W9-BGL-439

ALGEBRA
BOOK 2
WITH TRIGONOMETRY

A. M. WELCHONS □ W. R. KRICKENBERGER □ HELEN R. PEARSON □ ANN G. DUFFY □ JOHN M. McCAFFERY

GINN AND COMPANY

DESIGN AND PRODUCTION COORDINATION
Dimensions & Directions, Ltd.

COVER ILLUSTRATION   Herb Randle

TECHNICAL ILLUSTRATION   Vantage Art, Inc.

PHOTO RESEARCH   Helena Frost

CALCULATOR FEATURES   David Turinese

CAREER FEATURES   William H. Chernik

PHOTOGRAPHERS
x—Michal Heron; 46—Jean Claude Lejeunb/Stock Boston; 64—Michal Heron;
78—Timothy Eagan/Woodfin Camp & Assoc.; 116, 158, 202, 213—Michal
Heron; 230—Joel Gordon; 280—Hugh Rogers/Monkmeyer Photos, Inc.;
313—Fredrick Bodin/Stock Boston; 340—Watriss-Baldwin/Woodfin Camp &
Assoc.; 392—Mimi Forsyth/Monkmeyer Photos, Inc.; 430—Freda Leinwand/
Monkmeyer Photos, Inc.; 445—Edith Reichmann/Monkmeyer Photos, Inc.;
462, 494—Michal Heron; 512—Hugh Rogers/Monkmeyer Photos, Inc.;
529—U.S.D.A.; 546—Joel Gordon.

© Copyright, 1981, by Ginn and Company [Xerox Corporation]
All Rights Reserved
Home Office: Lexington, Massachusetts 02173
0-663-37310-7

CONTENTS

**CHAPTER 5 ■ GRAPHS, LINEAR EQUATIONS, FUNCTIONS,
AND RELATIONS**   **158**

**CHAPTER 6 ■ SYSTEMS OF LINEAR EQUATIONS
AND INEQUALITIES**   **202**

CHAPTER 1
THE REAL NUMBERS

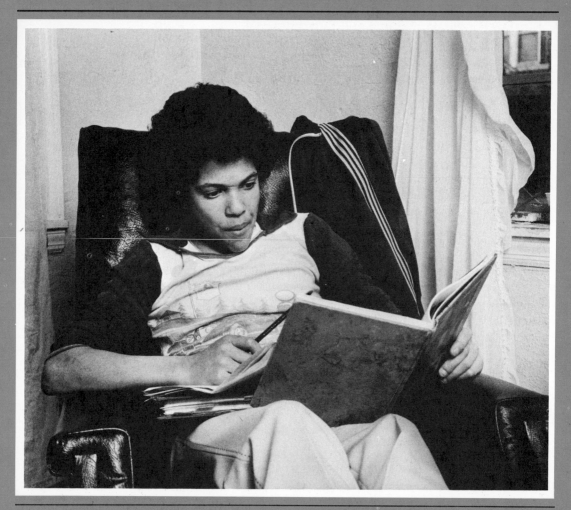

Time gets shorter as a person grows older. Take the time, while you have the time, and consider this statement, "Each day you live a smaller fraction of your life than you lived the day before." It can provide some interesting mathematical comparisons—and a message: Take the time while you have the time.

> **OBJECTIVES:** Identify whole numbers, positive and negative integers, and rational numbers. Add, subtract, multiply, and divide using these numbers.

1-1 NUMBERS AND THEIR GRAPHS

In all cultures people have been counting for as long as they have been talking. The numbers used are the **counting** or **natural numbers**, presently named 1, 2, 3, 4, and so on. In more recent history, 0 (zero) was created to represent the idea of there being no objects to count. Zero and the counting numbers form the **whole numbers**.

To represent the whole numbers, we mark congruent segments of a line. Then we match a point with 0, the next point to the right with 1, the next with 2, and so on.

Each point of such a **number line** is the **graph** of its matching number. A number is the **coordinate** of its matching point. When we draw the points for certain numbers, we **graph** the numbers.

EXAMPLE 1 Graph the even whole numbers less than 7.

SOLUTION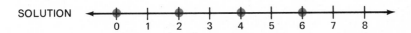

In a number line, shown below, the numbers for the points marked to the right of the point for zero are also called the **positive integers**. Marking congruent segments to the left of the zero point, as shown, locates points for the **negative integers**, −1, −2, −3, and so on. The positive integers, negative integers, and zero together are the **integers**.

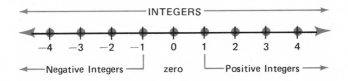

EXAMPLE 2 Graph the integers greater than −3 and less than 2.

SOLUTION

A **rational number** is a number that can be expressed in the form $\frac{a}{b}$, when a and b are integers and b is not zero. Since any integer, a, can be expressed as the fraction $\frac{a}{1}$, the rational numbers include the integers.

EXAMPLE 3 Which of these are rational numbers?

$$\tfrac{1}{2}, \; -5, \; 2\tfrac{1}{3}, \; -1.2, \; -\tfrac{13}{4}$$

SOLUTION $\frac{1}{2}$ already is in the form $\frac{a}{b}$.

Also, $-5 = \frac{-5}{1}$, $2\frac{1}{3} = \frac{7}{3}$, $-1.2 = \frac{-6}{5}$, and $-\frac{13}{4} = \frac{-13}{4}$.

Hence, each is a rational number.

The **real numbers** are the numbers that match all the points of the number line. Hence, the graph of the real numbers is the complete number line.

REAL NUMBERS

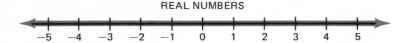

The real numbers include the rational numbers. They also include numbers that *cannot* be expressed in the form $\frac{a}{b}$, when a and b are integers. These are the **irrational numbers**. There are infinitely many irrational numbers. We shall be meeting them and working with them later in this book.

EXAMPLE 4 Draw the graph of the real numbers greater than -2.

SOLUTION

The ○ shows that the graph of -2 is not included. -2 is *not* greater than -2.

EXAMPLE 5 Draw the graph of the real numbers greater than or equal to $-3\frac{1}{2}$ and less than $1\frac{3}{4}$.

SOLUTION

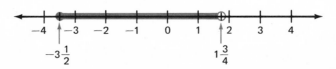

Each real number is associated with a real number called its **opposite**. If a number is positive, its opposite is negative. If a number is negative, its opposite is positive. The opposite of zero is zero. The graphs of two opposite numbers are the same distance from, but on opposite sides of, the point for zero.

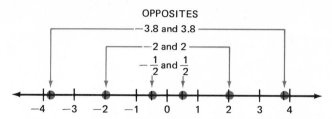

The symbol "$-$" is used to indicate the opposite of a number. The symbol "$-x$" may be read "the opposite of x".

The Opposite of x

When x represents a positive number $-x$ is negative.

When x represents a negative number $-x$ is positive.

EXAMPLE 6   Find and simplify $-x$ for $x = 9$; for $x = -9$.

SOLUTION   For $x = 9$, $-x = -9$.
For $x = -9$, $-x = -(-9)$. The opposite of -9 is 9. Thus, $-x = 9$.

The **absolute value** of a number is the distance of its graph from the point for zero in the number line. The absolute value of a positive number or zero is the number itself. The absolute value of a negative number is its opposite. The absolute value of a number is indicated with vertical bars, $|\quad|$.

ABSOLUTE VALUE

When x represents a positive number or zero, $|x| = x$.

When x represents a negative number, $|x| = -x$.

EXAMPLE 7   Simplify $|4|$. Simplify $\left|-\frac{11}{7}\right|$.

SOLUTION   Since 4 is positive, $|4| = 4$.
Since $-\frac{11}{7}$ is negative, $\left|-\frac{11}{7}\right| = -\left(-\frac{11}{7}\right)$, or $\frac{11}{7}$.

CLASSROOM EXERCISES

1. Which are rational numbers? $\frac{1}{3}$, -7, $4\frac{2}{3}$, $-\frac{15}{7}$, 2.6

2. Give $-x$ for $x = 13$.

3. Give $-x$ for $x = -13$.

Graph.

4. the whole numbers less than 8

5. the integers greater than -5 and less than 3

6. the real numbers less than 2

7. the real numbers greater than $-1\frac{1}{4}$ and less than or equal to $1\frac{1}{2}$

Simplify.

8. $-(2)$ **9.** $-(-8)$ **10.** $|0|$ **11.** $|-4.2|$ **12.** $\left|-\frac{7}{4}\right|$ **13.** $-|-3|$

EXERCISES

A **1.** Which are rational numbers? -6, -4.5, $2\frac{1}{3}$, 0, $\frac{3}{4}$, 0.4

2. Give $-x$ for $x = 4$.

3. Give $-x$ for $x = -4$.

Simplify.

4. $-(5)$ **5.** $-(7)$ **6.** $-(-9)$ **7.** $-(-10)$ **8.** $|7|$ **9.** $|4|$

10. $|-9.6|$ **11.** $|-8.2|$ **12.** $\left|-\frac{5}{6}\right|$ **13.** $\left|-\frac{3}{4}\right|$ **14.** $-|-2|$ **15.** $-|-10|$

Graph the numbers.

16. the odd integers greater than 6

17. the even integers greater than 8

18. the real numbers less than 2

19. the real numbers less than 4

20. the non-negative integers

21. the non-positive integers

22. the real numbers greater than 3 and less than 8

23. the real numbers greater than 2 and less than 9

24. the real numbers less than or equal to -4.5

25. the real numbers less than or equal to -1.5

B **26.** the real numbers with absolute value less than 3

27. the real numbers with absolute value greater than 3

28. the real numbers with absolute value greater than -3

29. the real numbers which are less than their absolute values

C **30.** Construct a line segment of length $\sqrt{2}$.

1-2 OPERATIONS AND THEIR PROPERTIES

The "equals" symbol, = , is used between two expressions for the same number. Since $a = b$ means that a and b represent the same number, we have the following property of equality.

THE SUBSTITUTION PROPERTY

When a and b represent the same number, a and b can replace each other in any expression.

Addition and multiplication are the basic **arithmetic operations**. They have certain properties that allow us to work with them easily.

COMMUTATIVE PROPERTIES

For any real numbers a and b,
$$a + b = b + a \quad | \quad a \cdot b = b \cdot a$$

ASSOCIATIVE PROPERTIES

For any real numbers a, b, and c,
$$(a + b) + c = a + (b + c) \quad | \quad (a \cdot b) \cdot c = a \cdot (b \cdot c)$$

DISTRIBUTIVE PROPERTY

For any real numbers a, b, and c,
$$a \cdot (b + c) = a \cdot b + a \cdot c$$

EXAMPLE 1   Use the Commutative Property of Multiplication to complete the following: $3 \cdot 5 = ? \cdot ?$

SOLUTION   The Commutative Property of Multiplication states that two factors in either order give the same product.
$$3 \cdot 5 = 5 \cdot 3$$

EXAMPLE 2   Use the Associative Property of Addition to help simplify $3\frac{3}{4} + \left(2\frac{1}{4} + 5\frac{1}{3}\right)$.

SOLUTION $3\frac{3}{4} + \left(2\frac{1}{4} + 5\frac{1}{3}\right) = \left(3\frac{3}{4} + 2\frac{1}{4}\right) + 5\frac{1}{3}$
$$= 6 + 5\frac{1}{3}$$
$$= 11\frac{1}{3} \cdot$$

EXAMPLE 3 Use the Distributive Property to help simplify $7\left(8 + \frac{3}{14}\right)$.

SOLUTION
$$7\left(8 + \tfrac{3}{14}\right) = 7 \cdot 8 + 7 \cdot \tfrac{3}{14}$$
$$= 56 + 1\tfrac{1}{2}$$
$$= 57\tfrac{1}{2}$$

Zero and one are numbers for which there are special properties for addition and multiplication.

IDENTITY PROPERTIES

For any real number a,

$$a + 0 = a \qquad\qquad a \cdot 1 = a$$

INVERSE PROPERTIES

For any real number a,

there is a number $-a$ such that $a + (-a) = 0$.

there is a number $\dfrac{1}{a}$

such that $a \cdot \dfrac{1}{a} = 1$,

provided that a is not zero.

THE ZERO PROPERTY

For any real number a, $\qquad a \cdot 0 = 0$

EXAMPLE 4 Simplify $10 \cdot 1$, $\quad 5.27 + 0$, $\quad 4 \cdot \frac{1}{4}$, $\quad (-39) + 39$, and $\frac{7}{15} \cdot 0$.

SOLUTION $\quad 10 \cdot 1 = 10 \qquad 5.27 + 0 = 5.27 \qquad 4 \cdot \tfrac{1}{4} = 1$

$$(-39) + 39 = 0 \qquad \tfrac{7}{15} \cdot 0 = 0$$

Parentheses, brackets, or the fraction bar in an expression tell us to do first the operations grouped by each of them. When there are no such *grouping symbols*, we should perform first all multiplication and division in order from left to right. Then we should perform all addition and subtraction, also in order from left to right.

EXAMPLE 5 Simplify $(2 + 4) \cdot 3$, $\quad 2 + (4 \cdot 3)$, $\quad$ and $\quad 2 + 4 \cdot 3$.

SOLUTION
$$(2 + 4) \cdot 3 = 6 \cdot 3 \qquad\qquad 2 + (4 \cdot 3) = 2 + 12$$
$$= 18 \qquad\qquad\qquad\qquad = 14$$

$$2 + 4 \cdot 3 = 2 + 12 \text{ (since we multiply before adding)}$$
$$= 14$$

EXAMPLE 6 Simplify $3 \cdot 4 - 10 \div 2$.

SOLUTION $\quad 3 \cdot 4 - 10 \div 2 = 12 - 5$
$$= 7$$

EXAMPLE 7 Simplify $5 - \dfrac{8+4}{3}$.

SOLUTION $\quad 5 - \dfrac{8+4}{3} = 5 - \dfrac{12}{3}$
$$= 5 - 4$$
$$= 1$$

EXAMPLE 8 Simplify $18 \div (6 - 3) + 1 + 2 \cdot 25$.

SOLUTION $\quad 18 \div (6 - 3) + 1 + 2 \cdot 25 = 18 \div 3 + 1 + 50$
$$= 6 + 1 + 50$$
$$= 57$$

ORDER OF ARITHMETIC OPERATIONS

1. Perform all operations that are included by the symbols of grouping ( ), [ ], or the fraction bar —.
2. Perform indicated multiplications and divisions in order from left to right.
3. Perform indicated additions and subtractions in order from left to right.

CLASSROOM EXERCISES

Use the Associative Property of Addition to simplify each expression.

1. $3\frac{2}{3} + \left(1\frac{1}{3} + 4\right)$ **2.** $6\frac{3}{4} + \left(\frac{1}{4} + 2\frac{1}{3}\right)$

Use the Commutative Property of Addition or Multiplication to complete each equation.

3. $9 + 6 = ? + ?$ **4.** $5 \times 7 = ? \times ?$

Use the Distributive Property to write the sum as a product.

5. $3 \cdot 4 + 3 \cdot 11 = ?$

Use the Distributive Property to write the product as a sum.

6. $17(4 + 11) = ?$

State the property suggested by each equation.

7. $\frac{1}{5} \times 5 = 1$ **8.** $29 + 0 = 29$ **9.** $56 \times 0 = 0$ **10.** $261 + (-261) = 0$

Simplify.

11. $4 \times 2 + 5 \times 6$ **12.** $60 \div (4 \times 3)$ **13.** $3 + 2 \cdot 6$ **14.** $8 - \dfrac{15+6}{3}$

EXERCISES

A Use the Associative Property of addition to simplify each expression.

1. $\frac{1}{3} + \left(3\frac{2}{3} + 15\frac{1}{4}\right)$ **2.** $4\frac{1}{2} + \left(2\frac{1}{2} + 10\frac{1}{3}\right)$ **3.** $1\frac{2}{7} + \left(\frac{5}{7} + 2\frac{1}{6}\right)$ **4.** $2\frac{1}{11} + \left(\frac{10}{11} + 4\frac{3}{10}\right)$

Use the Commutative Property of Addition or Multiplication to complete the equation.

5. $4 + 3 = ? + ?$ **6.** $20 \times 3 = ? \times ?$ **7.** $13 \times 0 = ? \times ?$

Write each sum as a product. Write each product as a sum.

8. $5 \cdot 10 + 5 \cdot 15$ **9.** $23 \cdot 15 + 23 \cdot 10$ **10.** $4(9 + 10)$ **11.** $7(15 + 20)$

Simplify.

12. $3 \times 2 + 4 \times 7$ **13.** $3 \times 9 - 8 \times 2$ **14.** $60 \div 4 \times 3$

15. $60 \times 4 \div 2$ **16.** $(3 + 2) \times 5$ **17.** $(4 + 6) \times 2$

18. $(60 \times 4) \div 2$ **19.** $(60 \div 4) \times 3$ **20.** $(8 \div 3 + 2) \times 0$

21. $(12 \div 7 + 6) \times 0$ **22.** $8 - \frac{21 + 4}{5}$ **23.** $9 - \frac{16 + 6}{11}$

24. $20 \div (7 - 2) + 3 + 2 \times 7$ **25.** $36 \div (11 - 2) + 1 + 2 \times 10$

B **26.** $|-3| \times 16 \div 6 - |-8|$ **27.** $\frac{7 + 3}{2} - \frac{10 + 2}{3}$ **28.** $(|-7| + 3) \cdot \frac{1}{(7 \times |-3|)}$

29. $14 \div 7 \times |-6| + 14 \div 7 \times (-|-6|)$ **30.** $\left[\left(4 + 1\frac{2}{3}\right) + \left(\frac{4}{3} + 2\right)\right] \times (40 \div 2 - 15) + 2 \cdot 4$

C A set of numbers is said to be *closed* under an operation if performing the operation on any two members of the set gives a member of the set.

31. Are the integers closed under division? Explain.

32. Is the set $\{1, -1\}$ closed under multiplication? under addition? Explain.

NAILS?, SCREENS?, PUTTY?

"How much will one cost?"

"Twenty cents," replied the clerk in the hardware store.

"And how much will twelve cost?" "Forty cents."

"Okay. I'll take nine hundred twelve."

"That will be sixty cents, please."

What was the customer buying?

1-3 ADDITION

The Properties of Addition discussed in the preceding section hold whether you are working with positive real numbers only, or with both positive and negative real numbers. We use absolute value to define addition when both positive and negative numbers are being considered.

ADDING POSITIVE AND NEGATIVE NUMBERS

1. If both are positive, add them as you always have. The sum is positive.

    $a + b = |a| + |b|$

2. If both are negative, add their absolute values. The sum is negative.

    $a + b = -(|a| + |b|)$

3. If one is positive and the other negative, but they are not opposites, find the difference of their absolute values. The result is positive or negative, to agree with the original number having the greater absolute value.

    $a + b = |a| - |b|$ if a is the positive number and $|a| > |b|$.

    $a + b = -(|a| - |b|)$ if a is the negative number and $|a| > |b|$.

EXAMPLE 1 Add -27 and -14.

SOLUTION Both numbers are negative. The sum is negative.

$$|-27| = 27$$
$$|-14| = \underline{14}$$
$$41$$

Add.

Therefore, $(-27) + (-14) = -41$.

EXAMPLE 2 Add -6.2 and 1.7.

SOLUTION Find the difference of the absolute values. The result is negative to agree with -6.2, since $|-6.2| > |1.7|$.

$$|-6.2| = 6.2$$
$$|\ 1.7| = \underline{1.7}$$
$$4.5$$

Subtract.

Therefore, $-6.2 + 1.7 = -4.5$.

EXAMPLE 3 Add $-\frac{1}{3}$ and $\frac{4}{5}$.

SOLUTION Find the difference of the absolute values. The result is positive to agree with $\frac{4}{5}$, since $|\frac{4}{5}| > |-\frac{1}{3}|$.

$$|\tfrac{4}{5}| = \tfrac{12}{15}$$
$$|-\tfrac{1}{3}| = \tfrac{5}{15}$$

Subtract. $\qquad \dfrac{\frac{7}{15}}{}$

Therefore, $-\frac{1}{3} + \frac{4}{5} = \frac{7}{15}$.

CLASSROOM EXERCISES

Simplify each sum.

1. $25 + (-10)$ **2.** $(-14) + (-62)$ **3.** $(-38) + (19)$ **4.** $(-16.4) + (12.2)$
5. $(-7) + 11$ **6.** $\frac{1}{4} + \left(-\frac{3}{4}\right)$ **7.** $\left(-\frac{2}{3}\right) + \left(-\frac{5}{12}\right)$ **8.** $-3\frac{1}{2} + 7\frac{3}{8}$

EXERCISES

A Simplify each sum.

1. $7 + (-6)$ **2.** $8 + (-2)$ **3.** $-3 + (-20)$ **4.** $-8 + (-9)$
5. $7 + (-7)$ **6.** $10 + (-10)$ **7.** $2.4 + (-3.8)$ **8.** $4.2 + (-6.6)$
9. $\frac{1}{2} + \left(-\frac{3}{4}\right)$ **10.** $\frac{2}{5} + \left(-\frac{3}{5}\right)$ **11.** $6\frac{1}{4} + (-7)$ **12.** $4\frac{1}{3} + (-5)$
13. $4.0 + (-0.8)$ **14.** $6.0 + (-0.4)$ **15.** $-7.6 + (-2.4)$ **16.** $-10.0 + (-2.1)$
17. $-7\frac{1}{4} + 4$ **18.** $-9\frac{1}{6} + 3$ **19.** $-2\frac{1}{4} + \left(-4\frac{1}{3}\right)$ **20.** $-6\frac{3}{5} + \left(-5\frac{5}{6}\right)$
B **21.** $-22 + 9 + (-14) + (-3)$ **22.** $62.4 + (-13.8) + (-25.4) + (-18.2)$

Simplify.

23. $(15.6 + (-3.6)) \div \left(6\frac{7}{12} + \left(-1\frac{1}{3}\right) + \left(-2\frac{1}{4}\right)\right)$ **24.** $|6 + (-|6 + (-|-6|)|)| + \left(-2\frac{1}{3}\right)$

C **25.** Show that the sum of any 3 consecutive integers has 3 as a factor.
26. Show that the sum of any two even integers is an even integer.
27. Show that the sum of any two odd integers is an even integer.
28. Show that the sum of an even integer and an odd integer is an odd integer.
29. Describe the sum of a number x and its absolute value. (Hint: What can you say when x is non-negative? negative?)

1-4 SUBTRACTION

The difference, $\boxed{a-b}$, of two real numbers a and b is the number $\boxed{c}$ for which $\boxed{c}+b=a$. In particular, $\boxed{[a+(-b)]}+b=a$. Therefore, when it is apparent that simplifying $a-b$ is not a straightforward exercise in arithmetic, represent $a-b$ as $a+(-b)$ and use the rules for adding positive and negative numbers.

EXAMPLE 1 Subtract 15 from 11.

SOLUTION Write $11-15$ as $11+(-15)$ and use the rules for addition.

$$11-15=11+(-15)$$
$$=-4$$

CHECK $-4+(15)\stackrel{?}{=}11$
$$11=11\quad\text{✓}$$

EXAMPLE 2 Subtract -2.3 from 6.0.

SOLUTION $6.0-(-2.3)=6.0+2.3$
$$=8.3$$

CHECK The check that $8.3+(-2.3)=6.0$ is left for the student.

EXAMPLE 3 Subtract 0.8 from -5.0.

SOLUTION $-5.0-0.8=-5.0+(-0.8)$
$$=-5.8$$

CHECK $-5.8+0.8\stackrel{?}{=}-5$
$$-5=-5\quad\text{✓}$$

EXAMPLE 4 Subtract -1.3 from -0.9.

SOLUTION $-0.9-(-1.3)=-0.9+1.3$
$$=0.4$$

CHECK The check is left for the student.

EXAMPLE 5 Subtract $\frac{4}{7}$ from $-\frac{5}{7}$

SOLUTION $-\frac{5}{7}-\frac{4}{7}=-\frac{5}{7}+\left(-\frac{4}{7}\right)$
$$=-\frac{9}{7}$$

CHECK $-\frac{9}{7}+\frac{4}{7}\stackrel{?}{=}-\frac{5}{7}$
$$-\frac{5}{7}=-\frac{5}{7}\quad\text{✓}$$

EXAMPLE 6 Subtract $-\frac{7}{8}$ from $\frac{2}{3}$.

SOLUTION $\quad \frac{2}{3} - \left(-\frac{7}{8}\right) = \frac{2}{3} + \frac{7}{8}$

$$= \frac{16}{24} + \frac{21}{24}$$

$$= \frac{37}{24}$$

CHECK $\quad$ The check that $\frac{37}{24} + \left(-\frac{7}{8}\right) = \frac{2}{3}$ is left for the student.

CLASSROOM EXERCISES

Simplify each difference.

1. $10 - 15$ **2.** $22 - (-13)$ **3.** $-6 - 7$ **4.** $27 - (-35)$

5. $-26.3 - 14.9$ **6.** $32.5 - (-19.4)$ **7.** $\frac{4}{5} - \frac{8}{5}$ **8.** $-\frac{1}{3} - \left(-\frac{1}{2}\right)$

EXERCISES

A   Simplify each difference.

1. $7 - (-4)$ **2.** $7 - (-6)$ **3.** $10 - 3$ **4.** $7 - 2$

5. $-8 - 4$ **6.** $-9 - 5$ **7.** $0 - (-9)$ **8.** $0 - (-6)$

9. $4 - (-4)$ **10.** $6 - (-6)$ **11.** $-30 - (-20)$ **12.** $-50 - (-30)$

13. $1 - (-100)$ **14.** $2 - (-40)$ **15.** $5 - (12)$ **16.** $7 - (15)$

17. $8 - 16$ **18.** $9 - 18$ **19.** $-7\frac{1}{2} - \left(-2\frac{1}{2}\right)$ **20.** $-3\frac{1}{2} - \left(-2\frac{1}{2}\right)$

21. $1\frac{7}{8} - 3$ **22.** $2\frac{4}{5} - 6$ **23.** $5.62 - (-2.12)$ **24.** $9.06 - (-1.11)$

B   Simplify.

25. $8 + 7 - (-6)$ **26.** $3 - (-6) + (-4)$ **27.** $1 - (-1) + 1$

28. $4 - 2 + (-6)$ **29.** $8 - 9 - 7$ **30.** $10 - (-8) + 3$

31. $4\frac{1}{2} - 2\frac{1}{4} + \left(-6\frac{1}{4}\right)$ **32.** $-8\frac{2}{3} - 6\frac{2}{5} + 5\frac{8}{9}$ **33.** $\left|-\frac{12}{13}\right| - 4\frac{1}{13} + \left(-6\frac{1}{39}\right)$

34. The highest recorded temperature is 56.6°C. This was recorded in Death Valley on July 10, 1913. In Vastok, Antarctica, on August 24, 1960, the lowest temperature of −88°C was recorded. Find the absolute value of the difference of the temperatures.

C   **35.** Show that if the sum of the digits of a two-digit number is subtracted from the number then the difference is divisible by 9.

36. Show that the difference between a three-digit number and the number obtained by reversing the order of the digits is divisible by both 9 and 11.

37. Find all values of x for which $|x| - x = 8$; for which $|x| - x = 0$.

1-5 MULTIPLICATION

The Properties of Multiplication discussed in Section 1-2 hold whether you are working only with positive factors, or with both positive and negative factors. When a negative number is a factor, we use absolute values to help determine the product.

MULTIPLYING POSITIVE AND NEGATIVE NUMBERS

1. Find if the product is positive or negative using these rules:
   a. The product of two positive numbers or two negative numbers is a positive number.
   b. The product of a positive number and a negative number is a negative number.
2. Use your findings from Step 1 with the product of the absolute values.

EXAMPLE 1   Multiply -16 and 7.

SOLUTION   One number is positive. The other is negative. The product is negative.

$$(-16)(7) = -(|-16| \cdot |7|)$$
$$= -(16 \cdot 7)$$
$$= -112$$

EXAMPLE 2   Multiply $\frac{2}{3}$ and $-\frac{5}{7}$.

SOLUTION   One number is positive. The other is negative. The product is negative.

$$\frac{2}{3} \cdot \left(-\frac{5}{7}\right) = -\left(\frac{2}{3} \cdot \frac{5}{7}\right)$$
$$= -\frac{2 \cdot 5}{3 \cdot 7}$$
$$= -\frac{10}{21}$$

EXAMPLE 3   Multiply -2.3 and -11.

SOLUTION   Both numbers are negative. The product is positive.

$$(-2.3)(-11) = (2.3)(11)$$
$$= 25.3$$

EXAMPLE 4   Find the product of -24, 5, and -1.

SOLUTION   You may first determine that the product is positive because there are two negative factors. Then multiply the absolute values.

Another way is to apply the rules for multiplying using two factors at a time.

$$(-24)(5)(-1) = (-120)(-1)$$
$$= 120$$

CLASSROOM EXERCISES

Simplify each product.

1. $(-4)(5)$ **2.** $(6.2)(3.1)$ **3.** $(32)(-3)$ **4.** $(-51)(-10.1)$
5. $\left(\frac{4}{7}\right)\left(-\frac{2}{9}\right)$ **6.** $\left(-\frac{3}{4}\right)\left(-5\frac{1}{8}\right)$ **7.** $\left(1\frac{5}{8}\right)\left(-3\frac{2}{7}\right)$ **8.** $(-1)(2)(-1)$

EXERCISES

Ⓐ Simplify each product.

1. $(4)(-3)$ **2.** $(5)(-2)$ **3.** $(-6)(4)$ **4.** $(-8)(2)$
5. $(-5)(-3)$ **6.** $(-4)(-3)$ **7.** $(5)(-6)$ **8.** $(6)(-7)$
9. $(-9)(-1)$ **10.** $(-10)(-1)$ **11.** $(-3)(-3)$ **12.** $(-2)(-2)$
13. $(2.1)(3.2)$ **14.** $(4.2)(6.1)$ **15.** $(-10.2)(3.1)$ **16.** $(-9.4)(2.1)$
17. $(-4.2)(-5.4)$ **18.** $(-3.1)(-5.1)$ **19.** $\left(\frac{2}{5}\right)\left(-\frac{3}{7}\right)$ **20.** $\left(\frac{2}{7}\right)\left(-\frac{2}{3}\right)$
21. $\left(-\frac{4}{9}\right)\left(-2\frac{2}{3}\right)$ **22.** $\left(-\frac{5}{6}\right)\left(-2\frac{1}{3}\right)$ **23.** $(-9)(2)(-1)$ **24.** $(-7)(3)(-1)$
25. $8(-2)(3)$ **26.** $7(-3)(4)$ **27.** $(-2)(-3)(-1)$ **28.** $(-1)(-4)(-5)$
29. $\left(-\frac{2}{3}\right)\left(-\frac{1}{7}\right)$ **30.** $\left(-\frac{4}{5}\right)\left(-\frac{6}{7}\right)$ **31.** $\left(-2\frac{1}{3}\right)\left(1\frac{5}{6}\right)$ **32.** $\left(-1\frac{1}{4}\right)\left(1\frac{1}{2}\right)$
33. $\left(\frac{2}{7}\right)\left(\frac{3}{5}\right)(-1)$ **34.** $\left(\frac{4}{9}\right)\left(\frac{5}{7}\right)(-1)$ **35.** $(1.1)(-2)(3)$ **36.** $(4.4)(-1)(3)$

Ⓑ Simplify.

37. $(-13)(-14)\left(\frac{1}{7}\right)$ **38.** $\left(1\frac{2}{3} - 1\frac{1}{5}\right) \times \left(-\frac{1}{3}\right) + \left(-\frac{4}{15}\right) \times \left(-\frac{2}{3}\right)$ **39.** $\frac{1}{2} \times \frac{1}{2} \times \frac{1}{2} - \frac{1}{3}$

Ⓒ **40.** Show that the product of two even integers is an even integer.

41. Show that the product of an even integer and an odd integer is an even integer.

42. Show that the product of two odd integers is an odd integer.

43. Which two expressions are equal: $x|x|$, $x|-x|$, $-x|x|$? Explain.

1-6 DIVISION

The quotient $a \div b$, $b \neq 0$, is the number c for which $c \cdot b = a$. Therefore, the quotient c is positive when b and a are both positive, or when b and a are both negative. The quotient c is negative when b is positive and a is negative, or when b is negative and a is positive.

factor	factor	product	dividend	divisor	quotient
c	b $=$	a	a $\div$	b $=$	c
+	+	+	+	+	+
+	−	−	−	−	+
−	+	−	−	+	−
−	−	+	+	−	−

The steps for dividing positive and negative numbers are similar to the steps for multiplying. First, find if the quotient is positive or negative. Then, use your findings with the quotient of the absolute values.

EXAMPLE 1   Divide 45 by -15.

SOLUTION   The dividend is positive.   The divisor is negative.   The quotient is negative.

$$\frac{45}{-15} = -\frac{|45|}{|-15|}$$

$$= -\frac{45}{15}$$

$$= -3$$

CHECK $(-15)(-3) \overset{?}{=} 45$

$45 = 45$ ✔

EXAMPLE 2   Divide -132 by 11.

SOLUTION   The dividend is negative.   The divisor is positive.   The quotient is negative.

$$\frac{-132}{11} = -\frac{132}{11}$$

$$= -12$$

CHECK $11 \cdot (-12) \overset{?}{=} -132$

$-132 = -132$ ✔

EXAMPLE 3   Divide -7.2 by -9.

SOLUTION   Both numbers are negative.   The quotient is positive.

$$\frac{-7.2}{-9} = \frac{7.2}{9}$$

$$= 0.8$$

CHECK $-9(0.8) \overset{?}{=} -7.2$

$-7.2 = -7.2$ ✔

EXAMPLE 4 Divide $-\frac{2}{3}$ by $\frac{4}{7}$.

SOLUTION One number is negative. The other is positive. The quotient is negative.

$$\left(-\frac{2}{3}\right) \div \frac{4}{7} = -\left(\frac{2}{3} \div \frac{4}{7}\right) \qquad \text{CHECK} \quad \frac{4}{7}\left(-\frac{7}{6}\right) \stackrel{?}{=} -\frac{2}{3}$$

$$= -\left(\frac{\overset{1}{\cancel{2}}}{3} \cdot \frac{7}{\underset{2}{\cancel{4}}}\right) \qquad \qquad \frac{\overset{2}{\cancel{4}}}{7}\left(-\frac{\overset{1}{\cancel{7}}}{\underset{3}{\cancel{6}}}\right) \stackrel{?}{=} -\frac{2}{3}$$

$$= -\frac{7}{6} \qquad \qquad \qquad -\frac{2}{3} = -\frac{2}{3} \quad ✔$$

CLASSROOM EXERCISES

Divide. Simplify each quotient.

1. -33 by 11

2. -56 by -8

3. 144 by -12

4. $\frac{1}{4}$ by $\frac{6}{11}$

5. $-\frac{1}{2}$ by $\frac{2}{3}$

6. $\frac{3}{5}$ by $-\frac{1}{3}$

7. $-\frac{3}{4}$ by $3\frac{1}{3}$

8. $-1\frac{2}{3}$ by -5

EXERCISES

A Simplify each quotient.

1. $10 \div 5$

2. $12 \div 6$

3. $(-12) \div (-3)$

4. $(-15) \div (-5)$

5. $14 \div (-7)$

6. $18 \div (-3)$

7. $-20 \div 5$

8. $-16 \div 8$

9. $18 \div 9$

10. $24 \div 6$

11. $5.6 \div (-2)$

12. $12.3 \div (-3)$

13. $\frac{2}{7} \div 4$

14. $\frac{5}{8} \div 10$

15. $-\frac{10}{11} \div 10$

16. $-\frac{9}{13} \div 9$

17. $8 \div \left(-\frac{1}{2}\right)$

18. $10 \div \left(-\frac{1}{3}\right)$

19. $\frac{2}{5} \div 1\frac{1}{3}$

20. $\frac{3}{7} \div 1\frac{1}{5}$

21. $-\frac{2}{3} \div \frac{5}{9}$

22. $-\frac{3}{7} \div \frac{5}{14}$

23. $-\frac{3}{5} \div \left(-1\frac{1}{10}\right)$

24. $-\frac{2}{3} \div \left(-1\frac{1}{6}\right)$

B Simplify.

25. $54 \div 9 \div 3$

26. $36 - [(6 \div 2) \cdot 3] - 12$

27. In a class of 30 students 17 are 16 years old, 6 are 15 years old, 5 are 17 years old, and 2 are 14 years old. Find the average age of the students.

C **28.** Find all numbers for x for which $\frac{|x|}{x} = 1$; for which $\frac{x}{|x|} = -1$.

1-7 POWERS AND ROOTS

When a product has two or more equal factors, it may be shown using an **exponent** and a **base**.

$$2 \cdot 2 \cdot 2 = 2^3 \qquad\qquad 5 \cdot 5 \cdot 5 \cdot 5 = 5^4$$

When a factor or term does not show an exponent, the exponent is understood to be 1.

$$5 = 5^1 \qquad 23 = 23^1 \qquad x = x^1 \qquad xy^2 = x^1y^2$$

EXAMPLE 1 Simplify 4^3.

SOLUTION $4^3 = 4 \cdot 4 \cdot 4$
$ = 64$

EXAMPLE 2 Simplify $\left(-\frac{1}{2}\right)^2$

SOLUTION $\left(-\frac{1}{2}\right)^2 = \left(-\frac{1}{2}\right)\left(-\frac{1}{2}\right)$
$\phantom{\left(-\frac{1}{2}\right)^2} = \frac{1}{4}$

When the base is a and the exponent is n, we say that a^n is the **nth power** of a.

$5^2 = 25$ 25 is the **second power** or **square** of 5.
$4^3 = 64$ 64 is the **third power** or **cube** of 4.
$7^4 = 2401$ 2401 is the **fourth power** of 7.
$a^n = y$ y is the **nth power** of a.

We also say that the base a is an **nth root** of a^n. The symbol $\sqrt[n]{}$ is used to designate an nth root of a number.

$5^2 = 25$ 5 is a **second root** or **square root** of 25. $\sqrt[2]{25} = 5$
$4^3 = 64$ 4 is a **third root** or **cube root** of 64. $\sqrt[3]{64} = 4$
$7^4 = 2401$ 7 is a **fourth root** of 2401. $\sqrt[4]{2401} = 7$
$a^n = y$ a is an **nth root** of y. $\sqrt[n]{y} = a$

EXAMPLE 3 Simplify $\sqrt[3]{-8}$.

SOLUTION   Since
$(-2)^3 = -8,$
$\sqrt[3]{-8} = -2.$

EXAMPLE 4 Find a square root of 9.

SOLUTION   Since each of 3^2 and $(-3)^2$ equals 9, each of 3 and -3 is a square root of 9.

$\sqrt[n]{a}$ is a **radical**. The symbol $\sqrt{}$ is the **radical sign**, n in $\sqrt[n]{a}$ is the **index**, and the number shown below the bar of the radical sign is the **radicand**. When the index is 2, it usually is not shown.

When n is an odd number there is only one real number that is the nth root of a. It is called the **principal nth root**. When n is even, as in Example 4, there are two real numbers that are nth roots of a positive number a. The principal nth root, $\sqrt[n]{a}$, is the positive nth root. $-\sqrt[n]{a}$ indicates the negative nth root.

index

$\sqrt[4]{16} = 2$ —— principal fourth root

radicand

index = 2 (not shown)

$\sqrt{9} = 3$ —— principal square root

radicand

EXAMPLE 5   Simplify $\sqrt[4]{81}$.

SOLUTION   We know $3^4 = 81$ and $(-3)^4 = 81$.
But $\sqrt[4]{81}$ indicates the principal fourth root of 81.
Hence, $\sqrt[4]{81} = 3$.

By comparing the definitions of principal square root and absolute value in this chart, we see that $\sqrt{a^2}$ is not necessarily a. Instead $\sqrt{a^2} = |a|$.

Principal Square Root	Absolute Value
When a is positive, $\sqrt{a^2} = a$	When a is positive, $|a| = a$
When a is negative, $\sqrt{a^2} = -a$	When a is negative, $|a| = -a$

EXAMPLE 6   Simplify $\sqrt{(-5)^2}$.

SOLUTION 1
$$\sqrt{(-5)^2} = \sqrt{25}$$
$$= 5$$

SOLUTION 2
$$\sqrt{(-5)^2} = |-5|$$
$$= 5$$

If a is a positive number such that $a^2 = 2$, then by our definition of square root, $a = \sqrt{2}$. It has been proven that a number such as $\sqrt{2}$ is not a rational number. It cannot be expressed in the form $\frac{a}{b}$, when a and b are integers. Thus, it is an example of an irrational number.

EXAMPLE 7 Which of the following are rational numbers?

a. $\sqrt{11}$ b. $\sqrt[3]{27}$ c. $\sqrt{(-7)^2}$ d. $\sqrt{0.4}$

SOLUTION a. There is no rational number a such that $a^2 = 11$. Therefore, $\sqrt{11}$ is not a rational number.

b. $\sqrt[3]{27} = 3$, a rational number.

c. $\sqrt{(-7)^2} = |-7|$, or 7, a rational number.

d. There is no rational number a such that $a^2 = 0.4$. Therefore, $\sqrt{0.4}$ is not a rational number.

CLASSROOM EXERCISES

Simplify.

1. $(2)^3$ **2.** $(-7)^2$ **3.** $\sqrt{(-8)^2}$ **4.** $\sqrt[3]{-27}$ **5.** $\sqrt{\dfrac{4}{25}}$ **6.** $\sqrt[3]{\dfrac{27}{64}}$

Is the number rational or irrational?

7. $\sqrt{13}$ **8.** $\sqrt[3]{-64}$ **9.** $\sqrt{0.2}$ **10.** $\sqrt{(-3)^2}$ **11.** $\sqrt{\dfrac{3}{27}}$ **12.** $\sqrt{6.25}$

EXERCISES

A Simplify.

1. $(5)^3$ **2.** $(4)^3$ **3.** $(-2)^3$ **4.** $(-5)^3$ **5.** $(-2)^2$

6. $(-3)^2$ **7.** $\left(-\dfrac{3}{2}\right)^3$ **8.** $\left(-\dfrac{2}{3}\right)^3$ **9.** $\sqrt{25}$ **10.** $\sqrt{4}$

11. $-\sqrt{64}$ **12.** $-\sqrt{16}$ **13.** $\sqrt[4]{625}$ **14.** $\sqrt[4]{1296}$ **15.** $\sqrt{(-4)^2}$

16. $\sqrt{(-9)^2}$ **17.** $\sqrt[3]{-1}$ **18.** $\sqrt[3]{-8}$ **19.** $\sqrt[3]{\dfrac{8}{27}}$ **20.** $\sqrt[3]{\dfrac{64}{27}}$

Is the number rational or irrational?

21. $\sqrt{3}$ **22.** $\sqrt[3]{125}$ **23.** $\sqrt{6}$ **24.** $\sqrt{\dfrac{25}{16}}$ **25.** $\sqrt[3]{4}$ **26.** $\sqrt{144}$

B Simplify.

27. $(-1)^6$ **28.** $(-1)^7$ **29.** $2^3 \cdot 3^2$ **30.** $(3a)^2$ **31.** $\sqrt[6]{64}$

32. $\sqrt[5]{-32}$ **33.** $\sqrt[4]{(-10)^4}$ **34.** $\sqrt{25-16}$ **35.** $\sqrt[4]{25-9}$ **36.** $\sqrt{\dfrac{4}{5}-\dfrac{4}{25}}$

C **37.** $\sqrt[6]{(-3)^6 x^6}$ **38.** $\sqrt[8]{\dfrac{(14)^8}{y^8}}$ **39.** $\sqrt[7]{(-2)^7 a^7}$ **40.** $\sqrt[9]{\dfrac{(3)^9}{x^9}}$

41. If n is even, show that $\sqrt[n]{a^n} = |a|$.

CHECKING YOUR UNDERSTANDING

WORDS AND SYMBOLS

absolute value, $|a|$
base, $(a)^n$
counting (natural) numbers
cube root, $\sqrt[3]{a}$
exponent, $a^{(n)}$
graph of a number
index of a radical, $\sqrt[n]{a}$

integers
irrational numbers
negative numbers
number line
opposite of a number a, $-a$
positive number
principal nth root, $\sqrt[n]{a}$

radical, $\sqrt[n]{a}$
radical sign $\sqrt{}$
radicand, $\sqrt[n]{(a)}$
rational number
real number
square root, $\sqrt{a}$
whole numbers

Properties of Addition and Multiplication

Associative   Commutative   Distributive   Identity   Inverse   Zero

CONCEPTS

■ Each point of the number line may be associated with a real number and each real number may be associated with a point of the number line. [1-1]

■ Each real number has an opposite, or inverse, with respect to addition. A number and its opposite have the same absolute value. Their sum is zero. [1-1, 1-2]

■ The absolute value of a non-zero number is positive. The absolute value of a negative number is its opposite. The absolute value of a number is the distance of its graph from the point for zero in the number line. [1-1]

■ Each non-zero real number has an inverse with respect to multiplication. Their product is one. [1-2]

■ When two symbols represent the same number, either may be used in place of the other. [1-2]

PROCESSES

■ Draw the graph of a given set of numbers. [1-1]

1. the whole numbers less than 4   **2.** the real numbers greater than $2\frac{1}{2}$

■ Find the opposite of a real number. Find the absolute value. [1-1]

3. -8 **4.** $\frac{3}{4}$ **5.** -6.7 **6.** 0

■ Simplify arithmetic expressions. [1-3 to 1-7]

7. $-7 + 2$ **8.** $\left(-\frac{1}{3}\right) + \left(-\frac{3}{4}\right)$ **9.** $2 - 9$ **10.** $(-0.8) - (-5.3)$

11. $4(-8)$ **12.** $\left(-\frac{2}{3}\right)\left(-5\frac{1}{4}\right)$ **13.** $-13 \div 4$ **14.** $\left(-\frac{2}{3}\right) \div \left(-\frac{2}{9}\right)$

15. $\sqrt{81}$ **16.** $\sqrt[3]{-\frac{8}{27}}$ **17.** $\sqrt{(-5)^2}$ **18.** $\sqrt{0.04}$

OBJECTIVES: Identify and simplify algebraic expressions. Add, subtract, multiply, and divide polynomials.

1-8 ALGEBRAIC EXPRESSIONS

A **variable**, usually a letter, is a symbol for a number. The **domain of the variable** is the set of numbers that are permitted to replace the variable.

A **term** is a constant, a variable, or an indicated product or quotient involving constants and variables. An **algebraic expression** is a term or an indicated sum or difference involving terms.

Terms				Algebraic Expressions	
10	x^2	$-6ab$	$\dfrac{1}{2}$	10	$x^2 - 6ab + \dfrac{1}{2}$
t	$2p$	$\dfrac{y}{2}$	$\dfrac{y^2}{z}$	$t + 2p$	$\dfrac{y}{2} - \dfrac{y^2}{z}$

Like terms are terms that contain the same variables with the same exponents.

Like Terms		Unlike Terms	
x, $2x$, and $-3x$	$10ab$, $-ab$, and $\dfrac{2}{3}ab$	$9x^2$ and $3x$	a, ab, and $-3ac$
$-3x^2y$, $7x^2y$, and $-x^2y$		$-3x^2y$, $7xy^2$, and $-x^2z$	

Algebraic expressions may be simplified by using the Distributive Property to combine like terms. Although the Distributive Property was stated in Section 1-2 using the one equation

$$a(b + c) = ab + ac,$$

other forms of the Property follow from it, the other properties of the real numbers, and the meaning of subtraction. For example,

$$(b + c)a = ba + ca \mid a(b - c) = ab - ac \mid a(b + c - d) = ab + ac - ad$$

EXAMPLE 1 Simplify $7x^2 - 11x^2 + 2x^2$. Use the Distributive Property.

SOLUTION $7x^2 - 11x^2 + 2x^2 = (7 - 11 + 2)x^2$
$$= -2x^2$$

The Commutative and Associative Properties of Addition allow you to rearrange terms in an expression before simplifying. It is usually helpful to arrange terms in descending or ascending powers of one variable.

EXAMPLE 2   Simplify $7 + 3b^2 - 6 + 5b^3 + 2b^2$.

SOLUTION
$$7 + 3b^2 - 6 + 5b^3 + 2b^2 = 7 - 6 + 3b^2 + 2b^2 + 5b^3$$
$$= 1 + (3 + 2)b^2 + 5b^3$$
$$= 1 + 5b^2 + 5b^3$$

EXAMPLE 3   Simplify $2x^2 - xy + y^2 + 2y^2 - x^2 - 3xy$.

SOLUTION
$$2x^2 - xy + y^2 + 2y^2 - x^2 - 3xy$$
$$= 2x^2 - x^2 - xy - 3xy + y^2 + 2y^2$$
$$= (2 - 1)x^2 + (-1 - 3)xy + (1 + 2)y^2$$
$$= x^2 - 4xy + 3y^2$$

CLASSROOM EXERCISES

Simplify.

1. $3x + 4x$
2. $10y^2 - 15y^2$
3. $11a^2 + 7a^3 - 3a + 4a^2 + 2a + 10$
4. $5ab + 2ab - 4ab$
5. $4c^2 - 2cd - d^2 + 5cd + 4d^2$
6. $3b^3 - a^2b + 2a^3 + 3a^2b - a^3$

EXERCISES

A   Simplify.

1. $8x - 5x$
2. $11y - 14y$
3. $5r^2 - 7r^2$
4. $9z^3 - 5z^3$
5. $-2c - 4c$
6. $-5t - 11t$
7. $\frac{1}{2}ab + \frac{1}{3}ab - ab$
8. $\frac{1}{4}bc + bc - \frac{1}{3}bc$
9. $3.2m^2n - 9.1m^2n$
10. $0.20n^2p - 0.47n^2p$
11. $3x + y - x$
12. $-5x - 2y + 2x$
13. $c^2 - c + 6 - 5c$
14. $10 - x^2 - 3x + 2x^2$
15. $4d^2 - 3 + 7d^3 + 4d^2 + 10$
16. $e + 11 - e^2 + 2e - 3e^2$
17. $p^2 - 4p + 2 - 2p^2 + 4p - 2$
18. $a^3 - 2a + 5 - 3a^3 + 2a - 5$
19. $8x^2 + 2ax + 1 - 2x^2 - 4ax$
20. $4by + 3 - 7b^2 - 11by + 3b^2$
21. $8x^2 - 3xy - 2x^2 + 8xy - 3y^2$
22. $8a^2 - 9ab + 4b^2 + 2ab - 3b^2$
23. $-6c^2 - 3cd + d^2 + 2c^2 + d^2$
24. $3y^2 + 2xy - x^2 + y^2 - 8xy$

B
25. $2(3 - x) - 4(x - 2y)$
26. $0.25(10x^2 + 4xy - 8y^2) + 4xy + y^2$
27. $x + 4[3 - (2 + 3x)]$
28. $(x + y) \div \left(1\frac{1}{6} - \frac{1}{3}\right) - \frac{1}{5}(x + 4)$

C
29. $\sqrt[8]{4x^8 - 3xy^7 - 3(x^8 - xy^7)}$
30. $6 + \sqrt[5]{32x^5} + 5x^2 - 3x$

1-9 ADDITION AND SUBTRACTION OF POLYNOMIALS

A term that is either a constant, a variable, or an indicated product of constants and variables is a **monomial**. An algebraic expression of one or more monomials is a **polynomial**. A polynomial of two terms is a **binomial**. A polynomial of three terms is a **trinomial**.

POLYNOMIALS

Monomials:	2, $-3x$, $11ab^2$, $\frac{1}{4}x$, $\sqrt{5}x$
Binomials:	$x + y$, $a^3 + 5$
Trinomials:	$s^3 + s^2 + s$, $5x^2 - 3x + 1$
Other Polynomials:	$s^4 + s^3 + s^2 + s$, $5x^2 - y^2 - 3x + 2y + 1$

To add polynomials, indicate the sum and combine like terms.

EXAMPLE 1 Add $x^2 + 2x + 2$ and $3x^2 + x - 5$.

SOLUTION $(x^2 + 2x + 2) + (3x^2 + x - 5) = x^2 + 3x^2 + 2x + x + 2 - 5$
$$= 4x^2 + 3x - 3$$

For addition, polynomials also may be arranged with like terms shown in columns. Then the sum is found for the terms in each column. The addition may be checked by replacing each variable by a number.

EXAMPLE 2 Add $2x^2 - xy + y^2$, $\quad -x^2 - 3xy + 2y^2$, $\quad$ and $8x^2 - 6y^2$. Check by using 2 for x and 3 for y.

SOLUTION

$$
\begin{array}{l}
2x^2 - xy + y^2 \\
-x^2 - 3xy + 2y^2 \\
8x^2 - 6y^2 \\
\hline
9x^2 - 4xy - 3y^2
\end{array}
$$

CHECK
$$
\left.
\begin{array}{l}
8 - 6 + 9 = 11 \\
-4 - 18 + 18 = {-4} \\
32 - 54 = -22
\end{array}
\right\} -15
$$
$$36 - 24 - 27 = -15$$

When subtracting a polynomial, you must subtract *each term* of the polynomial.

EXAMPLE 3 Subtract $7a - 5b$ from $2a + 4b$.

SOLUTION $(2a + 4b) - (7a - 5b) = 2a + 4b - 7a + 5b$
$$= 2a - 7a + 4b + 5b$$
$$= -5a + 9b$$

Like terms could also be arranged in columns for subtraction.

EXAMPLE 4 Subtract $x^3 - 4x^2 - 6x$ from $5x^3 - 3x$. Check by using 2 for x.

SOLUTION

$$
\begin{array}{r}
5x^3 \qquad - 3x \\
x^3 - 4x^2 - 6x \\
\hline
4x^3 + 4x^2 + 3x
\end{array}
$$

CHECK

$$
\begin{array}{rl}
40 \quad - \ 6 =& 34 \\
8 - 16 - 12 =& -20 \\
\hline
32 + 16 + \ 6 =& 54
\end{array}\Bigg\} 54
$$

ADDING AND SUBTRACTING POLYNOMIALS

1. Indicate the sum or difference.
2. Simplify by combining like terms.

CLASSROOM EXERCISES

Add.

1. $3x^2 + 10y^2$ and $4x^2 - 5y^2$

2. $8x^2 - 2x + \ 7$
$3x^2 + 4x - 10$

3. $3y^3 + 2y^2 \qquad + 1$
$-5y^3 \qquad + 2y - 7$
$2y^3 - 6y^2 \qquad + 4$

Subtract.

4. $-x + 3y$ from $9x - 7y$

5. $10ab - 4b$
$6ab - 7b$

6. $5x^2 + 8x - 2$
$-7x^2 - 7x + 4$

EXERCISES

A Add.

1. $5a - 3b$ and $2a + 6b$

2. $2y + 3z$ and $+8y - 4z$

3. $2y^2 - 3y + 4$ and $-4y^2 + 7y - 3$

4. $-3x^2 - 5x + 10$
$8x^2 + 3x - 11$

5. $7z^2 + 2z - \ 5$
$-5z^2 - 4z + 15$

6. $7a^2 - \ 3ab + 2b^2$
$-3a^2 + 11ab - 2b^2$

7. $8c^2 + 11cd + 9d^2$
$-7c^2 - 10cd + 3d^2$
$-5c^2 \qquad\qquad - 2$

8. $3m^2 - \ m - 6$
$-m^2 \qquad - 4$
$4m - 1$

9. $x^3 - 3x^2$
$-4x^3 - \ x^2 + \ 1$
$x^3 \qquad - 10$

10. $-3ab^2 + 7b^3 - \ 2$
$-a + 4ab^2 + 3b^3 - \ 3$
$3a \qquad + 2b^3 + 10$

11. $5r^2 - \ 2rs + 10s^2 - 1$
$-3r^2 \qquad - \ 7s^2 - 4$
$15rs + \ 3s^2 + 7$

12. $-x^2 - 2xy + 3y^2$
$-4x^2 + 3xy - \ y^2$
$-2x^2 - \ xy + \ y^2$

13. $-a^2 - 7ab + 4b^2$
$-8a^2 + 4ab - b^2$
$-2a^2 + 3ab + 2b^2$
$\overline{}$

14. $\frac{1}{3}x + \frac{3}{4}y - \frac{2}{5}z$
$\frac{1}{4}x + \phantom{\frac{3}{4}}y - \frac{1}{4}z$
$\frac{1}{2}x - \frac{3}{8}y - \frac{1}{10}z$
$\overline{\phantom{\frac{1}{2}x - \frac{3}{8}y - \frac{1}{10}z}}$

15. $\frac{1}{9}x - \frac{1}{3}y + \frac{1}{5}z$
$\frac{2}{3}x - \frac{1}{4}y + \frac{5}{6}z$
$-\frac{1}{2}x + \frac{1}{12}y - \frac{1}{15}z$
$\overline{\phantom{-\frac{1}{2}x + \frac{1}{12}y - \frac{1}{15}z}}$

Subtract.

16. $x^2 - 4x + 3$ from $4x^2 + 2x + 1$

17. $2k^2 - 3k + 5$ from $7k^2 - 8k - 4$

18. $2x^3 - 4x^2 + 6x - 7$ from $x^3 + 4x - 5$

19. $5r^3 + 2r^2 - 3r + 10$ from $-2r^3 - 3r + 10$

20. $3x + 6$
$x - 3$
$\overline{}$

21. $5a - 7$
$2a + 15$
$\overline{}$

$22 = 30$
$EVEN$

22. $2x^2 - 3x + 3$
$4x^2 - 7x - 5$
$\overline{}$

23. $3x^2 + 2x - 1$
$4x^2 + 5x + 4$
$\overline{}$

24. $3y^2 - 2y + 1$
$-3y^2 - 2y + 7$
$\overline{}$

25. $8a^2 - 3a + 2$
$-8a^2 - 3a + 6$
$\overline{}$

26. $3mn - 9n^2$
$-4m^2 - 5mn + 12n^2$
$\overline{}$

27. $-3a^2 - 7b^2$
$-5a^2 + 6ab - 7b^2$
$\overline{}$

28. $-x^3 - y^3$
$-2x^3 + x^2y - xy^2 + 2y^3$
$\overline{}$

29. $7b - c$
$-2a - 3b + 4c - 8d$
$\overline{}$

30. $\frac{1}{2}a + \frac{1}{3}b - \frac{1}{4}c$
$\frac{2}{3}a - \frac{1}{4}b - \frac{3}{4}c$
$\overline{\phantom{\frac{2}{3}a - \frac{1}{4}b - \frac{3}{4}c}}$

31. $\frac{1}{4}x + \frac{1}{8}y - \frac{1}{3}z$
$\frac{1}{3}x - \frac{1}{4}y - \frac{5}{9}z$
$\overline{\phantom{\frac{1}{3}x - \frac{1}{4}y - \frac{5}{9}z}}$

B **32.** Subtract $6a^2 - 3a + 7$ from 0.

33. Subtract $4a + b - c$ from $2a - b$.

34. From the sum of $2a + b$ and $3a - 4b$ take $5a + 2b$.

35. The sides of a triangle are $5a + b$, $2a - 3b$, and $a - 9b$. Find its perimeter.

36. The perimeter of a triangle is $5x^2 - x + 1$. Find the third side when one side is $x^2 + 2x + 3$ and another is $x^2 - 2x + 4$.

C Solve.

37. Find the perimeter of the figure at the right.

38. Find the sum of the lengths of the 12 edges of this rectangular solid.

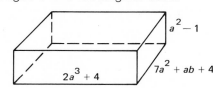

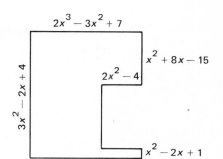

39. A four-digit number is chosen so that the difference found by subtracting the last digit (the units' digit) from the first digit is k and the difference found by subtracting the third digit from the second is $2k$, where k is positive. Another four-digit number is formed by reversing the digits in the original number. Write a simplified expression for the positive difference between the two numbers in terms of k.

12345678 KNOW YOUR CALCULATOR

An electronic calculator can be a very useful tool. To use one effectively, you should be familiar with its features. Some typical calculator keys are described below. Before proceeding, locate these keys on your calculator.

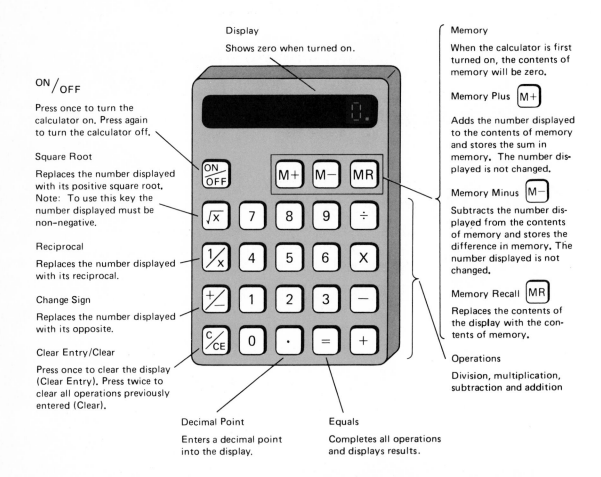

Display

Shows zero when turned on.

ON/OFF

Press once to turn the calculator on. Press again to turn the calculator off.

Square Root

Replaces the number displayed with its positive square root. Note: To use this key the number displayed must be non-negative.

Reciprocal

Replaces the number displayed with its reciprocal.

Change Sign

Replaces the number displayed with its opposite.

Clear Entry/Clear

Press once to clear the display (Clear Entry). Press twice to clear all operations previously entered (Clear).

Memory

When the calculator is first turned on, the contents of memory will be zero.

Memory Plus [M+]

Adds the number displayed to the contents of memory and stores the sum in memory. The number displayed is not changed.

Memory Minus [M−]

Subtracts the number displayed from the contents of memory and stores the difference in memory. The number displayed is not changed.

Memory Recall [MR]

Replaces the contents of the display with the contents of memory.

Operations

Division, multiplication, subtraction and addition

Decimal Point

Enters a decimal point into the display.

Equals

Completes all operations and displays results.

Remember, every calculator model is different. For particular questions, you should refer to the manual that comes with your calculator.

To use your calculator correctly you must understand the order in which it performs operations. Some calculators perform operations in the order we have agreed upon. (See Section 1-2.) Some perform operations in the order in which they are entered. When you press

$$9 \boxed{-} 3 \boxed{\div} 2 \boxed{=},$$

the result is 7.5 (that is, $9 - (3 \div 2)$) on a calculator that performs multiplication and division first, and then addition and subtraction. The result is 3 (that is, $(9 - 3) \div 2$) on a calculator that performs operations in the order in which they are entered.

The calculator memory provides an efficient way to save intermediate results for later use in a calculation. The change-sign key $\boxed{+/-}$ is useful in simplifying expressions involving subtraction and negative numbers.

The reciprocal key $\boxed{1/x}$ is useful in simplifying expressions involving division and fractions.

EXAMPLE Simplify $456 \div (67 - 29)$.

SOLUTION 1 Press $67 \boxed{-} 29 \boxed{=} \boxed{M+} 456 \boxed{\div} \boxed{MR} \boxed{=}$.
The display will show 12.

SOLUTION 2 Press $67 \boxed{-} 29 \boxed{=} \boxed{1/x} \boxed{\times} 456 \boxed{=}$.
The display will show 12.

EXERCISES

Simplify these with your calculator. Make sure the operations are performed in the order agreed upon in this book.

1. $407 - 13 \times 8$

2. $-81 - 5 \times 32 - 63$

3. $368 \div 23 - 14 \times 15$

4. $27 \times 8 - 288 \div 16$

5. $14 \times 12 + (-62) \times (-3)$

6. $360 \div 24 + 12 \times 13 + 351 \div 39$

7. $\dfrac{51}{136} - \dfrac{209}{152}$

8. $\dfrac{1}{15.94 - 2.4 \times 5.6}$

9. $\dfrac{-31.6 + 18.8}{17.63 - 11.23}$

10. $-93 + \dfrac{-158 + 1454}{12}$

11. $\dfrac{25}{137 - 4(136 - 154) - 109}$

12. $\dfrac{7 \times 8 - 168 \div 3}{-113 - (-148)}$

13. $\sqrt{84 \div (113 - 92)}$

14. $\sqrt{\dfrac{94 + (-418)}{-46 + (-54)}}$

15. $\sqrt{\dfrac{338 - 450}{379 - 554}}$

1-10 MULTIPLICATION AND DIVISION OF MONOMIALS

We use the meaning of exponents to help us multiply and divide monomials.

EXAMPLE 1 Multiply x^3 and x^4.

SOLUTION $x^3 \cdot x^4$

$= x \cdot x \cdot x \cdot x \cdot x \cdot x \cdot x$

$= x^7$

EXAMPLE 2 Divide x^5 by x^3.

SOLUTION $\dfrac{x^5}{x^3} = \dfrac{\overset{111}{\cancel{x}\cancel{x}\cancel{x}xx}}{\underset{111}{\cancel{x}\cancel{x}\cancel{x}}}$

$= x^2$

In general, when two terms have the same base, their exponents may be added for the product.

$$x^a \cdot x^b = \underbrace{xxx\ldots}_{\substack{a \\ \text{factors}}} \cdot \underbrace{xxx\ldots}_{\substack{b \\ \text{factors}}}$$

$$= \underbrace{xxxxxx\ldots}_{a+b \text{ factors}}$$

$$= x^{a+b}$$

When two terms have the same base, their exponents may be subtracted for the quotient.

When a is greater than b,

$$\frac{x^a}{x^b} = \frac{\overbrace{xxx\ldots}^{a \text{ factors}}}{\underbrace{xx\ldots}_{b \text{ factors}}}$$

$$= \underbrace{xxx\ldots}_{a-b \text{ factors}}$$

$$= x^{a-b}$$

$$\frac{x^b}{x^a} = \frac{\overbrace{xx\ldots}^{b \text{ factors}}}{\underbrace{xxx\ldots}_{a \text{ factors}}}$$

$$= \frac{1}{\underbrace{xxx\ldots}_{a-b \text{ factors}}}$$

$$= \frac{1}{x^{a-b}}$$

An expression such as $\dfrac{x^5}{x^5}$, $x \neq 0$, is equal to 1. Subtracting exponents gives $\dfrac{x^5}{x^5} = x^0$. For reasons such as this, a non-zero term with exponent zero is defined to be 1.

EXAMPLE 3 Simplify $\dfrac{x^3y^2}{xy^2}$.

SOLUTION **1**

$$\frac{x^3y^2}{xy^2} = \frac{\overset{1}{\cancel{x}}xx\overset{11}{\cancel{y}\cancel{y}}}{\underset{111}{\cancel{x}\cancel{y}\cancel{y}}}$$

$$= x^2$$

SOLUTION **2**

$$\frac{x^3y^2}{xy^2} = x^{3-1}y^{2-2}$$

$$= x^2y^0$$

$$= x^2$$

PROPERTY OF EXPONENTS FOR MULTIPLICATION

$$x^a \cdot x^b = x^{a+b}$$

PROPERTY OF EXPONENTS FOR DIVISION

For a greater than or equal to b and $x \neq 0$,

$$\frac{x^a}{x^b} = x^{a-b}, \qquad \frac{x^b}{x^a} = \frac{1}{x^{a-b}}.$$

Any factor of a product is called the **coefficient** of the other factors. The word "coefficient" usually is used to mean only the numerical coefficient when a constant occurs with variables.

coefficient of b

ab

coefficient of a

coefficient of b

$6ab$

coefficient of $6a$

$10x^2y$

numerical coefficient

To multiply or divide monomials, first multiply or divide their numerical coefficients.   Then multiply or divide the other factors using the properties of exponents.

EXAMPLE 4 Multiply $-3a^2b$ and $4ab^2$.

SOLUTION $(-3a^2b)(4ab^2) = -12(a^2b)(ab^2)$
$$= -12a^3b^3$$

EXAMPLE 5 Simplify $\dfrac{20x^4yz^3}{-10x^6yz^2}$.

SOLUTION $\dfrac{20x^4yz^3}{-10x^6yz^2} = \dfrac{-2y^{1-1}z^{3-2}}{x^{6-4}}$

$$= \frac{-2z}{x^2}$$

EXAMPLE 6 Simplify $\dfrac{4x^m}{-x}$.

SOLUTION $\dfrac{4x^m}{-x} = \dfrac{4x^m}{-1x}$

$$= -4x^{m-1}$$

CLASSROOM EXERCISES

Simplify each product.

1. $a^2 \cdot a^3$ **2.** $2m \cdot 4m$ **3.** $(4z)(-2z^2)$ **4.** $(5yz^2)(-3y^3z)$

Simplify each quotient.

5. $x^6 \div x^4$ **6.** $8y^3 \div 3y$ **7.** $20a^3b \div -4a^2b$ **8.** $x^b \div x^c$

EXERCISES

A   Simplify each product.

1. $x^4 \cdot x^5$ **2.** $a^{10} \cdot a^4$ **3.** $z^{10} \cdot z^4$ **4.** $c^8 \cdot c^3$

5. $c^x \cdot c^y$ **6.** $x^a \cdot x$ **7.** $(-3x)(4x)$ **8.** $(5y)(-2y)$

9. $(x^6)(-3x)$ **10.** $(d^5)(-2d)$ **11.** $(3.5t^3)(1.2t^5)$ **12.** $(7.1s^2)(1.1s^5)$

13. $(-2xy)(-3xy^4)$ **14.** $(-9x^3y)(-3xy)$ **15.** $x^{n+1} \cdot x^2$ **16.** $-2x^{m+1} \cdot 3x^{1-m}$

Simplify each quotient.

17. $\dfrac{x^7}{x}$ **18.** $\dfrac{c^8}{c}$ **19.** $\dfrac{-c^2}{c}$ **20.** $\dfrac{-x^{10}}{x^9}$ **21.** $\dfrac{x^{10}}{x^{10}}$ **22.** $\dfrac{a^3}{a^3}$

23. $\dfrac{0.8a^6}{0.2a}$ **24.** $\dfrac{1.2b^3}{0.4b^2}$ **25.** $\dfrac{20c^2t}{-4tc}$ **26.** $\dfrac{9r^2t}{-3rt}$ **27.** $\dfrac{-24abc}{-2ab}$ **28.** $\dfrac{-10rst}{-2rs}$

29. $(-x^2y) \div \dfrac{1}{3}xy$ **30.** $(-12xy) \div \dfrac{1}{4}y$ **31.** $28r^3s^3 \div 7r^2$

32. $\dfrac{-10x^my^n}{-5x^my}$ **33.** $\dfrac{-8a^nb^n}{-2ab^n}$ **34.** $\dfrac{x^{m+3}}{x^{m+1}}$

35. $\dfrac{a^{k+1}}{a^{k-1}}$ **36.** $\dfrac{-6a^hb^k}{3a^{-h}b^k}$ **37.** $\dfrac{14c^{n+1}d^m}{-7c^nd^{-m}}$

B   Simplify.

38. $(-2x)^3(3xy)^4$ **39.** $(5ab^2c)(-2abc^3)^2$ **40.** $(-4x)^4(3x^3) - (5x^5)(x^2)$

41. $\left(\dfrac{-6xy^3}{12x^2y^4}\right)^2$ **42.** $\dfrac{-14x^{2m}y^{3c}}{7x^{1-m}y^{-3c}}$ **43.** $\dfrac{(4x^ny^{n-1})^2}{8x^2y^{n-3}}$

C   **44.** Represent the area of a triangle whose base and height are both $a^{n+1}b^{k-4}$.

45. The distance traveled by a jet airplane is represented as $1.76x^{2m-3}y^{n+4}$. Its speed is $1.1x^{4-m}y^{-2n}$. Write an expression for the length of time of the flight. Simplify the expression.

1-11   MULTIPLICATION OF POLYNOMIALS

To multiply polynomials, arrange factors in descending or ascending powers of one variable.   Then use the Distributive Property.

EXAMPLE 1   Simplify $-(3x - 2)$.

   SOLUTION $-(3x - 2) = -3x - (-2)$
$$= -3x + 2$$

EXAMPLE 2   Multiply $4x^2$ and $2x^2 - 5x - 3$.

   SOLUTION $4x^2(2x^2 - 5x - 3) = (4x^2)(2x^2) - (4x^2)(5x) - (4x^2)(3)$
$$= 8x^4 - 20x^3 - 12x^2$$

EXAMPLE 3   Simplify $(2x - 3)(x + 3)$.

   SOLUTION $(2x - 3)(x + 3) = (2x - 3)x + (2x - 3)3$
$$= 2x \cdot x - 3 \cdot x + 2x \cdot 3 - 3 \cdot 3$$
$$= 2x^2 - 3x + 6x - 9$$
$$= 2x^2 + 3x - 9$$

EXAMPLE 4   Multiply $4a^2 + 3b^2 - 5ab$ and $a^2 - 2ab$.

   SOLUTION
$$
\begin{array}{l}
4a^2 - 5ab + 3b^2 \\
a^2 - 2ab \\
\hline
4a^4 - 5a^3b + 3a^2b^2 \\
- 8a^3b + 10a^2b^2 - 6ab^3 \\
\hline
4a^4 - 13a^3b + 13a^2b^2 - 6ab^3
\end{array}
$$

MULTIPLYING POLYNOMIALS

1.   Arrange factors in descending or ascending powers of one variable.
2.   Use the Distributive Property.

CLASSROOM EXERCISES

Multiply.

1. $(2a)(4a^2 - 3a + 9)$

2. $(3t^2)(5t - 15t^2 + 4t^3)$

3. $(x - 5)(x + 4)$

4. $(x^2 + 3x + 10)(2x + 4)$

5. $(x^2 + 4xy)(5x^2 + 2y^2 - xy)$

6. $(2mn - 5n)(3mn - 4m + 3)$

EXERCISES

Ⓐ Multiply.

1. $-3x^2(4x^3 + 5x^2 + 10)$
2. $-5x^2(2x^3 + 3x^2 + 1)$
3. $(3c + 1)(c + 2)$
4. $(4a - 5)(a + 7)$
5. $(x - 5)(x - 5)$
6. $(x - 7)(x - 7)$
7. $(2x + 3)(2x + 3)$
8. $(3x + 5)(3x + 5)$
9. $(x^2 - 2y)(x^2 - 5y)$
10. $(x^2 - 4y)(x^2 - 3y)$
11. $\left(\frac{1}{2}x^2 - y\right)\left(\frac{1}{3}x^2 - 2y\right)$
12. $\left(\frac{1}{5}x^2 - y\right)\left(\frac{1}{4}x^2 - 5y\right)$
13. $(2c - 4)(4c^2 + 5c + 9)$
14. $(7b + 1)(16b^2 - 8b + 5)$
15. $(2a^2 - ab + b^2)(a^2 - ab)$
16. $(5a^2 - 2ab + b^2)(2a^2 - ab)$
17. $(x^2 + x + 1)(x - 1)$
18. $(x^2 - x + 1)(x + 1)$

Ⓑ
19. $(a^2 + a - 1)(a^2 - a + 1)$
20. $(m^2 + n^2 - mn)(m^2 + mn + n^2)$
21. $(y)(y - 2)(y - 7)$
22. $-3y(y + 2)^2$
23. $(a^x + b^y)(a^x + b^y)$
24. $(y^{2a} + y^a + 1)(y^a + 1)$

25. Represent the volume of a cube having sides of length $3x - 4$.

Ⓒ 26. Find the value of k which makes the following statement true.
$(3x + k)(7x - k) = 21x^2 + 16x - k^2$

THE CENSUS TAKER

When a census-taker called at one house during the 1980 census, the following conversation took place with the father of the family.

"How many children do you have?" asked the census-taker.

"Three," replied the father honestly.

"What are their ages?" the census-taker asked next.

"I refuse to say," replied the father, "but I will tell you that the product of their ages is 36."

"That isn't very helpful," said the census-taker.

"All right then, I will tell you that the sum of their ages is the same as my house number."

The census-taker studied the number next to the door and after awhile replied, "I still don't know their ages."

"One more clue," said the father. "My oldest child is a boy."

The census-taker, who had never seen the children, pondered for a few minutes and then exclaimed, "Now I know! Thank you."

1. How old are the three children?   2. Explain how you found your answer.

1-12   DIVISION OF POLYNOMIALS

We may divide a polynomial by a monomial by dividing each of its terms by the monomial.

EXAMPLE 1   Divide $4x^2 + 2x + 6$ by 2.

SOLUTION $\dfrac{4x^2 + 2x + 6}{2} = \dfrac{4x^2}{2} + \dfrac{2x}{2} + \dfrac{6}{2}$

$= 2x^2 + x + 3$

EXAMPLE 2   Simplify $\dfrac{5x^3y - 15x^2y^2 + 5xy}{5xy}$.

SOLUTION $\dfrac{5x^3y - 15x^2y^2 + 5xy}{5xy} = \dfrac{5x^3y}{5xy} - \dfrac{15x^2y^2}{5xy} + \dfrac{5xy}{5xy}$

$= x^2 - 3xy + 1$

EXAMPLE 3   Divide $(a - b)x + 2(a - b)y + a - b$ by $a - b$.

SOLUTION $\dfrac{(a - b)x + 2(a - b)y + a - b}{a - b} = \dfrac{(a - b)x}{a - b} + \dfrac{2(a - b)y}{a - b} + \dfrac{a - b}{a - b}$

$= x + 2y + 1$

Also, we may divide a polynomial by another polynomial by using a process similar to division in arithmetic. The first step is to arrange the polynomial and its divisor in descending order of one variable.

EXAMPLE 4   Divide $7a + a^2 + 12$ by $a + 4$.

SOLUTION   In descending powers of a, we have
$(a^2 + 7a + 12) \div (a + 4)$.

$$
\begin{array}{r}
\boxed{a} + ③ \\
a + 4 \overline{\smash{)}a^2 + 7a + 12} \\
\underline{\boxed{a^2 + 4a}} \\
3a + 12 \\
\underline{③a + 12} \\
0
\end{array}
$$

CONCLUSION $(a^2 + 7a + 12) \div (a + 4) = a + 3$

The results of division may be checked by multiplying the quotient and the divisor, and then adding the remainder. The result of the check should be the dividend.

EXAMPLE 5   Divide $18a^2 + 11a + 6$ by $9a + 1$.   Check your results.

SOLUTION

$$
\begin{array}{r}
\boxed{2a} + ⓵ \longleftarrow \text{quotient} \\
9a + 1\overline{)18a^2 + 11a + 6} \longleftarrow \text{dividend} \\
\underline{\boxed{18a^2 + 2a}} \\
9a + 6 \\
\underline{(9a + 1)} \\
5 \longleftarrow \text{remainder}
\end{array}
$$

divisor

CHECK

$$(9a + 1)(2a + 1) + 5 \overset{?}{=} 18a^2 + 11a + 6$$
$$(9a + 1)2a + (9a + 1)1 + 5 \overset{?}{=} 18a^2 + 11a + 6$$
$$18a^2 + 2a + 9a + 1 + 5 \overset{?}{=} 18a^2 + 11a + 6$$
$$18a^2 + 11a + 6 = 18a^2 + 11a + 6 \quad ✔$$

In using the long division form, it is helpful to show zero for any missing term.

EXAMPLE 6   Simplify $\dfrac{x^3 + 27}{x - 3}$.   Check your work.

SOLUTION

$$
\begin{array}{r}
\boxed{x^2} + ⟨3x⟩ + \boxed{9} \\
x - 3\overline{)x^3 + 0x^2 + 0x + 27} \\
\underline{\boxed{x^3 - 3x^2}} \\
3x^2 + 0x \\
\underline{⟨3x^2 - 9x⟩} \\
9x + 27 \\
\underline{\boxed{9x - 27}} \\
54
\end{array}
$$

CHECK   The check is left for the student.

LONG DIVISION WITH POLYNOMIALS

1. Arrange dividend and divisor in descending order of one variable.
2. Insert zero for each term "missing" from the dividend.
3. Divide.
4. Simplify the quotient.
5. Check your result by multiplying the quotient and the divisor and then adding the remainder.   This result should be the dividend.

CLASSROOM EXERCISES

Divide.

1. $(3x^2 + 12x + 18) \div 3$

2. $(a^5 - 4a^3 - 2a^2) \div a^2$

3. $(8x^4y^2 + 4x^3y^2 + 2x^2y + 10xy) \div 2xy$

4. $3(x - y)^2 + 2(x - y) \div (x - y)$

5. $(6a^2 - 5a - 4) \div (2a + 1)$

6. $(y^2 - 2y - 18) \div (y + 3)$

7. $(5a + a^3 - 4)$ by $(a - 3)$

8. $(x^3 - 10)$ by $(x + 2)$

EXERCISES

A Divide.

1. $(5a^2 - 20) \div 5$

2. $(18x - 27) \div (-9)$

3. $(6a^3 - 12a^2 + 18a) \div a$

4. $(x^4 - 2x^3 + 4x^2) \div x$

5. $(30a^3 + 15a^2 + 20a) \div 5a$

6. $(14x^5 - 21x^3 + 7x^2) \div 7x$

7. $(5a^3b + 2a^2b^2) \div (-ab)$

8. $(32x^2y - 24x^2y^2) \div (-8xy)$

9. $[3(a - b) + n(a - b)]$ by $(a - b)$

10. $[(a + b)^2 + c(a + b)]$ by $(a + b)$

11. $[(x + y)^2 + 3(x + y)]$ by $(x + y)$

12. $[5(x - y) - m(x - y)]$ by $(x - y)$

13. $(x^2 + 4x + 4) \div (x + 2)$

14. $(a^2 + 6a + 9) \div (a + 3)$

15. $(10x^2 - x - 21)$ by $(2x - 3)$

16. $(21b^2 + b - 2) \div (3b + 1)$

17. $(4a^2 + 6a + 9) \div (2a - 5)$

18. $(15x^2 - x - 16) \div (5x + 3)$

19. $(21x^2 - 6x - 25) \div (7x + 5)$

20. $(15a^2 + 14a - 12) \div (3a + 4)$

21. $(x^6 - 13x^3 + 42) \div (x^3 - 7)$

22. $(x^8 - x^4 - 6) \div (x^4 - 3)$

23. $(x^3 + y^3) \div (x + y)$

24. $(x^3 - y^3) \div (x - y)$

25. $(c^3 - 27) \div (c - 3)$

26. $(d^3 + 8) \div (d + 2)$

27. $(16 - x - x^3)$ by $(4 + x)$

28. $(25 + x - x^3)$ by $(5 + x)$

29. $\dfrac{6a^3 + a^2 - 28a - 35}{2a - 5}$

30. $\dfrac{6b^3 - 8b^2 - 17b - 10}{3b + 2}$

B **31.** $(x^4 + 4y^4) \div (x^2 - 2xy + 2y^2)$

32. $(x^6 + x^4 - x^3 + x^2 + 1) \div (x^2 + x + 1)$

33. $(x^4 - 9x^2 + 16) \div (x^2 - 3x + 4)$

34. $(x^5 - 3x^2 - 52) \div (x^2 - 4)$

35. $(x^{2n} - x^n - 6) \div (x^n + 2)$

36. $(x^{2n} + 5x^n - 24) \div (x^n + 8)$

37. $\dfrac{2x^3 + x^4 - 6x^2 + 11x - 10}{x^2 + 2 - x}$

38. $(x^3 + a^3) \div (x + a)$

C **39.** $(a^{3n} + b^{3n}) \div (a^n + b^n)$

40. $(x^{3a} - y^{3a}) \div (x^a - y^a)$

41. $\dfrac{a^2(x - y) - 2a(x - y) + (x - y)}{(x - y)} \div (a - 1)$

42. Find an expression E such that $(x - 7)E = x^2 - 15x + 56$.

1-13 SIMPLIFYING ALGEBRAIC EXPRESSIONS

To simplify an algebraic expression containing parentheses, it often is good practice to first clear the expression of parentheses.

EXAMPLE 1 Simplify $15 + 2(x - 4)$.

SOLUTION $15 + 2(x - 4) = 15 + 2x - 8$
$$= 7 + 2x, \text{ or } 2x + 7$$

EXAMPLE 2 Simplify $3(x^2 - 3x + 2) - 2(10 - 4x^2)$

SOLUTION $3(x^2 - 3x + 2) - 2(10 - 4x^2) = 3x^2 - 9x + 6 - 20 + 8x^2$
$$= 11x^2 - 9x - 14$$

Algebraic expressions may contain one pair of grouping symbols, parentheses or brackets, between another. Although either can be removed first, often it is better to remove the inner symbol pair and combine like terms before removing the outer symbols.

EXAMPLE 3 Simplify $5x - [(3x + 1) - 3 - 2(2x - 3)]$.

SOLUTION
$$5x - [(3x + 1) - 3 - 2(2x - 3)]$$
$$= 5x - [3x + 1 - 3 - 4x + 6]$$
$$= 5x - [-x + 4]$$
$$= 5x + x - 4$$
$$= 6x - 4$$

Sometimes, it is useful to place parentheses in an expression to enclose some terms. When this is done, the result should be checked by *removing* the parentheses. The expression obtained should be the same as the original expression.

EXAMPLE 4 Enclose the last two terms of $a - b - c$ between parentheses preceded by $+$.

SOLUTION $a - b - c = a + (-b - c)$

CHECK $a + (-b - c) \overset{?}{=} a - b - c$
$$a - b - c = a - b - c \quad ✔$$

EXAMPLE 5 Enclose the last two terms of $a - b - c$ between parentheses preceded by $-$.

SOLUTION $a - b - c = a - (b + c)$

CHECK $a - (b + c) \overset{?}{=} a - b - c$
$$a - b - c = a - b - c \quad ✔$$

EXAMPLE 6 Enclose the last two terms of $a + b - c + d$ between parentheses preceded by $-$.

SOLUTION $a + b - c + d = a + b - (c - d)$

CHECK $a + b - (c - d) \overset{?}{=} a + b - c + d$
$a + b - c + d = a + b - c + d$ ✔

CLASSROOM EXERCISES

Simplify.

1. $4x + (5 - x)$

2. $7c - (3c - 1)$

3. $x(x - 2) - 3x(x + 2)$

4. $(3x^2 - 4x + 5) - (2x^2 - 3x + 9)$

Enclose the last two terms of each polynomial between parentheses preceded by $+$.

5. $x - y - 2z - a$

6. $2c + 9d - 5$

Enclose the last two terms of each polynomial between parentheses preceded by $-$.

7. $a - b - c - d$

8. $x - y - x^2 + y^2$

Simplify.

9. $7a - [(2a + 5) - 6 - (2a + 7)]$

10. $p + [3r + (3p - 4r) - 1]$

EXERCISES

Ⓐ Simplify.

1. $4x + (2 - x)$

2. $3a + (5 - a)$

3. $7c - (2c - 1)$

4. $2x - (x - 4)$

5. $3x(2x - 3) + 4x(x + 2)$

6. $x(x - 1) + 2x(x + 2)$

7. $2x^2(2x - 1) - x(x + 2)$

8. $3b^2(4b + 2) - b(b + 7)$

9. $8\left(\frac{1}{2}a - \frac{1}{4}b + \frac{1}{8}\right) - 6\left(\frac{2}{3}a - \frac{1}{6}b + \frac{1}{2}\right)$

10. $10\left(\frac{1}{5}x - \frac{1}{2}y + \frac{1}{10}\right) - 4\left(\frac{1}{4}x - \frac{1}{2}y + 8\right)$

Enclose the last two terms of each polynomial between parentheses preceded by $+$.

11. $m + n + p - q$

12. $c - d + e - f$

13. $b - a - ax + bx$

Enclose the last two terms of each polynomial between parentheses preceded by $-$.

14. $a + b - ac - bc$

15. $x^2 + 1 - ax^2 - a$

16. $a^2 - b^2 + a - b$

Simplify.

17. $(a - b) - [(b + c) - (a - c)]$

18. $(x - 2y) - [(2y + z) - (x - z)]$

19. $(x + y) - [2x - (x + y)]$

20. $(a + 2b) - [2a - (a + 2b)]$

21. $3x + [(2x - 4) - 4 - (2x - 4)]$

22. $10z + [(2z - 1) - 2 - (2z - 1)]$

23. $x(x + 2) - 3[(x + 1) - 4x(2x - 1)]$

24. $y(y + 1) - 4[(y + 2) - 3y(4y - 1)]$

B **25.** $3x^n(x - 4) - 2x^n(x + 5)$

26. $ab(a^2 - ab + b^2) - 3a(a^2b + ab^2)$

27. $(3c - 1)[(c + 2) - 4(c - 1)]$

28. $x^3 - 7[(2x^4 - x^3 + x^2) \div x] - 2(x^2 - 1)$

29. $2(a^3 - ab) - (a + b)(a^2 - ab + b^2)$

30. $6(x^2 - 1) - 4[(x^4 - 8x^2 + 15) \div (x^2 - 5)]$

C **31.** Find the number for k for which $2x - 3[x^2 - x((x - 3) + k)]$ simplifies to $-4x$.

32. Find the numbers for a and b for which $a(x^2 - 9) - 3[b - 5x(x - 10)]$ simplifies to $19x^2 - 150x - 42$.

CHECKING YOUR UNDERSTANDING

WORDS

algebraic expression	domain of a variable	term
binomial	monomial	trinomial
coefficient	polynomial	variable

CONCEPTS

■ Algebraic expressions containing like terms may be simplified. [1-8, 1-13]

■ When terms in a product or quotient have the same base, their exponents may be added or subtracted to simplify the product or quotient. [1-10]

■ The operations of addition, subtraction, multiplication, and division may be applied to polynomials. [1-9 to 1-12]

PROCESSES

■ Multiply or divide, using properties of exponents. [1-10]

1. $(x^5y^3)(x^2y^4)$ **2.** $(-3b^4)(2a^3b)$ **3.** $30x^2y^3 \div -10xy^2$ **4.** $\dfrac{-12r^2s^3t^4}{3rs^3t^7}$

■ Add, subtract, multiply, divide, and simplify polynomials. [1-8 to 1-13]

5. $(5x - 3y) + (2x + 7y)$ **6.** $(5x^2 + 2x) - (x^2 + 4x - 1)$ **7.** $(5x - 1)(3x + 4)$

8. $(a^2 + 4a - 5) \div (a + 5)$ **9.** $3x^2 - 2xy - x^2 + xy$ **10.** $2x - 3 + 3(x + 7)$

11. $xy - 5y(1 + x)$ **12.** $x - [5 - 2(x + 5) - 2x]$ **13.** $2x - [3(x + 3) - (2x - 1)]$

OBJECTIVE: Represent a situation given verbally with an algebraic expression.

1-14 PROBLEM SOLVING: WRITING ALGEBRAIC EXPRESSIONS

An algebraic expression can provide a mathematical description of a practical problem. Certain key words may indicate the operations to be used in writing the algebraic expression.

KEY WORDS FOR WRITING ALGEBRAIC EXPRESSIONS

Addition: sum, and, added, increased by

Subtraction: difference, decreased by, less

Addition or Subtraction: larger, smaller, greater than, less than,
                         more, fewer

Multiplication: product, factors, times, (fraction) of, twice, triple

Division: quotient, divisor

EXAMPLE 1 Write an algebraic expression for the sum of 5 and 4 times a number.

SOLUTION Use n for the number.
$$5 + 4n$$

EXAMPLE 2 Write an algebraic expression for 20 less than 5 times a number.

SOLUTION Use n for the number.
$$5n - 20$$

EXAMPLE 3 Express algebraically the product of 6 and the sum of $5x$ and y.

SOLUTION $6(5x + y)$

EXAMPLE 4 Express algebraically 3 more than the sum of the square of a number and twice the number.

SOLUTION Use n for the number.
$$n^2 + 2n + 3$$

EXAMPLE 5 Write an algebraic expression for a number which when added to n gives 56.

SOLUTION $56 - n$

CHECK $n + (56 - n) \overset{?}{=} 56$
$n + 56 - n \overset{?}{=} 56$
$56 = 56$ ✔

EXAMPLE 6 Write an algebraic expression for the value in cents of d dimes and $2q$ quarters.

SOLUTION $10d + 25(2q)$, or $10d + 50q$

EXAMPLE 7 Express algebraically the value of q quarters and twice as many nickels.

SOLUTION Since q is the number of quarters, $2q$ is the number of nickels.

$25q + 5(2q)$, which simplifies to $25q + 10q$, or $35q$

EXAMPLE 8 John is a years old. Sarah is 3 times as old. Represent the age of each 10 years ago.

SOLUTION Make a chart.

	Present Age	Age 10 Years Ago
John	a	$a - 10$
Sarah	$3a$	$3a - 10$

CLASSROOM EXERCISES

Write as an algebraic expression.

1. 5 more than twice a number

2. x divided by 2 fewer than x

3. 19 less than half a number

4. $\frac{5}{7}$ of the sum of a number and 13

5. one-fourth of a number decreased by two times the number

6. a number which when added to y gives 20

7. the value of x nickels and $2y$ quarters (in cents)

8. the age of John in 15 years if he is $3x$ years old now

9. 26 less 11 times the product of x and y

10. 13 greater than $\frac{1}{4}$ the difference of a and b

EXERCISES

A Write as an algebraic expression.

1. the sum of 3 times a number and 7

2. the sum of 5 times a number and 3

3. 7 added to two-thirds of a number

4. 11 added to five-sixths of a number

5. the product of 3 and the sum of $2x$ and 4

6. the product of 8 and the sum of $11y$ and 2

7. the value (in cents) of $2x$ half-dollars and y nickels

8. the value (in cents) of a quarters and $6b$ pennies

9. John's age in 15 years if he is now $x - 2$ years old

10. Mary's age 10 years ago if her present age is $y + 3$

11. 50 less 3 times the quotient of x and y

12. 47 less 8 times the quotient of a and b

13. 4 greater than 6 times the difference of a and b

14. 12 greater than 7 times the difference of b and a

15. y decreased by the product of x and 5 fewer than x

16. $3z$ decreased by the product of a and 2 fewer than a

17. a fraction with a denominator that is 3 less than a number and a numerator that is 2 less the number

18. a fraction with a denominator that is 4 less than a number and a numerator that is 3 less the number

19. the sum of two consecutive even integers

20. the sum of two consecutive odd integers

B **21.** Bill is 8 times his son's age. Express what Bill's age will be in 30 years.

22. The length of a rectangle is 2 more than 3 times the width. Express the area of the rectangle.

23. A sum of money consists of nickels, dimes and quarters. There are 8 more quarters than nickels and the number of dimes is 2 less than 3 times the number of nickels. Express the total value of the money.

24. Susan is $x - 4$ years old now. Peter is 3 times as old. Express Peter's age 5 years ago.

25. Let n represent the first of three numbers. The second number exceeds the first by 15 and the third number exceeds the second by $2n$. Express the product of the three numbers.

26. Two trains leave from the same town and travel in opposite directions. One train averages 110 kilometers per hour, the other 90 kilometers per hour. Express their distance apart after t hours.

27. The base of a triangle is represented by b. A second side is 2 more than the base and the third side is 8 less than twice the base. Write an expression for the perimeter.

C **28.** In a factory, Machine A produced n parts. Machine B produced 8 more than twice the number produced by A. Machine C produced 7 less than the number produced by B. Write an expression for the total number of parts produced. When the total number of parts produced is 59, find the number of parts produced by each machine.

CHAPTER REVIEW

Simplify. [1-1]

1. $|-41|$

2. $-\left(-\frac{2}{3}\right)$

3. $|16|$

Graph the numbers.

4. integers greater than -3

5. real numbers less than 5

6. real numbers less than 10.5 and greater than 2

Simplify the sum. Use the Associative Property of Addition. [1-2 to 1-9]

Write the product as a sum. Use the Distributive Property.

7. $\left(4\frac{1}{8} + 2\frac{6}{7}\right) + 3\frac{1}{7} = \underline{\quad ? \quad}$

8. $5(7 + 18)$

Simplify.

9. $5 - 2 \times 1 + 15 \div 3$

10. $100 \div 10 - 2 + 25$

11. $(3 + 17) \div 4 + (8 - 2)$

12. $29 + (-13)$

13. $-67 + (-48)$

14. $-15.8 + 4$

15. $-\frac{1}{3} + \frac{5}{3}$

16. $24 - 92$

17. $17.3 - (-26.4)$

18. $-152 - 37$

19. $\frac{3}{7} - \frac{8}{7}$

20. $14(-6)$

21. $(-3.2)(-9.6)$

22. $-\frac{1}{3}(50)$

23. $\left(-\frac{2}{3}\right)\left(\frac{1}{4}\right)\left(-\frac{9}{10}\right)$

24. $-16 \div 2$

25. $-72 \div -8$

26. $12.6 \div 2$

27. $\frac{4}{5} \div -\frac{1}{3}$

28. $(-3)^3$

29. $(-2)^4$

30. $\sqrt{121}$

31. $\sqrt{225}$

32. $4y^2 - 6y^2$

33. $5x^2 - 3x + 2x - 7$

34. $-2x^2 - 3x - 7 + 5x^2 + x - 3$

35. $(2x^2 + 3x + 4) + (-8x^2 - 7x + 15)$

36. $(4m^2 + 3mn - 9n^2) + (-2m^2 + 15n^2) + (10mn - 27m^2)$

37. $(8a^2 - 5ab - 7b^2) - (-3a^2 + 4ab + b^2)$

38. $(15hm + 4m^2) - (-6h^2 - 16hm - 3m^2)$

Simplify. [1-10, 1-11]

39. $y^3 \cdot y^7$

40. $(-3c^4)(5c^2)$

41. $(-10x^2y)(-2xy^5)$

42. $x^{10} \div x^5$

43. $-30a^2b \div (2ab)$

44. $10x^a \div (-2x^b)$

Multiply.

45. $-2a^3(5a^4 - 2a^3 + 3a)$

46. $(4x^2 - 2y^2)(4x^2 + 2y^2)$

47. $(3a - 1)(2a^2 + 3a - 5)$

Simplify. [1-12, 1-13]

48. $(y^3 + 4y^2 - 3y) \div y$

49. $(12x^2 + 20x - 8) \div (3x - 1)$

50. $(x^3 + 27) \div (x + 3)$

51. $-4x - 5(2x + 3)$

52. $x(x - 1) - 2x(x - 4)$

53. $(a - b) - 2[(b - c) - (a - c)]$

54. Enclose the last two terms of $x^4 - 2x^3 - 4x^2 - x + 1$ between parentheses preceded by $-$.

Write as an algebraic expression. [1-14]

55. 5 added to two-thirds of a number

56. 3 more than the sum of 7 and the cube of a number

57. the value (in cents) of $3q$ quarters and d dimes

58. Eric's age in 5 years if his present age is $y - 4$

CAPSULE REVIEW

Write the letter of the best response.

1. The property illustrated by $(2 + 3) + 7 = 2 + (3 + 7)$ is the
   a. Commutative Property of Addition   **b.** Commutative Property of Multiplication
   c. Associative Property of Addition   **d.** Associative Property of Multiplication
   e. Distributive Property

2. $150 \div 5 \times 2 - 4 + 9 =$
   a. 20   **b.** 210   **c.** -6 **d.** -20 **e.** 65

3. The sum of -13.4 and 15.8 is
   a. -29.2 **b.** -2.4 **c.** 2.4 **d.** 29.2 **e.** -29.4

4. The product of $\left(\frac{1}{3}\right)\left(-\frac{3}{4}\right)$, and $\frac{5}{8}$ is
   a. $-\frac{5}{32}$ **b.** $\frac{5}{32}$ **c.** $\frac{32}{5}$ **d.** $-\frac{32}{5}$ **e.** $-\frac{15}{6}$

5. $\sqrt{121} =$
   a. -11 **b.** 11 **c.** ± 11 **d.** $\sqrt{11}$ **e.** $-\sqrt{11}$

6. The sum of $-4a^3 - 3a + 11$ and $5a^3 + 9a - 15$ is
   a. $a^3 - 12a - 4$ **b.** $a^3 + 6a - 4$ **c.** $-a^3 + 6a - 4$ **d.** $a^3 - 6a - 4$ **e.** $a^3 + 6a + 4$

7. The product of $(-7a^3)$ and $3a^2 + 16a - 5$ is
   a. $-21a^5 - 112a^4 + 35a^3$ **b.** $-21a^5 + 112a^4 + 35a^3$ **c.** $21a^5 - 112a^4 + 35a^3$
   d. $-21a^5 - 112a^4 - 35a^3$ **e.** $21a^5 - 112a^4 - 35a^3$

8. When $2c^2 - c - 6$ is divided by $c - 2$ the quotient is
   a. $2c - 3$ **b.** $-2c - 3$ **c.** $2c + 3$ **d.** $-2c + 3$ **e.** $2c^2 + 3$

9. $6y + 3 - (y - 4 - 5y - 6) =$
   a. 13   **b.** -7 **c.** $2y + 13$ **d.** $2y - 7$ **e.** $10y + 13$

10. The algebraic expression for 36 less than 6 times the difference of x and y is
   a. $36 - 6(x + y)$ **b.** $36 - 6(x - y)$ **c.** $6(x + y) - 36$
   d. $6(x - y) - 36$ **e.** $36 + 6(x - y)$

CHAPTER TEST

1. Graph the real numbers greater than -3.

2. Give the absolute value of -5.7.

Simplify.

3. $\left(7 + \frac{3}{4}\right) \cdot 8$

4. $2 \cdot 3 + 4 \cdot 5$

Add.

5. -7 and 4

6. $-1\frac{1}{2}$ and $-\frac{3}{4}$

7. $3a^2 + 2ab - b^2$ and $a^2 - 3ab - 2b^2$

Subtract.

8. 5 from -3

9. -4 from 6

10. $4a^2 - b^2$ from $3a^2 + 5ab + b^2$

Multiply.

11. -5, 2, and -1

12. $-\frac{2}{3}$ and $\frac{3}{4}$

13. $-3a^2b$ and $4a^3b$

Divide.

14. -42 by -6

15. $\frac{3}{4}$ by $-\frac{1}{2}$

16. $-20a^6b^4$ by $-2a^2b$

Simplify.

17. 3^4

18. $\sqrt[3]{64}$

19. $8 + 3a - b + 2 + 4b$

20. $3x + 5x - 2x^2$

21. $5a - 3(b - a)$

22. $2a + 4(a - 3b)$

Multiply.

23. $3x$ and $5x - 2$

24. $x^2 + 2x$ and $x^2 - x + 3$

Divide.

25. $6a^2 - 4a$ by $2a$

26. $4a^2 + 4ab - 3b^2$ by $2a - b$

Write as an algebraic expression.

27. 10 less than 3 times a number

28. the sum of twice a number and the square of the number

Write the letter of the best response.

29. $10 \cdot \left(5 + \frac{8 - 4}{2}\right) =$

    a. 50   **b.** 54   **c.** 56   **d.** 70   **e.** 110

30. $-1\frac{1}{4} + 3 =$

    a. $-4\frac{1}{4}$ **b.** $-1\frac{3}{4}$ **c.** $1\frac{1}{4}$ **d.** $1\frac{3}{4}$ **e.** $2\frac{1}{4}$

31. $-5 - (-8) =$

    a. 13 **b.** 3 **c.** 0 **d.** -3 **e.** -13

32. $-\frac{1}{2} \cdot \frac{2}{3} =$

    a. $-\frac{2}{5}$ **b.** $-\frac{1}{3}$ **c.** $\frac{1}{6}$ **d.** $\frac{1}{3}$ **e.** $\frac{2}{5}$

33. $\frac{3}{10} \div \left(-\frac{9}{5}\right) =$

    a. $\frac{4}{5}$ **b.** $\frac{3}{2}$ **c.** $\frac{27}{50}$ **d.** -6 **e.** $-\frac{1}{6}$

34. Which is the graph of the integers greater than -3 and less than 2?

    a. 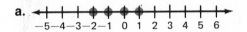   **b.**

    c.    **d.**

35. What is the third power of 8?

    a. 2 **b.** 11 **c.** 24 **d.** 64 **e.** 512

36. $x^2 + 3x - x - 2x^2 =$

    a. $-x^2 + 2x$ **b.** $3x^2 + 2x$ **c.** $x^2 + 2x$ **d.** $-x^2 + 3$ **e.** x^2

37. What is the sum of $5x^2 - 7x + 2$ and $3x^2 - x - 5$?

    a. $8x^2 + 8x + 7$ **b.** $8x^2 - 8x + 7$ **c.** $8x^2 - 8x - 3$

    d. $8x^2 - 6x - 3$ **e.** $8x^2 + 6x + 3$

38. What is the product of $3xy^2$ and $2x^3y^0$?

    a. $5x^3y^0$ **b.** $5x^4y$ **c.** $6x^3y^0$ **d.** $6x^3y^2$ **e.** $6x^4y^2$

39. What is the product of $x + 2$ and $2x - 3$?

    a. $2x^2 - 6$ **b.** $2x^2 + 6$ **c.** $2x^2 - x - 6$ **d.** $2x^2 + x - 6$ **e.** $2x^2 - 5x - 6$

40. What is $x^3 + 27$ divided by $x + 3$?

    a. $x^2 + 9$ **b.** $x^2 - 9$ **c.** $x^2 - 6x + 9$ **d.** $x^2 + 3x + 9$ **e.** $x^2 - 3x + 9$

41. $x^2 - x + 6 - (3x - 2) =$

    a. $x^2 - 2x + 4$ **b.** $x^2 - 4x + 4$ **c.** $x^2 - 4x + 8$

    d. $x^2 + 2x + 8$ **e.** $x^2 + 4x - 4$

42. What algebraic expression represents the product of a number and its cube?

    a. x^3 **b.** $x \cdot x^2$ **c.** $x \cdot x^3$ **d.** $x \cdot 3x$ **e.** $x \cdot 2x$

CHAPTER 2

FIRST-DEGREE EQUATIONS
AND INEQUALITIES
HAVING ONE VARIABLE

Audio technicians and engineers are responsible for the sound reproduced by various electronic recording and transmitting devices. Since vast amounts of entertainment and information are delivered electronically, it is a serious responsibility. A background in basic electronics is essential for the technician. A college degree requiring mathematical competence is necessary for the engineer.

OBJECTIVES: Solve first-degree equations and inequalities having one variable. Solve problems using equations and inequalities.

2-1 EQUATIONS, INEQUALITIES, AND SOLUTIONS

A mathematical sentence is a sentence that involves mathematical symbols and terms. A mathematical sentence showing that two expressions represent the same number is an equation. One showing that two expressions represent different numbers is an inequality. The symbols used in inequalities include $>$ to mean "is greater than," $<$ to mean "is less than," and $\neq$ to mean "is not equal to."

MATHEMATICAL SENTENCES

Equations	Inequalities
$4 + 5 = 9$	$16 - 10 < 7$
$3 \cdot 4 = 10 + 2$	$6 + 5 \neq 4 + 1$
$x + 3 = 16$	$21 + z < 48$
$3x + 8y = 24$	$16 - a > 9 + b$

A mathematical sentence that does not contain a variable gives information that is either true or false.

$4 + 5 = 9$ True $9 - 3 = 6 + 1$ False
$16 - 10 < 7$ True $7 - 3 > 5$ False

A sentence that contains a variable usually does not give enough information for determining whether the sentence is true or false. When the variable is replaced by a number from its domain, however, there is enough information. When the sentence is true, the number that replaced the variable is a **solution** of the equation or inequality. The set of all solutions is the **solution set**. The process of finding the solutions is called *solving* the equation or inequality.

EXAMPLE 1 Give the solution for $2x = 14$.

SOLUTION We know $2 \cdot 7 = 14$.
Thus, 7 is the solution.

EXAMPLE 2 Give the solutions for $2x > 14$.

SOLUTION We know that 2 times any number greater than 7 is a number greater than 14.
Thus, any number greater than 7 is a solution of $2x > 14$.

For some equations there are no solutions.

EXAMPLE 3   Give the solution for $x = x + 1$.

SOLUTION   Since no number equals one more than itself, the equation has no solution.

For some equations every number that may replace the variable gives a true sentence.   Such an equation is an **identity**.

EXAMPLE 4   Show that $3(x + 2) = 6 + 3x$ is an identity.

SOLUTION   Clear the left member of parentheses.
$$3(x + 2) = 6 + 3x$$
$$3x + 6 = 6 + 3x$$

Any number that replaces x gives a true sentence.   The equation is an identity.

An equation that is not an identity is a **conditional equation**.   There are some numbers that may replace the variable and give a sentence that is not true.

EXAMPLE 5   Show that $x + 2 = 7$ is a conditional equation.   Solve the equation.   Give the solution.

SOLUTION   Replace x by 3.

$$x + 2 \neq 7$$
$$3 + 2 \neq 7$$

Replace x by 5.

$$x + 2 = 7$$
$$5 + 2 = 7$$

Not all replacements for x give a true statement.   The equation is conditional.

The solution is 5.

CLASSROOM EXERCISES

Give the solution.

1. $3x = 12$ **2.** $3x > 12$ **3.** $2x = 5$

4. $2x < 5$ **5.** $2x + x < 3x$ **6.** $2(x + 1) = 2x + 2$

Show whether each equation is an identity or a conditional equation.   Give the solution for each.

7. $3x + x = 4x$ **8.** $3x + 1 = 4$ **9.** $4(2x + 1) = 8x + 4$

EXERCISES

A Give the solution.

1. $4x = 20$

2. $6x = 24$

3. $6x + 1 = 7$

4. $5x - 1 = 9$

5. $0.4x = 40$

6. $0.3x = 30$

7. $4x > 20$

8. $3x < 30$

9. $2x + 4x > 6x$

10. $7x + x < 8x$

11. $3(x + 1) = 3x + 3$

12. $4(x - 1) = 4x - 4$

13. $\frac{2}{3}x = 8$

14. $\frac{3}{4}x = 9$

15. $\frac{2}{3}x > \frac{2}{3}$

16. $\frac{3}{4}x < \frac{3}{4}$

17. $x^2 > 9$

18. $x^2 < 9$

Show whether each equation is an identity or a conditional equation. Give the solution for each.

19. $x + 3 = 3 + x$

20. $x - 5 = 5 - x$

21. $2x + 4x = 6x$

22. $9x - x = 8x$

23. $2x + 4 = 6$

24. $9x - 1 = 8$

25. $2x + 4x = 6$

26. $9x - x = 8$

27. $9x\left(\frac{1}{9}x\right) = x^2$

28. $6x\left(\frac{2x}{3}\right) = 4x^2$

29. $(2x)^2 = 2x^2$

30. $3x^2 = (3x)^2$

B Identify as an identity or a conditional equation.

31. $x(x + 4) = x^2 + 4x$

32. $y\left(y - \frac{1}{2}\right) = y^2 - \frac{1}{2}y$

33. $(a + b)^2 = a^2 + 2ab + b^2$

34. $(x - y)^2 = x^2 - 2xy + y^2$

35. $(a + b)(a - b) = a^2 - b^2$

36. $x^2 - y^2 = (x - y)(x + y)$

C **37.** $x^2 - a^2 = (a - x)(x - a)$

38. $4x^2 - a^2 = (2x - a)(2x + a)$

39. $c^x \cdot c^y = c^{x+y}$

40. $(c^x)^y = c^{xy}$

41. $x \cdot 0 = 0$

42. $x + 0 = x$

HOT OR COLD

"Can you tell me what the temperature has been at noon for the past five days?" Teri asked the weather reporter.

"I don't exactly recall," replied the weather reporter, "but I do remember that the temperature was different each day, and the product of the temperatures was 12."

Assuming that the temperatures are integers, what were they?

2-2 SOLVING FIRST-DEGREE EQUATIONS HAVING ONE VARIABLE

A first-degree equation is one in which the variable has only the exponent 1 after the equation has been cleared of fractions, parentheses, and radical signs. To solve such an equation, we systematically free the variable from the other numbers so that it stands alone in one member. To do this, we use the Properties of Equality.

PROPERTIES OF EQUALITY

For all real numbers a, b, and c,

1. If $a = b$, then $a + c = b + c$. Addition Property
2. If $a = b$, then $a - c = b - c$. Subtraction Property
3. If $a = b$, then $a \cdot c = b \cdot c$. Multiplication Property
4. If $a = b$, and $c \neq 0$, then $\dfrac{a}{c} = \dfrac{b}{c}$. Division Property

---

These properties allow us to add, subtract, multiply, or divide using the same number, c, in both members of an equation. However, if we divide both members by c, we must be sure that $c \neq 0$.

EXAMPLE 1 Solve $3n + 4 = 25$.

SOLUTION
$$3n + 4 = 25$$
Subtract 4 from both members.
$$3n + 4 - 4 = 25 - 4$$
$$3n = 21$$
Divide both members by 3.
$$\frac{3n}{3} = \frac{21}{3}$$
$$n = 7$$

CHECK
$$3n + 4 = 25$$
$$3(7) + 4 \overset{?}{=} 25$$
$$25 = 25 \quad \checkmark$$

When solving an equation, it is good practice to include a "Check". Replace the variable in the original equation by each number found as a "solution". When this results in a true sentence, you are assured that the number is indeed a solution.

EXAMPLE 2 Solve $3x - 7 = 5x + 3$.

SOLUTION

$$3x - 7 = 5x + 3$$

A_7 $3x - 7 + 7 = 5x + 3 + 7$ [Add 7 to both members.]

$$3x = 5x + 10$$

S_{5x} $3x - 5x = 5x + 10 - 5x$ [Subtract 5x from both members.]

$$-2x = 10$$

D_{-2} $\dfrac{-2x}{-2} = \dfrac{10}{-2}$ [Divide both members by -2.]

$$x = -5$$

CHECK

$$3x - 7 = 5x + 3$$
$$3(-5) - 7 \overset{?}{=} 5(-5) + 3$$
$$-22 = -22 \quad ✔$$

Sometimes, as done above, we shall use the letters A, S, M, and D with small, lower numerals, called *subscripts*, to refer to the properties of equality that we use in solving an equation. For example, S_{5x} above means that we subtract 5x from both members of the equation. We shall also use CT to mean "combine like terms."

EXAMPLE 3 Solve $2(y + 1) = 4 - (3y - 8)$.

SOLUTION

$$2(y + 1) = 4 - (3y - 8)$$
$$2y + 2 = 4 - 3y + 8$$

CT $2y + 2 = 12 - 3y$

A_{3y} $2y + 2 + 3y = 12 - 3y + 3y$

$$5y + 2 = 12$$

S_2 $5y + 2 - 2 = 12 - 2$

$$5y = 10$$

D_5 $\dfrac{5y}{5} = \dfrac{10}{5}$

$$y = 2$$

CHECK The check is left for the student.

When fractions are used for coefficients in an equation, both members usually are multiplied by the least common multiple (LCM) of the denominators to clear the fractions.

EXAMPLE 4 Solve $\frac{1}{3}x = \frac{1}{4}x - 2$.

SOLUTION

$$\frac{1}{3}x = \frac{1}{4}x - 2$$

M_{12} $12\left(\frac{1}{3}x\right) = 12\left(\frac{1}{4}x - 2\right)$

$$4x = 3x - 24$$

S_{3x} $4x - 3x = 3x - 24 - 3x$

$$x = -24$$

CHECK The check is left for the student.

Solving Simple Equations Containing Fractions and Parentheses

1. Clear the equation of fraction coefficients by multiplying both members by the least common multiple of the denominators.
2. Clear the equation of parentheses. (Sometimes it is better to clear parentheses *before* eliminating fraction coefficients.)
3. Proceed to solve the equation by combining like terms and using the properties of equality.
4. Check your result by replacing the variable in the original equation.

CLASSROOM EXERCISES

Solve and check.

1. $3k + 1 = 19$

2. $6x + 3 = 2x - 17$

3. $3(z + 1) = 8 - (z + 1)$

4. $7(x + 1) = 25 - (x + 2)$

5. $\frac{7}{12}x = \frac{1}{4}x - 2$

6. $\frac{1}{5}x = \frac{1}{4}x - 1$

EXERCISES

A Solve and check.

1. $5x + 2 = 37$

2. $6x + 2 = 38$

3. $3x - 5 = x + 7$

4. $3y + 5 = y - 1$

5. $x - 6 = 5x + 14$

6. $3c + 3 = 10c - 4$

7. $7x - 3 = 18$

8. $8x - 5 = 35$

9. $3 + 3y = 7 + 5y$

10. $2x + 4 = 6x + 12$

11. $5r = 10r - 15$

12. $4x = 8x - 12$

13. $2(y + 4) = 3y + 8$

14. $4(x - 3) = 5x - 12$

15. $\frac{2}{3}x - 7 = \frac{3}{4}x + 2$

16. $\frac{2}{5}x - 1 = \frac{7}{10}x + 2$

17. $4(x - 1) = 3(x + 2)$

18. $6(x + 2) = 3(x + 10)$

19. $20x = 10(5 - x)$

20. $9x + 1 = 2(1 + x)$

21. $2x - 5 - 6(x + 1) = 0$

22. $3x - 7 - 5(x + 2) = 0$

23. $\frac{x - 1}{2} = \frac{x + 1}{3}$

24. $\frac{2y - 1}{5} = \frac{y + 1}{2}$

B **25.** $6(2x + 3) - 3(x + 1) = 3(x + 2)$

26. $3(n + 1) + n^2 + 6 = n^2 + 12$

27. $\frac{2(3y - 4)}{5} - 8(y + 1) = \frac{5 - y}{4} + 35$

28. $\frac{x - 4}{2} - \frac{5x + 1}{3} + \frac{2x + 1}{3} = \frac{x - 2}{4}$

C **29.** $\frac{3n - 1}{4} - \frac{2n + 1}{5} - \frac{3(n + 1)}{4} + \frac{n + 5}{3} = 0$

30. $\frac{1}{x + 3} = \left(\frac{1}{2}\right)^3$

31. $\frac{1}{x} + \frac{1}{x + 1} = \frac{3}{x}$

2-3 SOLVING FIRST-DEGREE EQUATIONS CONTAINING PARAMETERS

When an equation contains two or more variables, we sometimes are interested in solving the equation for *one* of the variables in terms of the others. In this case we apply the name *parameter* to each of the other variables. In the process of solving for a variable, we treat the parameters as if they are constants.

EXAMPLE 1 Solve $3(x - b) = x + 3b$ for x.

SOLUTION

$$3(x - b) = x + 3b$$
$$3x - 3b = x + 3b$$

A_{3b} $\quad 3x - 3b + 3b = x + 3b + 3b$
$$3x = x + 6b$$

S_x $\quad\quad 3x - x = x + 6b - x$
$$2x = 6b$$

D_2 $\quad\quad\quad \dfrac{2x}{2} = \dfrac{6b}{2}$

$$x = 3b$$

CHECK
$$3(x - b) = x + 3b$$
$$3(3b - b) \overset{?}{=} 3b + 3b$$
$$6b = 6b \quad \vee$$

EXAMPLE 2 Solve $A = p(1 + rt)$ for r.

SOLUTION

$$A = p(1 + rt)$$
$$A = p + prt$$

S_p $\quad A - p = p + prt - p$
$$A - p = prt$$

D_{pt} $\quad \dfrac{A - p}{pt} = \dfrac{prt}{pt}$

$$\dfrac{A - p}{pt} = r \quad\quad\quad \text{CHECK} \quad \text{The check is left for the student.}$$

CLASSROOM EXERCISES

Solve for x or y.

1. $4y + 2k = 7(y - k)$

2. $6(2x + b) = 3x + 4b$

3. $\dfrac{1}{6}(x - c) = \dfrac{1}{3}x + c$

Solve for the indicated variable.

4. $p = s(1 - dt)$ for d

5. $F = ma$ for a

6. $S = \dfrac{a}{1 - r}$ for r

EXERCISES

$\boxed{A}$ Solve for x or y.

1. $bx = 2bc$ **2.** $4x = -8m$ **3.** $ax = b$ **4.** $ax = ab$

5. $x + a = b$ **6.** $5x - a = b$ **7.** $b^2x = 3b$ **8.** $mx = am^2$

9. $x + a = 3a$ **10.** $ax + b = b$ **11.** $rxt = c$ **12.** $ayb = f$

13. $y - c = 2$ **14.** $x + 1 = a$ **15.** $\frac{1}{2}x = p$ **16.** $\frac{1}{3}y = c$

17. $ax - b = c$ **18.** $ax + a = 7a$ **19.** $3(m - x) = x - 7m$ **20.** $rx + s = t$

21. $0.05x = 2h$ **22.** $0.07y = 21k$ **23.** $m^2x = m + 1$ **24.** $m^3x = m^2 + l$

Solve for the indicated variable.

25. $C = 2\pi r$ for r **26.** $A = \frac{\pi r^2 E}{180}$ for E **27.** $V = \frac{bh}{3}$ for h

28. $i = prt$ for r **29.** $W = I^2R$ for R **30.** $S = 2\pi rh$ for r

31. $S = 2\pi rh$ for h **32.** $S = 180(n - 2)$ for n **33.** $S = \frac{n}{2}(a + l)$ for a

34. $S = 2\pi r(r + h)$ for h **35.** $S = \frac{1}{2}gt^2$ for g **36.** $I = \frac{E}{R}$ for R

$\boxed{B}$ Solve for x or y.

37. $cy = c^{n+1}$ **38.** $x(2x - 3b) = 2x(x - b) + 3$ **39.** $-x(-3a - (-2)x) + 2(x^2 + a) = 0$

$\boxed{C}$ Solve for the indicated variable.

40. $S = \frac{n}{2}[2a + (n - 1)d]$ for a **41.** $R = \frac{2(E - f)}{mg}$ for E

42. $\frac{1}{x} + \frac{1}{a} = c$ for x **43.** $K = \frac{RTV^2 - aV + ab}{RT}$ for a

$\boxed{-0.5}$ # UNARY OPERATIONS

A *binary operation* is an operation that requires two numbers (called operands) to produce another number. Addition is an example. A *unary operation* is an operation that requires only one number (operand) to produce another. The calculator provides several examples of unary operations. One is "change sign." For any number, $\boxed{+/-}$ gives the opposite of the number.

Find other examples of unary operations on your calculator. Explain what each does.

2-4   PROBLEM SOLVING: USING FORMULAS

One way to use a formula is to find the number for one variable of the formula when the numbers for the other variables are known.

EXAMPLE 1   The formula $S = 180(n - 2)$ gives the sum, in degrees, of the measures of the angles of a convex polygon having n sides.   Find the sum of the measures of the angles of a polygon having 8 sides.

SOLUTION   For a polygon with 8 sides, $n = 8$.

$$S = 180(n - 2)$$
$$S = 180(8 - 2)$$
$$S = 180(6)$$
$$S = 1080$$

CONCLUSION   The sum of the measures of the angles of a polygon with 8 sides is 1080°.

Often we wish to find several numbers for one variable in a formula when we know several numbers for each of the other variables.   It saves time and is easier if we first solve the formula for the unknown variable.   Likewise, we should first solve for the unknown variable when we wish to use a calculator or computer.   Otherwise, it usually is easier to replace variables in the original formula and then solve for the required variable.

EXAMPLE 2   The sums of the angle measures for four convex polygons are 720°, 1080°, 1260°, and 1620°.   Find the number of sides of each polygon.   Use the formula from Example 1.

SOLUTION   First, solve $S = 180(n - 2)$ for n.

$$S = 180(n - 2)$$

D_{180} $\qquad \dfrac{S}{180} = n - 2$

A_2 $\qquad \dfrac{S}{180} + 2 = n$, or $n = \dfrac{S}{180} + 2$

Then replace S by each of the given numbers.

For $S = 720$, $n = \dfrac{720}{180} + 2$.   For $S = 1080$, $n = \dfrac{1080}{180} + 2$.

$\qquad\qquad\quad n = 6$ $\qquad\qquad\qquad\qquad\qquad\quad n = 8$

For $S = 1260$, $n = \dfrac{1260}{180} + 2$.   For $S = 1620$, $n = \dfrac{1620}{180} + 2$.

$\qquad\qquad\quad n = 9$ $\qquad\qquad\qquad\qquad\qquad\quad n = 11$

CONCLUSION   When the sum of the angle measures is 720°, the polygon has 6 sides. When the sum is 1080°, the polygon has 8 sides. When the sum is 1260°, the polygon has 9 sides. When the sum is 1620°, the polygon has 11 sides.

CHECK   Use 11 for n.
$$S = 180(n - 2)$$
$$1620 \stackrel{?}{=} 180(11 - 2)$$
$$1620 = 1620 \quad ✔$$

The other checks are left for the student.

CLASSROOM EXERCISES

Solve.

1. For a right triangle the hypotenuse length is given by the formula $c = \sqrt{a^2 + b^2}$. Find the hypotenuse length when $a = 20$ and $b = 21$.

2. Find the area of a rhombus for which the diagonal lengths are 17 and 12. Use the formula $A = \frac{1}{2}d_1 \cdot d_2$.

3. Use the formula in Exercise 2. Find d_2 when $A = 28$ and $d_1 = 7$; when $A = 25$ and $d_1 = 10$; when $A = 12$ and $d_1 = 6$; and when $A = 15$ and $d_1 = 3$.

EXERCISES

A   Solve.   Use 3.14 for π.

1. The formula for the volume of a sphere is $V = \frac{4}{3}\pi r^3$. Find the volume of a sphere whose radius is 2 meters.

2. In the formula for the Law of Falling Bodies, $s = \frac{1}{2}gt^2$, s represents the distance in meters that a body falls in t seconds. g represents the acceleration due to gravity (about 9.81 m/s²). A stone dropped from the top of a bridge strikes the water in 3 seconds. Find the distance from the top of the bridge to the water.

3. Find the volume of a cylindrical tank that is 10 meters high and that has a radius of 5 meters. Use the formula $V = \pi r^2 h$.

4. In the formula $W = I^2 R$, W is the number of watts, I the current in amperes, and R the resistance in ohms. Find the resistance of a 60-watt lamp which requires a $\frac{1}{2}$-ampere current.

5. Some hydrogen gas had a volume of 1843 cm³ when it was under a pressure of 0.2 megapascals. Find what its volume would be if the pressure were increased to 0.625 megapascals. Use the formula $\dfrac{V_1}{V_2} = \dfrac{P_2}{P_1}$.

6. Evaluate $C = \dfrac{E}{R_1 + R_2}$ to find E when $C = 22$, $R_1 = 4$ and $R_2 = 6$.

7. Use $C = 2\pi r$ to find the radius of a circle whose circumference is 25 cm.

8. Use $C = \pi d$ to find the diameter of a circle whose circumference is 36 cm.

B   9. Use the formula $A = \pi r^2$ to find the radius of a circle whose area is 78.5 m². Repeat for circles whose areas are 314 m² and 254.34 m².

10. Use $S = \frac{n}{2}[2a + (n - 1)d]$. Find a when $S = 165$, $n = 11$, and $d = 2$.

11. The formula $S = \pi r(r + l)$ gives the surface area of a cone with slant height

l and circular base radius *r*. Find the slant height when $S = 24\pi$ and $r = 3$.

12. The volume of the shell between two concentric spheres is given by $V = \frac{4}{3}\pi(r_2{}^3 - r_1{}^3)$ where r_2 and r_1 are the outer and inner radii respectively. Find r_1 when $V = 252\pi$ and $r_2 = 6$. Find r_1 when $V = 3528\pi$ and $r_2 = 15$.

13. The lengths of the sides of a triangle are 25, 7, and 24. Find the area. Use $A = \sqrt{s(s-a)(s-b)(s-c)}$ where $s = \frac{1}{2}(a + b + c)$ and the lengths of the sides are *a*, *b* and *c*.

$\boxed{\text{C}}$ **14.** Find the altitude of the cone of Exercise 11.

CHECKING YOUR UNDERSTANDING

WORDS AND SYMBOLS

conditional equation	formula	parameter
equation	identity	solution
first-degree equation	inequality, $>$, $<$, $\neq$	solution set

Properties of Equality

Addition Subtraction Multiplication Division

CONCEPTS

■ The Properties of Equality allow us to add, subtract, multiply, or divide both members of an equation by the same non-zero number. [2-2]

■ An equation containing one variable may be solved by using the Properties of Equality to replace the equation by one for which the solution is explicit. [2-2]

■ An equation in two variables often may be solved for one variable in terms of the other. [2-3]

PROCESSES

■ Check whether a given number is a solution of an equation. [2-1]

    1. $3(x - 2) - 17 = x + 5$ for $x = 14$ **2.** $2x - 6 = -2(3 - x)$ for any real number.

■ Solve an equation in one variable. Check the solution. [2-1 to 2-3]

    3. $6 + 2(y - 4) = 4(y - 2)$ **4.** $\frac{x}{5} - \frac{x - 3}{2} = -3$ **5.** $x - (1 - x) = x + (1 + x)$

    6. $3x + 1 = 3(x + 1) - 2$ **7.** $ad - 2bd = a$ for *d*   **8.** $x = y(w + 2z)$ for *z*

■ Evaluate a formula. [2-4]

    9. For $A = \frac{1}{2}h(a + b)$, find *a* when $A = 20$, $h = 10$, and $b = 1$.
    10. For $d = \frac{1}{2}at^2$, find *a* when $d = 12$ and $t = 2$.

2-5 SOLVING FIRST-DEGREE INEQUALITIES HAVING ONE VARIABLE

We solve first-degree inequalities in much the same way that we solve first-degree equations. We use the Properties of Inequality. One important difference from the Properties of Equality are the *two* cases needed for multiplication and division.

PROPERTIES OF INEQUALITY

For all real numbers a, b, and c,

1. If $a > b$, then $a + c > b + c$.   Addition Property
2. If $a > b$, then $a - c > b - c$.   Subtraction Property
3. If $a > b$ and $c > 0$, then $a \cdot c > b \cdot c$.   Multiplication Property
    If $a > b$ and $c < 0$, then $a \cdot c < b \cdot c$.
4. If $a > b$ and $c > 0$, then $\dfrac{a}{c} > \dfrac{b}{c}$.   Division Property

    If $a > b$ and $c < 0$, then $\dfrac{a}{c} < \dfrac{b}{c}$.

Notice that the inequality symbol is reversed when multiplying or dividing by a negative number (when $c < 0$).

EXAMPLE 1   Solve $3x - 5 > x + 2$.
Draw a graph showing the solutions.

SOLUTION

$$3x - 5 > x + 2$$
A_5 $3x - 5 + 5 > x + 2 + 5$
$$3x > x + 7$$
S_x $3x - x > x + 7 - x$
$$2x > 7$$
D_2 $\dfrac{2x}{2} > \dfrac{7}{2}$
$$x > \dfrac{7}{2}, \text{ or } x > 3\dfrac{1}{2}$$

CHECK   Replace x by a number greater than $3\dfrac{1}{2}$.

Use 4 for x. $3x - 5 > x + 2$

$$3(4) - 5 \overset{?}{>} 4 + 2$$
$$7 > 6 \quad ✔$$

GRAPH

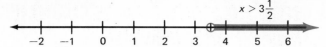

$x > 3\frac{1}{2}$

Recall that in a graph, ○ means that the point is not part of the graph. $3\frac{1}{2}$ is not a solution of the inequality. Hence, the point for $3\frac{1}{2}$ is not part of the graph.

The Properties of Inequality hold whether the inequality involves the symbol ">" or the symbol "<".

EXAMPLE 2 Solve $3(x - 3) < 5x - 13$.
Draw a graph showing the solutions.

SOLUTION

$$3(x - 3) < 5x - 13$$
$$3x - 9 < 5x - 13$$

A_9 $\qquad 3x - 9 + 9 < 5x - 13 + 9$
$$3x < 5x - 4$$

S_{5x} $\qquad 3x - 5x < 5x - 4 - 5x$
$$-2x < -4$$

D_{-2} $\qquad \dfrac{-2x}{-2} > \dfrac{-4}{-2}$
$$x > 2$$

CHECK Use 3 for x. $3(x - 3) \overset{?}{\underset{}{<}} 5x - 13$
$$3(3 - 3) \overset{?}{<} 5(3) - 13$$
$$0 < 2 \quad ✔$$

GRAPH

$x > 2$

CLASSROOM EXERCISES

Solve. Draw a graph showing the solutions.

1. $x + 3 > 2$ **2.** $x - 3 < 1$ **3.** $2x > 5$

4. $-3x > 9$ **5.** $4x - 6 > x + 3$ **6.** $2(x - 4) \leq 3x + 7$

EXERCISES

A Solve. Draw a graph showing the solutions.

1. $x + 7 > 2$ **2.** $x + 9 > 3$ **3.** $2x + 5 < 11$

4. $4x + 5 < 13$ **5.** $5x \leq 4x - 9$ **6.** $6x \leq 5x - 7$

7. $-5x < 4x - 9$ **8.** $-6x < 5x - 11$ **9.** $-2x + 5 < -3$

10. $-3x + 8 < -4$

11. $3x + 4 < 2x + 7$

12. $5x + 3 < 4x + 3$

13. $-3x + 1 \geq -8$

14. $-5x + 2 \geq -8$

15. $-4 + 8 < -3x + 12$

16. $-3 + 6 < -4x + 9$

17. $4(x - 2) > 5x + 1$

18. $6(x + 3) > 7x - 2$

19. $2(x - 3) \leq 5x + 4$

20. $4(x - 5) \leq 6x - 5$

21. $\dfrac{2}{3} - \dfrac{3}{4}x < \dfrac{1}{3}x - \dfrac{5}{12}$

22. $\dfrac{2}{5} - \dfrac{2}{15} < \dfrac{1}{10}x - \dfrac{1}{15}$

23. $\dfrac{2x + 3}{4} > 0$

24. $\dfrac{4x - 1}{5} > 0$

B Solve for x.

25. $\dfrac{x - 3}{2} + x > 4 - \dfrac{x - 5}{2}$

26. $\dfrac{5x - 3}{7} + 1 \geq \dfrac{x + 10}{3} - x$

27. $\dfrac{x - 6}{3} - \dfrac{x - 3}{2} - \dfrac{x - 2}{6} \leq 1$

28. $\dfrac{x - a}{3} + \dfrac{x + a}{4} - \dfrac{2x - a}{6} > \dfrac{a + 3}{3}$

29. $-3\left(\dfrac{x - 2}{3^2}\right) \leq x - 2$

30. $\dfrac{3(x - 5)}{12} + \dfrac{3}{4} > \dfrac{7}{8}(x + 7) - 11$

C **31.** $(x - 1)(x + 2) \leq (x + 3)(x - 4)$

32. $(x - 3)(x - 6) < x^2 - 9x + 23$

33. $3(2x - 1) > 2(3x + 4)$

34. $25 < \dfrac{1}{x^2}$

35. $\dfrac{(x + b)(x - b)}{b^2} - x(x + 2) > \dfrac{(1 - b)(1 + b)x(x + 1)}{b^2}$

36. Find all positive numbers which are larger than their squares.

CONSTRUCTING IRRATIONAL LENGTHS

A philosopher-mathematician of the Pythagorean school (about 500 B.C.) may have reasoned by using a diagram such as this.

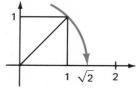

Of course, the idea of number line was not well developed at that time. Such a line was thought to contain points that corresponded to only the rational numbers. The Pythagoreans suggested that the length of the diagonal of the unit square, when transferred to the "number line," would identify a point in the "number line" that does not correspond to a rational number. This idea offered the foundation for the later development of the irrational numbers in a formal way (about 1875).

1. Make a construction that gives $\sqrt{3}$, $\sqrt{4}$, $\sqrt{5}$, and so on.

2. Use a reference. Relate the above concept to the *Archimedean Spiral*.

2-6 COMPOUND SENTENCES

A **compound sentence** is a sentence made from two or more simple sentences. The simple sentences may be connected by "and" or "or." A compound sentence with "and" is true only if each of the simple sentences is true. A compound sentence with "or" is true if at least one of the simple sentences is true.

COMPOUND SENTENCES

$2 + 4 = 6$ *and* $7 \cdot 4 > 27$	True, because both parts are true.
$2 + 4 = 6$ *and* $7 \cdot 4 < 27$	False, because one part is false.
$2 + 4 = 6$ *or* $7 \cdot 4 > 27$	True, because both parts are true.
$2 + 4 = 6$ *or* $7 \cdot 4 < 27$	True, because at least one part is true.
$2 + 4 \neq 6$ *or* $7 \cdot 4 < 27$	False, because both parts are false.

A solution of a compound sentence containing a variable is any number that can replace the variable and give a true sentence. A solution of a compound sentence with "and" is a solution that the simple sentences have in common. The graph for the compound sentence consists of the points that the graphs for the simple sentences have in common.

EXAMPLE 1 Solve $x + 2 > 5$ *and* $x < 6$. Draw a graph showing the solutions.

SOLUTION $x + 2 > 5$ *and* $x < 6$
$x > 3$ *and* $x < 6$

Any number greater than 3 *and* less than 6 is a solution.

GRAPH

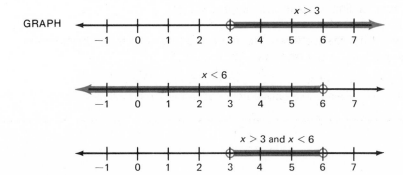

The compound sentence "$x > 3$ and $x < 6$" in Example 1 may be written in this form.

$$3 < x < 6$$

This is read, "x is greater than 3 and less than 6" or "x is between 3 and 6."

A solution of a compound sentence with "or" is a solution of either of the simple sentences. The graph for the compound sentence consists of the points that belong to the graph of either simple sentence.

EXAMPLE 2 Solve $x > 5$ *or* $x = 5$. Draw a graph showing the solutions.

SOLUTION 5 or any number greater than 5 is a solution of the sentence.

GRAPH

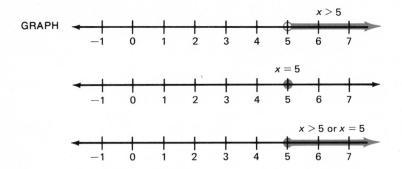

The sentence "$x > 5$ or $x = 5$" may be written $x \geq 5$ and is read "x is greater than or equal to 5". Similarly, the sentence "$x < 5$ or $x = 5$" may be written $x \leq 5$ and is read "x is less than or equal to 5."

EXAMPLE 3 Solve $2x + 4 < 0$ *or* $x - 3 \geq 0$. Graph the solution set.

SOLUTION $2x + 4 < 0$ or $x - 3 \geq 0$
$2x < -4$ or $x \geq 3$
$x < -2$ or $x \geq 3$

GRAPH

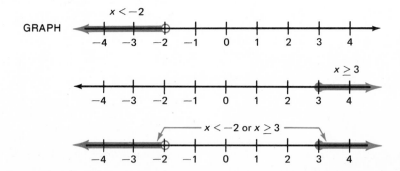

EXAMPLE 4   Solve $3x + 1 \le 10$ *and* $5x - 2 \ge -12$.   Graph the solution set.

SOLUTION $3x + 1 \le 10$ *and* $5x - 2 \ge -12$
$3x \le 9$ *and* $5x \ge -10$
$x \le 3$ *and* $x \ge -2$
$-2 \le x \le 3$

GRAPH

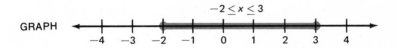

$$-2 \le x \le 3$$

CLASSROOM EXERCISES

Solve.   Draw a graph showing the solutions.

1. $x + 3 > 7$ and $x < 6$

2. $x + 5 > -1$ and $x + 3 < 4$

3. $x < 6$ or $x = 6$

4. $3x + 6 \le 0$ or $x - 8 > 0$

5. $3x + 1 \le 13$ and $4x - 1 \ge -9$

6. $x > 2$ or $x < 3$

EXERCISES

Ⓐ Solve.   Draw a graph showing the solutions.

1. $x + 6 > 8$ and $x < 5$

2. $x + 3 > 4$ and $x < 4$

3. $x > 1$ or $x + 3 < 3$

4. $x > 2$ or $x + 5 < 5$

5. $x + 1 > -3$ and $x + 3 < 5$

6. $x + 2 > -4$ and $x + 1 < 6$

7. $x > 6$ or $x = 6$

8. $x > 1$ or $x = 1$

9. $3x + 9 \le 0$ or $x - 3 \ge 0$

10. $4x + 16 \le 0$ or $x - 2 \ge 0$

11. $5x + 2 \le 17$ and $3x - 1 \ge 2$

12. $7x + 4 \le 25$ and $2x - 1 \ge 1$

13. $2x - 1 \le -3$ and $x + 1 > -6$

14. $4x - 3 \le -11$ and $x + 1 \ge -3$

15. $x < 6$ or $x > 1$

16. $x < 8$ or $x > 2$

Ⓑ **17.** $3x + 1 = 2(3x + 1)$ and $7x + 1 = 2(5x + 1)$

18. $7(x - 1) + 3(2x + 1) < 6x - 5$ or $x \ge -6$

19. $\dfrac{1 - x}{3} < x + 2$ and $\dfrac{1}{3}(9x + 1) \ge 15x - 17$

20. $\dfrac{x - 1}{3} + \dfrac{2x - 1}{4} < x$ or $-2x + 1 \ge x + 19$

Ⓒ **21.** $x > 1$ or $\left(x \le 2 \text{ and } x > \dfrac{3}{2}\right)$

22. $(x > 1 \text{ or } x \le 2)$ and $x > \dfrac{3}{2}$

23. $(x > 1 \text{ and } x \le 2)$ or $x > \dfrac{3}{2}$

24. $(x \ge 2 \text{ and } x < 5)$ and $(x > 3 \text{ and } x \le 8)$

MARINE SCIENCE AND OCEANOGRAPHY

The earth's surface is 70% water. Most is ocean. The oceans are a valuable resource for fossil fuels, foods, and a "highway" for transportation. Therefore, the study of oceans is crucial to the overall well-being of the human race.

Marine scientists study and analyze the physical, chemical, and biological components of the oceans. They use the principles and techniques developed in the natural sciences, mathematics, and possibly engineering to study the relationships that exist in the oceans.

Research carried out by marine scientists might lead to conclusions about

1. weather
2. fishing
3. mining
4. recreation
5. ship design
6. maps and charts

High school and college courses that are valuable to a marine scientist or oceanographer, include algebra, trigonometry, calculus, earth science, biology, and chemistry.

MATHEMATICAL SAMPLER

1. You are a marine scientist and you are comparing the *transport volume* of the Mississippi River and the Gulf Stream. Transport volume equals width × height (average depth) × velocity. $V_t = whv$. The particular portion of the Mississippi River under consideration has a width of 6 km, an average depth of 42 m, and a velocity of 2 meters per second. The Gulf Stream is approximately 22 km wide, has an average depth of 3250 m and a velocity of 4 kilometers per day. Which "river" has the greater transport volume?

2. You are a marine physicist. You must compute the period of a harmonic wave in Boston Harbor. T_n (period of harmonic wave) $= \dfrac{2l}{n\sqrt{gd}}$. The length (*l*) of the harbor is 7.6 kilometers. The number (*n*) of nodes of the harmonic wave is two. The average depth (*d*) of the harbor is 82.9 meters and *g* is the acceleration due to gravity (9.80 m/s²).

2-7 ABSOLUTE VALUE

Equations and inequalities sometimes include the absolute value of the variable. These are most easily solved by remembering that the absolute value of a number is the distance of its graph from the point for zero in the number line.

EXAMPLE 1   Solve $|x| = 3$.

SOLUTION   For a true sentence, a number for x must be 3 units from zero. There are two such numbers, 3 and -3.

Therefore, $x = 3$ or -3.

CHECK
$$|x| = 3$$
$$|3| \overset{?}{=} 3$$
$$3 = 3 \quad \checkmark$$

$$|x| = 3$$
$$|-3| = 3$$
$$3 = 3 \quad \checkmark$$

EXAMPLE 2   Solve $|x| = -2$.

SOLUTION   For a true sentence, a number for x must be -2 units from zero. Since distance is never negative, there is no such number.

The equation $|x| = -2$ has no solution.

EXAMPLE 3   Solve $|x + 5| > 3$. Draw a graph showing the solutions.

SOLUTION   For a true sentence, a number for x must be such that $x + 5$ is more than 3 units from zero.

Therefore,

$$x + 5 < -3 \quad \text{or} \quad x + 5 > 3$$
$$x < -8 \quad \text{or} \quad x > -2$$

GRAPH

CHECK   Use -9 for x.
$$|x + 5| > 3$$
$$|-9 + 5| \overset{?}{>} 3$$
$$|-4| \overset{?}{>} 3$$
$$4 > 3 \quad \checkmark$$

Use -1 for x.
$$|x + 5| > 3$$
$$|-1 + 5| \overset{?}{>} 3$$
$$|4| \overset{?}{>} 3$$
$$4 > 3 \quad \checkmark$$

EXAMPLE 4 Solve $|3 - x| < 2$.

SOLUTION For a true sentence, a number for x must be such that $3 - x$ is less than 2 units from zero.

Therefore, $3 - x > -2$ *and* $3 - x < 2$
$-x > -5$ and $\quad -x < -1$
$x < 5$ and $\quad\quad x > 1$
$1 < x < 5$

GRAPH

CHECK Use 3 for x. $|3 - x| < 2$
$|3 - 3| \overset{?}{<} 2$
$0 < 2$ ✔

CLASSROOM EXERCISES

Solve.

1. $|x| = 5$ **2.** $|x| = -5$ **3.** $|x + 1| = 4$
4. $|x + 2| > 4$ **5.** $|3 - x| < 6$ **6.** $|x - 1| > 2$

EXERCISES

Ⓐ Solve.

1. $|x| = 8$ **2.** $|x| = 9$ **3.** $|x - 1| = 4$
4. $|x - 1| = 6$ **5.** $|x + 3| = 2$ **6.** $|x + 4| = 1$
7. $|x| = -3$ **8.** $|x| = -1$ **9.** $|x - 6| > 2$
10. $|x - 8| > 3$ **11.** $|x + 4| > 3$ **12.** $|x + 5| > 2$
13. $|x - 6| < 2$ **14.** $|x - 8| < 3$ **15.** $|x + 3| < 2$
16. $|x + 4| < 1$ **17.** $|-x - 5| > 10$ **18.** $|-x - 3| > 12$
19. $|7 - x| \geq 1$ **20.** $|5 - x| \geq 1$ **21.** $|7 - x| < 1$
22. $|5 - x| < 1$ **23.** $|-x - 3| < 4$ **24.** $|-x - 7| < 9$
25. $|-x - 3| = 6$ **26.** $|-x - 11| = -3$ **27.** $|-x - 8| = -10$
28. $|-x - 4| = 13$ **29.** $\left|\dfrac{x}{3} + 2\right| \leq 3$ **30.** $|3 - 4x| = 5$
Ⓑ **31.** $|3x + 2| = 16$ **32.** $|3x + 7| \geq 0$ **33.** $|-17x + 81| < -1$
34. $|18x + 7| > 0$ **35.** $|-6x + 5| \leq 3$ **36.** $|13x - 5| \geq |-7|$

37. $\left| \dfrac{3x - 2}{4} \right| < a$ **38.** $\left| \dfrac{14 - 5x}{6} \right| \geq n$ **39.** $|3x + 1| = |7x - 4|$

Ⓒ **40.** $\dfrac{2}{|x + 4|} \geq 1$ **41.** $|x - 3| \leq |x - 1|$ **42.** $|x| + |x + 1| \geq 3$

CHECKING YOUR UNDERSTANDING

WORDS AND SYMBOLS

compound sentence, $\geq$, $\leq$, $a \leq x \leq b$

CONCEPTS

- The Properties of Inequality allow us to add, subtract, multiply, or divide both members of an inequality by the same non-zero number. However, when both members are multiplied or divided by a negative number, the inequality symbol is reversed. [2-5]

- An inequality may be solved by using the Properties of Inequality to replace the inequality by one for which the solutions are explicit. [2-5]

- A compound sentence using "and" is true when both simple sentences joined by "and" are true. A compound sentence using "or" is true when at least one of the simple sentences joined by "or" is true. [2-6]

- To solve an equation that includes the absolute value of an expression containing a variable, first rewrite the equation as a compound sentence without the absolute value symbol. Use the ideas that absolute value represents distance from the point for zero and such a distance may be in either of two directions. [2-7]

PROCESSES

- Solve an inequality in one variable. Draw a graph showing the solutions. [2-5]

  1. $-x + 2 < 2x - 7$ **2.** $5 + 3(1 - x) > 2X$ **3.** $\dfrac{5x}{2} - 3 > \dfrac{-5x}{6} + 2$

- Solve a compound sentence in one variable. Draw a graph showing the solutions. [2-6]

  4. $3x - 7 \leq 2$ **5.** $x - 2 \leq 0$ and $x + 1 \geq 0$

  6. $5(x + 1) < -10$ or $3x + 2 \geq 7$ **7.** $2x + 3 < 11$ and $x + 4 < 2x$

- Solve an equation or inequality involving the absolute value of an expression containing the variable. [2-7]

  8. $|x + 2| = 5$ **9.** $|x - 3| < 5$ **10.** $|2 - x| \geq 1$ **11.** $|x + 6| < 0$

2-8 PROBLEM SOLVING: USING EQUATIONS AND INEQUALITIES

Sometimes a problem situation may be represented by an equation or inequality in which a variable represents the answer sought. We find the answer by finding the solution of the equation or inequality. We check the answer by showing that it meets the conditions of the problem.

EXAMPLE 1 The sum of two numbers is 80. The sum of one-sixth of the smaller number and one-seventh of the larger number is 12. Find the numbers.

SOLUTION $\frac{1}{6}$ the smaller number plus $\frac{1}{7}$ the larger number is 12.

Use $\left[\begin{array}{l} s \quad \text{ for the smaller number.} \\ 80 - s \ \text{ for the larger number.} \end{array}\right.$

$\frac{1}{6}s + \frac{1}{7}(80 - s) = 12$ Now, solve the equation.

M_{42} $7s + 6(80 - s) = 504$
$7s + 480 - 6s = 504$
$s + 480 = 504$

S_{480} $s = 24.$ Also, $80 - s = 56.$

CONCLUSION The two numbers are 24 and 56.

CHECK The sum of 24 and 56 is 80.

$\frac{1}{6}(24) + \frac{1}{7}(56) \overset{?}{=} 12$
$12 = 12$ ✔

EXAMPLE 2 There are 1.6 liters of water in a 2-liter bottle. Tina can fill the bottle to overflowing with $\frac{1}{2}$ the water from her jar. How much water is in Tina's jar?

SOLUTION 1.6 liters plus one-half of the number of liters Tina has is at least 2 liters.

Use x for the number of liters of water in Tina's jar.

$1.6 + 0.5x \geq 2$
$0.5x \geq 0.4$
$x \geq 0.8$

CONCLUSION There is 0.8 liter or more water in Tina's jar.

CHECK Use 0.9 liter. Will adding half of the 0.9 liter to the 1.6 liters cause the bottle to overflow?

$1.6 + 0.5(0.9) \overset{?}{>} 2$
$2.05 > 2$ ✔

The meaning for the symbols used in solving a problem may be presented in chart form.

EXAMPLE 3   A man is four times as old as his daughter. Sixteen years from now he will be twice as old as his daughter. How old is each at present?

SOLUTION   The father's age in 16 years will equal twice the daughter's age in 16 years.

Use x for the daughter's age.

	Age Now	Age in 16 Years
Daughter	x	$x + 16$
Father	$4x$	$4x + 16$

$$4x + 16 = 2(x + 16)$$
$$4x + 16 = 2x + 32$$
$$2x = 16$$
$$x = 8$$

Also, $4x = 32$.

CONCLUSION   At present, the daughter is 8 years old.
The father is 32 years old.

CHECK   In 16 years the father will be 48 years old.
The daughter will be 24 years old.

$$48 \stackrel{?}{=} 2(24)$$
$$48 = 48 \quad \text{✔}$$

In many problems a special relationship exists among the quantities. Such a relationship often is expressed by a formula. For example, the diagram below represents a lever. Forces F_1 and F_2 are being applied at distances s_1 and s_2, respectively, from the fulcrum and on opposite sides of it. The lever balances when $F_1 s_1 = F_2 s_2$.

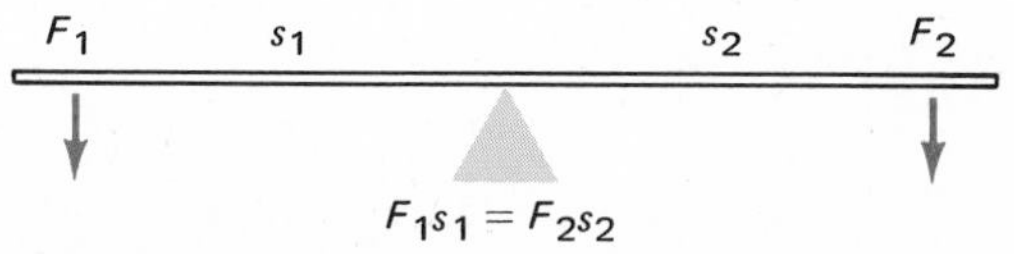

EXAMPLE 4 A bar 2.25 meters long is to be used as a lever. Where should the fulcrum be placed so that a force of 780 newtons will lift with a force of 1560 newtons?

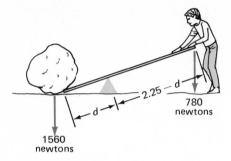

SOLUTION Use the formula $F_1 s_1 = F_2 s_2$. Replace F_1 by 1560. Replace F_2 by 780.

Use $\begin{bmatrix} d & \text{for the number of meters from the fulcrum} \\ & \text{to the object.} \\ 2.25 - d & \text{for the number of meters from the fulcrum} \\ & \text{to the person.} \end{bmatrix}$

$$1560d = 780(2.25 - d)$$
$$1560d = 1755 - 780d$$
$$2340d = 1755$$
$$d = 0.75$$

CONCLUSION To lift with a force of 1560 newtons, the fulcrum should be placed 0.75 meter from the object.

CHECK When the fulcrum is 0.75 meter from the object, it is 1.5 meters from the person. Does $F_1 s_1 = F_2 s_2$?

$$1560(0.75) \overset{?}{=} 780(1.5)$$
$$1170 = 1170 \ \blacktriangleright$$

EXAMPLE 5 A train leaves a station and travels at a rate of 72 kilometers per hour. Three hours later a second train leaves the station and travels at 120 kilometers per hour in the same direction. Use the formula $d\,(\text{distance}) = r\,(\text{rate}) \times t\,(\text{time})$ to find how long it will take the second train to overtake the first train.

SOLUTION

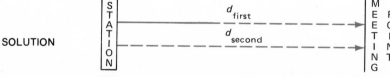

The distance traveled by each train is the same.

Use t for the time in hours needed for the second train to overtake the first.

	r	$\cdot$	t	$=$	d
First Train	72		$t + 3$		$72(t + 3)$
Second Train	120		t		$120t$

$$120t = 72(t + 3)$$
$$120t = 72t + 216$$
$$48t = 216$$
$$t = 4.5$$

CONCLUSION The second train will overtake the first train in 4.5 hours.

CHECK The check is left for the student.

EXAMPLE 6 How much pure alcohol must be added to 3 L of a 12%-alcohol solution to make a solution that is 25% alcohol?

SOLUTION Use n for the number of liters of pure alcohol needed.

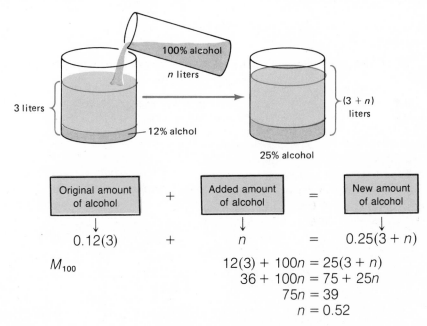

Original amount of alcohol	$+$	Added amount of alcohol	$=$	New amount of alcohol

$$0.12(3) \quad + \quad n \quad = \quad 0.25(3 + n)$$

M_{100}

$$12(3) + 100n = 25(3 + n)$$
$$36 + 100n = 75 + 25n$$
$$75n = 39$$
$$n = 0.52$$

CONCULSION 0.52 liter of pure alcohol should be added.

CHECK The check that adding 0.52 liter of alcohol gives a solution that is 25% alcohol is left for the student.

EXAMPLE 7 In Example 6, how much water should be added to make a solution that is *at most* 5% alcohol?

Use n for the number of liters of water needed.

SOLUTION

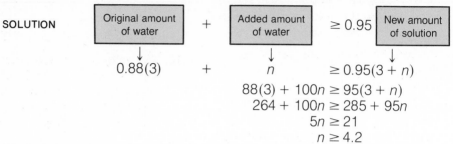

$$88(3) + 100n \geq 95(3 + n)$$
$$264 + 100n \geq 285 + 95n$$
$$5n \geq 21$$
$$n \geq 4.2$$

CONCLUSION   Adding at least 4.2 liters of water will give a solution that is at most 5% alcohol.

CLASSROOM EXERCISES

Solve.

1. The sum of two numbers is 72. The sum of $\frac{1}{4}$ the smaller and $\frac{1}{7}$ the larger is 12. Find the numbers.

2. Lucia is four times as old as her son. Twenty years from now she will be only twice as old as her son. Find the present age of each.

3. A bus leaves a terminal and travels at an average rate of 80 kilometers per hour. Two hours later a second bus leaves the terminal and travels at an average rate of 90 kilometers per hour in the same direction. Find the number of hours needed for the second bus to overtake the first bus.

4. A bar 3 meters long is to be used as a lever. Where should the fulcrum be placed so that a force of 400 newtons at one end will lift at the other end with a force of 1200 newtons?

5. How much pure alcohol must be added to 4 L of a 15%-alcohol solution to make a 20%-alcohol solution?

EXERCISES

A Solve.

1. The difference of two numbers is 16. 3 times the larger number equals 7 times the smaller. Find the numbers.

2. Find two numbers whose sum is 58 and whose difference is 16.

3. Two angles are complementary and the difference of their measures is 8 degrees. Find the measure of each angle.

4. Two angles are supplementary. The measure of one angle exceeds 3 times the measure of the other by 8 degrees. Find the measure of each angle.

5. The measure of one angle of a triangle exceeds the measure of a second angle by 14°. It also exceeds the measure of the third angle by 22°. Find the measures of the three angles.

6. The difference of three times the measure of an angle and five times the measure of its complement is to be less than 30°. Find the possible measures for the angle.

7. The perimeter of a rectangular garden is 100 meters. When the width is doubled and the length is decreased by 10 meters, the perimeter remains the same. Find the width and length of the garden.

8. Margaret is three times as old as her daughter. Eleven years from now she will be only twice as old as her daughter. Find the present age of each.

9. The combined ages of two brothers is 25 years. Three years ago the age of one brother exceeded twice the age of the other brother by one year. Find the present age of each brother.

10. Two cars leave the same place at the same time and travel in opposite directions. One of the cars is traveling 10 kilometers an hour faster than the other. After three hours they are 480 kilometers apart. Find the rate of each car in kilometers per hour.

11. Two trains, in stations that are 1060 kilometers apart, leave at the same time and travel toward each other, meeting in 4 hours. Their rates differ by 15 kilometers an hour. What is the rate of each train?

12. One car traveling at the rate of 60 kilometers an hour is 4 kilometers behind another car traveling at 50 kilometers an hour. In how many minutes will the faster car overtake the slower car?

13. Forces of 150 newtons and 90 newtons are to be applied to two ends of a 6-meter beam. Where should the fulcrum be placed so that the beam will balance?

14. A 500-newton force is applied to a beam 15 meters from the fulcrum. Find the force that must be applied to the beam on the other side of the ful-

crum and 20 meters from it so that the beam will balance.

15. A solution of water and acid is 90% acid. How much water should be added to 400 liters of the solution to make a solution that is 50% acid?

16. A mechanic has 500 liters of antifreeze solution that is 75% alcohol. The mechanic wishes to add water until the solution is 40% alcohol. How much water must be added?

17. A grocer blends two grades of tea. One is worth $2.40 a kilogram and the other $3.20 a kilogram. How much of each must be used to make a mixture of 50 kilograms to sell at $3.00 a kilogram?

B **18.** In Exercise 15, how much water should be added to the 400 liters to make a solution that is at most 40% acid?

19. A person drove a certain distance at 60 kilometers per hour and then that distance plus one more kilometer at 50 kilometers per hour. The total time for the trip was one hour. Find the distance traveled at 60 kilometers per hour.

C **20.** A new car tested for gasoline-efficiency will get 16 kilometers per liter of gasoline at 72 km/h and 15 kilometers per liter of gasoline at 90 km/h. On a 1170-kilometer trip, the time spent driving at 72 km/h is twice the time spent driving at 90 km/h. How many liters of gasoline are used?

21. Three solutions of acid in water have 6%, 8%, and 10% concentrations. Equal amounts of the first two are added to the third to form a 100-liter solution. How much of the first solution was used if the new concentration is between 7% and 9.5%?

CHAPTER REVIEW

Identify each equation as a conditional equation or as an identity. [2-1]

1. $x - 4 = 10$ **2.** $2(x + 7) = 2x + 14$ **3.** $\dfrac{2x}{3} = \dfrac{4x}{6}$ **4.** $4x = 5$

Solve and check. [2-2]

5. $4x - 7 = x + 8$ **6.** $2x + 3 = 4x - 4$ **7.** $2(y - 5) = 3y - 2$

8. $4 - (x - 6) = 3(x + 6)$ **9.** $\dfrac{2}{3}y - 5 = \dfrac{3}{4}y + 4$ **10.** $\dfrac{n - 2}{4} - \dfrac{2n + 3}{5} + \dfrac{5n}{2} = 13$

11. $0.3x + 2 = 17$ **12.** $0.04(x + 180) = 0.1x$ **13.** $6a - 2(2a + 5) = 6(5 + a)$

Solve for x. [2-3]   Solve for h.

14. $b^2 x = 4b$ **15.** $ax + bx = 3ax - c$ **16.** $A = \pi r^2 + 2\pi rh$

Evaluate. [2-4]

17. $l = a + (n - 1)d$ for $a = 3, n = 5, d = 4$ **18.** $S = \dfrac{ar^n - a}{r - 1}$ for $r = 2, a = 6, n = 4$

Solve.   Graph the solutions. [2-5]

19. $5x - 8 > x + 12$ **20.** $-3x + 7 < x - 5$ **21.** $2x - 3 - 3(x - 6) < 4$

Solve. [2-6]

22. $2x = 6$ and $x = 3$ **23.** $5x - 3 = 12$ or $5x - 3 = 13$ **24.** $2x - 3 = 9$ and $x > 0$

Solve.   Graph the solutions.

25. $2x - 3 > 1$ or $x < -5$ **26.** $x + 5 = 7$ or $x + 5 > 7$

27. $-x + 3 > 0$ and $3x - 1 > 2x$ **28.** $3x + 1 > -8$ and $x - 2 < 0$

29. $3x - 4 \le 2x - 8$ **30.** $4\left(x + \dfrac{3}{4}\right) \ge 3(x + 1)$

Solve and check. [2-7]

31. $|x - 1| = 3$ **32.** $|x + 2| > 2$ **33.** $|x - 1| \ge -3$ **34.** $|x - 4| \le 1$

Solve. [2-8]

35. One number is $\dfrac{5}{8}$ of another.   Twice the smaller number is 26 greater than the larger.   Find the numbers.

36. Find the measures in degrees of two supplementary angles, one of which has measure 15° more than the other.

37. John bicycles at the rate of 12 km/h and Bill at 15 km/h. John has a $\frac{1}{2}$-hour head start. How many hours will it take Bill to overtake John?

38. Twelve liters of a 12% salt solution are to be changed to a 15% solution. How many liters of water must be evaporated?

CAPSULE REVIEW

Write the letter of the best response.

1. Which equation or inequality has no solution?

    a. $3x + 6 = -3x + 6$ **b.** $3x + 6 > 3x - 6$

    c. $3x + 6 = 3x - 6$ **d.** $3x + 6 < -3x + 6$

2. Which Property of Equality is illustrated by the statement "$10 = 5(1 + 1)$, therefore $10 - 3 = 5(1 + 1) - 3$"?

    a. Addition Property   **b.** Multiplication Property

    c. Subtraction Property   **d.** Division Property

3. The solution of the equation $4(x - 2) - 3 = 2(x + 3) - 1$ is

    a. $x = 2$ **b.** $x = 12$ **c.** $x = -5$ **d.** $x = 8$

4. Which graph shows the solutions of the inequality $-3(x + 2) + 5 > -13$?

    a.

    b.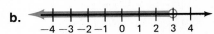

    c.

    d.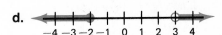

5. Which graph shows the solutions for $2(x + 2) < 10$ *and* $-3x - 6 < 0$?

    a.

    b.

    c.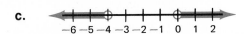

    d.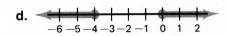

6. Which graph shows the solutions for $|2 + x| > 2$?

    a.

    b.

    c.

    d.

7. Raoul is $\frac{2}{5}$ as old as his father.   Ten years from now he will be half as old as his father.   Raoul's age in years is

a. 10   **b.** 50   **c.** 40   **d.** 20

CHAPTER TEST

---

1. Is $4(x + 2) = 4x + 8$ an identity?

2. Name the whole numbers less than 5 that are solutions of $3x - 2 < 6$.

Solve.

3. $2x - 5 = 25$ **4.** $3(x - 2) = 7x - 8$

5. $P = 2l + 2w$ for l **6.** $5(x - p) = x - 2p$ for x

7. The measure in degrees (d) of each angle of an n-sided regular polygon is given by the formula $d = \dfrac{180(n - 2)}{n}$.   Find the measure in degrees of each angle of a six-sided regular polygon.

8. The measure of each angle of a regular polygon is 135°.   How many sides does the polygon have?

Graph the solutions.

9. $3x + 4 < 5x - 6$ **10.** $3(x + 4) > 5x + 6$ **11.** $x + 2 > 3$ and $x < 7$

12. $2x > 6$ or $x < 2$ **13.** $|x + 2| \geq 5$ **14.** $|x - 3| \leq 2$

15. A train leaves a station and travels 60 km/h.   One hour later another train leaves traveling 80 km/h in the same direction.   How long will it take the second train to catch the first one?

16. An 8-kilogram mass and a 6-kilogram mass are placed on opposite ends of a 280-centimeter lever.   How far is the fulcrum from the 8-kilogram mass when the lever is balanced?

Write the letter of the best response.

17. Which of these is an identity?

a. $2x + x = 3$ **b.** $2x + x = 3x$ **c.** $2x + 3 = x$ **d.** $2x < 3$ **e.** $2x < 3x$

18. What is the solution of $\dfrac{x}{2} + \dfrac{5}{6} = \dfrac{x}{6}$?

a. -5 **b.** -2.5 **c.** -1 **d.** 1   **e.** 2.5

19. What does r equal if $rs + t = s$?

a. $\dfrac{t}{s - 1}$ **b.** $\dfrac{t}{1 + s}$ **c.** $\dfrac{t}{1 - s}$ **d.** $\dfrac{s - t}{s}$ **e.** $\dfrac{s + t}{s}$

20. The measure in degrees (d) of each angle of an n-sided regular polygon is given by the formula $d = 180 - \dfrac{360}{n}$. What is the measure in degrees of each angle of a 12-sided regular polygon?

a. 120   **b.** 136   **c.** 148   **d.** 150   **e.** 168

21. What is the graph of the solutions of $2(x - 3) < 3(x + 1)$?

a.

```
  ───┼──┼──○──┼──┼──┼──┼──┼──┼──►
   −10−9−8−7−6−5−4−3−2
```

b.

```
  ◄──┼──┼──○──┼──┼──┼──┼──┼──┼──►
   −10−9−8 −7−6−5−4−3−2
```

c.

```
  ◄──┼──┼──┼──┼──┼──┼──○──┼──┼──►
   −10−9−8−7−6−5−4−3−2
```

d.

```
  ◄──┼──┼──┼──┼──┼──┼──┼──○──┼──►
   −10−9−8−7−6−5−4−3−2
```

e.

```
  ◄──┼──┼──┼──┼──┼──┼──┼──○──┼──►
   −10−9−8−7−6−5−4−3−2
```

22. What is the graph of the compound sentence $x + 1 \geq 3$ or $x + 3 \leq 1$?

a.

```
  ◄──┼──○──┼──┼──┼──┼──○──┼──►
   −3−2−1  0  1  2  3  4  5
```

b.

```
  ◄──┼──●──┼──┼──┼──┼──●──┼──►
   −3−2−1  0  1  2  3  4  5
```

c.

```
  ◄──┼──○──┼──┼──┼──○──┼──┼──►
   −3−2−1  0  1  2  3  4  5
```

d.

```
  ◄──┼──○──┼──┼──┼──○──┼──┼──►
   −3−2−1  0  1  2  3  4  5
```

e.

```
  ◄──┼──●──┼──┼──┼──●──┼──┼──►
   −3−2−1  0  1  2  3  4  5
```

23. What is the graph of $|2x| \geq 6$?

a.

```
  ◄──┼──┼──┼──┼──●━━━━━━━━━━━━►
   −7−6−5−4−3−2−1  0  1  2  3  4  5  6  7
```

b.

```
  ◄──┼──┼──┼──┼──●━━━━━━●──┼──┼──►
   −7−6−5−4−3−2−1  0  1  2  3  4  5  6  7
```

c.

```
  ◄━━━━━━●──┼──┼──┼──●━━━━━━►
   −7−6−5−4−3−2−1  0  1  2  3  4  5  6  7
```

d.

```
  ◄──●──┼──┼──┼──┼──┼──●━━━━━━►
   −7−6−5−4−3−2−1  0  1  2  3  4  5  6  7
```

e.

```
  ◄──┼──●━━━━━━━━━━━●──┼──┼──►
   −7−6−5−4−3−2−1  0  1  2  3  4  5  6  7
```

24. A mother is three times as old as her son. Nine years ago she was 12 times his age. How old is the son now?

a. 7 years   **b.** 9 years   **c.** 11 years   **d.** 16 years   **e.** 33 years

CHAPTER 3
SPECIAL PRODUCTS, FACTORING, EQUATIONS

Those who provide personal services often are measured by the attention they pay to details. For some personal-service careers, attention to detail is an essential trait, as it would be for a watchmaker. Sometimes, it is valued as an "extra." In any case, paying attention to detail is a good habit, almost always is appreciated, and often brings its own rewards.

OBJECTIVE: Multiply two binomials.

3-1   THE PRODUCT OF TWO BINOMIALS

To multiply two polynomials, we must multiply each term of one polynomial by each term of the other.   For two binomials, the result will be a sum of four terms, two of which often may be combined.

EXAMPLE 1   Multiply $a + b$ and $c + d$.

SOLUTION 1

By the Distributive Property

$(a + b)(c + d)$
$= (a + b)c + (a + b)d$
$= ac + bc + ad + bd$

SOLUTION 2

Vertical Arrangement

$$\begin{array}{c} a \ + \ b \\ c \ + \ d \\ \hline ac + bc + ad + bd \end{array}$$

EXAMPLE 2   Multiply $2x + 3y$ and $x - 4y$.

SOLUTION 1

By the Distributive Property

$(2x + 3y)(x - 4y)$
$= (2x + 3y)x - (2x + 3y)4y$
$= 2x^2 + 3xy - 8xy - 12y^2$
$= 2x^2 - 5xy - 12y^2$

SOLUTION 2

Vertical Arrangement

$$\begin{array}{c} 2x \ + \ 3y \\ x \ - \ 4y \\ \hline 2x^2 + 3xy \\ - 8xy - 12y^2 \\ \hline 2x^2 - 5xy - 12y^2 \end{array}$$

The Short Method (FOIL)

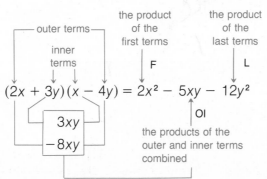

EXAMPLE 3 Multiply $3a + b$ and $2a - 5b$.

SOLUTION Product of **f**irst terms: $\quad 3a \cdot 2a = 6a^2$

Product of **o**uter terms: $\quad 3a \cdot (-5b) = -15ab$

Product of **i**nner terms: $\quad b \cdot (2a) = 2ab$

Product of **l**ast terms: $\quad b \cdot (-5b) = -5b^2$

$\left. \right\}$ Combined $\downarrow$ $-13ab$

$(3a + b)(2a - 5b) = 6a^2 - 13ab - 5b^2$

EXAMPLE 4 Multiply $2x - y$ and $2x + y$.

SOLUTION Product of **f**irst terms: $\quad 2x \cdot 2x = 4x^2$

Product of **o**uter terms: $\quad 2x \cdot y = 2xy$

Product of **i**nner terms: $\quad (-y)2x = -2xy$

Product of **l**ast terms: $\quad (-y)(y) = -y^2$

$\left. \right\}$ Combined $\downarrow$ 0

$(2x - y)(2x + y) = 4x^2 - y^2$

EXAMPLE 5 Square $5c - d$.

SOLUTION $(5c - d)^2 = (5c - d)(5c - d)$

$\qquad\qquad = 25c^2 - 10cd + d^2$

MULTIPLYING TWO BINOMIALS

1. Multiply the first terms.
2. Multiply the outer terms. Multiply the inner terms. Combine like terms, if any.
3. Multiply the last terms.

CLASSROOM EXERCISES

Multiply.

1. $(a + b)(c - d)$ 　　　 **2.** $(x + 3)(x + 1)$ 　　　 **3.** $(x + 2)(x - 3)$

4. $(4a + 2b)(a - 3b)$ 　　 **5.** $(3a - b)(3a + b)$ 　　 **6.** $(2x - 1)^2$

EXERCISES

A Multiply.

1. $(a - b)(x + y)$ 　　　 **2.** $(y + z)(x - w)$ 　　　 **3.** $(a + 3)(a + 2)$

4. $(b + 7)(b + 6)$ 　　　 **5.** $(x + 4)(x - 3)$ 　　　 **6.** $(w - 2)(w + 1)$

7. $(2a + b)(4a - 3b)$ 　 **8.** $(3x - 5y)(2x + y)$ 　 **9.** $(3x + 1)(2x - 5)$

10. $(2x - 9)(3x + 10)$ **11.** $(x - 6)(5x - 2)$ **12.** $(4x - 9)(x - 3)$

13. $\left(7x + \frac{1}{2}\right)(2x + 3)$ **14.** $\left(x + \frac{1}{3}\right)(6x + 3)$ **15.** $(1 - 7x)(1 + 9x)$

16. $(4 + 3x)(4 - 2x)$ **17.** $(2x - 3y)(5x - y)$ **18.** $(4x - 5y)(3x - y)$

19. $(7c + 3d)(7c + 4d)$ **20.** $(8x + 2y)(8x + 3y)$ **21.** $(7c + 3d)(7c - 3d)$

22. $(4x - 5y)(4x + 5y)$ **23.** $(2x - 3a)(2x + 3a)$ **24.** $(2b - 7c)(2b + 7c)$

25. $\left(x - \frac{1}{2}\right)\left(x + \frac{1}{2}\right)$ **26.** $\left(a - \frac{1}{7}\right)\left(a + \frac{1}{7}\right)$ **27.** $(3x - 5)^2$

28. $(2x + 4)^2$ **29.** $(x^2 + 0.5)^2$ **30.** $(y^2 - 0.1)^2$

B **31.** $(rs + 3)(rs - 1)$ **32.** $(3xy - 1)(4xy + 2)$ **33.** $(3 - c^2d)(5 - 4c^2d)$

34. $(1 - x^2y)(2 - 3x^2y)$ **35.** $(m^3n + 8)(m^3n - 6)$ **36.** $(7xy^2 - 3)(xy^2 + 4)$

37. $(a^n + 1)(a^n + 2)$ **38.** $(x^n + 2)(x^n + 3)$ **39.** $(a^{2n} - 1)(a^{2n} + 3)$

40. $(x^n - y^{3n})(x^n + 2y^{3n})$ **41.** $(x^{n+1} - 2)(x^{n+1} + 5)$ **42.** $(y^{k+3} + 1)(y^{k+3} - 2)$

43. $(x^n + y^n)^2$ **44.** $(x^n - y^n)^2$ **45.** $(x^m - y^n)(x^m + y^n)$

46. $(a^{2k} + b^k)(a^{2k} - b^k)$ **47.** $(B^a - A^b)(B^a - A^b)$ **48.** $(B^a + A^b)^2$

Solve for x.

49. $(x - 2)(x + 3) = x^2$ **50.** $(2x + 1)(x - 4) = 2x^2$

51. $(4x - 1)(4x + 1) = (8x - 1)(2x + 1)$ **52.** $(2x + 1)^2 = (2x - 3)(2x + 3)$

53. $(x - 4)^2 = (9 - x)^2$ **54.** $(2x - 3)(2x + 3) = (2x)^2$

C **55.** Simplify. $2^{(x-1)(x-5)} \cdot 2^{x(6-x)}$

56. Solve. $(2 + x^n)(3 - x^n) = x(x^{n-1} - 1) - (x^n - 4)(x^n + 4)$

57. Express $|x - 3| \cdot (x + 1)$ as a polynomial in x for $x < 3$.

Solve.

58. A rectangle has diagonal length x centimeters. The length of the rectangle is one centimeter less than the diagonal length. The width is 21 cm less than twice the diagonal length. Express the area of the rectangle as a polynomial in x.

$\boxed{15873}$ **THE NUMBER 15 873**

1. Find $15\,873 \cdot 21$.   **2.** Find $15\,873 \cdot 35$.   **3.** Find $15\,873 \cdot 56$.

4. Guess the solution of $15\,873x = 666\,666$. Explain.

3-2 SPECIAL PRODUCTS

The square of a binomial and the product of a sum and a difference of two terms are called *special products*.

$$(x + y)^2 = x^2 + 2xy + y^2$$
$$(x - y)^2 = x^2 - 2xy + y^2$$
$$(x + y)(x - y) = x^2 - y^2$$

The square of a binomial sum (or difference) is equal to the square of the first term, plus (minus) twice the product of the first and last terms, plus the square of the last term.

EXAMPLE 1 Square $x + 5$.

SOLUTION $(x + 5)^2 = x^2 + 2(5x) + 5^2$
$ = x^2 + 10x + 25$

EXAMPLE 2 Square $2x + y$.

SOLUTION $(2x + y)^2 = (2x)^2 + 2(2xy) + y^2$
$ = 4x^2 + 4xy + y^2$

EXAMPLE 3 Square $y - 6$.

SOLUTION $(y - 6)^2 = y^2 - 2(6y) + 6^2$
$ = y^2 - 12y + 36$

EXAMPLE 4 Square $x - 3y$.

SOLUTION $(x - 3y)^2 = x^2 - 2(3xy) + (3y)^2$
$ = x^2 - 6xy + 9y^2$

The product of the sum and the difference of two terms is equal to the square of the first term minus the square of the second term. The products of the outer and inner terms combine to be zero.

EXAMPLE 5 Multiply $x + 6$ and $x - 6$.

SOLUTION $(x + 6)(x - 6) = x^2 + 6x - 6x - 36$
$ = x^2 - 36$

EXAMPLE 6 Multiply $2a + 3b$ and $2a - 3b$.

SOLUTION $(2a + 3b)(2a - 3b) = 4a^2 - 9b^2$

CLASSROOM EXERCISES

Square.   Multiply.

1. $x + 6$ **2.** $a - 3b$ **3.** $3x + 5$ **4.** $(x - 3)(x + 3)$ **5.** $(2a + 10b)(2a - 10b)$

EXERCISES

A Square.

1. $x + 3$ **2.** $a + 5$ **3.** $x - 4$ **4.** $c - 6$

5. $h + 7$ **6.** $2 + m$ **7.** $1 - y$ **8.** $y - 8$

9. $h - x$ **10.** $a + 5b$ **11.** $c + 11d$ **12.** $x - \dfrac{1}{2}$

Multiply.

13. $(x + 1)(x - 1)$ **14.** $(x - 2)(x + 2)$ **15.** $(y - 5)(y + 5)$

16. $(c + 8)(c - 8)$ **17.** $(5a - x)(5a + x)$ **18.** $(3y - w)(3y + w)$

19. $(c + 2d)(c - 2d)$ **20.** $(m - 3n)(m + 3n)$ **21.** $\left(3c + \dfrac{2}{3}\right)\left(3c - \dfrac{2}{3}\right)$

B Square.

22. $ab + 1$ **23.** $xy + 3$ **24.** $cd - 9$ **25.** $mn - 7$

26. $x - ab$ **27.** $c + xy$ **28.** $x^a + y^b$ **29.** $0.5x^6 - 0.1y^2$

Multiply.

30. $(x^n - 4)(x^n + 4)$ **31.** $(a^m b^n + 1)(a^m b^n - 1)$ **32.** $(3a^x - 2b^y)(3a^x + 2b^y)$

Solve for x.

33. $(x + 3)(2x + 1) \geq 2x^2$ **34.** $(4x - 5)(x + 1) > 4x^2$

35. $(2x - 3)(2x + 3) > (2x + 3)^2$ **36.** $(3 - 2x)(3 + 2x) < -4x^2 - 5x$

C Solve.

37. The square picture is centered in the cardboard so that its edges are parallel to the edges of the cardboard. The length of the side of the picture is 1 cm less than the length of the side of the cardboard. The area of the exposed cardboard is 25 cm². Find the length of a side of the picture.

38. Simplify. $\dfrac{x^{(y-3)(y-3)}}{x^{y(y-6)}}$

39. Show that the difference of the squares of two consecutive odd integers is divisible by 8.

3-3   BINOMIALS USED AS MONOMIALS

The recognition and use of patterns is an important part of the study of mathematics.   You have learned the pattern for distributing multiplication by a monomial over a polynomial.   For example,

$$a(b + c + d) = ab + ac + ad.$$

You can use this pattern to simplify multiplying a polynomial by a binomial.   To do this, treat a binomial as a monomial, then apply the pattern for carrying out the operation.

EXAMPLE 1   Find the product of $2a + b$ and $x + y + z$.

SOLUTION   Treat $(2a + b)$ as a monomial and use the Distributive Property.

$$(2a + b)(x + y + z)$$
$$= (2a + b)x + (2a + b)y + (2a + b)z$$
$$= 2ax + bx + 2ay + by + 2az + bz$$

You may treat a binomial as a monomial to find other products also.

EXAMPLE 2   Find the product of $(c + d) + 1$ and $(c + d) - 1$.

SOLUTION   Treat $(c + d)$ as a monomial.   Use the pattern for finding the product of the sum and difference of two numbers. In general, $(x + y)(x - y) = x^2 - y^2$.
For this case, $[(c + d) + 1][(c + d) - 1] = (c + d)^2 - 1^2$
$$= c^2 + 2cd + d^2 - 1.$$

EXAMPLE 3   Find the product of $(a + b) - 3$ and $(a + b) + 5$.

SOLUTION   Treat $(a + b)$ as a monomial.   Use the pattern for the product of two binomials.

$$[(a + b) - 3][(a + b) + 5]$$
$$= (a + b)^2 + 5(a + b) - 3(a + b) - 15$$
$$= (a + b)^2 + 2(a + b) - 15$$
$$= a^2 + 2ab + b^2 + 2a + 2b - 15$$

EXAMPLE 4   Find the product of $x + y - t$ and $x - y + t$.

SOLUTION   Use parentheses to form a binomial from each expression.

$$(x + y - t)(x - y + t) = [x + (y - t)][x - (y - t)]$$
$$= x^2 - (y - t)^2$$
$$= x^2 - (y^2 - 2yt + t^2)$$
$$= x^2 - y^2 + 2yt - t^2$$

CLASSROOM EXERCISES

Multiply.

1. $(3x + 1)(a + b + c)$

2. $((x + y) - 2)((x + y) + 2)$

3. $[(y + z) + 6][(y + z) + 2]$

4. $(w + y - 4)(w + y + 4)$

EXERCISES

A Multiply.

1. $(x + y)(a + b + c)$

2. $(a - b)(c + d + e)$

3. $(2x - 1)(m + n - p)$

4. $(3x + 1)(r - s + t)$

5. $[(c + d) - 5][(c + d) + 5]$

6. $[(x + y) - 8][(x + y) + 8]$

7. $[(2a - b) - m][(2a - b) + m]$

8. $[(3m - n) - c][(3m - n) + c]$

9. $[c + (m + n)][c - (m + n)]$

10. $[2x + (m + 2n)][2x - (m + 2n)]$

11. $[1 - (r - s)][1 + 2(r - s)]$

12. $[3 + (x - y)][2 - 3(x - y)]$

13. $(x + y + 3)(x + y + 3)$

14. $(a + b + 6)(a + b + 6)$

15. $(3r + 2s + 7)(3r + 2s - 8)$

16. $(4x + 5y + 1)(4x + 5y - 3)$

17. $(h - k + 4)(h + k - 4)$

18. $(a - b + 9)(a + b - 9)$

19. $(3x - 4y - 5z)(3x + 4y + 5z)$

20. $(3a + b + d)(3a - b - d)$

B **21.** $(x^2 - x - 6)(x^2 - x + 6)$

22. $(x^2 + 2x - 1)(x^2 + 2x + 5)$

23. $(x^2 - xy + y^2)(x^2 + xy + y^2)$

24. $(x^2 - x + 1)(x^2 + x - 1)$

25. $(x^2 + x + 1)(x^2 + x + 1)$

26. $(x^2 - x + 1)(x^2 + x + 1)$

27. $(|-3|x - y - |6|)(|3|x + y + |-6|)$

28. $(x^n + y^k - 1)(x^n + y^k + 1)$

29. $(2x^{n+1} - 3y^n + 5)^2$

30. $(x^m - y^n + z^n)(x^m + y^n - z^n)$

Solve.

31. A rectangle has length given by the sum of two numbers and width given by the difference of these two numbers. Another rectangle has the same width but a length which is two more units than the length of the first rectangle. Find the amount by which the square of the length of the diagonal of the second rectangle exceeds the square of the length of the diagonal of the first rectangle.

C **32.** Multiply. $(w + x - y - z)(w + x + y + z)$

33. Solve. $(3x^2 + 1 - x)(3x^2 + 1 + x) - (3x^2 - 1)(3x^2 + 1) = 0$

34. Simplify. $(x^2 + bx + b^2)(x^2 - bx + b^2)$

OBJECTIVE: Factor polynomials completely.

3-4 COMMON MONOMIAL AND BINOMIAL FACTORS

Factoring a number is the process of finding two or more expressions whose product equals the number.

Number	Factors	Reason
10	5 and 2	$10 = 5 \cdot 2$
$x^2 + 2x$	x and $x + 2$	$x^2 + 2x = x(x + 2)$
$a^2 - b^2$	$a + b$ and $a - b$	$a^2 - b^2 = (a + b)(a - b)$
$6x^2 - 7xy - 5y^2$	$3x - 5y$ and $2x + y$	$6x^2 - 7xy - 5y^2 = (3x - 5y)(2x + y)$

When an expression, such as $x + y + z$, is multiplied by a monomial, such as $2a$, each term of the expression is multiplied by the monomial.

$$2a(x + y + z) = 2ax + 2ay + 2az$$

On the other hand, when the terms of an expression have a common factor, the expression can be factored. One factor will be the common factor. The other may be found by dividing each term of the expression by the common factor.

$$2r^3 - 2r^2s + 2rs^2 = 2r(r^2 - rs + s^2). \qquad 2r \text{ is a common factor.}$$

The **greatest common factor** (GCF) is the largest number by which each of two or more numbers is divisible. The greatest common factor of $2r^3 - 2r^2s + 2rs^2$ is $2r$.

EXAMPLE 1 Factor $7x^2 - 21x$.

SOLUTION The greatest common factor of the two terms is $7x$.
$$7x^2 - 21x = 7x \cdot x - 7x \cdot 3$$
$$= 7x(x - 3)$$

EXAMPLE 2 Factor $6a^2b^2 - 12a^3b + 30a^3b^4$.

SOLUTION The GCF of $\qquad$ 6, $\quad$ 12, and $\qquad$ 30 is 6.
The GCF of $\qquad a^2,\quad a^3,$ and $\qquad a^3$ is a^2.
The GCF of $\qquad b^2,\qquad b,$ and $\qquad b^4$ is b.
The GCF of $6a^2b^2$, $12a^3b$, and $30a^3b^4$ is $6a^2b$.
$$6a^2b^2 - 12a^3b + 30a^3b^4 = 6a^2b(b - 2a + 5ab^3)$$

Sometimes the GCF will include a binomial.

EXAMPLE 3 Factor $a(x - y) + b(x - y)$.

SOLUTION The GCF of the two terms is $(x - y)$.
$$a(x - y) + b(x - y) = (x - y)(a + b)$$

EXAMPLE 4 Factor $3(x + 2y)^2 - 6(x + 2y)$.

SOLUTION The GCF is $3(x + 2y)$.
$$3(x + 2y)^2 - 6(x + 2y) = 3(x + 2y)(x + 2y - 2)$$

CLASSROOM EXERCISES

Factor.

1. $5x^2 - 25x$
2. $18a^2 - 9a$
3. $2xc + 4c$
4. $ex^2 + e$
5. $bx^2 + bx + 2b$
6. $d^2x^3 + dx^2 + dx$
7. $4c^2d^2 - 12cd^2 + 28c^2d^4$
8. $3x^5y - 13x^3y^2 + 15x^3y^3$
9. $a^2b^2x^2 - a^2b^2x + a^2b^2$
10. $a(b + c) + b(b + c)$
11. $m(a - 2) - n(a - 2)$
12. $(x - 1)h - 2(x - 1)$

EXERCISES

A Factor.

1. $6x - 12$
2. $3y - 21$
3. $x^2 - x$
4. $a^2 + a$
5. $\pi R - \pi r$
6. $eE - ex$
7. $4abx - 4bx$
8. $3ab^2y + 3ay$
9. $a^2bc - ab^2$
10. $xzy^2 - z^2y$
11. $5m^2 - 10m$
12. $6z^2 - 36z$
13. $7cd - 14c^2d^2$
14. $4xy + 16xy^2$
15. $8a^3 - 16a^2$
16. $9y^2 - 18y^3$
17. $x^2y - xy^2$
18. $b^2a + ba^2$
19. $15x^3 - 10x^2 + 5x$
20. $10y^3 - 6y^2 + 2y$
21. $\pi r^2 + \pi rh$
22. $2wl + 2hl^2$
23. $\frac{1}{3}\pi r^2 + \frac{1}{3}\pi R^2 + \frac{1}{3}\pi rR$
24. $\frac{1}{4}eb^2 - \frac{1}{4}eB^2 + \frac{1}{4}ebB$
25. $2x^3c^2 - 2x^3c + 2x^3d^2$
26. $10x^2y^2 + 5xy^2 - 5y^3$
27. $x^{m+1} - x^m$
28. $y^{x+3} + y^x$
29. $y^{2m} - y^m$
30. $c^x - 3c^{3x}$
31. $h^2 - 4h^{n+2}$
32. $a^4 - 3a^{m+4}$
33. $x^k - 6x^{k+3}$
34. $y^n + 7y^{n+6}$
35. $2a^2 - 6a^2y$
36. $3z^2 - 12z^3y$
37. $7ab^m - 21ac^{c+1}b^c$
38. $3x^{n+1} + 6xy^mz^n$
39. $2x^2y + 4a^2x + 6a^2y^2$
40. $4ab^2 - 4bc + 4c^2a$
41. $18m^x - 27x^{2m}$
42. $16y^{2b} + 24b^{3y}$
43. $x(a - y) - c(a - y)$
44. $c(a - b) + d(a - b)$
45. $x^2(x - 4) - y^2(x - 4)$

46. $y^2(x + 2) - x^2(x + 2)$ **47.** $m(x^2 - 9) - (x^2 - 9)$ **48.** $c^2(c + 3) - 9(c + 3)$

49. $4(p + 2) - y(p + 2)$ **50.** $2(b - 3) + x(b - 3)$ **51.** $(t^2 + 2) + r^2(t^2 + 2)$

52. $(x^2 - 9) - y^2(x^2 - 9)$ **53.** $a(m + n) - b(m + n) - c(m + n)$

B **54.** $x^3y^2 + 5xy^3 - 2x^3y^2 + xy^3$ **55.** $x^my^n - 3x^{m+1}y^n + 2x^my^n + 3y^n$

56. $a^3b^2 - 3ab^2 + ab + 3(a^3b^2 + ab^2 + ab)$ **57.** $x^{k+3}y^{4k} - x^3(x^ky^{4k} + x^n + y^n)$

58. $\frac{1}{3}(c^2d^2 - cd) - \frac{2}{3}(6c^2d^2 + 5cd)$ **59.** $3y^2 - (2x - 3y)(5x - y)$

60. $9a^2 - d^2 - (3a + b + d)(3a - b - d)$ **61.** $a^2(x^a - y^b) - c^2(x^a - y^b)$

C **62.** Show that the total surface area of a closed right circular cylinder is $2\pi r(h + r)$ when r is the radius of the base and h is the height.

Factor.

63. $x^n(a + b) - y^n(a + b)$ **64.** $(x + 1)^3y^m + (x + 1)^2z^n$

65. $x^my^{n+2}z^{k+1} + x^{2m}y^{n+3}z^k + x^my^nz^{k-1}$

POLYGONAL NUMBERS

Numbers that are related to sets of dots that suggest polygonal shapes are *polygonal numbers*.

The first few *triangular numbers* are
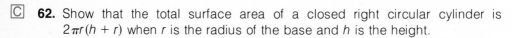
1   3   6   and   10.

The first few *square numbers* are

1   4   9   and   16.

The first few *pentagonal numbers* are 1

5   12   and   22.

1. What number is common to all sets of polygonal numbers?
2. What are the next 5 triangular numbers?
3. What are the next 5 square numbers?
4. What are the next 5 pentagonal numbers?

3-5 FACTORING TRINOMIALS

Some trinomials of the form $ax^2 + bxy + cy^2$ can be factored into two binomial factors. To do so we reverse the method used in finding the product.

EXAMPLE 1 Factor $x^2 - 2x - 15$.

SOLUTION If there are to be two binomial factors, the product of the first terms must be x^2.

$$x^2 - 2x - 15 = (x \quad ?)(x \quad ?)$$

The last terms of the binomial factors must be two numbers whose product is -15 and whose sum is -2. Two such numbers are -5 and 3. Thus,

$$x^2 - 2x - 15 = (x - 5)(x + 3).$$

CHECK $x^2 - 2x - 15 \stackrel{?}{=} (x - 5)(x + 3)$
$x^2 - 2x - 15 = x^2 - 2x - 15$ ✔

EXAMPLE 2 Factor $10x^2 - 23xy + 12y^2$.

SOLUTION The product of the first terms of two binomial factors must be $10x^2$.

$$10x^2 - 23xy + 12y^2 = (10x \quad ?)(x \quad ?)$$
$$\text{or}$$
$$10x^2 - 23xy + 12y^2 = (5x \quad ?)(2x \quad ?)$$

The last terms must be negative factors of 12. The sum of the products of these two factors and the two factors of 10 must be -23.

Pairs of factors of 10	Pairs of negative factors of 12
10 and 1	-12 and -1
5 and 2	-6 and -2
	-4 and -3

By trial, we find $\underbrace{5(-3)}_{\text{outer}} + \underbrace{2(-4)}_{\text{inner}} = -23$. Thus,

$$10x^2 - 23xy + 12y^2 = (5x - 4y)(2x - 3y).$$

CHECK $10x^2 - 23xy + 12y^2 \stackrel{?}{=} (5x - 4y)(2x - 3y)$
$10x^2 - 23xy + 12y^2 = 10x^2 - 23xy + 12y^2$ ✔

A polynomial that cannot be factored is a **prime polynomial**.

EXAMPLE 3   Factor $x^2 + 3x + 6$.

SOLUTION $x^2 + 3x + 6 = (x\quad?)(x\quad?)$

The product of the last terms must be 6 and their sum 3. Try 6 and 1.

$x^2 + 3x + 6 \stackrel{?}{=} (x + 6)(x + 1)$

CHECK $x^2 + 3x + 6 \neq x^2 + 7x + 6$

Try 3 and 2.

$x^2 + 3x + 6 \stackrel{?}{=} (x + 3)(x + 2)$

CHECK $x^2 + 3x + 6 \neq x^2 + 5x + 6$

CONCLUSION   There are no other possibilities to consider. $x^2 + 3x + 6$ is prime.

Sometimes, the two binomial factors are the same. If so, the trinomial is a **perfect-square trinomial**. A perfect-square trinomial is easy to recognize. Two of its terms are perfect squares. Its other term is twice the product of square roots of the perfect-square terms.

perfect-square terms

$$a^2x^2 + 2abxy + b^2y^2 = (ax + by)(ax + by)$$
$$= (ax + by)^2$$

twice the product of
square roots of the
perfect-square terms

EXAMPLE 4   Factor $x^2 - 8x + 16$.

SOLUTION   perfect-square terms

$$x^2 - 8x + 16 = (x - 4)(x - 4)$$

twice the product of
square roots of the
perfect-square terms

The $-8x$ in the trinomial tells us to use the *negative* square root of 16

$$x^2 - 8x + 16 = (x - 4)^2$$

EXAMPLE 5   Factor $4c^2 - 20cd + 25d^2$.

SOLUTION $4c^2 - 20cd + 25d^2 = (2c - 5d)(2c - 5d)$
$$= (2c - 5d)^2$$

CLASSROOM EXERCISES

Factor.

1. $x^2 + x - 6$

2. $y^2 - 3y - 4$

3. $21 + 4x - x^2$

4. $10 + 7b + b^2$

5. $3x^2 + 10x - 8$

6. $36z^2 - z - 21$

7. $y^2 + 5y + 7$

8. $z^2 + 4z + 12$

9. $y^2 - 10y + 25$

10. $a^2 + 12a + 36$

11. $4x^2 + 12x + 9$

12. $9c^2 - 24cd + 16d^2$

EXERCISES

A Factor when possible.

1. $m^2 - 2m - 24$

2. $y^2 - 4y - 32$

3. $c^2 - 12 - 4c$

4. $x^2 - 20 - x$

5. $b^2 + 12 - 7b$

6. $y^2 + 12 - 8y$

7. $h^2 - 9h + 20$

8. $z^2 - 5z + 6$

9. $k^2 - k - 6$

10. $x^2 - 3x - 70$

11. $x^2 + x - 30$

12. $y^2 + 4y - 12$

13. $x^2 + 3x - 18$

14. $z^2 + z - 20$

15. $42 - 13x + x^2$

16. $30 - 11y + y^2$

17. $20 - 8b - b^2$

18. $24 - 5z - z^2$

19. $8 + 2y - y^2$

20. $24 + 2b - b^2$

21. $200 + 30z + z^2$

22. $48 + 19a + a^2$

23. $2x^2 + 7x + 3$

24. $3z^2 + 5z + 2$

25. $10x^2 + 17x + 3$

26. $6b^2 + 17b + 7$

27. $3x^2 - 10x + 8$

28. $5y^2 - 21y + 18$

29. $8a^2 + 2a - 21$

30. $15b^2 + 14b - 16$

31. $2p^2 - 3p - 5$

32. $7x^2 + 4x - 3$

33. $3c^2 + 4c - 7$

34. $7x^2 - 4x - 3$

35. $x^2 + 2xy - 15y^2$

36. $a^2 + ab - 12b^2$

37. $x^2 - 2xy - 15y^2$

38. $a^2 - ab - 12b^2$

39. $m^2 - mn - 56n^2$

40. $c^2 - bc - 72b^2$

41. $x^2 + 7x + 9$

42. $b^2 + 6b + 13$

43. $2c^2 - 3cd - 2d^2$

44. $3x^2 - 8xy - 3y^2$

45. $2a^2 - 5ab + 2b^2$

46. $5z^2 - 26zw + 5w^2$

47. $1 - 6x + 9x^2$

48. $1 - 10c + 25c^2$

49. $x^2 + 2x + 1$

50. $c^2 + 8c + 16$

51. $x^2 - 2x + 1$

52. $x^2 - 8x + 16$

53. $c^2 + 2cd + d^2$

54. $z^2 + 2zw + w^2$

55. $c^2 - 2cd + d^2$

56. $z^2 - 2zw + w^2$

57. $2x^2 - x - \frac{3}{8}$

58. $5g^2 - g - \frac{6}{125}$

59. $2x^2 + 4xy + y^2$

60. $3c^2 + 5cd + d^2$

B **61.** $x^2y^2 - 7xy + 10$

62. $c^2d^2 - 10cd + 16$

63. $5x^2y^2 - xy - 4$

64. $a^{2n} + 10a^n + 16$

65. $x^{2a} - x^a - 20$

66. $2x^{2a} + x^a - 3$

67. $a^{4x} - 6a^{2x} + 9$

68. $3x^{2n} - 13x^n y + 4y^2$

69. $3x^4y^4 - 13x^2y^2 - 30$

Find the principal square root.

70. $\sqrt{x^2 - 8x + 16}$

71. $\sqrt{h^2 + 4h + 4}$

72. $\sqrt{9x^2 - 24x + 16}$

73. $\sqrt{36 + 36x + 9x^2}$

74. $\sqrt{4a^{2x} + 4a^x + 1}$

75. $\sqrt{c^2 - 5c + \frac{25}{4}}$

C Factor.

76. $6x^{2n} + 37x^n y^m + 45y^{2m}$

77. $28y^{4x} + 64y^{2x}z^w - 15z^{2w}$

78. $(2y + 1)^2 + 5(2y + 1) + 6$
(Hint: Treat $2y + 1$ as x.)

79. $(3w + 4)^4 - 10(3w + 4)^2 + 9$

80. Find the principal square root of $x^2 - 20xy + 100y^2$ for $x < 10y$.

99980001   SEQUENCES BY ADDITION

In the following sequences of numbers, each term, except the first, is found by adding a constant to the previous term.

5, 8, 11, 14, 17, . . .   11, 18, 25, 32, 39, . . .
21, 30, 39, 48, 57, . . .   94, 86, 78, 70, 62, . . .

The "constant" feature of your calculator can be useful when working with this type of sequence. The *flow chart* shows how to use your calculator to generate the successive terms.

Use the "constant" feature of your calculator to find the following.

1. The 12th term in 5, 12, 19, 26, 33, . . .

2. The 10th term in 13, 104, 195, 286, 377, . . .

3. The 27th term in 83, 189, 295, 401, 507, . . .

4. The 12th term in 207, 192, 177, 162, 147, . . .

5. The 9th term in 391, 354, 317, 280, 243, . . .

6. The 15th term in 119, 107, 95, 83, 71, . . .

7. The 28th term in 256, 211, 166, 121, 76, . . .

8. The 10th term in 0.42, 4.13, 7.84, 11.55, 15.26, . . .

9. The 40th term in 104.3, 101.6, 98.9, 96.2, 93.5, . . .

10. The 15th term in $\frac{1}{2}, \frac{3}{4}, 1, \frac{5}{4}, \frac{3}{2}, \ldots$

11. The 12th term in $3, \frac{11}{3}, \frac{13}{3}, 5, \frac{17}{3}, \ldots$

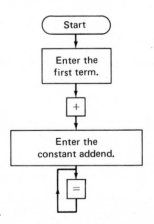

3-6 THE DIFFERENCE OF TWO SQUARES

If the sum of two numbers is multiplied by their difference, the product is the difference of their squares.

$$(a + b)(a - b) = a^2 - b^2$$

$$
\begin{array}{r}
a + b \\
a - b \\
\hline
a^2 + ab \\
- ab - b^2 \\
\hline
a^2 \qquad - b^2
\end{array}
$$

This shows that a difference of two squares may be factored into two binomials, one a sum and the other a difference. The terms of the two factors will be square roots of the terms of the expressions being factored.

EXAMPLE 1 Factor $9x^2 - 25$.

SOLUTION This is the difference of two squares.
Use the pattern $a^2 - b^2 = (a + b)(a - b)$.
$$9x^2 - 25 = (3x)^2 - 5^2$$
$$= (3x + 5)(3x - 5)$$

EXAMPLE 2 Factor $x^2 - 16y^2$.

SOLUTION $x^2 - 16y^2 = x^2 - (4y)^2$
$$= (x + 4y)(x - 4y)$$

EXAMPLE 3 Factor $x^{2n} - 4y^{2n}$.

SOLUTION $x^{2n} - 4y^{2n} = (x^n)^2 - (2y^n)^2$
$$= (x^n + 2y^n)(x^n - 2y^n)$$

FACTORING THE DIFFERENCE OF TWO SQUARES

1. Find a square root of each square.
2. Write the sum of the square roots as one factor.
Write the difference of the square roots as the other factor.

CLASSROOM EXERCISES

Factor.

1. $y^2 - 25$ **2.** $a^2 - 100$ **3.** $25x^2 - 1$

4. $16y^2 - 49$ **5.** $a^2 - 25b^2$ **6.** $c^2 - 36d^2$

7. $81x^2 - y^2$ **8.** $100y^2 - z^2$ **9.** $c^2 - \frac{1}{4}d^2$

10. $b^{2n} - 9c^{2n}$ **11.** $x^{2n} - 16y^{2n}$ **12.** $a^{2n} - 121b^{2n}$

EXERCISES

Ⓐ Factor.

1. $y^2 - 4$ **2.** $x^2 - 9$ **3.** $m^2 - 1$

4. $b^2 - 36$ **5.** $1 - y^2$ **6.** $16 - a^2$

7. $x^2 - 49$ **8.** $y^2 - 64$ **9.** $4x^2 - 1$

10. $9c^2 - 16$ **11.** $81 - 16y^2$ **12.** $25 - 36a^2$

13. $x^2 - 0.25$ **14.** $y^2 - 0.81$ **15.** $c^2 - d^2$

16. $a^2 - x^2$ **17.** $a^2b^2 - c^2$ **18.** $x^2y^2 - m^2$

19. $1 - 100x^2$ **20.** $4 - 9y^2$ **21.** $16x^2y^6 - 25$

22. $36a^4b^6 - 1$ **23.** $9 - 64c^4$ **24.** $49 - 25x^4$

25. $25b^{2n} - a^2$ **26.** $81y^{2k} - z^2$ **27.** $16a^2 - 49b^{4m}$

28. $4x^2 - 25y^{4n}$ **29.** $4a^{6n} - 81b^{2n}$ **30.** $25c^{4n} - 9d^{2n}$

31. $y^{2m} - 0.01$ **32.** $a^{2x} - 0.04$ **33.** $m^{4x} - n^{2y}$

Ⓑ **34.** $a^{6m} - b^{2n}$ **35.** $\frac{4}{9}a^2 - \frac{25}{36}b^2$ **36.** $\frac{9}{49}x^2 - \frac{16}{9}y^2$

37. $\frac{1}{100}y^{2n} - \frac{4}{9}z^{2k}$ **38.** $\frac{1}{25}h^{2k} - \frac{81}{16}a^{2b}$ **39.** $9x^4y^8 - 16z^6$

Ⓒ **40.** $4a^{2k}b^{2m} - 25c^{2h}$ **41.** $a^{2x+2} - b^{2y+2}$ **42.** $25x^6 - 2y^4$

43. $(x + y)(x - y) - k(2x - k)$ **44.** $(10x^2y^2 - 8xz^2 - 6z^2) - (9x^2y^2 - 8xz^2 - 2z^2)$

45. $A^{8x^2+24x+18} - B^{2y^2+4y+2}$ **46.** $(a^2 + 4ab + 4b^2)^2 - (a^2 - 4ab + 4b^2)^2$

47. Give the area of the region between the two equilateral triangles as a product.

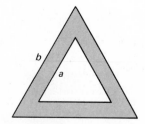

3-7   THE SUM AND DIFFERENCE OF TWO CUBES

Study this multiplication and division.

$$
\begin{array}{rl}
a^2 - ab + b^2 & \\
\underline{a + b} & \\
a^3 - a^2b + ab^2 & \\
\underline{a^2b - ab^2 + b^3} & \\
a^3 \qquad\qquad + b^3 &
\end{array}
\qquad\qquad
\begin{array}{r}
a^2 - ab + b^2 \\
a+b{\overline{\smash{)}\,a^3 + 0 + 0 + b^3}} \\
\underline{a^3 + a^2b} \\
-a^2b \\
\underline{-a^2b - ab^2} \\
ab^2 + b^3 \\
\underline{ab^2 + b^3} \\
0
\end{array}
$$

These show that the sum of two cubes may be factored with one factor being a binomial sum.   The terms of this sum are the cube roots of the terms of the expression being factored.

$$a^3 + b^3 = (a + b)(a^2 - ab + b^2)$$

In like manner, we can show that the difference of two cubes may be factored with one factor being a difference.   The terms of the difference are the cube roots of the terms of the expression being factored.

$$a^3 - b^3 = (a - b)(a^2 + ab + b^2)$$

EXAMPLE 1   Factor $y^3 + 64$.

SOLUTION   Use the pattern for factoring the sum of two cubes.
$$
\begin{aligned}
y^3 + 64 &= y^3 + 4^3 \\
&= (y + 4)(y^2 - 4y + 4^2) \\
&= (y + 4)(y^2 - 4y + 16)
\end{aligned}
$$

EXAMPLE 2   Factor $8x^3 - 27$.

SOLUTION   Use the pattern for factoring the difference of two cubes.
$$
\begin{aligned}
8x^3 - 27 &= (2x)^3 - 3^3 \\
&= (2x - 3)[(2x)^2 + 3(2x) + 3^2] \\
&= (2x - 3)(4x^2 + 6x + 9)
\end{aligned}
$$

EXAMPLE 3   Factor $a^3 - 125b^6$.

SOLUTION   Use the pattern for factoring the difference of two cubes.
$$
\begin{aligned}
a^3 - 125b^6 &= a^3 - (5b^2)^3 \\
&= (a - 5b^2)[a^2 + a(5b^2) + (5b^2)^2] \\
&= (a - 5b^2)(a^2 + 5ab^2 + 25b^4)
\end{aligned}
$$

FACTORING THE SUM OF TWO CUBES

1. Write the sum of the cube roots as one factor.

2. Use this pattern to write the other factor.

$$a^3 + b^3 = (a + b)(a^2 - ab + b^2)$$

FACTORING THE DIFFERENCE OF TWO CUBES

1. Write the difference of the cube roots as one factor.

2. Use this pattern to write the other factor.

$$a^3 - b^3 = (a - b)(a^2 + ab + b^2)$$

CLASSROOM EXERCISES

Factor.

1. $c^3 + 8$ **2.** $27x^3 + 8$ **3.** $64a^3 - b^3$ **4.** $c^3 - 8d^6$

EXERCISES

A Factor.

1. $a^3 - 1$ **2.** $x^3 - 8$ **3.** $a^3 + 1$ **4.** $x^3 + 8$

5. $c^3 + 27$ **6.** $a^3 + 125$ **7.** $m^3 - 27$ **8.** $y^3 - 125$

9. $m^3 - n^3$ **10.** $m^3 + n^3$ **11.** $8x^3 - 1$ **12.** $64x^3 - 1$

13. $8y^3 + 27$ **14.** $27a^3 + 125$ **15.** $x^3 - 216$ **16.** $b^3 - 343$

17. $a^3 + \frac{1}{8}$ **18.** $y^3 + \frac{1}{27}$ **19.** $a^3b^3 + c^3$ **20.** $x^3y^3 - m^3$

21. $y^6 + 8$ **22.** $a^6 + 27$ **23.** $8a^3 + 27b^3$ **24.** $64c^3 + 125d^3$

25. $x^3 - 64y^6$ **26.** $m^3 - 27n^6$ **27.** $b^3 + 27a^6$ **28.** $y^3 + 64z^6$

B **29.** $x^{3a} + 1$ **30.** $y^{3c} + 1$ **31.** $y^{3b} - 64$

32. $z^{3d} - 8$ **33.** $\frac{1}{8}a^3 - \frac{1}{27}b^3$ **34.** $0.001c^3 - 0.008d^3$

35. $\frac{1}{343}a^{3x}b^{3y} - \frac{1}{8}c^6$ **36.** $x^6 - y^6$ **37.** $a^5 - 8a^2$

C **38.** $(2x + 1)^3 - (x + 1)^3$ (Hint: Let $a = 2x + 1$ and $b = x + 1$.)

39. $(x + y)^3 + (x - y)^3$ **40.** $x^{6n} - y^{6n}$ **41.** $(x + 1)^6 - (x - 1)^6$

42. Find the volume of the spherical shell bounded by concentric spheres when the difference of the radii of the outer and inner spheres is 1 cm.

3-8 COMPLETE FACTORING

When any polynomial is to be factored, it should be factored *completely*. The first step is to find the greatest common monomial factor of the terms of the polynomial. When the factoring is complete, all the factors should be prime.

EXAMPLE 1 Factor $2x^2 - 6x$ completely.

SOLUTION The GCF of the two terms is $2x$.
$$2x^2 - 6x = 2x(x - 3)$$

EXAMPLE 2 Factor $6x^3 + 21x^2 - 45x$ completely.

SOLUTION $6x^3 + 21x^2 - 45x = 3x(2x^2 + 7x - 15)$
$$= 3x(2x - 3)(x + 5)$$

To help you factor completely, you should watch for the special types of polynomials. These include the perfect-square trinomial, the difference of two squares, and the sum or difference of two cubes.

EXAMPLE 3 Factor $a^5 - 16a$ completely.

SOLUTION Find the greatest common monomial factor. Then use the pattern for factoring the difference of two squares.
$$a^5 - 16a = a(a^4 - 16)$$
$$= a(a^2 + 4)(a^2 - 4)$$
$$= a(a^2 + 4)(a + 2)(a - 2)$$

EXAMPLE 4 Factor $x^6 - y^6$ completely.

SOLUTION Use the pattern for factoring the difference of two squares. Then use the patterns for factoring the sum of two cubes and the difference of two cubes.
$$x^6 - y^6 = (x^3)^2 - (y^3)^2$$
$$= (x^3 + y^3)(x^3 - y^3)$$
$$= (x + y)(x^2 - xy + y^2)(x - y)(x^2 + xy + y^2)$$

You should watch also for special ways to group the terms of a polynomial to help you recognize whether it is a special type.

EXAMPLE 5 Factor $3x - 3y - ax + ay$ completely.

SOLUTION Find the GCF of the first two terms. Find the GCF of the last two terms. Then treat $x - y$ as a monomial.
$$3x - 3y - ax + ay = 3(x - y) - a(x - y)$$
$$= (x - y)(3 - a)$$

EXAMPLE 6 Factor $(x - y)^2 - 9$ completely.

SOLUTION Treat $(x - y)$ as a monomial.
Use the pattern for factoring the difference of two squares.

$$(x - y)^2 - 9 = (x - y)^2 - 3^2$$
$$= [(x - y) + 3][(x - y) - 3]$$
$$= (x - y + 3)(x - y - 3)$$

EXAMPLE 7 Factor $c^2 - 9 - 2cd + d^2$ completely.

SOLUTION Rearrange the terms and use patterns for factoring.

$$c^2 - 9 - 2cd + d^2 = c^2 - 2cd + d^2 - 9$$
$$= (c - d)^2 - 3^2$$
$$= [(c - d) + 3][(c - d) - 3]$$
$$= (c - d + 3)(c - d - 3)$$

EXAMPLE 8 Factor $4x^2 - 4y^2 + 4y - 1$ completely.

SOLUTION $4x^2 - 4y^2 + 4y - 1 = 4x^2 - (4y^2 - 4y + 1)$
$$= (2x)^2 - (2y - 1)^2$$
$$= [2x + (2y - 1)][2x - (2y - 1)]$$
$$= (2x + 2y - 1)(2x - 2y + 1)$$

EXAMPLE 9 Factor $(x + y)^2 + 3(x + y) - 28$ completely.

SOLUTION Treat the expression as a trinomial by treating $(x + y)$ as a monomial.

$$(x + y)^2 + 3(x + y) - 28 = [(x + y) + 7][(x + y) - 4]$$
$$= (x + y + 7)(x + y - 4)$$

FACTORING A POLYNOMIAL COMPLETELY

1. Find the greatest common monomial factor, if any.

2. Determine whether any binomial is

   a. the difference of two squares
   b. the difference of two cubes
   c. the sum of two cubes.   Then factor.

3. Determine whether any trinomial is

   a. a perfect-square trinomial
   b. the product of two binomial factors.   Then factor.

4. Determine whether terms may be regrouped so that a binomial may be treated as a monomial.   Then proceed as in Step 2 or 3.

CLASSROOM EXERCISES

Factor completely.

1. $5a^2 - 10a$

2. $x^4 - x^2$

3. $(a + 1)(b + 2) - (a + 1)(b + 3)$

4. $d^6 - 1$

5. $(2x + y)^2 + 5(2x + y)$

6. $a^2(x + 1) - b^2(x + 1)$

7. $(a - c)^2 - 9$

8. $x^2 + 2xy + y^2 - 16$

9. $(a + b)^2 - (a + b) - 12$

EXERCISES

A Factor completely.

1. $4x + 12$

2. $a^2 - 7a$

3. $a^2b + ab^2$

4. $c^3d - c^2d^2$

5. $5m^2 - 30m - 30$

6. $7n^2 + 7n + 14$

7. $cx^2 - 4c$

8. $dz^2 - 9d$

9. $8m^2 - 11m + 3$

10. $14n^2 - 10n - 4$

11. $4k^2 - 16$

12. $5c^2 - 125$

13. $y^3 - 9y$

14. $a^3 - 16a$

15. $2a^3 - 2$

16. $3z^3 + 3$

17. $3x^3 + 24$

18. $2d^3 + 16$

19. $abx^3 - 27ab$

20. $9x^3 - 72$

21. $x^6 + y^6$

22. $a^6 + 1$

23. $(c - 3d)^2 + (c - 3d)$

24. $(2x - 1)^2 + b(2x - 1)$

25. $(5 - c)^2 + 2(5 - c)$

26. $(4 - g)^2 - 3(4 - g)$

27. $y^2(x + 2) - x^2(x + 2)$

28. $c^2(c + 3) - 9(c + 3)$

29. $cx + cy + bx + by$

30. $4a + 4b + xa + xb$

31. $mx + my - nx - ny$

32. $ca + cb - 3a - 3b$

33. $x^3 + x + x^2 + 1$

34. $c^3 - c - c^2 + 1$

35. $3y^3 - 6y^2 - 3y + 6$

36. $2a^2x - 2x - 6a^2 + 6$

37. $5a^3 + 2a^2 - 15a - 6$

38. $x^3 + 2x^2 + 3x + 6$

39. $a - a^2 - a^3 + a^4$

40. $a^3 - 4a^2 - a + 4$

41. $(x + y)^2 - c^2$

42. $(a + b)^2 - d^2$

43. $x^2 - (y + 1)^2$

44. $a^2 - (b + 2)^2$

45. $a^2 + 2ab + b^2 - c^2$

46. $x^2 + 2xy + y^2 - z^2$

47. $x^2 - 6x + 9 - 4y^2$

48. $y^2 - 4y + 4 - 25z^2$

49. $1 - x^2 - 2xy - y^2$

50. $4 - a^2 - 2ab - b^2$

51. $x^2 - c^2 - y^2 + 2cy$

52. $m^2 + 2np - p^2 - n^2$

53. $(a + b)^2 + 7(a + b) + 12$

54. $(c + d)^2 + 11(c + d) + 30$

55. $(m - n)^2 + (m - n) - 30$

56. $(c - 3d)^2 + 3(c - 3d) - 10$

57. $x^2 - (a - b)^2$

B **58.** $(a^3 + a^2 + a)^5 - 81(a^3 + a^2 + a)$

59. $x^4(b^2 + b + 3) - y^4(b^2 + b + 3)$

60. $12(z^2 - z + 5)^2 + 20(z^2 - z + 5) + 3$

61. $4(3a^2 + a + 1)^2 + 28(3a^2 + a + 1) + 49$

62. $cb^2 + cb + c - db^2 - db - d$

63. $x^2a^3 - 9a^3 + x^2a + x^2 - 9a - 9$

64. $m^2 - h^2 + n^2 - 2mn + 2hk - k^2$

65. $r^2 + t^2 - 4m^2 + 4m - 1 - 2rt$

66. $(x^2 + 1)^3 - x^3 + 3x^2 - 3x + 1$

67. $(a^2 + a + 1)^3 - 1$

C **68.** $a^4 + 4b^4$ (Hint: Insert $4a^2b^2$)

69. $(x + y)^4 + (x + y)^2 + 1$

3-9 THE REMAINDER AND FACTOR THEOREMS

The Remainder Theorem and the Factor Theorem help us factor some polynomials that do not yield to any of the factoring methods we have studied so far. Since the Remainder Theorem is needed for the Factor Theorem, the Remainder Theorem is presented first.

THE REMAINDER THEOREM

The remainder found when a polynomial in x is divided by the binomial $x - a$ is the same as the value of the polynomial for $x = a$.

EXAMPLE 1   Find the remainder for $(x^2 - 3x - 18) \div (x - 2)$.

SOLUTION 1   Use long division to find the remainder.

$$
\begin{array}{r}
x - 1 \\
x - 2 \overline{)\, x^2 - 3x - 18} \\
\underline{x - 2x} \\
-\ x - 18 \\
\underline{-\ x + 2} \\
-20
\end{array}
$$

The remainder is -20 when the divisor is $x - 2$.

SOLUTION 2   Use the Remainder Theorem. Evaluate $x^2 - 3x - 18$ for $x = 2$.

$$
\begin{aligned}
x^2 - 3x - 18 &= 2^2 - 3(2) - 18 \\
&= 4 - 6 - 18 \\
&= -20
\end{aligned}
$$

The polynomial value is -20 for $x = 2$.

Therefore, by The Remainder Theorem, the remainder is -20 when the divisor is $x - 2$.

EXAMPLE 2   Find the remainder for $(x^2 - 3x - 18) \div (x + 3)$.

SOLUTION   The remainder when dividing by $x + 3$, or $x - (-3)$, equals the value of the polynomial for $x = -3$.

$$
\begin{aligned}
x^2 - 3x - 18 &= (-3)^2 - 3(-3) - 18 \\
&= 0
\end{aligned}
$$

The remainder is 0 when the divisor is $x + 3$.

Since the divisor $x + 3$ in Example 2 gives a remainder 0, $x + 3$ is a factor of $x^2 - 3x - 18$. This result helps us to understand the Factor Theorem.

THE FACTOR THEOREM

If a polynomial in x has value zero for $x = a$, then $x - a$ is a factor of the polynomial.

The Factor Theorem provides a way to find binomial factors of any polynomial in one variable.

EXAMPLE 3 Factor $x^3 - 5x^2 + 6$ completely.

SOLUTION   We seek factors of the form $x - a$. Try values for a that are factors of 6: 1, -1, 2, -2, 3, -3, 6, -6.

Is $x - 1$ a factor? Replace x by 1.
$$x^3 - 5x^2 + 6 = 1^3 - 5(1)^2 + 6$$
$$= 1 - 5 + 6$$
$$= 2$$

Since the polynomial value is not zero, $x - 1$ is not a factor.

Is $x + 1$ a factor? Replace x by -1.
$$x^3 - 5x^2 + 6 = (-1)^3 - 5(-1)^2 + 6$$
$$= -1 - 5 + 6$$
$$= 0$$

Since the polynomial value is zero, $x + 1$ is a factor.
By division, $x^3 - 5x^2 + 6 = (x + 1)(x^2 - 6x + 6)$.
The trinomial $x^2 - 6x + 6$ is prime. The factoring is complete.

EXAMPLE 4 Factor $x^5 + 32$.

SOLUTION   Replace x by 1: $\quad x^5 + 32 = 1^5 + 32$
$$= 33$$

Replace x by -1: $\quad x^5 + 32 = (-1)^5 + 32$
$$= 31$$

Replace x by -2: $\quad x^5 + 32 = (-2)^5 + 32$
$$= -32 + 32$$
$$= 0$$

$x + 2$ is a factor of $x^5 + 32$.
By division, $x^5 + 32 = (x + 2)(x^4 - 2x^3 + 4x^2 - 8x + 16)$.

CLASSROOM EXERCISES

Find the remainder.

1. $(x^2 + 5x + 4) \div (x - 3)$ **2.** $(a^2 - 3a + 2) \div (a + 2)$

Factor. Use the Factor Theorem.

3. $a^3 + 4a^2 + 4a + 1$ **4.** $2y^3 - y^2 - 2y - 3$ **5.** $z^3 + 2z^2 + z + 2$

EXERCISES

A Find the remainder.

1. $x^2 + 6x + 8 \div x + 2$ **2.** $x^2 - 7x + 12 \div x - 5$

Factor. Use the Factor Theorem.

3. $x^3 + x^2 + 4$ **4.** $x^3 - 2x^2 + 3$ **5.** $x^3 + 4x - 5$

6. $x^3 - 2x - 4$ **7.** $2x^2 - x - 1$ **8.** $x^2 - x - 2$

9. $x^5 + y^5$ **10.** $a^5 - y^5$ **11.** $2x^3 - 54$

12. $3y^3 + 81$ **13.** $x^2 - 9$ **14.** $25 - z^2$

15. $x^2 + 2x - 3$ **16.** $x^2 + 4x - 5$ **17.** $x^3 - 2x^2 - 19x + 20$

18. $x^3 + 7x^2 - 14x - 48$ **19.** $a^5 - 1$ **20.** $a^5 + 1$

B **21.** $x^3 - 3x^2 + 3x - 2$ **22.** $y^3 + 2y^2 + 3y + 2$ **23.** $x^7 - y^7$

24. $x^4y^2 - 3x^3y^2 - \frac{1}{8}xy^2 + \frac{3}{8}y^2$ **25.** $ax^5 + 625ax^4 - \frac{a}{625}x - a$

Find the principal square root.

26. $\sqrt{x^4 - 2x^3 - 11x^2 + 12x + 36}$ **27.** $\sqrt{x^6 + 2x^5 + 3x^4 + 4x^3 + 3x^2 + 2x + 1}$

C Factor.

28. $x^3 + x^2y - xy^2 - xc^2 - y^3 + c^2y$ **29.** $(x^2 + 1)^3 - 2(x^2 + 1)^2 - 19(x^2 + 1) + 20$

SO YOU THINK YOU KNOW ALGEBRA!

The mass of a certain male basketball player averages 45 kilograms for every meter of height. He and his coach collectively are 62 years old. The coach now is twice as old as the player was when the coach was half as old as the player will be when the coach is 80. The coach's age now is two-fifths of the player's mass. How tall is the basketball player?

3-10 THE LEAST COMMON MULTIPLE

The **least common multiple** (LCM) of two or more terms is the product of their different prime factors, each taken the greatest number of times it occurs for any one of the terms.

Numbers	Prime Factors	Factors of LCM	LCM of the Numbers
4	2, 2		
6	2, 3	2, 2, 3, 5	60
15	3, 5		
$3x^3$	3, x, x, x		
$15x^2$	3, 5, x, x	3, 5, 5, a, x, x, x	$75ax^3$
$25ax$	5, 5, a, x		

EXAMPLE 1   Find the LCM of $4a^3$, $7a^2b$, and $2ab$.

SOLUTION   The LCM of 4, 7, and 2 is $2^2 \cdot 7$, or 28.
The LCM of a^3, a^2, and a is a^3.
The LCM of b and b is b.
Therefore, the LCM of $4a^3$, $7a^2b$, and $2ab$ is $28a^3b$.

EXAMPLE 2   Find the LCM of $2a^3 - 18a$,
$4a^2 + 6a - 18$, and $a^2 - 6a + 9$.

SOLUTION

$2a^3 - 18a$	$4a^2 + 6a - 18$	$a^2 - 6a + 9$
$= 2a(a^2 - 9)$	$= 2(2a^2 + 3a - 9)$	$= (a - 3)^2$
$= 2a(a + 3)(a - 3)$	$= 2(a + 3)(2a - 3)$	

The LCM must include the factors
$2, a, a + 3, (a - 3)^2, 2a - 3$.
Therefore, the LCM is $2a(a + 3)(2a - 3)(a - 3)^2$.

Finding the Least Common Multiple of Two or More Terms

1. Factor each term completely.

2. For each different factor, list the highest power that occurs in any one of the terms.

3. Form the product of the factors listed in Step 2. This product is the LCM of the terms in Step 1.

CLASSROOM EXERCISES

Find the least common multiple.

1. 15, 25, and 50

2. $15x^2y$, $25x^3y^2$, and $50x$

3. $72a^2b$, $6ab^2$, and ab^3

4. $(x + 1)(x - 2)$ and $(x + 1)^2(x + 3)$

5. $x^2 - 3x + 2$, $x^2 - x - 2$, and $x^2 - 2x - 3$

6. $2y^2 + 14y + 24$, $3y^2 - 27$, and $y^2 + 7y + 12$

EXERCISES

A   Find the least common multiple.

1. 20, 30, and 45

2. 18, 27, and 36

3. $20a^2b^3$, $30b$, and $45a^4$

4. $18x^2y^2$, $27x^3y$, and $36xy^5$

5. $8xy$, $12x^2$, and $18y^2$

6. $10wz^2$, $12w^2z^2$, and $15wz^3$

7. $15a^2bc^3$ and $20a^3bc^4$

8. $35xy^2z$ and $14y^3z$

9. $(a + b)(c - d)^2$ and $(m + n)(c - d)$

10. $(x - y)(x - 3y)$ and $(x - 3y)^2(w + z)$

11. $x^2 - y^2$, $2x + 2y$, and $x^2 + 2x + y^2$

12. $a^2 - b^2$, $a^3 - ab^2$, and $a^2 + ab^2$

13. $x^2 + 3x$, $x^2 - 9$, and $x^2 - 3x$

14. $y^3 - 25y$, $y^2 + 5y$, and $y^2 - 5y$

15. $(a + b)^2$, $(a - b)^2$, and $(a + b)(a - b)$

16. $(x + y)^3$, $2(x + y)^2$, and $3(x + y)$

17. $m^2 - 5m + 6$ and $m^2 - 4m + 4$

18. $x^2 - 4x - 21$ and $x^2 + 6x + 9$

19. $c^2 - 16$, $c^2 - c - 12$, and $c^2 - 9$

20. $2 - x - x^2$, $1 - x^2$, and $4 - x^2$

21. $x^3 + y^3$, $x + y$, and $x^2 - xy + y^2$

22. $a^3 - b^3$, $a - b$, and $a^2 + ab + b^2$

23. $2x^2 + x - 3$ and $x^3 - x^2 - x + 1$

24. $a^3 + a^2 - a - 1$ and $a^2 - 2a + 1$

B   **25.** $2x^2 + 4xy + 2y^2 - 2$ and $5x + 5y + 5$

26. $36 - (a + b)^2$ and $(a + b)^2 + 12(a + b) + 36$

27. $b^3 + b^2 - 2$ and $b^2 - 2b + 1$

28. $z^3 + z^2 - 3z - 6$ and $z^3 + 4z^2 + 6z + 3$

29. $a^2 + 4ab + 4b^2 - 81$ and $(a + 2b)^2 - 18(a + 2b) + 81$

30. $3x^2 + 3y^2$, $2x^4 - 2x^2y^2 + 2y^4$, and $4x^4 - 4x^2y^2 + 4y^4$

Find the least common multiple of the denominators.

31. $\dfrac{1}{3x + 12}$, $\dfrac{2x + 3}{x^2 + 9x + 20}$, $\dfrac{3}{5x + 25}$, and $\dfrac{7x^2 + 2x + 1}{2x^2 + 20x + 50}$

C   Find the least common multiple.

32. $x^4 + 5x^2 + 9$ and $x^3 + 2x - 3$

33. $x^3 + x^2 - 5x + 3$, $x^2 + x - 2$, and $x^4 + 7x^3 + 18x^2 + 20x + 8$

34. $4(a^4 + 1)^4 - 29(a^4 + 1)^2 + 25$ and $a^8 + 4a^4 + 4$

CHECKING YOUR UNDERSTANDING

WORDS AND SYMBOLS

common monomial factor   greatest common factor, GCF   prime polynomial
complete factoring   least common multiple, LCM   special product
difference of two squares   perfect-square trinomial   sum and difference of two cubes

CONCEPTS

- A polynomial in x that has value zero for $x = a$ has $x - a$ as a factor. [3-9]

- The difference of two squares is the product of the sum and difference of their square roots. [3-2]

PROCESSES

- Multiply polynomials. [3-1, 3-2]

  1. $(2x - 1)(x + 3)$ **2.** $(x + y)^2$ **3.** $(y - 3x)(y + 3x)$ **4.** $5 - (x + y)5 + (x + y)$

- Find common monomial factors of the terms of a polynomial. Find binomial factors. Factor completely. Use the Factor Theorem. [3-4 to 3-10]

  5. $6a^2b^2 + 15ab^3 + 3ab^2$ **6.** $x^2 + 4x - 21$ **7.** $6x^2 - x - 15$

  8. $4y^2 - 20y + 25$ **9.** $4x^2 - 81y^2$ **10.** $x^3 - 8$

  11. $27x^3 + 1$ **12.** $x^3 - 3x^2 - x + 3$ **13.** $49y^2 - y^6$

- Find the least common multiple. [3-10]

  14. Find the LCM of $6x^3 + 18x^2$, $12x^2 + 12x - 72$, and $9x^2 - 18x$.

NUMBER PATTERNS

Give the next three members of each pattern.

1. 1, 5, 9, 13, _?_, _?_, _?_   **2.** 2, 4, 8, 16, 32, _?_, _?_, _?_

3. 5, 6, 8, 11, 15, _?_, _?_, _?_   **4.** 24, −12, 6, −3, _?_, _?_, _?_

5. 2, 5, 11, 23, 47, _?_, _?_, _?_   **6.** 0, 1, 1, 2, 3, _?_, _?_, _?_

7. 0.7, 0.21, 0.063, _?_, _?_, _?_   **8.** 3, 5, 7, 11, 13, 17, _?_, _?_

9. 8, 5, 4, 9, 1, 7, _?_, _?_   **10.** O, T, T, F, F, S, S, _?_, _?_, _?_

OBJECTIVE: Use factoring to solve equations.

3-11 SPECIAL PRODUCTS AND FACTORING IN EQUATIONS

The patterns for writing special products may be helpful for simplifying some equations quickly and efficiently.

EXAMPLE 1   Solve $(2x - 1)^2 - (x + 1)^2 = 3(x + 2)(x - 2)$

SOLUTION

$$(2x - 1)^2 - (x + 1)^2 = 3(x + 2)(x - 2)$$
$$(4x^2 - 4x + 1) - (x^2 + 2x + 1) = 3(x^2 - 4)$$
$$4x^2 - 4x + 1 - x^2 - 2x - 1 = 3x^2 - 12$$
$$3x^2 - 6x = 3x^2 - 12$$
$$-6x = -12$$
$$x = 2$$

CHECK
$$(2x - 1)^2 - (x + 1)^2 = 3(x + 2)(x - 2)$$
$$(2(2) - 1)^2 - (2 + 1)^2 \overset{?}{=} 3(2 + 2)(2 - 2)$$
$$0 = 0 \quad \vee$$

The patterns for factoring may be needed for solving some equations and for simplifying a solution.

EXAMPLE 2   Solve $ax + b^2 = a^2 + bx$ for x.

SOLUTION

$$ax + b^2 = a^2 + bx$$
$$ax - bx = a^2 - b^2$$
$$(a - b)x = (a + b)(a - b)$$
$$D_{a-b} \atop (a-b \neq 0) \qquad x = a + b$$

CHECK   The check is left for the student.

The steps for solving some equations may include both multiplying and factoring.

EXAMPLE 3   Solve $b(x - b) = x - (2 - b)$ for x.

SOLUTION

$$b(x - b) = x - (2 - b)$$
$$bx - b^2 = x - 2 + b$$
$$bx - x = b^2 + b - 2$$
$$(b - 1)x = (b - 1)(b + 2)$$
$$D_{b-1} \atop (b-1 \neq 0) \qquad x = b + 2$$

CHECK   The check is left for the student.

Factoring may be helpful in solving some formulas for certain variables.

EXAMPLE 4 Solve the formula $A = P + Prt$ for P.

SOLUTION $\qquad A = P + Prt$

$$A = P(1 + rt)$$

$$\frac{A}{1 + rt} = P$$

$$\text{or, } P = \frac{A}{1 + rt}$$

CHECK $\quad A = P + Prt$

$$A \overset{?}{=} \frac{A}{1 + rt} + \frac{A}{1 + rt}(rt)$$

$$A \overset{?}{=} \frac{A + Art}{1 + rt}$$

$$A \overset{?}{=} \frac{A(1 + rt)}{1 + rt}$$

$$A = A \quad ✔$$

CLASSROOM EXERCISES

Solve for x.

1. $(x + 1)^2 + (x + 3)^2 = 2(x - 1)(x + 3)$

2. $cx + 4b^2 = c^2 + 2bx$

3. $cx + cd = 2c^2 - d^2 + dx$

4. $a(x - a) = x + 2a - 3$

5. Solve $p = S - Sdt$ for S.

EXERCISES

[A] Solve and check.

1. $(x + 2)^2 - (2x + 1) = (x - 3)(x + 3)$

2. $(2y + 1)^2 + (y - 2) = (2y - 1)(2y + 1)$

3. $(3x + 1)^2 + (x - 2)^2 = 2(5x - 1)(x + 2)$

4. $(4x - 1)^2 - (2x + 3)^2 = (3x + 1)(4x + 1)$

5. $(2x - 1)^2 - (x - 3)(3x + 2) = x^2 - 5$

6. $(x + 6)(2x + 3) - (x + 5)(2x - 1) = 11$

7. $(y + 6)(y - 6) - y(y - 5) = 29$

8. $(y + 3)(y - 1) - (y + 2)(y - 2) = 0$

9. $(x + 4)(x - 5) + (x + 2)(x - 6) = 2x^2 - 2$

10. $(2x - 1)(x - 3) - 3(x - 1)(x + 2) = 29 - x^2$

11. $(x - 4)(2x + 1) + (x + 1)(3x - 2) = 5x^2 - 30$

12. $(x + 1)(x^2 - x + 1) + 3x = x^3 - 5$

Solve for x or y.

13. $(c - d)y = c^2 - 2cd + d^2$

14. $(a - b)x = a^2 + ab - 2b^2$

15. $cx + x = (c + 1)(c - 1)$

16. $cy + y = (c + 1)^2$

17. $bx - b^2 = 3x + b - 12$

18. $ax - a^2 = -2x - 5a - 14$

19. $b^2(ay - 1) = a^2(1 - ay)$

20. $b^2 - a^2 = ab^2y - a^3y$

21. $a^2 - ax - b^2 = bx$

22. $c^2 - cx - d^2 = -dx$

23. $a^3 - bx = ax - b^3$

24. $ax - 8 = a^3 - 2x$

Solve.

25. $T = mg - mf$ for m

26. $T = 2\pi r^2 + 2\pi rh$ for h

27. $2A = h(b + c)$ for h

28. $S = \pi rl + \pi r'l$ for l

29. $r(s - l) = s - a$ for s

30. $k(m - t) = t + b$ for t

31. $A = \pi R^2 - \pi r^2$ for R; for r; for $R - r$

32. $A = \frac{1}{2}h(b + b')$ for h; for b; for b'

B Solve for x.

33. $a^2x + x = a^3 - 2a^2 - 2a - ax - 3$

34. $(x - a)(x^2 + ax + a^2)(x + a)(x^2 - ax + a^2) + 2x = x^6 + bx$

35. $(5x - 1)^2 - (x + 3)^2 = 8(3x + 1)(x - 1)$

36. Solve for x^{2n}. $(cx^n - ay^m)(cx^n + ay^m) + 9d^2 = c^4 + 3dx^{2n} - a^2y^{2m}$

C **37.** Solve for $x^2 + 1$. $x^2a^2 = a^2(a - 1)(a + 1) + b^2(4a^2 - 3x^2) + 3b^2(b - 1)(b + 1)$

38. Solve for $x + y$. $(x + 7)a^2 - 3(x + 3) + y(a - 3) = a(a^3 - ya - x)$

⌷.∃∃∃∃∃∃   REPEATING DECIMALS

Since your calculator can display only finitely many digits, it will show $\frac{2}{3}$ (press 2 ÷ 3 =) as one of the following.

$$0.6666667 \quad \text{or} \quad 0.6666666$$

In the first case the calculator rounded in the last decimal place shown. In the second case the calculator discarded any digits beyond the last one shown.

Enter $\frac{2}{3}$ on your calculator to check whether it rounds.

A calculator that does not round will give different results for $\frac{1}{6} \times 6$ (Press 1 ÷ 6 × 6 =) and $6 \times \frac{1}{6}$ (Press 6 × 1 ÷ 6 =). In such cases you should learn to interpret the results.

1. What result does your calculator display for 1 ÷ 6 × 6 = ?

2. What result does your calculator display for 6 × 1 ÷ 6 = ?

What *whole number* or *fraction* could these most likely represent on a calculator?

3. 0.3333332

4. 2.6666666

5. −7.9999998

6. 0.9999999

7. −2.4999996

8. 0.0699999

3-12 SOLVING EQUATIONS BY FACTORING

Factoring is useful in solving second-degree equations in one variable. First, we collect the terms so they are in one member of the equation, leaving zero as the other member. Then we factor and use the following property.

$$\text{If } a \cdot b = 0, \text{ then } a = 0 \text{ or } b = 0.$$

This property states that if a product is zero, then at least one of the factors must be zero.

EXAMPLE 1   Solve $x^2 = 3x$.

SOLUTION

$$x^2 = 3x$$
$$x^2 - 3x = 0$$
$$x(x - 3) = 0$$

Since the product of x and $x - 3$ is zero, x could be zero or $x - 3$ could be zero.

$$x = 0 \qquad \text{or} \qquad x - 3 = 0$$
$$x = 3$$

CHECK

$x^2 = 3x$	$x^2 = 3x$
$0^2 \stackrel{?}{=} 3(0)$	$3^2 \stackrel{?}{=} 3(3)$
$0 = 0 \ ✔$	$9 = 9 \ ✔$

EXAMPLE 2   Solve $6x^2 + 15x = 9$.

SOLUTION

$$6x^2 + 15x = 9$$
$$6x^2 + 15x - 9 = 0$$
$$3(2x^2 + 5x - 3) = 0$$
$$3(2x - 1)(x + 3) = 0$$
$$(2x - 1)(x + 3) = 0$$

$$2x - 1 = 0 \qquad \text{or} \qquad x + 3 = 0$$
$$2x = 1 \qquad\qquad\qquad x = -3$$
$$x = \tfrac{1}{2}$$

CHECK

$6x^2 + 15x = 9$	$6x^2 + 15x = 9$
$6\left(\tfrac{1}{2}\right)^2 + 15\left(\tfrac{1}{2}\right) \stackrel{?}{=} 9$	$6(-3)^2 + 15(-3) \stackrel{?}{=} 9$
$\tfrac{3}{2} + \tfrac{15}{2} \stackrel{?}{=} 9$	$54 - 45 \stackrel{?}{=} 9$
$9 = 9 \ ✔$	$9 = 9 \ ✔$

EXAMPLE 3 Solve $(2x + 1)(x - 1) - (x - 1)^2 = 4$.

SOLUTION

$$(2x + 1)(x - 1) - (x - 1)^2 = 4$$
$$(2x^2 - x - 1) - (x^2 - 2x + 1) = 4$$
$$2x^2 - x - 1 - x^2 + 2x - 1 = 4$$
$$x^2 + x - 6 = 0$$
$$(x - 2)(x + 3) = 0$$

$$x - 2 = 0 \quad \text{or} \quad x + 3 = 0$$
$$x = 2 \quad \mid \quad x = -3$$

CHECK The check is left for the student.

SOLVING A SECOND-DEGREE EQUATION IN ONE VARIABLE

1. Collect the terms in one member so that the other member is zero.
2. Simplify and factor.
3. Set each factor equal to zero and solve the resulting equations.
4. Check your results by substituting in the original equation.

CLASSROOM EXERCISES

Solve by factoring.

1. $5x - 15 = 0$

2. $x^2 = 5x$

3. $2x^2 + 3x = 2 \quad \frac{1}{2}$,

4. $30x^2 - 11x = -1$

5. $x^2 + ax - 6a^2 = 0$

6. $x^2 + 3ax + 2a^2 = 0$

7. $(2x + 3)^2 - (x + 1)^2 = 3(x + 2)(x - 2)$

8. $(5x + 2)(x - 2) - (x - 2)^2 = 112$

EXERCISES

Ⓐ Solve by factoring.

1. $6x - 30 = 0$

2. $-7x + 14 = 0$

3. $x^2 = -3x$

4. $z^2 = -5z$

5. $x^2 - 10x + 24 = 0$

6. $2y^2 + 8y + 7 = 0$

7. $c^2 + 5c = 24$

8. $m^2 - 2m = 15$

9. $x^2 = 3x - 2$

10. $x^2 + 5 = 6x$

11. $y - 6 = -y^2$

12. $y^2 = -12y - 32$

13. $15y^2 = y + 6$

14. $2y^2 + 5 = -11y$

15. $80 + 2x = x^2$

16. $2c^2 = 20c - 18$

17. $4x^2 + 49 = -28x$

18. $3c^2 + 3 = 6c$

19. $3x^2 + 15x = 42$

20. $4z^2 + 20z = 144$

21. $10x^2 - 65x + 30 = 0$

22. $(2x + 3)^2 - (2x + 3)(2x + 1) = 0$

23. $(4x - 1)(4x + 3) - (4x - 1)^2 = 0$

24. $(2x + 1)^2 - (x - 3)^2 = -15$

25. $(7y + 2)^2 - (y + 4)^2 = -14$

26. $(3x + 2)^2 - (x - 5)^2 = 0$

27. $(5z - 3)^2 - (2z + 1)^2 = 0$

Solve for x or y.

28. $8y^2 + 5cy - 3c^2 = 0$

29. $2y^2 - 5ay - 7a^2 = 0$

30. $x^2 + bx = -10b^2$

31. $5x^2 - 2a^2 = 3ax$

B   **32.** $(x - 2)(x^2 + 2x + 4) + x(2x - 9) + 4 = (x + 1)(x^2 - x + 1)$

33. $(y^2 + 9)(y - 3)(y + 3) + x(2xy^2 + 3x + 18) = (x^2 + y^2)^2 - x^4$

34. Solve for $x + y$. $x^2 + 2xy + y^2 - 25z^2 = 0$

C   **35.** Solve for x^n. $4x^{2n} - 48x^n + 140 = 0$

36. Find all positive consecutive integers a, b, c, such that $a^2 + b^2 = c^2$.

37. Solve for x. $x^4 + 2x^3 - 13x^2 - 14x + 24 = 0$
(Hint: Use the Factor Theorem.)

38. $V = \frac{1}{4}\pi^2(a + b)(b - a)^2$ gives the volume of a torus while $S = \pi^2(b^2 - a^2)$ gives the surface area. For $V = S$ and $a = 1$, find b.

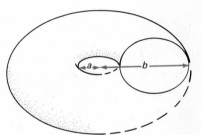

SPECIAL FACTORING

Certain polynomials may be changed into factorable form by adding and then subtracting the same term. This process forms the difference of two squares, one of which is a perfect square trinomial.

EXAMPLE   Factor $a^4 + 4b^4$

SOLUTION   Add $4a^2b^2$ as a "middle" term to form a perfect square. Be sure to subtract $4a^2b^2$ also. Then factor.

$$a^4 + 4b^4 = a^4 + 4a^2b^2 + 4b^4 - 4a^2b^2$$
$$= (a^2 + 2b^2)^2 - 4a^2b^2$$
$$= (a^2 + 2b^2 + 2ab)(a^2 + 2b^2 - 2ab)$$

Factor these.

1. $x^4 + 4y^4$

2. $4x^4 + y^4$

3. $a^4 + a^2 + 1$

4. $c^4 + c^2 + 1$

5. $a^4 + a^2b^2 + b^4$

6. $x^4 + x^2y^2 + y^4$

7. $4x^4 + 3x^2 + 1$

8. $y^4 - 7y^2 + 1$

9. $9c^4 + 5c^2 + 1$

10. $4x^4 + 4x^2 + 25$

11. $4x^4 - 29x^2 + 25$

12. $y^4 - 17y^2 + 64$

CHAPTER REVIEW

Multiply. [3-1 to 3-3]

1. $(x - 3)(x + 4)$ **2.** $(2y - 4)(3y + 2)$ **3.** $(4x + 5)(3x - 2)$

4. $(x - 2y)(x + 2y)$ **5.** $(x - ab)(x + ab)$ **6.** $(2x + 3)(2x + 3)$

7. $(x^2 + 3)^2$ **8.** $\left(x - \frac{1}{2}\right)^2$ **9.** $(3x - 1)^2$

10. $[(a + b) - 2][(a + b) + 3]$ **11.** $[3 - (x - 4)][2 + (x - 4)]$

12. $(5x - 2y - 1)(5x - 2y + 3)$ **13.** $(2x + y + 3)(x - y - 3)$

Factor. [3-4 to 3-7]

14. $12x^2 - 6x$ **15.** $5x^3 - 2x^2 - 3x$ **16.** $4x^3 - 64x$

17. $x^2 + 3x + 2$ **18.** $x^2 - 5x - 6$ **19.** $y^2 - y - 20$

20. $16 - 6b - b^2$ **21.** $3x^2 + 4x + 1$ **22.** $6x^2 - x - 5$

23. $2x^2 - 9xy - 5y^2$ **24.** $6x^2 - 5x - 4$ **25.** $x^2 + x + \frac{1}{4}$

26. $a^2 - 49$ **27.** $4x^2 - 9$ **28.** $100 - 81y^2$

29. $x^2y^2 - m^2$ **30.** $x^{2n} - 1$ **31.** $a^{2m} - b^{4n}$

32. $x^3 + 1$ **33.** $27 - y^3$ **34.** $8x^3 - 1$

35. $27y^3 - 8$ **36.** $x^{3m} - 8$ **37.** $a^6 + 27$

Factor completely. [3-8]

38. $3x^2 + 9x - 15$ **39.** $a^3 - 9a$ **40.** $a^4 - b^4$

41. $x^6 - 1$ **42.** $8a^3 - 2a$ **43.** $a^2(x - 1) - (x - 1)$

Find the remainder. [3-9]

44. $(x^2 - 7x + 3) \div (x - 2)$ **45.** $(3x^2 - 11x + 6) \div (x - 3)$ **46.** $(x^3 - x^2 - 8) \div (x - 2)$

Factor using the Factor Theorem.

47. $x^3 - 2x^2 - 5x + 10$ **48.** $x^3 - 12x + 9$ **49.** $x^3 + 2x^2 - 9x - 18$

Find the Lowest Common Multiple for each. [3-10]

50. $12a^2, 2a^3, 5ab$ **51.** $25a^3b^2, 35ab^3$ **52.** $(x - y)^2, x^2 - y^2, ax + ay$

Solve for x. [3-11]

53. $(2x - 1)(x + 5) + (x + 3)(3x - 1) = 5x^2 + 26$ **54.** $mx + l = ml + x$

55. $(3x - 1)^2 - (x + 5)(x - 4) = 8x^2 - 7$

Solve for b.

56. $c^2 - 6b = 3c - 2bc$

Solve for s.

57. $as + a = ar^n + rs$

Solve by factoring. [3-12]

58. $y^2 = 4y$

59. $x^2 - 4x - 21 = 0$

60. $x^2 - 6x = -9$

61. $2x^2 - 5x = 12$

62. $x^3 - 4x = 0$

63. $12y^2 = 8y + 7$

CAPSULE REVIEW

Write the letter of the best response.

1. If $(x + c)(x + 3) = x^2 + dx - 12$, then
   a. $c = 2$ and $d = 5$
   b. $c = -4$ and $d = -1$
   c. $c = -6$ and $d = 4$
   d. $c = 4$ and $d = 7$

2. The square of $(2x + 3y)$ is
   a. $4x^2 + 12xy + 9y^2$
   b. $4x^2 + 6xy + 9y^2$
   c. $4x^2 - 12xy + 9y^2$
   d. $4x^2 + 12x^2y^2 + 9y^2$

3. Which of the following is not equal to $[(x + 3) + 1] \cdot [(x + 3) - 1]$?
   a. $(x + 4)(x + 2)$
   b. $(x + 3)^2 - 1^2$
   c. $(x + 1)^2 - 3^2$
   d. $x^2 + 6x + 8$

4. The Greatest Common Factor of $12x^4y^3z$, $18x^2y^4z$ and $42x^2y^3z^2$ is
   a. $6x^2y^3z$
   b. $9x^2y^3z$
   c. $3xy^3z$
   d. $6x^2y^3z^2$

5. Which of these trinomials is neither prime nor a perfect square?
   a. $x^2 + x + 1$
   b. $x^2 + 2x + 2$
   c. $x^2 + 2x + 1$
   d. $x^2 + 3x + 2$

6. A factored form of $a^{4t} - b^{6t}$ is
   a. $(a^2 - b^3)^{2t}$
   b. $(a^{2t} - b^{3t})^2$
   c. $a^{2t}(a^{2t} - b^{4t})$
   d. $(a^{2t} + b^{3t})(a^{2t} - b^{3t})$

7. When $16x^4 - y^4$ is factored completely, the result is
   a. $(4x^2 - y^2)^2$
   b. $(4x^2 + y^2)(2x + y)(2x - y)$
   c. $(4x^2 + y^2)(4x^2 - y^2)$
   d. $4(x^2 + y^2)(x + y)(x - y)$

8. Which of these binomials is a factor of $x^3 + 5x^2 + 9x + 9$?
   a. $x + 1$
   b. $x - 2$
   c. $x + 3$
   d. $x - 1$

9. The solutions of the equation $2x^2 = 5x + 3$ are
   a. $x = -\frac{1}{2}, x = 3$
   b. $x = -2, x = \frac{1}{3}$
   c. $x = 1, x = 4$
   d. $x = 0, x = 5$

CHAPTER TEST

Find the product.

1. $(x + 2y)(x + y)$ **2.** $(2x - 5)(2x + 5)$ **3.** $((x + y) + 2)(x + y) - 2)$

4. $2x + 3$ and $x - 1$ **5.** $((x + y) + 3)$ and $((x + y) + 4)$

6. Square $3x + 2$.

Factor.

7. $4x^2 + 6x + 8$ **8.** $6x^3 + 12x^2 + 9x$ **9.** $x^2 - 3x - 10$ **10.** $4x^2 + 5x + 1$

11. $x^2 - 36$ **12.** $4x^2 - 9y^2$ **13.** $x^3 - 1$ **14.** $x^3 + 8$

Factor completely.

15. $x^3 + 5x^2 + 4x$ **16.** $x^4 - 16$

17. Is $x - 2$ a factor of $x^4 - x^3 - 8$?

18. Find the remainder when $x^5 + 3x$ is divided by $x - 1$.

19. Find the Least Common Multiple of $3ab$, $6a^2b$, and $10b$.

20. Find the Least Common Multiple of $a^2 + 2ab + b^2$ and $a^2 - b^2$.

Solve.

21. $(x + 3)^2 - (x + 2)^2 = 3(x - 6)$ **22.** $rt = 2t - 5$ for t

23. $x^2 - 6x = 0$ **24.** $(x + 1)(x - 3) = x - 5$

Write the letter of the best response.

25. What is the product of $(2x - 5)(x + 2)$?

     a. $2x^2 - 9x - 10$ **b.** $2x^2 - 3x - 10$ **c.** $2x^2 - x - 10$

     d. $2x^2 - 10$ **e.** $2x^2 + 9x - 10$

26. What is the product of $(x - 3y)(x - 3y)$?

     a. $x^2 - 9y^2$ **b.** $x^2 + 9y^2$ **c.** $x^2 - 6xy - 9y^2$

     d. $x^2 + 6xy + 9y^2$ **e.** $x^2 - 6xy + 9y^2$

27. What is the product of $(5 + (x + y))(5 - (x + y))$?

     a. $25 - x^2 - y^2$ **b.** $25 - x^2 + y^2$ **c.** $25 - x^2 - 2xy - y^2$

     d. $25 - x^2 + 2xy - y^2$ **e.** $25 + x^2 - 2xy + y^2$

28. How is $14x^3 + 21x^2 + 35x$ written in completely factored form?

     a. $7x(2x^2 + 3x + 5)$ **b.** $7(2x^3 + 3x^2 + 5x)$ **c.** $x(14x^2 + 21x + 35)$

     d. $14x(x^2 + 3x + 5)$ **e.** $x^2(14x + 3x + 5)$

29. Which of these trinomials is prime?

    a. $x^2 + 6x + 12$ **b.** $x^2 + 7x + 12$ **c.** $x^2 + 8x + 12$

    d. $x^2 + 13x + 12$ **e.** $x^2 - x - 12$

30. What are the factors of $x^2 - 16$?

    a. $x - 4$ and $x - 4$ **b.** $x + 4$ and $x + 4$ **c.** $x - 4$ and $x + 4$

    d. x and 4 **e.** x^2 and -16

31. What is the missing factor? $x^3 - 27 = (x - 3)(\ ?\ )$

    a. $x^2 - 3x + 9$ **b.** $x^2 + 3x + 9$ **c.** $x^2 + 9$

    d. $x^2 - 9$ **e.** $x^2 - 6x + 9$

32. What are the factors of $(x + y)^2 + 7(x + y)$?

    a. $x + y$ and x and 7 **b.** $(x + y)^2$ and 7 **c.** $x + y$ and 7

    d. $(x + y)^2$ and $7(x + y)$ **e.** $x + y$ and $x + y + 7$

33. What is the remainder when $x^3 + x^2 + 5$ is divided by $x - 1$?

    a. 3   **b.** 5   **c.** 7   **d.** 9   **e.** 10

34. What is the Least Common Multiple of $3x^2y$, $6xy^2$, and $8xy$?

    a. $48x^2y^2$ **b.** $24x^2y^2$ **c.** $144xy$ **d.** $144x^4y^4$ **e.** $18xy$

35. What does x equal if $bx + x - 2 = b(b + 3) - x$ and $b \neq -2$?

    a. $\dfrac{b^2 + 3b + 2}{b}$ **b.** $\dfrac{b^2 + 5}{b}$ **c.** $b + 3$ **d.** $b + 1$ **e.** $b - 3$

36. What are the solutions of $(3x + 1)(x - 1) = (x + 1)(x + 2) - 5$?

    a. $-\frac{1}{3}$ and 1   **b.** -2 and -1 **c.** 1 and 2   **d.** $\frac{1}{2}$ and 2   **e.** $-\frac{1}{3}$ and -2

CHAPTER 4
FRACTIONS AND
FRACTIONAL EQUATIONS

Several developments are serving to improve medical services in our country. These include employment of increasing numbers of technicians, physicians' assistants, and nurse practitioners, use of new medicines and new medical techniques, and the increased involvement of physicians in group practice. Many improvements are the results of studies to improve the time- and cost-effectiveness of these procedures.

OBJECTIVES: Add, subtract, multiply, divide and simplify fractions that contain variables.

4-1 RATIONAL EXPRESSIONS

A rational number is a number that may be represented in the fraction form $\frac{a}{b}$ for which a and b are integers and $b \neq 0$. Similarly, a **rational expression** is an expression that may be represented in the fraction form $\frac{P}{Q}$ where P and Q are polynomials. For $\frac{P}{Q}$, the domain of any variable used in Q must exclude numbers for which Q is zero.

Rational Numbers		Rational Expressions			
2	0.6	$3a$	$\dfrac{3}{5}$	$\dfrac{2}{t}$	$x^2 + 5x + 4$
$2\dfrac{1}{2}$	$-\dfrac{3}{4}$	$\dfrac{4x + 1}{3y}$		$\dfrac{x^2 + 7x - 3}{6x^2 - 11x + 4}$	

Just as $\frac{a}{b}$, $-\frac{-a}{b}$, $-\frac{a}{-b}$, and $\frac{-a}{-b}$ are four ways to represent a rational number using the integers a and b, so $\frac{P}{Q}$, $-\frac{-P}{Q}$, $-\frac{P}{-Q}$, and $\frac{-P}{-Q}$ are four ways to represent a rational expression using the polynomials P and Q.

EXAMPLE 1 Represent $\dfrac{1 - x}{y - 1}$ in three other ways.

SOLUTION

$$\frac{1 - x}{y - 1}$$
$$= -\frac{-(1 - x)}{y - 1}$$
$$= -\frac{-1 + x}{y - 1}$$
$$= -\frac{x - 1}{y - 1}$$

$$\frac{1 - x}{y - 1}$$
$$= -\frac{1 - x}{-(y - 1)}$$
$$= -\frac{1 - x}{-y + 1}$$
$$= -\frac{1 - x}{1 - y}$$

$$\frac{1 - x}{y - 1}$$
$$= \frac{-(1 - x)}{-(y - 1)}$$
$$= \frac{-1 + x}{-y + 1}$$
$$= \frac{x - 1}{1 - y}$$

EXAMPLE 2 Represent $-\dfrac{3}{a-b}$ in three other ways.

SOLUTION

$$-\frac{3}{a-b}$$

$$= \frac{-3}{a-b}$$

$$-\frac{3}{a-b}$$

$$= \frac{3}{-(a-b)}$$

$$= \frac{3}{-a+b}$$

$$= \frac{3}{b-a}$$

$$-\frac{3}{a-b}$$

$$= -\frac{-3}{-(a-b)}$$

$$= -\frac{-3}{-a+b}$$

$$= -\frac{-3}{b-a}$$

EXAMPLE 3 Complete: $\dfrac{x+y-z}{x-3} = -\dfrac{?}{x-3}$

SOLUTION $\dfrac{x+y-z}{x-3} = -\dfrac{-(x+y-z)}{x-3}$

$$= -\frac{-x-y+z}{x-3}$$

$$= -\frac{z-x-y}{x-3}$$

When a numerator or a denominator is in factored form, an even number of factors in either, or both, may be multiplied by -1. The resulting fraction is equal to the original fraction. When an odd number of factors is multiplied by -1, the resulting fraction equals the opposite of the original fraction.

EXAMPLE 4 Complete. $\dfrac{(a-2)(b-3)(c-4)}{6} = \dfrac{(2-a)??}{6}$

SOLUTION An even number of factors must be multiplied by -1.

$$\frac{(a-2)(b-3)(c-4)}{6} = \frac{(2-a)(3-b)(c-4)}{6}$$

$$\text{or } \frac{(2-a)(b-3)(4-c)}{6}$$

FRACTION FORMS

For any fraction, $\dfrac{a}{b}$, -1 may be introduced as a factor in any two $\square$ positions without changing the value of the fraction.

$$\square\,\frac{\square\,a}{\square\,b}$$

CLASSROOM EXERCISES

Represent each rational expression in three other ways.

1. $\dfrac{1}{2}$ **2.** $-\dfrac{s}{3}$ **3.** $\dfrac{a-3}{3-b}$ **4.** $-\dfrac{5}{2y-x}$

Give the missing terms or factors.

5. $\dfrac{x-3}{z-x-y} = -\dfrac{x-3}{?}$ **6.** $\dfrac{(a-4)(b-5)(6-c)}{8} = \dfrac{(4-a)\,?\,?}{8}$

EXERCISES

A Represent each rational expression in three other ways.

1. $\dfrac{x-2}{2-y}$ **2.** $\dfrac{4-b}{a-3}$ **3.** $\dfrac{x-6}{x-y}$ **4.** $\dfrac{8-b}{b-a}$

Give the missing terms or factors.

5. $\dfrac{(a-3)(b-4)(c-1)}{5} = \dfrac{?\,?\,(1-c)}{5}$ **6.** $\dfrac{(x-1)(y-6)(z-3)}{2} = \dfrac{?\,?\,(3-z)}{2}$

7. $\dfrac{(3-y)(4-z)(x-2)}{8} = -\dfrac{(3-y)\,?\,?}{8}$ **8.** $\dfrac{(u-2)(v-1)(w-4)}{6} = -\dfrac{?\,(v-1)\,?}{6}$

9. $\dfrac{(a-b)(c-d)}{3} = -\dfrac{?\,?}{3}$ **10.** $\dfrac{(x-y)(y-z)}{4} = -\dfrac{?\,?}{4}$

B **11.** $\dfrac{(a-1)(b-2)}{(c-3)(d-4)} = \dfrac{?\,?}{(3-c)(4-d)}$ **12.** $\dfrac{x-(y-z+w)}{x-w} = -\dfrac{?}{x-w}$

13. $\dfrac{(b-(c-d))-a}{b+d} = -\dfrac{?}{b+d}$ **14.** $\dfrac{(a-b)-(c+d)}{a-c} = \dfrac{?}{c-a}$

15. $\dfrac{(x-1)^2}{2-x} = \dfrac{?}{x-2}$ **16.** $\dfrac{(a+2)(3-a)}{(2-a)(a+3)(a-4)} = \dfrac{?\,(a+2)}{(a-2)(a+3)(a-4)}$

C **17.** In how many different ways may $\dfrac{(a-1)(a-2)(a-3)(a-4)(a-5)}{6} = \dfrac{?}{6}$

be completed? Use only the factors $(a-k)$ or $(k-a)$, $k = 1, 2, 3, 4, 5,$ in the numerator.

18. Does $\dfrac{(a-b)^n}{(b-a)^n} = 1$ or -1? **19.** Does $(-1)^n(a-b)^n = (b-a)(a-b)^{n-1}$ or $(b-a)^n$?

4-2   SIMPLIFYING FRACTIONS

The numerator and denominator are the **terms** of a fraction.   A fraction is in *lowest terms* when its numerator and denominator have no common integral factor except 1 and -1.   A fraction may be *reduced* to a fraction in lowest terms by eliminating common factors other than 1 and -1 from the numerator and denominator.   To do this, we use the rule for multiplying with fractions and the Multiplication Property of One.

$$\frac{ac}{bc} = \frac{a}{b} \cdot \frac{c}{c} \quad \text{(rule for multiplying with fractions)}$$

$$= \frac{a}{b} \cdot 1$$

$$= \frac{a}{b} \quad \text{(Multiplication Property of One)}$$

Once the above process is understood, it may be modified into a shorter and faster method for reducing a fraction.

EXAMPLE 1   Simplify $\dfrac{2a^2b}{8ab^2}$ by reducing to lowest terms.

SOLUTION
$$\frac{2a^2b}{8ab^2} = \frac{a \cdot 2ab}{4b \cdot 2ab}$$

$$= \frac{a}{4b} \cdot \frac{2ab}{2ab}$$

$$= \frac{a}{4b} \cdot 1$$

$$= \frac{a}{4b}$$

Shorter Method

$$\frac{\overset{1 \cdot a \cdot 1}{\cancel{2a^2b}}}{\underset{4 \cdot 1 \cdot b}{\cancel{8ab^2}}} = \frac{a}{4b}$$

EXAMPLE 2   Simplify $\dfrac{a^2 - 4b^2}{a^2 - ab - 2b^2}$ by reducing to lowest terms.

SOLUTION   Factor both the numerator and denominator to find their common factors.

$$\frac{a^2 - 4b^2}{a^2 - ab - 2b^2} = \frac{(a + 2b)\overset{1}{\cancel{(a - 2b)}}}{(a + b)\underset{1}{\cancel{(a - 2b)}}}$$

$$= \frac{a + 2b}{a + b}$$

Caution: You may be tempted to "reduce" further by writing $\dfrac{\cancel{a} + 2\cancel{b}}{\cancel{a} + \cancel{b}}$.   This is incorrect.   Neither a nor b is a *factor* of either the numerator or the denominator.

EXAMPLE 3 Simplify $\dfrac{7x^2 - x^3 - 12x}{x^4 - 16x^2}$.

SOLUTION $\dfrac{7x^2 - x^3 - 12x}{x^4 - 16x^2} = \dfrac{-x^3 + 7x^2 - 12x}{x^4 - 16x^2}$

$$= \dfrac{-x(x^2 - 7x + 12)}{x^2(x^2 - 16)}$$

$$= \dfrac{\overset{-1}{\cancel{-x}}(x-3)\overset{1}{\cancel{(x-4)}}}{\underset{x}{x^2}(x+4)\underset{1}{\cancel{(x-4)}}}$$

$$= \dfrac{-(x-3)}{x(x+4)}, \text{ or } \dfrac{3-x}{x(x+4)}$$

EXAMPLE 4 Simplify $\dfrac{x^3 + 8}{x^2 - 4}$.

SOLUTION $\dfrac{x^3 + 8}{x^2 - 4} = \dfrac{\overset{1}{\cancel{(x+2)}}(x^2 - 2x + 4)}{\underset{1}{\cancel{(x+2)}}(x - 2)}$

$$= \dfrac{x^2 - 2x + 4}{x - 2}$$

CLASSROOM EXERCISES

Simplify.

1. $\dfrac{25a^2b^4}{5a^3b^4}$

2. $\dfrac{4x^5y^2}{6x^7y}$

3. $\dfrac{x^2 - 2x - 3}{x^2 + 3x + 2}$

4. $\dfrac{2x^2 - 11x - 6}{x^2 - 5x - 6}$

5. $\dfrac{a^3 + 3a^2 - 4a}{2a^3 + 11a^2 + 12a}$

6. $\dfrac{x^3 + 1}{x + 1}$

EXERCISES

A Simplify.

1. $\dfrac{21}{91}$

2. $\dfrac{69}{115}$

3. $\dfrac{9x^7y^{10}}{36x^{10}y^3}$

4. $\dfrac{7x^4y^3}{28x^2y^4}$

5. $\dfrac{22x^7y^6}{11x^4y^4}$

6. $\dfrac{81x^4y^5}{9xy^3}$

7. $\dfrac{-16x^6y^9}{8x^6y^{11}}$

8. $\dfrac{20x^8y^4}{-5x^8y^5}$

9. $\dfrac{ab}{ax - ay}$

10. $\dfrac{cx + cy}{cd}$

11. $\dfrac{m^2 - m - 12}{m^2 + 10m + 21}$

12. $\dfrac{x^2 + x - 6}{x^2 - 3x - 18}$

13. $\dfrac{x^2 - 9}{x + 3}$

14. $\dfrac{10 - y}{100 - y^2}$

15. $\dfrac{8x^2 - 2x - 1}{6x^2 - 5x + 1}$

16. $\dfrac{-x^2 + x + 6}{2x^2 - 13x + 21}$

17. $\dfrac{-6x^2 + 7x + 5}{2x^2 + 27x + 13}$

18. $\dfrac{a^3 - ab^2}{a^2 - 2ab + b^2}$

19. $\dfrac{x^2 - 2xy + y^2}{y^3 - yx^2}$

20. $\dfrac{3x^3 - 11x^2 + 10x}{25 - 9x^2}$

21. $\dfrac{a^2 - (b - 2)^2}{4 - (a - b)^2}$

22. $\dfrac{(c - 3)^2 - b^2}{(b - c)^2 - 9}$

23. $\dfrac{ax}{a^2x^2 - ax}$

24. $\dfrac{x^3 + 27}{21 + x - 2x^2}$

25. $\dfrac{x^3 - 8}{-3x^2 + 7x - 2}$

26. $\dfrac{am + an + bm + bn}{m^3 + n^3}$

27. $\dfrac{x^3 - y^3}{2x^2 - 2y^2}$

28. $\dfrac{a^3 + b^3}{9a^2 - 9b^2}$

29. $\dfrac{xy - 3x - 2y + 6}{y^3 - 27}$

30. $\dfrac{2b - 2a + ab - a^2}{8 + a^3}$

31. $\dfrac{a^3 + b^3}{a^4 + a^2b^2 + b^4}$

32. $\dfrac{a^3 - b^3}{a^4 + a^2b^2 + b^4}$

B **33.** $\dfrac{2 + a + 2a^2 + a^3}{a^3 - 5a^2 + a - 5}$

34. $\dfrac{3a^3 + 8a^2 + 5a}{3a^2 - a - 10}$

35. $\dfrac{a^4 - 16}{a^6 + 64}$

36. $\dfrac{2x^6 + 5x^3 - 3}{1 - 4x^6}$

37. $\dfrac{a^3 + 3a^2b + 3ab^2 + b^3}{a^3 + 2a^2b + ab^2}$

38. $\dfrac{x^2 - 2xy + y^2 - z^2}{z^2 - x^2 + y^2 + 2yz}$

39. $\dfrac{x^3 + 12x^2y + 48xy^2 + 64y^3}{x^4 + 8x^3y + 16x^2y^2}$

40. $\dfrac{x^{12} - y^{12}}{x^6 - y^6}$

41. $\dfrac{x^{2n} - 81y^{2n}}{x^n - 9y^n}$

42. $\dfrac{b^{2x} + b^x c^x - 2c^{2x}}{3b^{2x} + 7b^x c^x + 2c^{2x}}$

43. $\dfrac{x^4y^4 - 13x^2y^2 + 36}{x^3y^3 - 2x^2y^2 - 9xy + 18}$

C **44.** $\dfrac{x^8 - 1}{(x^5 + x^4 + x + 1)(x^3 - x^2 + x - 1)}$

45. $\dfrac{x^5 - x^4 + x^3 - x^2 + x - 1}{x^6 - 1}$

46. $\dfrac{x^n - 1}{x - 1}$

47. $\dfrac{x^n - 1}{x + 1}$

(HINT: For Exercises 46 and 47 try different values for n.   Watch for a pattern.)

WEATHER OR NOT

One pleasant evening in a large city, a woman left her apartment on the corner to take her dog for a walk. She began her stroll leisurely enough, but after she completed the first side of her around-the-block walk, the weather began to change. She walked a bit faster on the second side, faster still on the third side, and very briskly on the fourth side until she was back inside her apartment. If the city block is 0.1 kilometer on a side, and the woman walked at a rate of 2 km/h, 4 km/h, 6 km/h, and 8 km/h on each side of the square block respectively, what was her average speed for the entire walk?

4-3 MULTIPLICATION WITH FRACTIONS

You may multiply fractions by multiplying their numerators and multiplying their denominators.

$$\frac{a}{b} \cdot \frac{c}{d} = \frac{ac}{bd}, \; b \neq 0, \; d \neq 0.$$

As with arithmetic fractions, it is good practice to reduce the product of algebraic fractions to lowest terms.

EXAMPLE 1 Simplify $\dfrac{2a^2}{3b} \cdot \dfrac{15b^2}{8a}$.

SOLUTION $\dfrac{2a^2}{3b} \cdot \dfrac{15b^2}{8a} = \dfrac{\overset{1 \cdot a}{\cancel{2a^2}} \cdot \overset{5 \cdot b}{\cancel{15b^2}}}{\underset{1 \cdot 1 \; \cdot \; 4 \cdot 1}{\cancel{3b} \cdot \cancel{8a}}}$

$$= \frac{5ab}{4}$$

Using the above rule, factors of the numerators (denominators) of two fractions are also the factors of the numerator (denominator) of the product before simplifying. Eliminating common factors in the numerators and denominators *before* multiplying shortens the process for finding the product in lowest terms.

EXAMPLE 2 Multiply $\dfrac{ab - b^2}{2a}$ and $\dfrac{2a + 2b}{a^2b - b^3}$.

SOLUTION $\dfrac{ab - b^2}{2a} \cdot \dfrac{2a + 2b}{a^2b - b^3} = \dfrac{\overset{1 \quad 1}{\cancel{b}(a - b)}}{\underset{1}{2a}} \cdot \dfrac{\overset{1 \; \cdot \; 1}{2(a + b)}}{\underset{1 \; \cdot \; 1 \; \cdot \; 1}{\cancel{b}(a + b)(a - b)}}$

$$= \frac{1}{a}$$

CLASSROOM EXERCISES

Simplify.

1. $\dfrac{2x^3}{5y} \cdot \dfrac{10y^2}{6x}$

2. $\dfrac{7a^2}{3b^3} \cdot \dfrac{6b^2}{a}$

3. $\dfrac{12c^4}{7d^2} \cdot \dfrac{21dc}{4}$

4. $\dfrac{4(a + b)}{(a - b)} \cdot \dfrac{(a - b)}{2(a + b)}$

5. $\dfrac{3(x - y)}{(x + y)} \cdot \dfrac{2(x + y)}{(x - y)}$

6. $\dfrac{4x - x^2}{3y} \cdot \dfrac{xy + y^2}{4 - x}$

7. $\dfrac{x^2 - x^2a}{a^3} \cdot \dfrac{2a^2}{x - xa}$

EXERCISES

A Simplify.

1. $\dfrac{6a^2}{5b} \cdot \dfrac{45b^3}{18a^3}$

2. $\dfrac{9x^3}{4y^2} \cdot \dfrac{32y^3}{81x^4}$

3. $\dfrac{7c^{2+n}}{11a^2} \cdot \dfrac{132a^3}{56c^{3+n}}$

4. $\dfrac{d^{3+k}}{6c^3} \cdot \dfrac{30c^5}{7d^{3+k}}$

5. $a^2b\left(\dfrac{3}{4ab^2}\right)$

6. $2xy^3\left(\dfrac{6}{x^2y}\right)$

7. $y \cdot \dfrac{x}{y}$

8. $2a \cdot \dfrac{b}{a}$

9. $\dfrac{3}{a-b} \cdot \dfrac{(a-b)^2}{18}$

10. $\dfrac{4}{(x+y)^2} \cdot \dfrac{(x+y)}{16}$

11. $\dfrac{m-n}{m^2-1} \cdot \dfrac{m+1}{m^2-n^2}$

12. $\dfrac{b^3}{a^2-b^2} \cdot \dfrac{a+b}{4ab}$

13. $\dfrac{x^2-8x+15}{8} \cdot \dfrac{6}{x^2-10x+21}$

14. $\dfrac{5}{a^2-7a+12} \cdot \dfrac{a^2-10a+24}{15}$

15. $\dfrac{y^2-y-6}{2y^2+8y+8} \cdot \dfrac{6}{4y^2-36}$

16. $\dfrac{5}{2x^2+12x+18} \cdot \dfrac{x^2-2x-15}{5x^2-125}$

17. $\dfrac{(a+b)^3}{a^3+b^3} \cdot \dfrac{a^2-ab+b^2}{a^2+2ab+b^2}$

18. $\dfrac{x^2-2x-8}{x^4-x^3} \cdot \dfrac{x^3-4x^2+4x}{5x^2-30x+40}$

19. $\dfrac{a^x}{a-b} \cdot \dfrac{b-a}{a}$

20. $\dfrac{x-3y}{x} \cdot \dfrac{x^n}{3y-x}$

B **21.** $\dfrac{x^2-6x+5}{xy^2-y^2} \cdot \dfrac{xy}{35-2x-x^2}$

22. $\dfrac{20-a-a^2}{ab^2} \cdot \dfrac{ab^3-b^3a^2}{a^2+a-20}$

23. $\dfrac{abx^2-aby^2}{x^2+2xy+y^2} \cdot \dfrac{xy-y^2}{x^2-2xy+y^2}$

24. $\dfrac{b^2-ab}{b^2-2ab+a^2} \cdot \dfrac{xb^2-xa^2}{xb^2+2xba+xa^2}$

25. $\dfrac{x^2y-16y^3}{x^2+3xy-4y^2} \cdot \dfrac{y-x}{xy^2-4y^3}$

26. $\dfrac{dc^2-d^3}{c^2-3cd+2d^2} \cdot \dfrac{2d-c}{c^2+2cd+d^2}$

C **27.** $\dfrac{a^6+b^6}{a^3-b^3} \cdot \dfrac{a-b}{a^2+b^2}$

28. $\dfrac{x^2+xy}{x^2-xy+y^2} \cdot \dfrac{x^3-y^3}{x^6-y^6}$

29. $\dfrac{a^2-2ab+b^2-c^2}{a^2+2ab+b^2-c^2} \cdot \dfrac{a+b+c}{c+b-a}$

30. $\dfrac{x^{4n}+6x^{2n}-27}{c^2-c^2x} \cdot \dfrac{cx^{2n+1}-cx^{2n}+3cx-3c}{x^{8n}-81}$

DINNER DATE

Seven good friends dine in the same restaurant. All are eating there today, but each one does not eat at this restaurant every day. In fact, Al eats there every day, Barb eats there every other day, Carl eats there every third day, and so on to the last person, Georgia, who eats there every seventh day. Today they agree that the next time they are all at this restaurant, they will have a party. In how many days from today will this celebration take place?

4-4   DIVISION WITH FRACTIONS

The **reciprocal**, or **multiplicative inverse**, of the number $\frac{a}{b}$ is $\frac{b}{a}$ ($a \neq 0, b \neq 0$). The product of reciprocals is 1.

RECIPROCALS

3 and $\frac{1}{3}$ $\frac{1}{p}$ and $\frac{p}{1}$, or p $\frac{xy}{z}$ and $\frac{z}{xy}$ $\frac{2a+5}{5}$ and $\frac{5}{2a+5}$

To divide one fraction by another, multiply the dividend by the reciprocal of the divisor.

$$\frac{\frac{a}{b}}{\frac{c}{d}} = \frac{\frac{a}{b} \cdot \frac{d}{c}}{\underbrace{\frac{\cancel{c}}{\cancel{d}} \cdot \frac{\cancel{d}}{\cancel{c}}}_{1}}. \quad \text{Therefore,} \quad \frac{\frac{a}{b}}{\frac{c}{d}} = \frac{a}{b} \cdot \frac{d}{c}.$$

$$\frac{a}{b} \div \frac{c}{d} = \frac{a}{b} \cdot \frac{d}{c}, \ b \neq 0, \ c \neq 0, \ d \neq 0.$$

EXAMPLE 1   Divide $\frac{4ab}{15c}$ by $\frac{2a}{5}$.

SOLUTION $\dfrac{4ab}{15c} \div \dfrac{2a}{5} = \dfrac{\overset{2 \cdot 1}{\cancel{4ab}}}{\underset{3}{\cancel{15c}}} \cdot \dfrac{\overset{1}{\cancel{5}}}{\underset{1 \cdot 1}{\cancel{2a}}}$

$= \dfrac{2b}{3c}$

EXAMPLE 2   Divide $\frac{a^3 - ab^2}{4}$ by $\frac{a^2 - 2ab + b^2}{8}$.

$\dfrac{a^3 - ab^2}{4} \div \dfrac{a^2 - 2ab + b^2}{8} = \dfrac{a\overset{a+b}{\cancel{(a^2 - b^2)}}}{\underset{1}{\cancel{4}}} \cdot \dfrac{\overset{2}{\cancel{8}}}{\underset{a-b}{\cancel{(a-b)^2}}}$

$= \dfrac{2a(a+b)}{a-b}, \text{ or } \dfrac{2a^2 + 2ab}{a-b}$

CLASSROOM EXERCISES

Simplify.

1. $\dfrac{6a^2c}{7b} \div \dfrac{3ac}{14}$

2. $\dfrac{15x^2z}{6y^3} \div \dfrac{10xz^2}{3y^2}$

3. $\dfrac{4(x+3)^2}{5(y-1)} \div \dfrac{(x+3)^4}{(y-1)}$

4. $\dfrac{xy^2z^3}{7} \div \dfrac{x^2y^3z}{21}$

5. $\dfrac{x^2-xy}{6} \div \dfrac{x^2+xy-2y^2}{8}$

6. $\dfrac{a^2b-b^3}{14} \div \dfrac{a^2+4ab+3b^2}{2}$

EXERCISES

A Simplify.

1. $\dfrac{6x^2y^3}{5a^3b} \div \dfrac{2xy}{15a^2b^2}$

2. $\dfrac{4z^2w}{7cd^3} \div \dfrac{2zw^3}{c^2d^2}$

3. $\dfrac{12m^{x+2}}{n^2} \div 6m^{x+2}$

4. $\dfrac{18x^{a+3}}{7y^2} \div \dfrac{3x^a}{14y^2}$

5. $\dfrac{x+y}{y^{n+1}} \div \dfrac{x^2-y^2}{y^{n+2}}$

6. $\dfrac{c^{m+2}}{a-b} \div \dfrac{c^{m+1}}{a^2-b^2}$

7. $\dfrac{m^2-mn}{n} \div \dfrac{m}{n}$

8. $\dfrac{a^2+ab}{b} \div \dfrac{a}{b}$

9. $\dfrac{b^2-2b+1}{6} \div (b^2-1)$

10. $\dfrac{a^4-b^4}{a^2} \div (a^2-b^2)$

11. $(x^2-4) \div \dfrac{3x^2+3x-6}{x-1}$

12. $(x^4-y^4) \div \dfrac{x^2-y^2}{x^4-x^2y^2+y^4}$

13. $\dfrac{t}{t-3} \div \dfrac{t^4}{2}$

14. $\dfrac{y^6}{5} \div \dfrac{y-1}{10}$

15. $\dfrac{y^2-x^2}{y^2} \div \dfrac{x+y}{2y}$

16. $\dfrac{2t}{4t^2-1} \div \dfrac{6t^3}{6t+3}$

17. $\dfrac{1-m}{m-3} \div \dfrac{m^4-1}{12m-36}$

18. $\dfrac{x-2}{x-5} \div \dfrac{4-x^2}{3x-15}$

19. $\dfrac{4x^2+8x+3}{2x^2-5x+3} \div \dfrac{1-4x^2}{6x^2-9x}$

20. $\dfrac{25-9y^2}{8y^2-4y} \div \dfrac{10-21y+9y^2}{2y^2-y}$

21. $\dfrac{a^3-8}{a^2-2a+4} \div (a^2-4)$

22. $\dfrac{m^3+8n^3}{14} \div \dfrac{m^2+4mn+4n^2}{21}$

B 23. $\dfrac{(a-b)^3}{b^3+c^3} \div \dfrac{a^2-2ab+b^2}{b^2-bc+c^2}$

24. $\dfrac{x^3-y^3}{(x+y)^3} \div \dfrac{x^2+xy+y^2}{x^2+2xy+y^2}$

25. $\dfrac{x^2+y^2-z^2-2xy}{x^2+y^2-z^2+2xy} \div \dfrac{x-y-z}{(x+y-z)^2}$

26. $\dfrac{a^2-b^2}{a^2} \cdot \dfrac{a^2-ab+b^2}{a^2} \div \dfrac{a^3+b^3}{a^{4x}}$

27. $\dfrac{m^2+2m+1}{m^2+4m} \cdot \dfrac{m^2-16}{m^2-3m-4} \div \dfrac{m^2-2m-3}{m^2-m}$

28. $\dfrac{2a^2-8a-ab+4b}{2a^2-6a-ab+3b} \div \dfrac{2a^2-8a+ab-4b}{a^2-4a}$

C 29. $\dfrac{x^{2n}-9}{x^{2n}+x^n-42} \cdot \dfrac{x^{2n}-6x^n}{x^{2n}+4x^n-21} \div \dfrac{x^{2n}-2x^n-15}{x^{2n}+14x^n+49}$

30. $\dfrac{x^4+4x^3-4x^2+4x-5}{x^2+3x-10} \div \dfrac{x^2+3x-4}{x^4+2x^3-7x^2+2x-8}$

4-5 ADDITION AND SUBTRACTION WITH FRACTIONS

To add or subtract fractions having a common denominator, add or subtract their numerators.

To add or subtract fractions having different denominators, first replace the fractions by other fractions for the same numbers so that all denominators are the same. To keep the work as simple as possible, use the **least common denominator** (LCD). The LCD is the LCM of the denominators. (See Section 3-10.)

EXAMPLE 1 Simplify $\dfrac{3x}{5} - \dfrac{x}{10} + \dfrac{x}{2}$.

SOLUTION The LCD is 10.

$$\frac{3x}{5} - \frac{x}{10} + \frac{x}{2} = \frac{6x}{10} - \frac{x}{10} + \frac{5x}{10}$$

$$= \frac{6x - x + 5x}{10}$$

$$= \frac{10x}{10}$$

$$= x$$

EXAMPLE 2 Simplify $\dfrac{1}{a} + \dfrac{1}{ab} + \dfrac{1}{b}$.

SOLUTION The LCD is ab.

$$\frac{1}{a} + \frac{1}{ab} + \frac{1}{b} = \frac{b}{ab} + \frac{1}{ab} + \frac{a}{ab}$$

$$= \frac{a + b + 1}{ab}$$

EXAMPLE 3 Simplify $\dfrac{a}{a^2 - 2ab + b^2} - \dfrac{b}{a^2 - b^2}$.

SOLUTION

$$\frac{a}{a^2 - 2ab + b^2} - \frac{b}{a^2 - b^2}$$

$$= \frac{a}{(a - b)^2} - \frac{b}{(a + b)(a - b)} \qquad \text{The LCD is } (a - b)^2(a + b).$$

$$= \frac{a(a + b)}{(a - b)^2(a + b)} - \frac{b(a - b)}{(a - b)^2(a + b)}$$

$$= \frac{a^2 + ab - ab + b^2}{(a - b)^2(a + b)}$$

$$= \frac{a^2 + b^2}{(a - b)^2(a + b)}$$

EXAMPLE 4 Simplify $\dfrac{1}{6x} + \dfrac{1}{3x-6} - \dfrac{1}{2x+4}$.

SOLUTION

$\dfrac{1}{6x} + \dfrac{1}{3x-6} - \dfrac{1}{2x+4}$

$= \dfrac{1}{6x} + \dfrac{1}{3(x-2)} - \dfrac{1}{2(x+2)}$ The LCD is $6x(x-2)(x+2)$.

$= \dfrac{(x-2)(x+2)}{6x(x-2)(x+2)} + \dfrac{2x(x+2)}{6x(x-2)(x+2)} - \dfrac{3x(x-2)}{6x(x-2)(x+2)}$

$= \dfrac{x^2 - 4 + 2x^2 + 4x - 3x^2 + 6x}{6x(x-2)(x+2)}$

$= \dfrac{10x - 4}{6x(x-2)(x+2)}$

$= \dfrac{5x - 2}{3x(x-2)(x+2)}$

CLASSROOM EXERCISES

Simplify.

1. $\dfrac{3}{4} + \dfrac{1}{2}$ **2.** $\dfrac{2}{c} - \dfrac{3}{c}$ **3.** $\dfrac{3}{x+1} + \dfrac{2}{x+1}$ **4.** $1 + \dfrac{b}{c}$

5. $\dfrac{a}{b} - 1$ **6.** $\dfrac{2x}{x-1} - \dfrac{2}{x-1}$ **7.** $\dfrac{1}{a} + \dfrac{1}{b}$ **8.** $\dfrac{1}{c} - \dfrac{1}{d}$

9. $\dfrac{x}{x-y} - \dfrac{y}{x+y}$ **10.** $\dfrac{3x-12}{x+5} + \dfrac{2x}{x^2+10x+25}$ **11.** $\dfrac{1}{5a} - \dfrac{1}{4a-2} + \dfrac{3}{2a-1}$

EXERCISES

A Simplify.

1. $\dfrac{a}{2} + \dfrac{b}{4} + \dfrac{c}{6}$ **2.** $\dfrac{x}{7} + \dfrac{y}{9} + \dfrac{z}{21}$ **3.** $\dfrac{3}{2x^3} - \dfrac{2}{3x^2} + \dfrac{1}{x}$

4. $\dfrac{7}{3y^2} - \dfrac{2}{y} + \dfrac{1}{9y^3}$ **5.** $\dfrac{1}{x} + \dfrac{1}{y} + \dfrac{1}{z}$ **6.** $\dfrac{1}{a} - \dfrac{1}{b} + \dfrac{1}{c}$

7. $\dfrac{4x-7}{8} - \dfrac{3x-5}{12}$ **8.** $\dfrac{2b-5}{12} + \dfrac{4b-1}{20}$ **9.** $\dfrac{x-5}{4x} - \dfrac{3x-1}{x}$

10. $\dfrac{6-b}{7b} - \dfrac{2b-3}{b}$ **11.** $\dfrac{2c}{3-2c} + 1$ **12.** $1 + \dfrac{a}{1-a}$

13. $\dfrac{5a+3b}{2a^2b} - \dfrac{3a+4b}{ab^2}$ **14.** $\dfrac{2w+y}{3w^3y^2} - \dfrac{4w-3y}{2wy^3}$ **15.** $x - 5 - \dfrac{2+13x}{3x}$

16. $\dfrac{2 + 5x}{3x} - 2x + 3$

17. $\dfrac{x^2 - 5}{x^3 - 1} - \dfrac{x + 1}{x^2 + x + 1}$

18. $\dfrac{4 + a^2}{a^3 + 1} - \dfrac{a + 1}{a^2 - a + 1}$

19. $a + \dfrac{a - 2}{3 - a} + \dfrac{4 - a^2}{a^2 - 9}$

20. $\dfrac{z - 5}{4 - z} + z - \dfrac{z - 2}{z^2 - 16}$

21. $\dfrac{x}{x^2 - 16} - \dfrac{x + 1}{x^2 - 5x + 4}$

22. $\dfrac{3}{12 + x - x^2} + \dfrac{2}{x^2 - 9}$

23. $\dfrac{2}{b^2 - ab} + \dfrac{2}{a^2 - ab}$

24. $\dfrac{5}{5x - x^2} - \dfrac{2}{x^2 - 25}$

25. $\dfrac{2s}{t^2 - s^2} - \dfrac{s}{t - s} + \dfrac{t}{t + s}$

26. $\dfrac{b}{a^2 - b^2} - \dfrac{a}{b - a} + \dfrac{b}{b + a}$

$\boxed{\text{B}}$ **27.** $\dfrac{1}{x + y} + \dfrac{1}{x - y} - \dfrac{2x}{x^2 - y^2}$

28. $\dfrac{2x^3}{x^6 - y^6} - \dfrac{1}{x^3 - y^3} - \dfrac{1}{x^3 + y^3}$

29. $\dfrac{t - 3}{t^2 - 3t + 2} - \dfrac{t - 2}{t^2 - 4t + 3} - \dfrac{t - 1}{t^2 - 5t + 6}$

30. $\dfrac{s - 1}{s^2 - 9s + 20} + \dfrac{4s - 5}{s^2 - 8s + 15} - \dfrac{3s - 6}{s^2 - 7s + 12}$

31. $\dfrac{a}{1 - a^3} + \dfrac{1}{a^2 - 1} - \dfrac{2}{a^2 + a + 1}$

32. $\dfrac{4x - 4}{x^2y - x^2d - y + d} - \dfrac{2 - 2x}{xy + y - xd - d}$

$\boxed{\text{C}}$ **33.** $\left(\dfrac{x + 2}{x^2 + 2x - 3} \div \dfrac{x - 1}{x^2 + 5x + 6}\right) - \dfrac{4x + 4}{x^2 - 2x + 1}$

34. $\left(\dfrac{3y - 1}{6y^2 - 11y - 10} \cdot \dfrac{9y^2 - 4}{12y - 4}\right) - \dfrac{1}{2y^2 - 5y}$

35. For $x = \dfrac{2t}{1 + t^2}$ and $y = \dfrac{1 - t^2}{1 + t^2}$, show that the value of $x^2 + y^2$ is independent of the value of t.

 **SEQUENCES BY MULTIPLICATION**

In the following sequences of numbers, each term except the first is found by multiplying the preceding term by a constant.

3, 9, 27, 81, 243, . . .   4, 20, 100, 500, 2500, . . .
12, −24, 48, −96, 192, . . .   100, 50, 25, 12.5, 6.25, . . .

The "constant" feature of your calculator can be useful when working with this type of sequence. The flow chart shows how to use your calculator to generate the successive terms.

Use the "constant" feature of your calculator to find the 10th term in each sequence.

1. 5, 25, 125, 625, . . .   **2.** −5, −20, −80, −320, . . .

3. 8, −24, 72, −216, . . .   **4.** −9, 36, −144, 576, . . .

5. 256, 128, 64, 32, . . .   **6.** 19 683, 6561, 2187, . . .

7. 4.8, 7.2, 10.8, 16.2, . . .   **8.** 10.24, 2.56, 0.64, 0.16, . . .

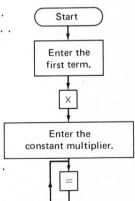

4-6 MIXED EXPRESSIONS

A **mixed expression** is one that has a fraction as one term and non-fractions as other terms.

MIXED EXPRESSIONS

$$2 + \frac{1}{3} \qquad\qquad \frac{1}{a} + a \qquad\qquad 2x - 3 - \frac{5}{x+4}$$

When working with mixed expressions, it often is useful to represent the mixed expression as a fraction.

EXAMPLE 1 Multiply $\frac{1}{x} - 1$ and $x + 1 + \frac{1}{x}$.

SOLUTION $\left(\frac{1}{x} - 1\right)\left(x + 1 + \frac{1}{x}\right) = \frac{1-x}{x} \cdot \frac{x^2 + x + 1}{x}$

$$= \frac{1 - x^3}{x^2}$$

EXAMPLE 2 Divide $2 - \frac{1}{x} - \frac{6}{x^2}$ by $4 - \frac{9}{x^2}$.

SOLUTION $\left(2 - \frac{1}{x} - \frac{6}{x^2}\right) \div \left(4 - \frac{9}{x^2}\right) = \frac{2x^2 - x - 6}{x^2} \div \frac{4x^2 - 9}{x^2}$

$$= \frac{2x^2 - x - 6}{\overset{}{\underset{1}{\cancel{x^2}}}} \cdot \frac{\overset{1}{\cancel{x^2}}}{4x^2 - 9}$$

$$= \frac{\overset{1}{\cancel{(2x + 3)}}(x - 2)}{\underset{1}{\cancel{(2x + 3)}}(2x - 3)}$$

$$= \frac{x - 2}{2x - 3}$$

CLASSROOM EXERCISES

Simplify.

1. $\left(1 - \frac{y}{x}\right)\left(1 + \frac{y}{x}\right)$ **2.** $\left(\frac{a}{2} + 1\right)\left(a - 2 + \frac{4}{a}\right)$ **3.** $\left(\frac{x^2}{a} - a\right) \div \left(\frac{x}{a^2} - \frac{1}{a}\right)$

EXERCISES

A Simplify.

1. $\left(x - \dfrac{1}{x}\right) \div \left(x + \dfrac{1}{x} - 2\right)$ **2.** $\left(\dfrac{1}{y} - y\right) \div \left(\dfrac{1}{y} - 2 + y\right)$ **3.** $\left(1 - \dfrac{2}{3a}\right)\left(\dfrac{9a}{9a^2 - 4}\right)$

4. $\left(\dfrac{5}{6} + \dfrac{1}{a}\right)\left(\dfrac{4a}{25a^2 - 36}\right)$ **5.** $\left(\dfrac{1}{x} + \dfrac{1}{y}\right) \div \left(\dfrac{1}{x} - \dfrac{1}{y}\right)$ **6.** $\left(\dfrac{2}{m} - \dfrac{2}{n}\right) \div \left(\dfrac{1}{m} + \dfrac{1}{n}\right)$

7. $\left(c - \dfrac{cy}{x}\right) \div \left(c^2 - \dfrac{c^2 y}{x}\right)$ **8.** $\left(a + \dfrac{a}{b}\right) \div \left(1 + \dfrac{1}{b}\right)$ **9.** $(m^2 + m - 1)\left(1 - \dfrac{1}{m} + \dfrac{1}{m^2}\right)$

10. $\left(\dfrac{1}{x} - 1\right) \div (x - 1)$ **11.** $\left(\dfrac{1}{z} - 4\right) \div (4z - 1)$ **12.** $(x^2 - 2x - 1)\left(1 - \dfrac{2}{x} + \dfrac{1}{x^2}\right)$

13. $\left(\dfrac{x}{y} - \dfrac{y}{x}\right)\left(x - \dfrac{x^2}{x + y}\right)$ **14.** $\left(\dfrac{a}{b} - \dfrac{b}{a}\right)\left(a - \dfrac{a^2}{a - b}\right)$ **15.** $\left(1 + \dfrac{a + b}{a - b}\right)\left(1 - \dfrac{a - b}{a + b}\right)$

16. $\left(a - 5 + \dfrac{8}{a + 1}\right)\left(a + 2 + \dfrac{4}{a - 3}\right)$ **17.** $\left(\dfrac{-15}{x + 1} + x + 3\right)\left(\dfrac{75}{x + 6} + x - 14\right)$

18. $\left(a - \dfrac{3b^2}{a - 2b}\right) \div \left(a - 2b - \dfrac{b^2}{a - 2b}\right)$ **19.** $\left(x + 10z + \dfrac{-26z^2}{x - z}\right) \div \left(\dfrac{x - z}{3} - \dfrac{4z^2}{3x - 3z}\right)$

B **20.** $\left(\dfrac{t^2 - 1}{t^3 - 1} + \dfrac{t - 1}{t^2 + t + 1}\right) \div \left(\dfrac{t + 1}{t^2 - t + 1} - \dfrac{t^2 - 1}{t^3 + 1}\right)$ **21.** $\left(\dfrac{x}{y} + \dfrac{1}{x}\right)\left(x - \dfrac{x^3}{x^2 + y}\right)$

22. $\left(\dfrac{m}{n} - 1\right)\left(1 + \dfrac{m}{n}\right) \div \left(\dfrac{n}{m} - \dfrac{m}{n}\right)$ **23.** $(a + 1)\left[\dfrac{1}{a^2 - 1} + 1 - \dfrac{1}{2(a - 1)}\right]$

C **24.** $\left(\dfrac{-5}{x^4 - 15x^2 + 49} - 1\right) \div \left(\dfrac{1 - x}{x^2 - 7 + x} + 1\right)$

25. $\left(x + 7 - \dfrac{9x^2 + 63x - 198}{x^3 - 2x^2 - 5x + 6}\right)\left(x + 2 + \dfrac{13x^2 - 5x - 62}{x^3 - x^2 - 22x + 40}\right)$

EVENS AND ODDS

An even integer has 2 as a factor. We may *represent* an even integer by the term $2n$ in which n represents some integer. Similarly, when we *obtain* an expression having the form $2n$, n an integer, we are assured that $2n$ represents an even integer. Since an odd integer differs from an even integer by 1, expressions like $2n + 1$ or $2n - 1$ represent odd integers.

Show that

1. squares of even integers are even; squares of odd integers are odd.
2. products of even integers are even; products of odd integers are odd.

4-7 COMPLEX FRACTIONS

A **complex fraction** is one that has a fraction in either the numerator or the denominator, or in both.

COMPLEX FRACTIONS

$$\dfrac{\frac{1}{x}}{\frac{1}{y}} \qquad \dfrac{\frac{x+1}{x}}{5} \qquad \dfrac{a-b}{\frac{a}{b}} \qquad \dfrac{1+\frac{s}{t}}{1-\frac{s^2}{t^2}}$$

To replace a complex fraction by a simple fraction, (1) multiply both numerator and denominator of the complex fraction by the LCD of all the fractions in both the numerator and denominator, or (2) divide the numerator by the denominator.

EXAMPLE 1 Simplify $\dfrac{1+\frac{1}{x}}{\frac{2}{x^2}-\frac{1}{2x}}$.

SOLUTION 1 The LCD of $\dfrac{1}{x}$, $\dfrac{2}{x^2}$, and $\dfrac{1}{2x}$ is $2x^2$.

$$\frac{1+\frac{1}{x}}{\frac{2}{x^2}-\frac{1}{2x}} = \frac{2x^2\left(1+\frac{1}{x}\right)}{2x^2\left(\frac{2}{x^2}-\frac{1}{2x}\right)}$$

$$= \frac{2x^2+2x}{4-x}$$

SOLUTION 2 $\dfrac{1+\frac{1}{x}}{\frac{2}{x^2}-\frac{1}{2x}} = \dfrac{\frac{x+1}{x}}{\frac{4-x}{2x^2}}$

$$= \frac{x+1}{\overset{}{\underset{1}{\cancel{x}}}} \cdot \frac{\overset{x}{\cancel{2x^2}}}{4-x}$$

$$= \frac{(x+1)2x}{4-x}, \text{ or } \frac{2x^2+2x}{4-x}$$

CLASSROOM EXERCISES

Simplify.

1. $\dfrac{\frac{1}{8} + 1}{\frac{1}{8} - 1}$

2. $\dfrac{2 + \frac{1}{a}}{\frac{1}{a^2} - \frac{3}{a}}$

3. $\dfrac{1 - \frac{1}{c^2}}{\frac{1}{c} - \frac{1}{c^2}}$

4. $\dfrac{\frac{1}{3a} - \frac{1}{b}}{\frac{1}{a} + \frac{1}{2b}}$

EXERCISES

A Simplify.

1. $\dfrac{\frac{1}{2} + 1}{\frac{1}{2} - 1}$

2. $\dfrac{9 - \frac{1}{4}}{3 + \frac{1}{2}}$

3. $\dfrac{\frac{1}{x} + y}{\frac{1}{x} - y}$

4. $\dfrac{a - \frac{1}{b}}{b - \frac{1}{a}}$

5. $\dfrac{1 + \frac{a}{b}}{1 - \frac{a^2}{b^2}}$

6. $\dfrac{1 - \frac{x}{y}}{\frac{x - y}{y}}$

7. $\dfrac{\frac{a^2 b}{c^2}}{\frac{ab^2}{c^2}}$

8. $\dfrac{\frac{1}{x} + \frac{1}{y}}{\frac{1}{x} - \frac{1}{y}}$

9. $\dfrac{a + 1}{1 + \frac{1}{a}}$

10. $\dfrac{a - 1}{a - \frac{1}{a}}$

11. $\dfrac{a + \frac{a}{b}}{1 + \frac{1}{b}}$

12. $\dfrac{x^2 - \frac{1}{x}}{x^3 - \frac{1}{x^3}}$

13. $\dfrac{\frac{x^2}{6} + \frac{5x}{12} - 1}{\frac{x^2}{4} + \frac{11x}{12} - \frac{1}{3}}$

14. $\dfrac{x - 3 + \frac{2}{x}}{x - 4 + \frac{3}{x}}$

15. $\dfrac{\frac{x^3 + 27}{x^2 - 9}}{\frac{x^2 - 3x + 9}{x + 3}}$

16. $\dfrac{\frac{a^2 + 2a + 4}{a - 2}}{\frac{a^3 - 8}{a^2 - 4}}$

B **17.** $\dfrac{\frac{x}{1 + x} - \frac{1 - x}{x}}{\frac{x}{1 + x} + \frac{1 - x}{x}}$

18. $\dfrac{\frac{a^2}{a^2 + b^2} - 1}{\frac{ab}{a + b} - b}$

19. $\dfrac{\frac{x^2 - 3xy}{a^2 - 1}}{\frac{9y^2 - 6xy + x^2}{1 + a}}$

20. $\dfrac{\frac{3a + b}{a - b} - 3}{1 - \frac{a - 3b}{a + b}}$

21. $\dfrac{\frac{x - 1}{x + 1} - \frac{x + 1}{x - 1}}{\frac{x + 1}{x - 1} - \frac{x - 1}{x + 1}}$

22. $\dfrac{\left(1 - \frac{3x}{x + y}\right) \div \left(\frac{y - 5x}{x + y}\right)}{\left(\frac{2}{5} + \frac{\frac{3}{5}y}{y - 5x}\right)}$

C **23.** $\dfrac{\frac{x}{1 - x^3} + \frac{1}{x^2 - 1} - \frac{2}{x^2 + x + 1}}{-2 + \frac{1}{x^2 - 1}}$

24. $\dfrac{\left(1 - \frac{2}{a + b}\right)\left(1 + \frac{2}{a + b}\right)}{\left(a + 3b + \frac{4b^2 - 4}{a - b}\right)}$

25. $1 + \dfrac{1}{2 + \dfrac{1}{2 + \dfrac{1}{2 + \dfrac{1}{2 + \frac{1}{2}}}}}$

26. $1 - \dfrac{1}{2 - \dfrac{1}{2 - \dfrac{1}{2 - \dfrac{1}{2 - \frac{1}{2}}}}}$

27. $1 + \dfrac{1}{2 - \dfrac{1}{2 + \dfrac{1}{2 - \dfrac{1}{2 + \frac{1}{2}}}}}$

CHECKING YOUR UNDERSTANDING

WORDS AND SYMBOLS

complex fraction
mixed expression

least common denominator, LCD
lowest terms fraction
multiplicative inverse

rational expression
reciprocal

CONCEPTS

■ For any fraction, -1 may be introduced as a factor in the numerator or the denominator, or both, an even number of times. The value of the fraction will remain unchanged. When -1 is introduced an odd number of times, the resulting fraction is the opposite of the original fraction. [4-1]

■ Fractions whose terms involve algebraic expressions may be added, subtracted, multiplied, divided, and simplified according to the rules and methods that apply to arithmetic fractions. [4-1 to 4-7]

PROCESSES

■ Introduce factors of -1 in a fraction so that the resulting fraction equals the original fraction. [4-1]

1. $\dfrac{5}{x-1} = \dfrac{?}{1-x}$ **2.** $\dfrac{(a-3)(b+4)}{10} = -\dfrac{?\,?}{-10}$ **3.** $\dfrac{(x-y)(2x-3y)}{2x-y} = \dfrac{(y-x)\,?}{?}$

■ Add, subtract, multiply, divide, and simplify fractions whose terms contain algebraic expressions. [4-1 to 4-7]

4. $\dfrac{-15a^2b}{5ab^2}$ **5.** $\dfrac{2y^3 + 10y^2 + 12y}{y^3 + 6y^2 + 9y}$ **6.** $\dfrac{2}{x^2 + 5x + 6} + \dfrac{1}{x^2 - 9}$

7. $\dfrac{2}{x} + \dfrac{4}{3-x} - \dfrac{4+4x}{2x}$ **8.** $\dfrac{x+2y}{x^2+xy} - \dfrac{y-2x}{x^2-y^2}$ **9.** $\dfrac{a^3b^2}{c} \cdot \dfrac{c^4}{a^4b}$

10. $\dfrac{a^3 - ab^2}{a+b} \cdot \dfrac{a}{a^2 - 2ab + b^2}$ **11.** $\dfrac{x^3 - 1}{x^3} \div \dfrac{x-1}{x}$

12. $\dfrac{x^2 + 4x + 4}{3x} \div \dfrac{x^2 + x - 2}{6}$ **13.** $\left(x - \dfrac{1}{x}\right)\left(\dfrac{1}{x-1} + 1\right)$

14. $\left(3x - 1 - \dfrac{2}{x}\right) \div \left(1 + \dfrac{2}{3x}\right)$ **15.** $\dfrac{\dfrac{1}{x} + \dfrac{1}{y}}{\dfrac{1}{x} - \dfrac{1}{y}}$

OBJECTIVES: Solve fractional equations. Solve problems using fractional equations.

4-8 SOLVING FRACTIONAL EQUATIONS

A **fractional equation** is one in which the variable appears in a denominator.

FRACTIONAL EQUATIONS

$$\frac{1}{x} = 2 \qquad 7 + \frac{3}{x} = 8 \qquad x + \frac{1}{x} = 2 \qquad \frac{-1}{x-2} = x \qquad \frac{x}{x+2} + \frac{1}{x} = 1$$

To solve a fractional equation, first reduce each fraction to lowest terms. Then, multiply both members of the equation by the LCM of the denominators to clear the equation of fractions.

EXAMPLE 1 Solve $\dfrac{3x^2}{x^2 - 2x} = 1$.

SOLUTION Factor the denominator and reduce the fraction.

$$\frac{3x^2}{x^2 - 2x} = 1$$

$$\frac{3x^2}{\overset{x}{x}(x-2)} = 1$$

$$M_{x-2} \quad \frac{3x}{x-2}(x-2) = x-2$$

$$3x = x - 2$$
$$2x = -2$$
$$x = -1$$

CHECK

$$\frac{3x^2}{x^2 - 2x} = 1$$

$$\frac{3(-1)^2}{(-1)^2 - 2(-1)} \overset{?}{=} 1$$

$$\frac{3}{1+2} \overset{?}{=} 1$$

$$1 = 1 \quad ✔$$

EXAMPLE 2 Solve $\dfrac{2x}{x+1} = 2 - \dfrac{5}{2x}$.

SOLUTION The LCM of the denominators is $2x(x+1)$.

$$\frac{2x}{x+1} = 2 - \frac{5}{2x}$$

$$M_{2x(x+1)} \quad \frac{2x \cdot 2x\overset{1}{\cancel{(x+1)}}}{\underset{1}{\cancel{x+1}}} = 2 \cdot 2x(x+1) - \frac{5 \cdot \overset{1}{\cancel{2x}}(x+1)}{\underset{1}{\cancel{2x}}}$$

$$4x^2 = 4x^2 + 4x - 5x - 5$$
$$x = -5$$

CHECK

$$\frac{2x}{x+1} = 2 - \frac{5}{2x}$$

$$\frac{2(-5)}{-5+1} \overset{?}{=} 2 - \frac{5}{2(-5)}$$

$$2\frac{1}{2} = 2\frac{1}{2} \quad ✔$$

EXAMPLE 3 Solve $\dfrac{3x}{x^2-9} - \dfrac{6-x}{x^2+3x} = \dfrac{4}{x+3}$.

SOLUTION Factor the denominators to help find their LCM.

$$\frac{3x}{x^2-9} - \frac{6-x}{x^2+3x} = \frac{4}{x+3}$$

$$\frac{3x}{(x+3)(x-3)} - \frac{6-x}{x(x+3)} = \frac{4}{x+3}$$

The LCM of the denominators is $x(x+3)(x-3)$.

$$M_{x(x+3)(x-3)} \quad 3x^2 - (6-x)(x-3) = 4x(x-3)$$
$$3x^2 + x^2 - 9x + 18 = 4x^2 - 12x$$
$$3x = -18$$
$$x = -6$$

CHECK The check is left for the student.

CLASSROOM EXERCISES

Solve.

1. $\dfrac{5a}{3a+a^2} = 1$

2. $\dfrac{-6y^2}{y^2+4y} = 2$

3. $\dfrac{3b}{b+1} = 3 + \dfrac{-2}{b}$

4. $\dfrac{1}{x-6} + \dfrac{2}{x+6} = \dfrac{3}{x}$

5. $\dfrac{2x-3}{x^2-4} + \dfrac{4}{x(x^2-4)} = \dfrac{2}{x}$

6. $\dfrac{4a+15}{a^2-25} + \dfrac{5}{a+5} = \dfrac{9a+10}{a^2+5a}$

EXERCISES

A Solve.

1. $\dfrac{10b}{b^2 + b} = 1$

2. $\dfrac{4y^2}{y^2 - 2y} = 3$

3. $\dfrac{5}{x} = \dfrac{6}{x} - \dfrac{1}{2}$

4. $\dfrac{7}{2x} + \dfrac{1}{3} = \dfrac{1}{x} + \dfrac{7}{6}$

5. $\dfrac{x}{x + 1} + \dfrac{3x - 2}{x} = 4$

6. $\dfrac{y}{y - 1} + \dfrac{2(y - 1)}{y} = 3$

7. $\dfrac{3}{x} - \dfrac{1}{x - 2} = \dfrac{2}{x + 2}$

8. $\dfrac{1}{y} + \dfrac{2}{y + 1} = \dfrac{3}{y + 2}$

9. $\dfrac{6}{3x - 1} + \dfrac{1}{2} = \dfrac{14}{6x - 2}$

10. $\dfrac{4}{1 + 4y} - \dfrac{1}{3} = \dfrac{1}{3 + 12y}$

11. $\dfrac{1}{x^2 + 8} = \dfrac{1}{x^2 + 4x + 4}$

12. $\dfrac{6t - 2}{2t - 1} = \dfrac{9t}{3t + 1}$

13. $\dfrac{4}{x - 3} + \dfrac{2x}{x^2 - 9} = \dfrac{1}{x + 3}$

14. $\dfrac{6x^2 - 2x + 5}{3x^2 - 2} = 2$

15. $\dfrac{5}{y - 2} + \dfrac{4y}{y^2 - 4} = \dfrac{2}{y + 2}$

16. $\dfrac{8a^2 - 3a + 6}{2a^2 - 3} = 4$

17. $\dfrac{3x}{x^2} - \dfrac{5}{x + 6} = \dfrac{1}{x^2 + 6x}$

18. $\dfrac{2(x + 1)}{(x + 1)^2} - \dfrac{2}{x} = \dfrac{1}{x^2 - x}$

Solve for the variable indicated.

19. $\dfrac{x}{a} = b$ for x

20. $\dfrac{a}{x} = b$ for x

21. $F = \dfrac{wa}{g}$ for g

22. $a = \dfrac{V - V_0}{t}$ for V_0

23. $V = \dfrac{Q}{r_1} - \dfrac{Q}{r_2}$ for Q

24. $\dfrac{E}{e} = \dfrac{R + r}{r}$ for e

25. $S = \dfrac{a - ar^n}{1 - r}$ for a

26. $\dfrac{1}{P} = \dfrac{1}{f_1} + \dfrac{1}{f_2}$ for P

27. $\dfrac{1}{R} = \dfrac{1}{r_1} + \dfrac{1}{r_2} + \dfrac{1}{r_3}$ for R

Solve.

B **28.** $\dfrac{x^2 + 1}{x^2 - 1} - \dfrac{2}{x + 1} = \dfrac{x}{x - 1}$

29. $\dfrac{4x + 3}{x^2 - x - 6} + \dfrac{x - 4}{x + 2} = \dfrac{x}{x - 3}$

30. $\dfrac{x^2}{x^3 - 1} + \dfrac{x}{x^2 + x + 1} - \dfrac{2}{x - 1} = 0$

31. $\dfrac{x}{x - 3} - \dfrac{2x + 1}{x - 4} + \dfrac{x^2}{x^2 - 7x + 12} = 0$

32. $20x + 27 + \dfrac{21}{x - 1} = \dfrac{5x - 2}{x - 1}$

33. $\dfrac{x}{x + 1} - \dfrac{7}{x^2 + x} = \dfrac{-3}{x}$

34. $\dfrac{3x - 12}{4x^2 - 9} - \dfrac{3x}{4x^2 - 16x + 15} < 0$

35. $\dfrac{x^3 - 6x + 2}{x^4 + 2x^2 + 1} - \dfrac{x}{x^2 + 1} > 0$

C **36.** $\dfrac{-55}{4x^3 - 8x^2 - 20x + 24} + \dfrac{11}{4x^3 - 24x^2 + 44x - 24} = \dfrac{4}{x^2 - 4}$

37. $\dfrac{4 - 3x}{x^4 - 7x^2 + 9} + \dfrac{3}{x^3 - 2x^2 - 2x + 3} = 0$

4-9 LOSING AND GAINING SOLUTIONS

Two equations are **equivalent** when they have the same solutions. Equivalent equations result when we apply the Properties of Equality to an equation or when we simplify either member. We solve an equation by a process of writing equivalent equations until we have an equation or a compound sentence whose solution is explicit.

> EQUIVALENT EQUATIONS
>
> $3(x - 2) - (x - 4) = -6$ ←———————— Solution is not explicit.
> $3x - 6 - x + 4 = -6$
> $2x = -4$
> $x = -2$ ←———————— Solution is explicit.

EXAMPLE 1 Solve $x^2 = 4x$.

SOLUTION 1
$$x^2 = 4x$$
$$x^2 - 4x = 0$$
$$x(x - 4) = 0$$
$$x = 0 \quad \text{or} \quad x - 4 = 0$$
$$x = 4$$

CHECK
$$x^2 = 4x$$
$$(0)^2 \stackrel{?}{=} 4(0)$$
$$0 = 0 \quad ✔$$

SOLUTION 2
$$x^2 = 4x$$
$$D_x \quad \frac{x^2}{x} = \frac{4x}{x}$$
$$x = 4$$

$$x^2 = 4x$$
$$(4)^2 \stackrel{?}{=} 4(4)$$
$$16 = 16 \quad ✔$$

In solution 2, zero was "lost" as a solution when members of the equation were divided by x. The Division Property permits division by non-zero numbers only. The equations $x^2 = 4x$ and $\frac{x^2}{x} = \frac{4x}{x}$ are not equivalent.

EXAMPLE 2 Solve $(x - 1)(x - 2) = x - 1$

SOLUTION
$$(x - 1)(x - 2) = x - 1$$
$$x^2 - 3x + 2 = x - 1$$
$$x^2 - 4x + 3 = 0$$
$$(x - 3)(x - 1) = 0$$
$$x - 3 = 0 \quad \text{or} \quad x - 1 = 0$$
$$x = 3 \quad | \quad x = 1$$

CHECK
$$(x - 1)(x - 2) = x - 1$$
$$(3 - 1)(3 - 2) \stackrel{?}{=} 3 - 1$$
$$2 = 2 \quad ✔$$

$$(x - 1)(x - 2) = x - 1$$
$$(1 - 1)(1 - 2) \stackrel{?}{=} 1 - 1$$
$$0 = 0 \quad ✔$$

In Example 2, had we first divided both members by $x - 1$, we would have obtained $x - 2 = 1$, or $x = 3$. We would have "lost" 1 as a solution. The equations

$$(x - 1)(x - 2) = x - 1 \text{ and } \frac{(x - 1)(x - 2)}{(x - 1)} = \frac{x - 1}{x - 1}$$

are not equivalent. The number 1 cannot be allowed as a replacement for x when dividing by $x - 1$.

You should remember that, in general, it is possible to "lose" a solution for an equation when you *divide* both members by an expression containing the variable. Similarly, you should be aware that you may "gain" a solution when you *multiply* both members of an equation by an expression containing the variable.

EXAMPLE 3 Solve $x - 3 + \dfrac{1}{x - 2} = \dfrac{(x - 3)^2}{x - 2}$.

SOLUTION

$$x - 3 + \frac{1}{x - 2} = \frac{(x - 3)^2}{x - 2}$$

$$M_{x-2} \qquad (x - 2)(x - 3) + \cancel{(x - 2)}\frac{1}{\cancel{x - 2}} = \cancel{(x - 2)}\frac{(x - 3)^2}{\cancel{x - 2}}$$

$$x^2 - 5x + 6 + 1 = x^2 - 6x + 9$$
$$x = 2$$

CHECK

$$x - 3 + \frac{1}{x - 2} = \frac{(x - 3)^2}{x - 2}$$

$$2 - 3 + \frac{1}{2 - 2} \overset{?}{=} \frac{(2 - 3)^2}{2 - 2}$$

$$-1 + \frac{1}{0} \overset{?}{=} \frac{1}{0}$$

CONCLUSION Since a denominator 0 is meaningless, there is no solution of the equation.

For the above example, 2 was "gained" as an apparent solution when both members of the equation were multiplied by $x - 2$. The Multiplication Property permits multiplication by any number, including zero, but it does not assure that the original equation and the equation that results from multiplying by zero are equivalent. In fact, they seldom are equivalent.

A "solution" that is "gained" in the process of solving an equation is called an **extraneous solution**. Extraneous solutions are detected by checking each apparent solution in the original equation.

CLASSROOM EXERCISES

Solve and check.

1. $y^2 = 5y$

2. $a^2 - 8a + 15 = a - 5$

3. $6x^2 - 5x - 4 = 2x + 1$

4. $\dfrac{3x - 5}{x - 5} - 1 = \dfrac{10}{x - 5}$

5. $y - 4 + \dfrac{1}{y - 3} = \dfrac{(y - 4)^2}{y - 3}$

6. $\dfrac{2}{a - 1} + \dfrac{2a}{a^2 - 1} = \dfrac{1}{a + 1}$

EXERCISES

A Solve and check.

1. $x^2 = 3x$

2. $y^2 = 2y$

3. $z^2 = -4z$

4. $w^2 = -7w$

5. $x^2 + 4x - 5 = x + 5$

6. $y^2 - 3y - 18 = y - 6$

7. $a - 2 + \dfrac{1}{a - 1} = \dfrac{(a - 2)^2}{a - 1}$

8. $z - 6 + \dfrac{1}{z - 5} = \dfrac{(z - 6)^2}{z - 5}$

9. $3x^2 - x - 10 = x - 2$

10. $2x^2 - x - 21 = x + 3$

11. $4x^2 - 12x + 9 = 2x - 3$

12. $25z^2 - 90z + 81 = 5z - 9$

13. $\dfrac{4}{x - 1} + \dfrac{1}{x - 2} = \dfrac{1}{x^2 - 3x + 2}$

14. $\dfrac{-6}{x - 3} + \dfrac{9}{x - 2} = \dfrac{-6}{x^2 - 5x + 6}$

15. $y + 2 - \dfrac{(y + 2)^2}{y + 1} = \dfrac{-1}{y + 1}$

16. $\dfrac{(b + 5)^2}{b + 4} - \dfrac{1}{b + 4} = b + 5$

17. $\dfrac{x^2 - 6x + 9}{x - 2} = x - 3 + \dfrac{2}{x - 2}$

18. $\dfrac{x^2 + 8x + 16}{x + 3} = x + 4 + \dfrac{2}{x + 3}$

19. $\dfrac{5}{x - 4} - \dfrac{1}{x + 4} = \dfrac{-2x}{x^2 - 16}$

20. $\dfrac{8}{z + 10} - \dfrac{2z}{z^2 - 100} = \dfrac{-1}{z - 10}$

21. $\dfrac{4}{y - 1} + \dfrac{y}{y^2 - 1} = \dfrac{1}{y + 1}$

22. $\dfrac{6}{a - 3} + \dfrac{2}{a - 2} = \dfrac{1}{a^2 - 5a + 6}$

23. $\dfrac{1}{x} = 0$

24. $\dfrac{1}{b - 2} = 0$

B **25.** $(3x + a + b)^2 - 4 = 0$

26. $(4x - 3)^2 = (4x - 3)^4$

27. $x^2 - 5 + \dfrac{4}{x^2 - 4} = \dfrac{(x^2 - 2)^2}{x^2 - 4}$

28. $\dfrac{1}{x - 2} - \dfrac{x}{x^2 + 4} = \dfrac{x^2 + 9x + 10}{x^4 - 16}$

29. $\dfrac{1}{y^2 - y} + \dfrac{y - 2}{y^2 + 3y - 4} = \dfrac{-4}{y^2 + 4y}$

30. $\dfrac{1}{x - 3} + \dfrac{1}{x^2 - 6x + 9} = \dfrac{12}{x^3 - 9x^2 + 27x - 27}$

C **31.** $\dfrac{(x^2 + x - 2)(x^2 - x - 1)}{x^2 + x + 2} = 1$

32. $\dfrac{-25y^2 + 25}{4y^4 - 29y^2 + 25} = \dfrac{25 - 29y}{4y^3 - 4y^2 - 25y + 25}$

⌈ 0.833333 ⌉ "APPROACHING" A NUMBER

The terms of the sequence $\frac{1}{2}, \frac{2}{3}, \frac{3}{4}, \frac{4}{5}, \frac{5}{6}, \ldots$, are said to "approach" the number 1. We can find the terms to be *as close to* 1 as we wish them to be (but not necessarily equal to 1) by selecting them far enough along in the sequence.

To find the number, if any, that a sequence approaches, it may be necessary to check a large number of terms. We can do this on a calculator by checking the decimal representation for each term.

The terms of each of these sequences "approach" some number. Find the number.

1. $\frac{1}{2}, \frac{1}{4}, \frac{1}{6}, \frac{1}{8}, \frac{1}{10}, \cdots$

2. $\frac{1}{3}, \frac{1}{9}, \frac{1}{27}, \frac{1}{81}, \frac{1}{243}, \cdots$

3. $1, -\frac{1}{2}, \frac{1}{3}, -\frac{1}{4}, \frac{1}{5}, \cdots$

4. $\frac{2}{1}, \frac{3}{2}, \frac{4}{3}, \frac{5}{4}, \frac{6}{5}, \cdots$

5. $\frac{5}{3}, \frac{7}{7}, \frac{9}{11}, \frac{11}{15}, \frac{13}{19}, \cdots$

6. $\frac{7}{3}, \frac{10}{5}, \frac{13}{7}, \frac{16}{9}, \frac{19}{11}, \cdots$

7. $\frac{3}{4}, \frac{5}{7}, \frac{7}{10}, \frac{9}{13}, \frac{11}{16}, \cdots$

8. $\frac{6}{9}, \frac{11}{15}, \frac{16}{21}, \frac{21}{27}, \frac{26}{33}, \cdots$

Sometimes, the nth term of a sequence will be given. This is especially helpful when the pattern followed by the terms of the sequence is not clear. It also is helpful for finding the number, if any, that the terms of the sequence approach. Instead of examining the sequence term-by-term, you may replace n in the nth term by numbers that are as large as you wish.

Find the number that each sequence approaches.

9. $\frac{2}{8}, \frac{6}{13}, \frac{10}{18}, \cdots, \frac{4n-2}{5n+3}, \cdots$

10. $1, \frac{1}{2}, \frac{5}{12}, \cdots, \frac{n^2+1}{3n^2-n}, \cdots$

11. $\frac{2}{3}, \frac{4}{9}, \frac{8}{27}, \cdots, \frac{2^n}{3^n}, \cdots$

12. $\frac{1}{4}, \frac{25}{16}, \frac{61}{36}, \cdots, \frac{7n^3-6}{4n^3}, \cdots$

13. $\frac{1}{8}, \frac{2}{16}, \frac{3}{24}, \cdots, \frac{n}{8n}, \cdots$

14. $-2, -\frac{2}{3}, -\frac{30}{53}, \cdots, \frac{n(n^2+1)}{1-2n^3}, \cdots$

The following sequence approaches a familiar number. Find the number. (Have patience, the sequence approaches the number "slowly.")

15. $4, 4 - \frac{4}{3}, 4 - \frac{4}{3} + \frac{4}{5}, 4 - \frac{4}{3} + \frac{4}{5} - \frac{4}{7}, \cdots$

4-10 PROBLEM SOLVING: USING FRACTIONAL EQUATIONS

Problems that involve the contribution of an unknown fractional part to a joint effort can be solved by using fractional equations.

EXAMPLE 1 It took 27 hours to plow a field with the old tractor. It takes $10\frac{4}{5}$ hours to plow the field using the old and new tractors together. How long would it take to plow the field using only the new tractor?

SOLUTION The sum of the fractional parts of the field plowed by each tractor is 1 (the whole field).

Use t for the number of hours needed to plow the field using the new tractor.

	rate	· time	= work done
Old Tractor	$\frac{1}{27}$	$10\frac{4}{5}$	$10\frac{4}{5}\left(\frac{1}{27}\right)$
New Tractor	$\frac{1}{t}$	$10\frac{4}{5}$	$10\frac{4}{5}\left(\frac{1}{t}\right)$

$$\text{Work}_{\text{O.T.}} + \text{Work}_{\text{N.T.}} = 1$$

$$10\frac{4}{5}\left(\frac{1}{27}\right) + 10\frac{4}{5}\left(\frac{1}{t}\right) = 1$$

$$\frac{54}{5}\left(\frac{1}{27} + \frac{1}{t}\right) = 1$$

$M_5 \qquad 54\left(\frac{1}{27} + \frac{1}{t}\right) = 5$

$M_{27t} \qquad 54(t + 27) = 135t$

$$54t + 1458 = 135t$$

$$1458 = 81t$$

$$18 = t$$

CONCLUSION The plowing would take 18 hours with the new tractor.

CHECK $\frac{1}{27}$ plus $\frac{1}{18}$, or a total of $\frac{5}{54}$, of the field could be plowed in one hour by the two tractors together. At this rate will the whole field be plowed in $10\frac{4}{5}$ hours?

$$10\frac{4}{5}\left(\frac{5}{54}\right) \stackrel{?}{=} 1$$

$$\frac{54}{5} \cdot \frac{5}{54} \stackrel{?}{=} 1$$

$$1 = 1 \quad \text{✓}$$

EXAMPLE 2 The denominator of a fraction is 5 greater than the numerator. When 3 is added to both terms of the fraction, the new fraction is equal to $\frac{1}{2}$. Find the fraction.

SOLUTION $\frac{\text{numerator} + 3}{\text{denominator} + 3}$ is equal to $\frac{1}{2}$.

Use $\begin{bmatrix} n & \text{for the numerator of the fraction.} \\ n + 5 & \text{for the denominator of the fraction.} \end{bmatrix}$

$$\frac{n + 3}{n + 5 + 3} = \frac{1}{2}$$

$$\frac{n + 3}{n + 8} = \frac{1}{2}$$

$M_{2(n+8)}$ $\qquad 2n + 6 = n + 8$

$$n = 2$$

Also, $n + 5 = 7$.

CONCLUSION The fraction is $\frac{2}{7}$.

CHECK $\frac{2 + 3}{7 + 3} \stackrel{?}{=} \frac{1}{2}$

$$\frac{1}{2} = \frac{1}{2} \quad ✔$$

CLASSROOM EXERCISES

Solve.

1. Tom can mow a lawn in 5 hours. His friend can mow the same lawn in 6 hours. How long does it take to mow the lawn when they work together?

2. The denominator of a fraction is one more than the numerator. When 4 is added to the numerator and 6 is added to the denominator the result equals $\frac{3}{4}$. Find the fraction.

3. Sue can build a table in 12 hours. When she works with Bob, it takes $6\frac{2}{3}$ hours to build a table. How long does it take Bob to build a table?

4. The denominator of a certain fraction is 8 less than the numerator. When 3 is subtracted from both the numerator and the denominator, the resulting fraction equals 3. Find the fraction.

EXERCISES

Ⓐ Solve.

1. The numerator of a fraction is 4 less than the denominator. When both numerator and denominator are increased by 6, the resulting fraction equals $\frac{2}{3}$. Find the fraction.

2. The denominator of a fraction is 3 less than twice the numerator. When the

numerator is increased by 8 and the denominator by 35, the resulting fraction equals $\frac{1}{3}$. Find the fraction.

3. Ann can process a batch of film in 8 hours. Barbara can do the work in 10 hours. How long will it take them together to process the film?

4. Juan can assemble a bicycle in 10 minutes. It takes Sol 15 minutes for the same task. How long does it take when they work together?

5. Two painters can do a piece of work in 8 hours. One painter can do the work alone in 14 hours. How long would it take the other painter to do the work alone?

6. When 12 is subtracted from both terms of a fraction, the result equals $\frac{3}{17}$. When 5 is added to the numerator of the fraction, the result equals $\frac{1}{2}$. Find the fraction.

7. When 13 is subtracted from both terms of a fraction, the result equals 16. When 1 is subtracted from the numerator of the fraction, the result equals 2. Find the fraction.

8. The speed of an airplane in still air is 450 km/h. How far west can it go and return in 3 hours when the wind is blowing from the west at 50 km/h?

9. An airplane has enough fuel for a safe flying time of 88 minutes. Its air speed flying east is 300 km/h and returning is 250 km/h. How far east may it be flown?

10. A boat makes a round trip across a lake in 4 hours. Going across, the boat averages 10 km/h. Returning, it averages 15 km/h. How far is it across the lake?

11. One girl can mow a lawn in 1 hour. She and her sister can mow the lawn in 20 minutes. How long would it take the sister to mow the lawn alone?

12. When working together, two pumps can fill a swimming pool in 24 hours. When operated alone, one pump requires 20 hours more than the other to fill the pool. How long would it take each pump alone to fill the pool?

13. Two people can complete a task in $2\frac{2}{3}$ days when they work together. Working alone one person takes 4 days more than the other. Find the number of days it takes each to complete the task.

14. A tank can be filled by an inlet pipe in 4 hours and emptied by a drain pipe in 6 hours. How long will it take to fill the tank when both pipes are open?

15. A tank can be filled by an inlet pipe in 8 hours when the drain pipe is open and in 5 hours when the drain pipe is closed. How long will it take to empty a full tank when the inlet pipe is closed?

B 16. Albert, Mary, and Charles can do a piece of work in 3 days. Albert could do the same piece of work alone in 8 days, and Mary in 10 days. How many days would it take Charles to do the work?

17. A mixing vat can be filled by 2 pipes in 4 hours and 5 hours, respectively, and can be emptied by a third pipe in 6 hours. How many hours will it take to fill the mixing vat when all the pipes are used?

18. Working together, two persons can complete a task in 30 days. Working alone, it takes the second person 3 weeks more than twice the number of weeks it takes the first person. Find the number of 7-day weeks it takes each person working alone.

19. How many minutes after 5 o'clock will the hands of a clock first be together? Suggestion: Use x for the number of minute units that the minute hand travels. Then $\frac{x}{12}$ is the number of minute units that the hour hand travels, and $x - \frac{x}{12} = 25$.

20. How soon after 7 o'clock will the hour and minute hands of a clock first be together?

21. How soon after 8 o'clock will the hands of a clock first be opposite each other?

22. When 260 is divided by a certain number, the quotient is 15 and the remainder is 5. Find the number.

23. One automobile travels 10 km/h faster than a second automobile. The first automobile travels 320 km in the same time the second automobile travels 240 km. Find the rate of each automobile.

24. The sum of the numerator and denominator of a certain fraction is 104. The fraction reduced to lowest terms is $\frac{9}{17}$. Find the fraction.

25. Two fractions represent positive numbers. Their sum equals $\frac{17}{21}$. The first fraction is the reciprocal of one more than twice the denominator of the second fraction. The numerator of the second fraction is one less than its denominator. Find the fractions.

C **26.** Martha can walk a kilometer in 3 minutes less time than her sister. Also, she can walk 5 kilometers while her sister walks 4 kilometers. Find the rate of each in kilometers per hour.

27. When working together Anne, Bernice, and Christine can do a piece of work in 1 hour and 20 minutes. To do the work alone, Christine would need twice as much time as Anne and 2 hours more than Bernice. How long would it take each working alone to complete the work?

28. A bus travels east for 250 km and then heads north for 352 km. Its rate going north is 6 km/h less than its rate going east. When the total time for the trip is 13 hours, find the speed of the bus going east.

ON ABSOLUTE VALUE

Two definitions for absolute value are as follows.

$$|x| = \begin{cases} x \text{ if } x \geq 0 \\ -x \text{ if } x < 0 \end{cases} \qquad |x| = \max\{x, -x\}$$

1. Interpret the meaning of max $\{x, -x\}$. **2.** Are these definitions equivalent?

One other useful expression using absolute value is $\frac{x}{|x|}$.

3. What is the value of $\frac{x}{|x|}$ for any positive number? any negative number?

4-11   PROBLEM SOLVING: PROPORTIONS

Ratios are used to compare numbers. The ratio comparing a to c, $c \neq 0$, may be written a to c, $a:c$,   or $\frac{a}{c}$.

The fraction form, $\frac{a}{c}$, is a convenient form for working with ratios, because much of what we do with fractions may be applied to ratios. The fraction form also suggests that the ratio a to c may be regarded as the quotient $a \div c$. This we shall do often, keeping in mind that every ratio involves *two* numbers. Also, the two numbers should represent "like" quantities.

EXAMPLE 1   The farmer collected 2 dozen white eggs and 8 brown eggs. Write a ratio in simplest form to compare the number of white eggs to the number of brown eggs.

SOLUTION $\dfrac{\text{number of white eggs}}{\text{number of brown eggs}} = \dfrac{24}{8}$

Just as with the fraction $\frac{24}{8}$, the simplest form

for the ratio $\frac{24}{8}$ is $\frac{3}{1}$, or 3 to 1.

A **proportion** is an equation whose two members are ratios. The numbers in one ratio are said to be *in proportion to* or *proportional to* the numbers in the other ratio.

The proportion $\dfrac{a}{b} = \dfrac{c}{d}$ may be written $\overset{\displaystyle\longmapsto \text{extremes} \longleftarrow}{\underset{\text{means}}{a : b \;\; = \;\; c : d.}}$

The terms a and d of the proportion are called the **extremes** and the terms b and c are called the **means**. When b and c are the same number, that number is the **mean proportional** between a and d.

Multiplying both members of the proportion

$$\frac{a}{b} = \frac{c}{d} \quad \text{by } bd \text{ gives} \quad \underset{\substack{\text{the product of} \\ \text{the extremes}}}{ad} = \underset{\substack{\text{the product} \\ \text{of the means}}}{bc}$$

> In any proportion, the product of the extremes is equal to the product of the means.

EXAMPLE 2   Can $\frac{9}{20}$ and $\frac{14}{35}$ be the two members of a proportion?

SOLUTION $\frac{9}{20} \overset{?}{=} \frac{14}{35}$

$9 \cdot 35 \overset{?}{=} 20 \cdot 14$

$315 \neq 280$

CONCLUSION   Since the product of the extremes would not equal the product of the means, $\frac{9}{20}$ and $\frac{14}{35}$ are not the two members of a proportion.

EXAMPLE 3   For what value of z is $\dfrac{8}{5z - 4} = \dfrac{2}{z + \frac{1}{2}}$ a proportion?

SOLUTION   Solve the equation for z.

$\dfrac{8}{5z - 4} = \dfrac{2}{z + \frac{1}{2}}$

$8\left(z + \frac{1}{2}\right) = (5z - 4)2$

$8z + 4 = 10z - 8$

$12 = 2z$

$6 = z$

CHECK $\dfrac{8}{5z - 4} = \dfrac{2}{z + \frac{1}{2}}$

$\dfrac{8}{5(6) - 4} \overset{?}{=} \dfrac{2}{6 + \frac{1}{2}}$

$\dfrac{8}{26} \overset{?}{=} \dfrac{2}{\frac{13}{2}}$

$\dfrac{4}{13} = \dfrac{4}{13}$ ✔

EXAMPLE 4   When 7 kilograms of flour cost $2.73, what should 5 kilograms cost if the prices are proportional to the amounts of flour?

SOLUTION   Use c for the cost in dollars of 5 kilograms.

$\dfrac{7}{5} = \dfrac{2.73}{c}$

$7c = 5(2.73)$

$c = \dfrac{5(2.73)}{7}$

$c = 1.95$

CHECK $\dfrac{7}{5} \overset{?}{=} \dfrac{2.73}{1.95}$

$7(1.95) \overset{?}{=} 5(2.73)$

$13.65 = 13.65$ ✔

CONCLUSION   5 kilograms of flour should cost $1.95.

From geometry we know that the lengths of corresponding sides of similar figures are proportional.

EXAMPLE 5   Triangles *ABC* and *DEF* are similar.

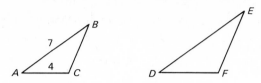

Side *DE* is 2 units greater than *AB*.
How long is side *DF*?

SOLUTION   The lengths *AB* and *DE* are proportional to the lengths *AC* and *DF*.

$$\frac{AB}{DE} = \frac{AC}{DF}$$

$$\frac{7}{9} = \frac{4}{DF}$$ CHECK $\frac{7}{9} \stackrel{?}{=} \frac{4}{\frac{36}{7}}$

$$7 \cdot DF = 36$$

$$DF = 5\frac{1}{7}$$ $\frac{7}{9} \stackrel{?}{=} 4 \cdot \frac{7}{36}$

CONCLUSION   *DF* is $5\frac{1}{7}$ units long. $\frac{7}{9} = \frac{7}{9}$ ✔

CLASSROOM EXERCISES

Express as a ratio in simplest form.

1. 4 to 16   **2.** 3 kilometers to 500 meters   **3.** 15 grams to 1 kilogram

Which are the two members of a proportion?

4. $\frac{6}{18}$ and $\frac{8}{24}$ **5.** $\frac{6}{17}$ and $\frac{2}{5}$ **6.** $\frac{7}{3}$ and $\frac{42}{18}$

Find the number for *x* which gives a proportion.

7. $\frac{x}{3} = \frac{5}{7}$ **8.** $\frac{x+1}{2} = \frac{7}{6}$ **9.** $\frac{6}{x+2} = \frac{4}{2x-3}$

10. 4 kilograms of bologna cost $9.16. Find the cost for 7 kilograms at the same price per kilogram.

11. In the diagram $\overline{DE} \parallel \overline{BC}$. $\triangle ADE \sim \triangle ABC$.
Find *AD* for *DE* = 3, *BC* = 5, and *AB* = 6.

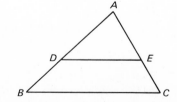

EXERCISES

A Express as a ratio in simplest form.

1. 2 meters to 1 kilometer   **2.** 10 minutes to 3 hours   **3.** $x^2 + 2x$ to $x^2 - 4$

4. the measure in degrees of one angle of an equilateral triangle to 180

5. 0.25 degrees to 5 degrees   **6.** a number $2x$ to another number $5x$

7. the circumference of a circle to the diameter

Solve.

8. The sum of two numbers is 126. Their ratio is 2 to 5. Find the numbers. (Hint: Use $2x$ for the smaller number.)

9. Lois does $\frac{3}{4}$ as much work as Raymond. How should they divide the $50.75 that they are paid for their work?

10. The ratio of the number of postal cards sorted by machine A each minute to the number of postal cards sorted by machine B each minute is 5 to 3. Together the two machines sort 160 cards per minute. How many are sorted per minute by each machine?

11. The ratio of the width of a rectangular field to its length is 5 to 6. Find the dimensions of the field when its perimeter is 220 meters.

12. For line segment AB that is 10 centimeters long, the ratio of AC to AB is 0.618. Find AC and CB.

Which are the two members of a proportion?

13. $\frac{3}{4}$ and $\frac{4}{5}$ **14.** $\frac{6}{9}$ and $\frac{18}{27}$ **15.** $\frac{2}{5}$ and $\frac{4}{15}$ **16.** $2:3$ and $16:24$

Find the number for x which gives a proportion.

17. $\frac{x}{7} = \frac{3}{8}$ **18.** $\frac{4}{9} = \frac{x}{2}$ **19.** $\frac{3x + 2}{2} = \frac{x - 1}{1}$ **20.** $\frac{2x + 3}{4} = \frac{x - 5}{3}$

Solve. Use a proportion.

21. 22 kilograms of loin roast costs $14.80. How much does 15.4 kilograms of loin roast cost?

22. 6.5 kilograms of butter costs $5.65. How much does 9.1 kilograms cost?

23. 70 meters of fencing cost $133. Find the cost for 49 meters.

24. Hogs with a mass of 1746 kilograms sold for $742.32. For how much would hogs with a mass of 2231 kilograms have sold?

25. The circumference of one circle is 250 centimeters. Find the circumference of another circle whose diameter is $3\frac{1}{2}$ times that of the first one.

26. Grace received $51.75 for 15 hours of work. What would she have received for $13\frac{2}{3}$ hours of work?

27. Three pens sell for 78 cents. Find the selling price for 8 pens.

28. The width of a rectangle is 12 meters. A similar rectangle has dimensions 6 meters by 8 meters. Find the length of the first rectangle.

29. The lengths of the sides of a triangle are 15 centimeters, 18 centimeters, and 24 centimeters. The length of the shortest side of a similar triangle is 10 centimeters. Find the length of its longest side.

30. A tree 46 meters high casts a shadow 27 meters long. How long is the shadow of a tower that is 24 meters high?

In the diagram at the right, $\overline{DE}\|\overline{BC}$ and $\triangle ADE \sim \triangle ABC$.

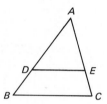

31. $AD = 8$, $AB = 20$, and $AE = 6$. Find EC.

32. Find AE when $EC = 24$, $AD = 24$, and $BD = 16$.

33. Find DE when $BC = 18$, $AD = 10$, and $AB = 15$.

34. Find BC when $DE = 18$, $DB = 10$, and $AD = 20$.

B The areas of two similar polygons are proportional to the squares of their corresponding sides. For quadrilateral T, for example,

$$\frac{\text{area }(T)}{\text{area }(T')} = \frac{a^2}{a'^2}.$$

35. The area of a polygon is 176 square meters. One of the sides of a similar polygon is $\frac{3}{4}$ as long as the corresponding side of the first polygon. Find the area of the similar polygon.

36. The area of a pentagon is 224 square centimeters. One of the sides of a similar pentagon is $\frac{5}{4}$ as long as the corresponding side of the first pentagon. Find the area of the similar pentagon.

$\triangle ABC$ is a right triangle having $\overline{CD} \perp \overline{AB}$. $\overline{AB}$ is the hypotenuse. In geometry, it is proved that b is the mean proportional (geometric mean) between a and x.

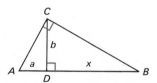

37. Find x when $a = 4$ and $b = 12$.

38. Find x when $a = 2.5$ and $b = 1.5$.

39. Find a when $x = 3$ and $b = 9$.   **40.** Find a when $x = 4$ and $b = 6$.

41. Find b when $a = 9$ and $x = 4$.   **42.** Find b when $a = 25$ and $x = 4$.

43. These two hexagons are similar. Each side of the smaller hexagon is $\frac{2}{3}$ as long as the corresponding side of the larger hexagon. Find the ratio of the area of the shaded part to the area of the larger hexagon.

44. Solve. $\dfrac{x^2 + x - 6}{x^2 + x - 2} = \dfrac{x^2 + 4x + 3}{x^2 + 3x - 4}$

45. For $\dfrac{x}{y} = \dfrac{a}{b}$, show that $\dfrac{x}{y} = \dfrac{x + a}{y + b}$.

CHECKING YOUR UNDERSTANDING

WORDS AND SYMBOLS

equivalent equations

fractional equation

proportion, $\dfrac{a}{b} = \dfrac{c}{d}$

extraneous solution

means of a proportion, $\dfrac{a}{\boxed{b}} = \dfrac{\boxed{c}}{d}$

extremes of a proportion, $\dfrac{\boxed{a}}{b} = \dfrac{c}{\boxed{d}}$

mean proportional, $\dfrac{a}{\boxed{b}} = \dfrac{\boxed{b}}{c}$

CONCEPTS

■ Solving an equation often involves the process of writing equivalent equations until there is one whose solution is explicit. [4-9]

■ Dividing both members of an equation by an expression involving a variable may result in solutions of the equation being "lost." Multiplying both members by such an expression may result in solutions being "gained." [4-9]

■ For any proportion, the product of the extremes equals the product of the means. [4-11]

PROCESSES

■ Solve fractional equations. Check for lost or gained solutions. [4-8, 4-9]

1. $\dfrac{1}{x}(x + 1) = \dfrac{1}{x}$
   2. $\dfrac{-3}{y - 4} - \dfrac{1}{2} = \dfrac{7}{3 - y}$
   3. $\dfrac{x^2 - 6}{x + 3} + \dfrac{x - 3}{x} = \dfrac{-9}{x^2 + 3x}$

■ Solve problems using fractional equations and proportions. [4-10, 4-11]

4. For what values of y does $\dfrac{y + 2}{3y + 5} = \dfrac{y - 2}{y - 5}$?

5. The denominator of a fraction is 1 less than twice the numerator. When 1 is subtracted from the numerator and 2 added to the denominator, the result equals $\dfrac{2}{5}$. Find the fraction.

CHAPTER REVIEW

Represent each fraction in three different ways. [4-1]

1. $-\dfrac{2}{3}$ **2.** $\dfrac{a-1}{b-1}$ **3.** $-\dfrac{5}{x-y}$ **4.** $\dfrac{1-x}{x-1}$

Simplify. [4-2 to 4-7]

5. $\dfrac{3x^2y^3}{9xy^2}$ **6.** $\dfrac{-2^3ab^2}{4a^2b}$ **7.** $\dfrac{8ab^2}{4a^2b-8ab^2}$ **8.** $\dfrac{a^2-b^2}{a^2-2ab-3b^2}$

9. $\dfrac{27a^2b}{5c}\cdot\dfrac{15c^2}{3ab^2}$ **10.** $\dfrac{a^3-4a}{6b}\cdot\dfrac{3b^2}{a^2+a-6}$ **11.** $\dfrac{6x^2-5x-6}{6x^2}\cdot\dfrac{9x^3}{9x^2+27x+14}$

12. $\dfrac{5x}{4y}\div 2xy$ **13.** $\dfrac{6}{a^2-4a}\div\dfrac{-2a}{a^2-3a-4}$ **14.** $\dfrac{x^3-8}{3a}\div\dfrac{x^2+2x+4}{9ab}$

15. $\dfrac{x+7}{6}-\dfrac{2x-3}{6}$ **16.** $\dfrac{4x}{9}-\dfrac{x}{3}+\dfrac{5x}{6}$ **17.** $\dfrac{6x}{x^2-25}+2-\dfrac{3}{x-5}$

18. $\left(1+\dfrac{1}{a-1}\right)\left(\dfrac{1}{a-2}+1\right)$ **19.** $\left(\dfrac{1}{n}+1\right)\div\left(2+n+\dfrac{1}{n}\right)$ **20.** $(m^2+m+1)\left(1-\dfrac{1}{m}-\dfrac{1}{m^2}\right)$

21. $\dfrac{\frac{x^2-y^2}{2x}}{\frac{x+y}{x^2}}$ **22.** $\dfrac{\frac{1}{a}+\frac{1}{b}}{\frac{a}{b}-\frac{b}{a}}$ **23.** $\dfrac{x+\frac{27}{x^2}}{x-3+\frac{9}{x}}$

Solve and check. [4-8, 4-9]

24. $\dfrac{15}{2x-1}=3$ **25.** $\dfrac{x^2+1}{x^2-9}=\dfrac{x+7}{x-3}$ **26.** $\dfrac{n}{n-2}=1-\dfrac{1}{n}$

27. $x^2=9x$ **28.** $x^3=2x^2-x$ **29.** $\dfrac{x+1}{x-1}=\dfrac{x}{3}+\dfrac{2}{x-1}$

Solve. [4-10, 4-11]

30. A mechanic's helper takes twice as long as the mechanic to do a job. Working together they take 6 hours to do the job. How long will it take each to do the whole job alone?

31. The sum of a number and its reciprocal is 2.9. Find the number.

32. The sum of two numbers is 450. Their ratio is 4 to 5. Find the numbers.

33. The dimensions of one rectangle are 60 centimeters and 96 centimeters. Find the longer dimension of a similar rectangle whose shorter dimension is 10 centimeters.

CAPSULE REVIEW

Write the letter of the best response.

1. Which of the following is not equivalent to $\dfrac{(c-3)(d+1)}{(m-4)}$?

a. $\dfrac{(3-c)(-1-d)}{(4-m)}$ **b.** $\dfrac{(3-c)(-1-d)}{(m-4)}$ **c.** $-\dfrac{(3-c)(d+1)}{(m-4)}$ **d.** $\dfrac{(3-c)(d+1)}{(4-m)}$

2. Which of the following represents $\dfrac{m^2+4m-21}{3+2m-m^2}$ in lowest terms?

a. $\dfrac{m+7}{3-m}$ **b.** $\dfrac{m+6}{2m+1}$ **c.** $\dfrac{m-3}{1+m}$ **d.** $-\dfrac{m+7}{m+1}$

3. In simplified form, $\dfrac{x+1}{x+2}-\dfrac{x+2}{x+3}=$

a. $\dfrac{8x+7}{(x+2)(x+3)}$ **b.** $\dfrac{-1}{(x+3)}$ **c.** $-\dfrac{1}{(x+2)(x+3)}$ **d.** $\dfrac{2x+3}{(x+2)}$

4. In simplified form, $\dfrac{3-\dfrac{2}{y}}{3+\dfrac{2}{y}}=$

a. $\dfrac{-3y-2}{3y+2}$ **b.** $\dfrac{3y}{2}$ **c.** $\dfrac{3y-2}{3y+2}$ **d.** $\dfrac{y-1}{y+1}$

5. The solution(s) of the equation $\dfrac{x-3}{2x}+\dfrac{1}{3}=\dfrac{3x-7}{2x}$ is (are)

a. $\dfrac{1}{3}$ **b.** 3 **c.** $\dfrac{2}{5}$ and $\dfrac{7}{5}$ **d.** -5 and 2

6. The solution(s) of the equation $1+\dfrac{12}{x^2-4}=\dfrac{3}{x-2}$ is (are)

a. 1 and 2 **b.** 1 **c.** 1 and 4 **d.** -3

7. For what value of y does $\dfrac{5}{6y+8}=\dfrac{2}{5y+\dfrac{7}{3}}$?

a. $\dfrac{1}{3}$ **b.** -3 **c.** $\dfrac{4}{5}$ **d.** 1

8. When $E=RI+\dfrac{rl}{n}$, $n=$

a. $\dfrac{rl}{E+RI}$ **b.** $\dfrac{RI-E}{r}$ **c.** $\dfrac{RI+E}{r}$ **d.** $\dfrac{rl}{E-RI}$

CHAPTER TEST

1. Represent $\dfrac{-x}{2}$ three different ways.

2. Complete $\dfrac{a-b}{1-x} = \dfrac{?}{x-1}$.

Simplify.

3. $\dfrac{3x}{x^2 - 3x}$

4. $\dfrac{x^2 - 7x + 12}{x^2 - 2x - 3}$

5. $\dfrac{2x^3}{5y} \cdot \dfrac{15y^2}{14x^2}$

6. $\dfrac{x^2 - y^2}{2x} \cdot \dfrac{3x}{(x-y)^2}$

7. $\dfrac{4xy^2}{5} \div \dfrac{x^2 y}{10}$

8. $\dfrac{x^2 + 5x + 4}{4} \div \dfrac{x^2 + 6x + 8}{6}$

9. $\dfrac{x}{2} + \dfrac{x}{6} - \dfrac{x}{3}$

10. $\dfrac{5}{x+3} + \dfrac{3}{x+2}$

11. Write $x + 2 + \dfrac{1}{x}$ as a fraction.

12. Divide $x + 3 + \dfrac{2}{x}$ by $1 + \dfrac{2}{x}$.

Simplify.

13. $\dfrac{1 + \frac{3}{x}}{\frac{3}{x^2}}$

14. $\dfrac{x + 4 + \frac{3}{x}}{1 + \frac{1}{x}}$ ✓

Solve.

15. $\dfrac{3x}{x+1} = 4$

16. $\dfrac{4}{x} + \dfrac{x}{x+2} = 1$

17. $\dfrac{1}{x-3} + \dfrac{1}{x} = 1 + \dfrac{3}{x^2 - 3x}$

18. Are $x(x+5) = 0$ and $x + 5 = 0$ equivalent equations? Explain.

19. The denominator of a fraction is 9 greater than the numerator. When both terms of the fraction are increased by 2, the new fraction equals $\dfrac{1}{2}$. Find the fraction.

20. The numerator of a fraction is 3 less than the denominator. When both terms of the fraction are increased by 1, the new fraction equals $\dfrac{2}{3}$. Find the fraction.

21. For what value of x is $\dfrac{8}{x-2} = \dfrac{6}{x-3}$ a proportion?

22. The two triangles pictured are similar. Find x. $\longrightarrow$

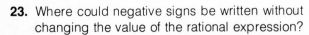

Write the letter of the best response.

23. Where could negative signs be written without changing the value of the rational expression?

$\dfrac{x+3}{y-8} = \boxed{r}\,\dfrac{\boxed{s}\,(x+3)}{\boxed{t}\,(y-8)}$

    a. r **b.** s **c.** t **d.** r and s **e.** r, s, and t

24. $\dfrac{x^2}{x^3 + x^2} =$

   a. $\dfrac{1}{x}$ **b.** $\dfrac{1}{x^3}$ **c.** $\dfrac{1}{x^4}$ **d.** $\dfrac{1}{x + 1}$ **e.** $\dfrac{1}{x + x^2}$

25. $\dfrac{x^2 + 2x + 1}{5} \cdot \dfrac{10}{x^2 + 3x + 2} =$

   a. $\dfrac{2}{x + 1}$ **b.** $\dfrac{2(x + 1)}{x + 2}$ **c.** $\dfrac{x + 1}{x}$ **d.** $\dfrac{2(2x + 1)}{3x + 2}$ **e.** $\dfrac{5}{x + 1}$

26. $\dfrac{x^2 + 3x + 2}{6}$ divided by $\dfrac{x^2 + 4x + 3}{3}$ gives

   a. $\dfrac{2(x + 2)}{x + 3}$ **b.** $\dfrac{x + 2}{2(x + 3)}$ **c.** $\dfrac{3x + 2}{2(4x + 3)}$ **d.** $\dfrac{1}{2(x + 1)}$ **e.** $\dfrac{2(x + 3)}{x + 2}$

27. $\dfrac{3}{2x + 2} + \dfrac{7}{4x + 4} =$

   a. $\dfrac{6x + 13}{4x + 4}$ **b.** $\dfrac{5}{2x + 2}$ **c.** $\dfrac{13}{3x + 3}$ **d.** $\dfrac{5}{3x + 3}$ **e.** $\dfrac{13}{4x + 4}$

28. $\left(1 + \dfrac{1}{x}\right)\left(x - 1 + \dfrac{1}{x}\right) =$

   a. $x + \dfrac{2}{x}$ **b.** $x - 1 + \dfrac{1}{x^2}$ **c.** $x + \dfrac{1}{2x}$ **d.** $\dfrac{x^3 - 1}{x^2}$ **e.** $\dfrac{x^3 + 1}{x^2}$

29. $\dfrac{1 + \dfrac{2}{x}}{x + 5 + \dfrac{6}{x}} =$

   a. $\dfrac{1}{x + 3}$ **b.** $\dfrac{1}{(x + 2)^2}$ **c.** $\dfrac{x + 2}{x^2}$ **d.** $\dfrac{x^2}{x + 2}$ **e.** $\dfrac{1}{x^2(x + 3)}$

30. What is the solution of $\dfrac{x}{x^2 + x} + \dfrac{5}{x} = \dfrac{5}{x + 1}$?

   a. $-1\dfrac{1}{4}$ **b.** -2 **c.** -5 **d.** 5 **e.** $\dfrac{1}{4}$

31. What are the solutions of $\dfrac{1}{x - 2} + \dfrac{2}{x} = 1 + \dfrac{2}{x^2 - 2x}$?

   a. 3 only   **b.** 2 only   **c.** 2 and 3   **d.** 0 and 2   **e.** 0, 2, and 3

32. The numerator of a fraction is 5 less than the denominator. If both terms of the fraction are increased by 4, the new fraction equals $\dfrac{1}{2}$. What is the denominator of the original fraction?

   a. 2   **b.** 4   **c.** 6   **d.** 8   **e.** 10

33. For what value of x is $\dfrac{11}{x + 3} = \dfrac{5}{x - 3}$ a proportion?

   a. 4   **b.** 5   **c.** 6   **d.** 7   **e.** 8

CUMULATIVE REVIEW

Give the word or symbol to complete each sentence.

1. $-x$ is the ___?___ of x.

2. $3x - 4 < -2x + 1$ is called an ___?___.

3. 4 is the ___?___ of 16.

4. $40x^2y^3$ is the ___?___ of $8x^2y$ and $10xy^3$.

5. In $\frac{e}{t} = \frac{t}{s}$, t is the ___?___.

6. $x^2 - 9$ ___?___ $(x - 3)(x + 3)$.

Briefly answer each question. Refer to the concept suggested.

7. $(y^2)^4 = y^8$. Why?

8. To solve $|3x - 1| = 4$, you solve the compound sentence $3x - 1 = 4$ or $3x - 1 = -4$. Why?

9. When $-x < 6$, $x > -6$. Why?

10. $\frac{x - 2}{x^2 - 4} = \frac{1}{x + 2}$ unless $x = \pm 2$. Why?

11. $-0 = 0$. Why?

12. -5 is a solution of $2 - x \geq 7$. Why?

Simplify.

13. $|-6|$

14. $\sqrt[3]{-8}$

15. $\sqrt[4]{(-6)^4}$

16. $3x - 4y + 8x + y$

17. $(x^2y)^3 \cdot (x^5y)$

18. $\frac{x^3 + 3x^2 - 6x + 2}{x - 1}$

19. $3x^2 - x - (-2x^2 + 3x - 1)$

20. $4x - [4(x - 1) - 3(x + 2)]$

Solve.

21. $|5x - 4| \leq 11$

22. $|-3x + 7| > 2$

Factor completely.

23. $12x^3y^4 - 24x^2y^5 + 4xy^4$

24. $25x^2 - 30xy + 9y^2$

25. $20x^2 - 2x - 6$

26. $6x^3 - 5x^2 - 4x$

Solve.

27. $12 + 3(x - 3) = 5(x + 2)$

28. $w = z(a - 2x)$, for x

29. $\frac{4}{x - 3} + \frac{1}{x - 1} = \frac{5}{x^2 - 4x + 3}$

30. $\frac{x^2 - 2}{x + 2} + \frac{x - 2}{x} = \frac{-4}{x^2 + 2x}$

Solve.

31. Two cars leave the same place at the same time and travel in opposite directions. One travels at 50 kilometers per hour and the other at 40 kilometers per hour. In how many hours will they be 315 kilometers apart?

32. A carpenter and helper can add a room to a house in 4 days by working together. It takes 6 days if the carpenter works alone. How long would it take the helper working alone?

Write the letter of the best response.

33. $5 - 2(7 - 12) =$

    a. -15 **b.** -5 **c.** -21 **d.** 15 **e.** 3

34. The solution to $3(x - 1) \le 6$ or $-2(x + 1) < 3$ is

    a. $x < -\dfrac{5}{2}$ **b.** all real numbers   **c.** $-\dfrac{5}{2} < x \le 3$

    d. $x \le 3$ or $x > 5$ **e.** $-\dfrac{2}{5} < x \le 3$

35. $x^2 - 4 = (x - 2)(x + 2)$ is an example of

    a. a perfect square   **b.** a conditional equation   **c.** a ratio

    d. a first degree equation   **e.** an identity.

36. The Lowest Common Denominator of $\dfrac{1}{x^3 + 4x^2}, \dfrac{1}{3x^2y + 13xy + 4y}$, and $\dfrac{1}{3x^2 + x}$ is

    a. $3x^4y + x^3y$ **b.** $x^2y(3x + 1)(x + 4)$ **c.** $x^3y(3x + 1)(x + 4)$

    d. $3x^3y + 13x^2y + 4xy$ **e.** $x^3y(3x + 1)^2(x + 4)$

37. Find all values of x for which $\dfrac{x}{x + 2} = \dfrac{x}{3x - 1}$ is a proportion.

    a. $\dfrac{2}{3}$ **b.** $0, \dfrac{2}{3}$ **c.** $\dfrac{3}{2}$ **d.** $\dfrac{3}{2}, 0$ **e.** none of these

38. Which of the following is not equal to $\dfrac{x - 3}{4 - x}$?

    a. $-\dfrac{3 - x}{4 - x}$ **b.** $\dfrac{x}{4 - x} - \dfrac{3}{x - 4}$ **c.** $\dfrac{x}{4 - x} + \dfrac{3}{x - 4}$ **d.** $\dfrac{3 - x}{x - 4}$ **e.** $-\dfrac{x - 3}{x - 4}$

39. When $x < \dfrac{2}{3}$, then $|2 - 3x|$ equals

    a. $3x - 2$ **b.** $-3x - 2$ **c.** $2 - 3x$ **d.** $2 + 3x$ **e.** none of these

40. What does T equal when $\dfrac{1}{T} = \dfrac{1}{A} - \dfrac{1}{B}$?

    a. $\dfrac{A - B}{AB}$ **b.** $A - B$ **c.** $\dfrac{B - A}{AB}$ **d.** $B - A$ **e.** $\dfrac{AB}{B - A}$

41. What is the solution of $\dfrac{1}{x - 3} = \dfrac{6}{x^2 - 9} - \dfrac{6}{x + 3}$?

    a. $x = 3$ **b.** $x = 2$ **c.** $x = -1$ or 4 **d.** $x = -2$ **e.** no solution

42. What is $\dfrac{6}{x^2 - 7x + 12} - \dfrac{x + 1}{x^2 - 4x}$ simplified?

    a. $-\dfrac{x - 1}{x(x - 4)}$ **b.** $\dfrac{3 + 8x - x^2}{x^3 - 7x^2 + 12x}$ **c.** $\dfrac{x^2 - 8x - 3}{x^3 - 7x^2 + 12x}$ **d.** $\dfrac{-x^2 + 8x - 3}{x^3 - 7x^2 + 12x}$

CHAPTER 5
GRAPHS, LINEAR EQUATIONS, FUNCTIONS, AND RELATIONS

A challenge to both management and employees in manufacturing is to make work interesting when it could be dull. One way is to vary the tasks and machines for which each employee is responsible. The requirement is that the employee be flexible in, and management be sensitive to, skills, attitudes, and personal relationships.

OBJECTIVE: Match ordered pairs of numbers and points in a plane.

5-1 THE REAL NUMBERS AND THE POINTS OF A PLANE

Two perpendicular number lines intersecting at zero may be used to match each point of a plane with two real numbers. One line usually is shown to be horizontal and the other vertical. Each is a **coordinate axis**. Their point of intersection is the **origin**. The plane is the **coordinate plane**. The four parts of the plane separated from each other by the axes are called **quadrants**.

TERMS ASSOCIATED WITH THE COORDINATE PLANE

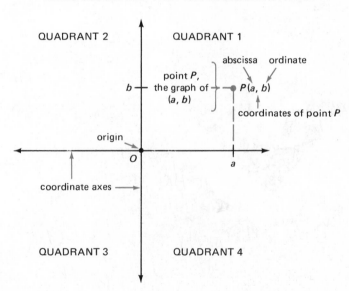

As indicated in the diagram above, a point, P, in the coordinate plane corresponds to an ordered pair of real numbers, (a, b). The first number, a (the **abscissa**), names a point in the horizontal axis. The second number, b (the **ordinate**), names a point in the vertical axis. The two numbers are the **coordinates** of the point P. The point is the **graph** for the number pair.

One way to find the ordered pair for a point, *A*, as shown in this diagram, is to move first horizontally from the origin to the point directly below *A*. Then move vertically to *A*. Thus, point *A* corresponds to 2 in the horizontal axis and 1 in the vertical axis. The coordinates of *A* are (2, 1).

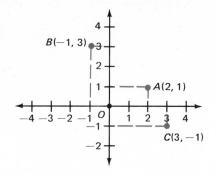

The process is similar for finding the point for an ordered pair such as (−1, 3). First move from the origin to the point for −1 in the horizontal axis. Then move up or down, parallel to the vertical axis, to the point that matches the point for 3. Notice that the ordered pair (−1, 3) matches point *B* while the ordered pair (3, −1) matches point *C*.

EXAMPLE 1 Give the coordinates of *A*, *B*, *C*, and *D*.

SOLUTION   The coordinates of *A* are (4, −5).

The coordinates of *B* are (−6, 1).

The coordinates of *C* are (0, 3).

The coordinates of *D* are (−2, 0).

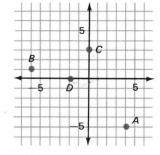

The process of drawing the graph for a number pair is called *graphing* or *plotting* the number pair.

EXAMPLE 2 Graph (−1, 0), (4, 4), (−3, −6), and (5, −6).

SOLUTION

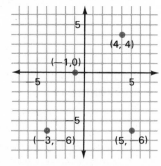

CLASSROOM EXERCISES

Give the coordinates of each point.

1. *A* **2.** *B* **3.** *C* **4.** *D*

5. *E* **6.** *F* **7.** *G*

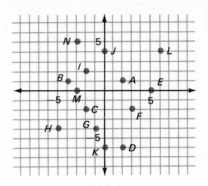

Use graph paper. Plot these points.

8. $A(-1, 4)$ **9.** $B(7, 3)$ **10.** $K(-5, 6)$

11. $F(-4, -3)$ **12.** $D(3, 0)$

EXERCISES

 Give the coordinates of *A, B, C* and *D*.

1. 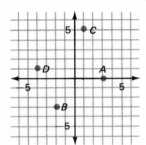 **2.** 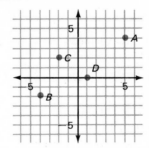 **3.**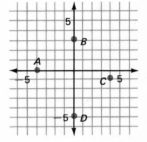

Use graph paper. Plot these points.

4. $A(1, 2), B(-3, -2), C(4, -1), D(-2, 1)$ **5.** $D(3, 1), K(3, -2), N(-1, -1), T(-1, 3)$

B Graph.

6. the set of ordered pairs with first coordinate 3

7. the set of ordered pairs with second coordinate -1

8. the set of ordered pairs each with equal first and second coordinates.

9. the set of ordered pairs 4 units from the origin

10. Three of the vertices of a rectangle are $(1, 1)$, $(1, 5)$, and $(4, 5)$. Find the coordinates of the fourth vertex.

11. $A(5, 8)$, $B(3, 2)$ and $C(7, 2)$ are the vertices of a triangle. Find the length of the median to side *BC*.

C **12.** Graph the set of all ordered pairs for which the second coordinate of each is less than or equal to the first coordinate.

13. Points $A(\sqrt{3}, 1)$, $B(1, \sqrt{3})$, $C(-1, \sqrt{3})$, $D(-\sqrt{3}, 1)$, $E(-\sqrt{3}, -1)$, $F(-1, -\sqrt{3})$, $G(1, -\sqrt{3})$, and $H(\sqrt{3}, -1)$ are vertices of an octagon. The vertices are contained in a circle having the origin, *O*, as its center. Find the radius length for the circle, $m \angle COB$, and $m \angle BOA$.

5050 SUMMING THE TERMS OF A SEQUENCE

The sum of the terms of a sequence may be found quickly by using a calculator. The flow chart on the left shows how to find the sum when each term of a sequence is equal to the previous term plus a constant. The flow chart on the right shows how to find the sum when each term is equal to the previous term multiplied by a constant.

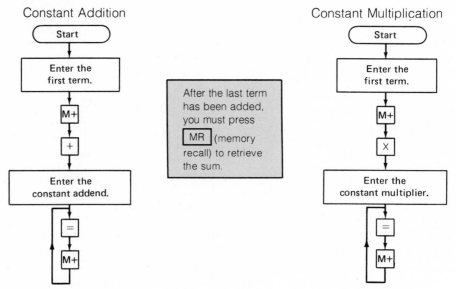

Constant Addition

Constant Multiplication

After the last term has been added, you must press MR (memory recall) to retrieve the sum.

Use your calculator. Find the sum of the first 10 terms of each sequence.

1. 5, 11, 17, 23, . . .

2. 3, 12, 48, 192, . . .

3. $5\frac{3}{4}, 4, 2\frac{1}{4}, \frac{1}{2}, . . .$

4. $-6, 18, -54, 162, . . .$

5. $1, \frac{1}{2}, \frac{1}{4}, \frac{1}{8}, . . .$

6. $1, -\frac{1}{2}, \frac{1}{4}, -\frac{1}{8}, . . .$

By saving money as shown in the chart, how much is saved

Day	1	2	3	4	⋯
Save	1¢	2¢	4¢	8¢	⋯

7. in 7 days?

8. in 14 days?

9. in 21 days?

A ball dropped from rest in a vacuum would fall approximately 4.9 m the first second and 9.8 m farther in each succeeding second. That is, it would fall 4.9 m the first second, 14.7 m the second second, 24.5 m the third second, and so on.

10. How far would the ball fall in 10 seconds?

> **OBJECTIVES:** Identify, find solutions for, and graph linear equations in two variables. Find slope and intercepts for a line. Write an equation for a line.

5-2 FIRST-DEGREE EQUATIONS HAVING TWO VARIABLES

A first-degree equation in two variables is one that can be written in this *standard form*.

$$Ax + By = C$$

In this form, x and y are the variables and A, B, and C are constants with A and B not both zero. When the coefficients for x and y in a first-degree equation are rational numbers, the standard form often is written with A, B, and C as integers.

FIRST-DEGREE EQUATIONS HAVING TWO VARIABLES

	Standard Form
$y = 2x - 4$	$2x - y = 4$
$\dfrac{y}{2} - \dfrac{2x}{3} = 1$	$-4x + 3y = 6$
$y - 3 = 0$	$y = 3$

The coefficient of x is 0.

A solution of an equation in two variables is an ordered pair of numbers that give a true sentence when they replace the variables. The graph for the equation is the graph for all its solutions. When the variables in the equation are x and y, the number for x is the first member of an ordered-pair solution and the number for y the second member. Since the first member also corresponds to a point on the horizontal axis of the coordinate plane, the horizontal axis is called the **x-axis**. Similarly, the vertical axis is called the **y-axis**.

The graph for a first-degree equation in two variables is a line in the coordinate plane. Conversely, every line in the coordinate plane is the graph of some first-degree equation. Hence, these equations are called **linear equations**.

To graph a linear equation, simply find some solutions, graph their points, and draw the line containing the points. It is enough to graph two solutions. However, a third solution should be graphed to act as a check.

EXAMPLE 1   Draw the graph for $2x - y = 4$.

SOLUTION   Solve the equation for y.

$$2x - y = 4$$
$$-y = -2x + 4$$
$$y = 2x - 4$$

Use three numbers for x.
Find corresponding numbers
for y.

x	y
-2	-8
0	-4
2	0

GRAPH   Graph two points.
Check that the third
point is in the same
line.   If so, draw that
line.

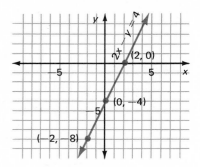

EXAMPLE 2   Draw the graph for $x = 3$.

SOLUTION   The line for $x = 3$ is the same line as that for $x + 0y = 3$.
The equation $x + 0y = 3$ shows, however, that the num-
bers for x will be 3 no matter what number is used for y.

x	y
3	-4
3	$\frac{1}{2}$
3	5

GRAPH

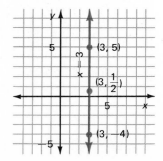

The graph is parallel
to the y-axis and 3
units to the right of it.

Linear equations may be given in variables other than x and y.   For
the graph of such an equation, you may use either axis for either variable.   The choice depends upon what you wish to show with the graph.

EXAMPLE 3 Draw the graph for $p + 2q = 6$.

SOLUTION 1 Solve for p. Make a table. Then graph.

$$p + 2q = 6$$
$$p = -2q + 6$$

q	p
4	-2
3	0
0	6

GRAPH

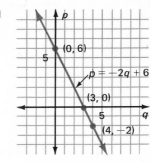

$p = -2q + 6$
(0, 6)
(3, 0)
(4, −2)

SOLUTION 2 Solve for q. Make a table. Then graph.

$$p + 2q = 6$$
$$2q = -p + 6$$
$$q = -\frac{1}{2}p + 3$$

p	q
-2	4
0	3
6	0

GRAPH

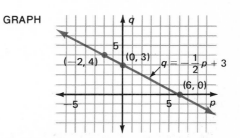

$q = -\frac{1}{2}p + 3$
(−2, 4)
(0, 3)
(6, 0)

GRAPHING A LINEAR EQUATION

1. Find three solutions of the equation.
2. Graph two solutions. Draw the line containing the two points.
3. Check to see that the point for the third solution is also in the line.

CLASSROOM EXERCISES

Draw the graph for each equation.

1. $x - 5y = 3$ **2.** $x - 1 = 0$ **3.** $2x + 3y = 6$

4. Graph $3s + t = 9$ with t plotted against s.

5. Graph $3s + t = 9$ with s plotted against t.

EXERCISES

A Draw the graph for each equation.

1. $x + y = 5$ **2.** $x + y = 9$ **3.** $2x + y = 5$

4. $3x + y = 7$ **5.** $2x - y = 5$ **6.** $3x - y = 7$

7. $x - 2y = 4$ **8.** $x - 4y = 8$ **9.** $x = 0$

10. $x = -2$ **11.** $y = -1$ **12.** $y = 0$

13. $3x + y = 0$ **14.** $5x + y = 0$ **15.** $2x + 3y = 12$

16. $3x + 5y = 15$ **17.** $7x + 2y = -28$ **18.** $4x + 5y = -40$

19. $\frac{1}{2}x + 3y = 7$ **20.** $\frac{1}{3}x + 5y = 9$ **21.** $\frac{1}{2}x - \frac{1}{3}y = 1$

22. Graph $3p + q = 6$ with p plotted against q.

23. Graph $3p + q = 6$ with q plotted against p.

24. Graph $\frac{u}{4} + \frac{v}{5} = 4$ with u plotted against v.

25. Graph $\frac{u}{4} + \frac{v}{5} = 4$ with v plotted against u.

B Write each equation in standard form. Draw its graph.

26. $3y = x + 5$ **27.** $2x - 7 = 3y$ **28.** $\frac{1}{4}x = \frac{1}{7}y - 2$

29. $y = |-3|x + 2$ **30.** $x(y - 1) = y(x + 1)$ **31.** $x(x - 1) = x(x + 2) + y$

C **32.** $\dfrac{x^2 - 2x - 3}{x - 3} = y$ **33.** $\dfrac{1}{x} = 2 - \dfrac{y}{x}$

34. Graph $y = |2x - 4|$.   **35.** Graph $y = \begin{cases} 2x - 4 & \text{for } x \geq 2 \\ -(2x - 4) & \text{for } x < 2 \end{cases}$

GOOD INCOME

Suppose you accept a job for which there are several salary plans. The plans are represented by these graphs. In each, t represents time spent working, and A represents amount of income. Which would you prefer?

a.   b.   c.   d.   e.

      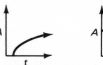

5-3 THE SLOPE OF A LINE

When talking about a roof, a hill, or some other object that is slanted, we often speak of its *slope*, or *steepness*. The word "slope" also is used to help describe a line in the coordinate plane. To understand the slope of a line, you may find it helpful to associate the word "slope" with the word "steepness."

The **slope of a nonvertical line** in the coordinate plane is the ratio of the difference of the y-coordinates to the difference of the x-coordinates for any two points of the line. Imagine that a point can move along the line. The slope of the line is the ratio of the *change* in the y-coordinate of the point to the change in its x-coordinate. The Greek letter Δ (capital *delta*) is used to suggest difference or amount of change. Hence,

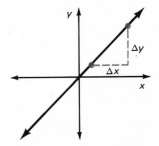

$$\text{slope} = \frac{\Delta y}{\Delta x}.$$

EXAMPLE 1 Find the slope of the line for $y = x$.

SOLUTION The line for $y = x$ looks like this.

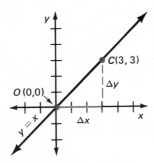

The number pairs $(0, 0)$ and $(3, 3)$ name points O and C, respectively, in the line. Imagine a point moving from O to C. Its y-coordinate increases from 0 to 3. Its x-coordinate also increases from 0 to 3.

$$\text{slope} = \frac{\Delta y}{\Delta x}$$

$$= \frac{3}{3}$$

$$= 1$$

CONCLUSION The slope of the line for $y = x$ is 1.

EXAMPLE 2   The line for $2x - 3y = -4$ is shown.   Find its slope.

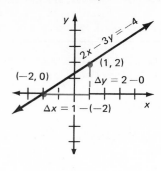

SOLUTION   First we choose two points $(-2, 0)$ and $(1, 2)$ in the line.   The difference of their y-coordinates is $2 - 0$, or 2.   The difference of their x-coordinates is $1 - (-2)$, or 3.

$$\text{slope} = \frac{\Delta y}{\Delta x}$$

$$= \frac{2 - 0}{1 - (-2)}$$

$$= \frac{2}{3}$$

CONCLUSION   The slope of the line for $2x - 3y = -4$ is $\frac{2}{3}$.

The slope, $\frac{2}{3}$, of the line in Example 2 tells us that the line is not as steep as the line with slope 1 (Example 1).   It tells us that, as we move from point to point along the line, the y-coordinates change only $\frac{2}{3}$ as much as do the corresponding x-coordinates.

Examples 1 and 2 illustrate that a line slanting upward to the right has positive slope.   As we move from point to point in such a line, both coordinates increase or both decrease.   A line that slants downward to the right has negative slope.   As we move from point to point in such a line, one coordinate increases while the other decreases.

EXAMPLE 3   The line for $y = -\frac{1}{2}x + 3$ is shown.   Find its slope.

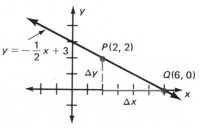

SOLUTION 1 $P(2, 2)$ and $Q(6, 0)$ are two points of the line.   Imagine a point moving from P to Q.   The y-coordinate *decreases* by 2.   The x-coordinate increases by 4.   Therefore,

$$\text{slope} = \frac{\Delta y}{\Delta x}$$

$$= \frac{-2}{4}, \text{ or } -\frac{1}{2}$$

SOLUTION 2   We get the same ratio by subtracting coordinates.

$$\text{slope} = \frac{\Delta y}{\Delta x}$$

$$= \frac{0 - 2}{6 - 2}$$

$$= -\frac{1}{2}$$

CONCLUSION   The slope of the line for $y = -\frac{1}{2}x + 3$ is $-\frac{1}{2}$.

A line that is horizontal has slope zero since the y-coordinates of its points are all the same.   A line that is vertical has *no slope* since the x-coordinates of its points are all the same.

Horizontal Line	Vertical Line
$\text{slope} = \frac{\Delta y}{\Delta x}$	$\text{slope} = \frac{\Delta y}{\Delta x}$
$= \frac{0}{\Delta x}$	$= \frac{\Delta y}{0}$, which is meaningless.
$= 0$	

EXAMPLE 4   The lines for $y = 5$ and $x = 2$ are shown.
Find the slope of each.

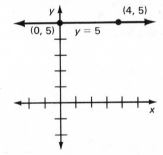

SOLUTION

The points $(0, 5)$ and $(4, 5)$ belong to the line for $y = 5$.

$$\text{slope} = \frac{\Delta y}{\Delta x}$$

$$= \frac{5 - 5}{4 - 0}$$

$$= 0$$

The points $(2, 1)$ and $(2, 3)$ belong to the line for $x = 2$.

$$\text{slope} = \frac{\Delta y}{\Delta x}$$

$$= \frac{\Delta y}{2 - 2}, \text{ or } \frac{\Delta y}{0},$$

which is meaningless.

CONCLUSION   The slope of the line for $y = 5$ is 0.
The line for $x = 2$ has no slope.

FINDING THE SLOPE OF A LINE

1. Select two points A and B with coordinates (x_A, y_A) and (x_B, y_B) in the line.

2. Find $\dfrac{\Delta y}{\Delta x}$ when Δy represents the difference of the y-coordinates of A and B and Δx the difference of the x-coordinates.

   $$\text{Slope} = \frac{\Delta y}{\Delta x}$$

   $$= \frac{y_A - y_B}{x_A - x_B}, \text{ or } \frac{y_B - y_A}{x_B - x_A}$$

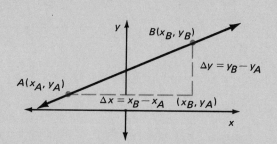

3. When A and B have the same x-coordinate $(x_A = x_B)$, $\Delta x = 0$, $\dfrac{\Delta y}{\Delta x}$ is meaningless, and the line has no slope. It is parallel to the y-axis.

CLASSROOM EXERCISES

Find the slope of each line.

1.

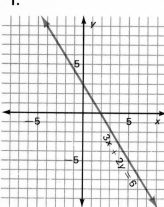

2.

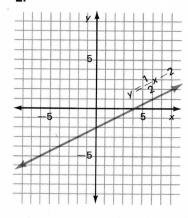

3.

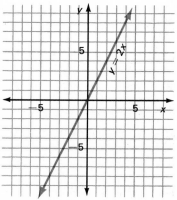

Draw the graph for each. Find the slope.

4. $-2x + y = 4$

5. $-3y = 4x$

6. $x + 4 = 0$

7. the line containing the points $(-1, 2)$ and $(3, 6)$

EXERCISES

A Find the slope of each line.

1.
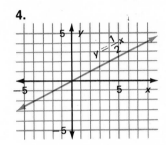

2.
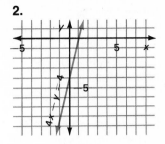

3.
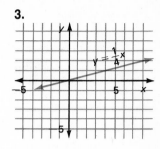

4.
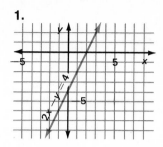

5.
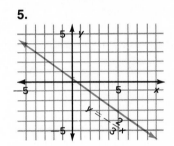

6.
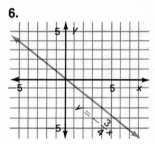

Draw the graph for each equation.   Find the slope.

7. $-2x + y = 6$

8. $-3x + y = 9$

9. $-4x + 2 = y$

10. $-6x + 3 = y$

11. $y + 5 = 0$

12. $-y + 2 = 0$

13. $-x + 3 = 0$

14. $x + 1 = 0$

15. $y = 2x - 2$

Find the slope of the line containing each pair of points.

16. $(2, -3)$ and $(-1, 4)$

17. $(3, -1)$ and $(-2, 3)$

18. $\left(\frac{1}{2}, 3\right)$ and $\left(\frac{3}{8}, 3\right)$

B Find the slope of the line for each equation.

19. $|3|x + |-7|y = 21$

20. $\sqrt{2}x - y = \sqrt{2}$

21. $x(x + 1) + y = x^2 + y - 2$

Suppose $(3, 9)$ and (t, t^2) are two points in a line.   Find t

22. for the line to have slope -7.

23. for the line to have no slope.

24. The slope of the line containing $\left(3, \frac{3}{4}\right)$ and $\left(t, \frac{t}{t + 1}\right)$ is 5.   Find t.

25. The line containing points $(4, -3)$ and $(2, y)$ has slope no greater than 6.   Find the possible values for y.

26. Are the points $(7, 0)$, $(-1, 6)$, and $(-5, 9)$ collinear?   Explain.

C **27.** For what value of k are $(1, 5)$, $(k, 4k)$, and $(0, -2)$ collinear?

28. For what values of k does the line for $|k - 2|x + 3y = 10$ have slope -2?

5-4 THE SLOPE-INTERCEPT FORM, $y = mx + b$

The **x-intercept** of a line in the coordinate plane is the x-coordinate of its point of intersection with the x-axis. The **y-intercept** is the y-coordinate of the point of intersection with the y-axis.

Linear equations of the form $x = b$ have graphs that are parallel to the y-axis. There is no y-intercept. All other linear equations may be written in the form $y = mx + b$. This is the **slope-intercept form** for an equation of a line, since m is the slope and b is the y-intercept of its graph.

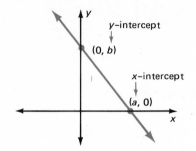

EXAMPLE 1 Find the slope of the line for $y = 3x + 5$. Find the y-intercept. Find the x-intercept. Draw the graph.

SOLUTION This table shows several solutions for $y = 3x + 5$.

x	y
-2	-1
-1	2
0	5
1	8
2	11

As numbers for x change 1 unit, numbers for y change 3 units.

Thus, slope $= \dfrac{\Delta y}{\Delta x}$

$= \dfrac{3}{1}$, or 3.

The slope of the line for $y = \boxed{3}x + 5$ is $\boxed{3}$.

For the y-intercept, x must be zero.

When $x = 0$, $y = 5$ as shown in the table above.

For the x-intercept, y must be zero.

$$y = 3x + 5$$
$$0 = 3x + 5$$
$$-3x = 5$$
$$x = -\frac{5}{3}$$

The line for $y = 3x + \boxed{5}$ has y-intercept $\boxed{5}$, and x-intercept $-\frac{5}{3}$.

GRAPH The line must contain $\left(-\frac{5}{3}, 0\right)$ and $(0, 5)$.

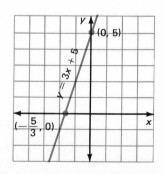

Understanding the slope-intercept form saves much of the effort in finding information about the graph of a linear equation. For the equation of Example 1, for example, we can find that the slope is 3 and the y-intercept is 5 simply by examining the equation.

$$\overset{\overset{\text{slope}}{\downarrow}}{y = 3\underset{\underset{y\text{-intercept}}{\uparrow}}{x + 5}} \qquad\qquad \overset{\overset{\text{slope}}{\downarrow}}{y = m\underset{\underset{y\text{-intercept}}{\uparrow}}{x + b}}$$

We can find the x-intercept by remembering that the number for y is 0.

$$0 = 3x + 5 \qquad\qquad 0 = mx + b$$
$$\underset{\underset{x\text{-intercept}}{\uparrow}}{-\frac{3}{5} = x} \qquad\qquad \underset{\underset{x\text{-intercept}}{\uparrow}}{-\frac{b}{m} = x}$$

EXAMPLE 2 Find the slope and y-intercept of the line for
$3x - 2y = 10$.

SOLUTION Solve for y.
$$3x - 2y = 10$$
$$-2y = -3x + 10$$
$$y = \tfrac{3}{2}x - 5$$

The slope is $\tfrac{3}{2}$. The y-intercept is -5.

The slope-intercept form provides an efficient way to write an equation for a line.

EXAMPLE 3 Write an equation for the line having slope $-\tfrac{2}{3}$ and y-intercept 4.

SOLUTION $m = -\tfrac{2}{3}, b = 4$
$$y = mx + b$$
$$y = -\tfrac{2}{3}x + 4, \text{ or } 2x + 3y = 12$$

The slope-intercept form also provides a convenient method for drawing the graph of a linear equation. First, plot the point for the y-intercept. Then use the slope to locate another point.

EXAMPLE 4 Draw the line for $2y - 3x = 6$.

SOLUTION   Write the equation in slope-intercept form.

$$2y - 3x = 6$$
$$2y = 3x + 6$$
$$y = \frac{3}{2}x + 3$$

The slope is $\frac{3}{2}$.   The y-intercept is 3.

Plot a point at $(0, 3)$.   From that point, locate another point by changing the x-coordinate 2 units and the y-coordinate 3 units.   The second point is $(2, 6)$.

GRAPH   Use the two points to draw the line.

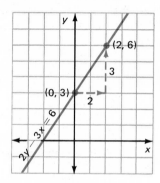

EXAMPLE 5 Draw the line for $y = 4 - 3x$.

SOLUTION   The slope-intercept form for the equation is

$$y = -3x + 4.$$

Plot a point at $(0, 4)$.   Since the slope is -3, or $\frac{-3}{1}$, change the x-coordinate by 1 and the y-coordinate by -3 to find another point, $(1, 1)$.

GRAPH

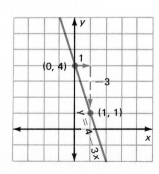

The slope-intercept form is useful in working with equations in variables other than x and y. For a graph, however, we must keep in mind which variable refers to which axis. When we want to draw a graph showing variable C *plotted against* variable n, we use the horizontal axis for n, the vertical axis for C, and solve the equation for C in terms of n.

EXAMPLE 6 Mr. Wood's car ran out of gasoline. At a gasoline station, he found that he would have to pay $0.25 per liter and leave a $5.00 deposit for the container he had to borrow. The equation

$$C = 0.25n + 5.00$$

gives the number of dollars, C, he needs in order to get n liters of gasoline. Draw the graph for this equation.

GRAPH

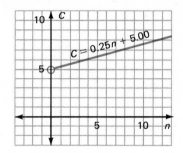

EXAMPLE 7 Use the information from Example 6. Suppose Mr. Wood wanted to know how much gasoline he could buy for a certain amount of money. Draw a graph to show the relationship.

SOLUTION Solve $C = 0.25n + 5.00$ for n. Then graph.

$$C = 0.25n + 5.00$$
$$100C = 25n + 500$$
$$100C - 500 = 25n$$
$$4C - 20 = n$$

GRAPH

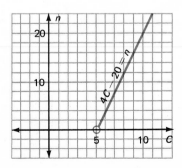

CLASSROOM EXERCISES

Find the x- and y-intercepts.

Find the slope and y-intercept.

1. $y = 4x + 3$ **2.** $3x + 5y = 15$ **3.** $y = -3x + 1$ **4.** $y = 3$

Find an equation for the line having slope m and y-intercept b.

Graph. Use the slope-intercept form.

5. $m = -\frac{3}{4}, b = 5$ **6.** $m = \frac{8}{5}, b = -2$ **7.** $y = -3x + 1$ **8.** $y = 2x + 1$

9. The cost of renting some garden equipment is $5.00 plus 60 cents per hour. Make a graph of cost plotted against time. Make a graph of time plotted against cost.

EXERCISES

Ⓐ Find the x- and y-intercepts.

1. $y - 3x = 6$ **2.** $2y - 5x = 10$ **3.** $x - y = 6$ **4.** $x + y = 2$

5. $y = 2x - 1$ **6.** $y = -3x + 2$ **7.** $y = 3$ **8.** $y = -5$

Find the slope and y-intercept.

9. $y = 2x + 4$ **10.** $y = -3x + 7$ **11.** $x + 2y = 1$ **12.** $2x - 9y = 18$

13. $3x - 4y = 24$ **14.** $x + 5y = 2$ **15.** $2y + 1 = 0$ **16.** $4 - 2y = 0$

Find an equation for the line having slope m and y-intercept b.

17. $m = -2, b = 0$ **18.** $m = \frac{1}{3}, b = -2$ **19.** $m = -\frac{1}{2}, b = 7$

20. $m = \frac{2}{3}, b = 0$ **21.** $m = -\frac{1}{2}, b = 6$ **22.** $m = -1, b = 3$

Graph. Use the slope-intercept form.

23. $y = 3x - 6$ **24.** $y = 8 - 2x$ **25.** $y = 6 + x$

26. $y - 4x = 0$ **27.** $y + x = 0$ **28.** $4y = 6 - 2x$

29. Graph. Use the same coordinate system.

$y = \frac{1}{2}x + 3$ $2y - x = 8$ $2y = x + 10$

30. Assume the average rate of travel for an automobile is 60 kilometers per hour. Write an equation which expresses the relation between d, the distance traveled by the automobile, and h, the number of hours that it travels. Make a graph of d plotted against h. Make a graph of h plotted against d.

31. At Magens Bay Beach there is a 150-meter-wide border of sand along the water. The beach loses 3 meters of sand per year due to erosion. Graph the width of the beach, w, plotted against t, the number of years.

B **32.** Graph. Use the same coordinate system. Which graphs do not intersect?

$y - 3x = 5$ $\qquad\qquad$ $y + 2x = 6$ $\qquad\qquad$ $y - 3x = -5$

33. Write each of the equations of Exercise 32 in slope-intercept form. How are the first and third equations alike?

34. It can be proved that two lines are parallel if their slopes are equal. For which of the following are the graphs parallel?

$20y - 15x = -35$ $\qquad$ $12y - 9x + 8 = 0$ $\qquad$ $15y - 10x = 9$

35. Graph. Use the same coordinate system. Which graphs are not parallel?

$2y + x = -4$ $\qquad\qquad$ $x + 2y = 12$ $\qquad\qquad$ $y - 2x = 1$

36. It can be proved that two lines are perpendicular if the product of their slopes is -1. Without drawing either graph, tell whether the graphs of $3y + 7x = 10$ and $y + 2 = \frac{3}{7}x$ intersect. Explain.

37. A line is perpendicular to $4x - 3y = 2$. Its y-intercept is 3. Write an equation for the line.

38. A company finds that it costs $5000 to produce 100 items and $7500 to produce 200 items. Assume that the graph relating cost to the number of items produced is a line. Graph cost, C, plotted against the number of items produced, n. Write an equation for C in terms of n.

C **39.** In parallelogram $ABCD$, $A = (0, 0)$, $B = (13, 0)$, $C = (18, 12)$, and $D = (5, 12)$. Show that $ABCD$ is a rhombus. (HINT: Consider the diagonals.)

40. The line $|h - 2|x + |k - 1|y = 10$ has slope -2. Find all ordered pairs (h, k) such that $h + k = 20$.

41. Use the information from Exercise 31. When the beach erodes to a width of 102 meters, the Beach Improvement Association begins to widen the beach at the rate of 1.5 meters per year. Graph the width of the beach, w, plotted against t, the number of years. Write an equation relating w to t.

NO CALCULATOR ALLOWED

Compute the value of $36\,984^2 - 36\,983^2$ in under 30 seconds.

5-5 THE POINT-SLOPE FORM AND TWO-POINT FORM

When we know the *slope*, m, of a line and the coordinates, (x_1, y_1), of *any point* in the line, we can find an equation of the line.

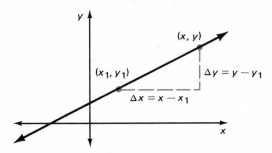

Choose (x, y) to represent any point other than (x_1, y_1) in the line. Then $\dfrac{y - y_1}{x - x_1}$ represents m. We may write

$$\frac{y - y_1}{x - x_1} = m \quad \text{or} \quad y - y_1 = m(x - x_1),$$

and then simplify. Since one point and the slope are all that is needed, $y - y_1 = m(x - x_1)$ is the **point-slope form** for the equation of a line.

EXAMPLE 1 Find an equation of the line containing the point $(2, -3)$ and having slope 2.

SOLUTION Begin with

$$\frac{y - y_1}{x - x_1} = m \quad \text{or} \quad y - y_1 = m(x - x_1).$$

$$\frac{y - (-3)}{x - 2} = 2 \quad \text{or} \quad y - (-3) = 2(x - 2)$$

Either form gives
$$y + 3 = 2x - 4$$
$$y = 2x - 7$$

CHECK $y = 2x - 7$ is the slope-intercept form. The slope of the line is 2. Does the line contain $(2, -3)$?

$$y = 2x - 7$$
$$-3 \overset{?}{=} 2(2) - 7$$
$$-3 = -3 \quad ✔$$

When we know the coordinates, (x_1, y_1) and (x_2, y_2), of any two points of a line, we also can find an equation for the line. We choose (x, y)

to represent any other point in the line. Then each of

$$\frac{y - y_1}{x - x_1}, \frac{y - y_2}{x - x_2}, \text{ and } \frac{y_2 - y_1}{x_2 - x_1}$$

represents the slope of the line. We may write, for example,

$$\frac{y - y_1}{x - x_1} = \frac{y_2 - y_1}{x_2 - x_1} \quad \text{or} \quad y - y_1 = \frac{y_2 - y_1}{x_2 - x_1}(x - x_1)$$

and then simplify. Since two points are all that is needed,

$$y - y_1 = \frac{y_2 - y_1}{x_2 - x_1}(x - x_1)$$

is the **two-point form** of an equation for a line.

EXAMPLE 2 Find an equation of the line containing points $(-2, 1)$ and $(3, 4)$.

SOLUTION Begin with

$$\frac{y - y_1}{x - x_1} = \frac{y_2 - y_1}{x_2 - x_1} \quad \text{or} \quad y - y_1 = \frac{y_2 - y_1}{x_2 - x_1}(x - x_1)$$

$$\frac{y - 1}{x - (-2)} = \frac{4 - 1}{3 - (-2)} \quad \text{or} \quad y - 1 = \frac{4 - 1}{3 - (-2)}(x - (-2))$$

Either form gives

$$y - 1 = \frac{3}{5}(x + 2)$$

$$5y - 5 = 3x + 6$$

$$-3x + 5y = 11$$

CHECK

$$-3x + 5y = 11$$
$$-3(-2) + 5(1) \stackrel{?}{=} 11$$
$$11 = 11 \quad ✔$$

$$-3x + 5y = 11$$
$$-3(3) + 5(4) \stackrel{?}{=} 11$$
$$11 = 11 \quad ✔$$

CLASSROOM EXERCISES

Find an equation of the line having slope m and containing the given point.

Find an equation of the line containing the pair of points.

1. $(1, -4), m = 3$ **2.** $(-3, 0), m = -\frac{1}{2}$ **3.** $(1, -2)$ and $(4, 5)$ **4.** $(4, 0)$ and $(0, 2)$

EXERCISES

Find an equation of the line having slope m and containing the given point.

1. $(3, 2), m = \frac{3}{2}$ **2.** $(2, -1), m = -\frac{1}{2}$ **3.** $(-2, -5), m = \frac{1}{4}$

4. $(0, 2), m = 5$ **5.** $(2, 5), m = 0$ **6.** $(-2, 6), m$ is undefined.

Find an equation of the line containing the pair of points.

7. $(2, 3)$ and $(5, 7)$ **8.** $(-1, 2)$ and $(3, 4)$ **9.** $(5, 0)$ and $(0, 7)$

10. $(0, 0)$ and $(5, 6)$ **11.** $(-4, -4)$, and $(0, 0)$ **12.** $(-1, -1)$, and $(-4, -1)$

B **13.** A line contains the points $(3, 1)$ and $(5, 7)$. Write an equation in slope-intercept form. Find the y-intercept.

14. A line contains the points $(0, b)$ and $(a, 0)$, where $a \neq 0$ and $b \neq 0$. Write the equation so that the right member is ab. Divide both members of the equation by ab. The result is an equation of a line in "intercept form."

15. A line contains the point $(2, -3)$ and is parallel to the line $y = -\frac{1}{2}x + 6$. Write an equation for the line.

16. A line contains the point $(9, -1)$ and is perpendicular to the line $2y = 3x - 7$. Write an equation for the line.

17. The coordinates of the vertices A, B, and C of a right triangle are $(3, -4)$, $(-2, -4)$, and $(-2, 8)$ respectively. Write an equation for the line containing the hypotenuse.

18. Line l is perpendicular to the line $3x - 4y = 12$. Line l intersects $3x - 4y = 12$ at a point where the x-coordinate is -2. Write an equation for line l.

19. Points $(2, -3)$, $(-7, 9)$ and (x, y) are collinear. Give the equation of the line in standard form.

C **20.** The coordinates of A, B, and C are $(2, 0)$, $(5, 4)$, and $(0, k)$ respectively. Find the value for k that makes $AC + BC$ the smallest possible distance.

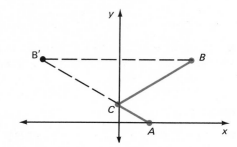

21. Let m_1 denote the slope of the line containing $(0, 0)$ and (x, y). Let m_2 denote the slope of the line containing $(0, 5)$ and (x, y). Find the equation of all points (x, y) when $m_1 + m_2 = \frac{2}{3}$.

THE FOUR STORES

In a certain city there are four unusual stores named Alpha, Beta, Gamma, and Delta. Each store charges one dollar to enter and one dollar to exit. A man enters Alpha and spends half of his money on purchases in the store. He leaves Alpha and proceeds to the other three stores and does the same thing. When he leaves the last one he finds he has no money left.

How much did he have when he started his shopping?

CHECKING YOUR UNDERSTANDING

WORDS AND SYMBOLS

abscissa	linear equation	quadrant
coordinate axis	ordered pair (a, b)	slope
coordinate plane	ordinate	x- and y-intercepts
coordinates of a point	origin	x and y axes

Forms of a Linear Equation

slope-intercept	point-slope	two-point

CONCEPTS

■ Each point of the coordinate plane may be associated with an ordered pair of real numbers. Each ordered pair of real numbers may be associated with one point of the coordinate plane. [5-1]

■ Each line in the coordinate plane may be represented by a first-degree equation in two variables. Every such equation may be represented by a line in the coordinate plane. The points in the line for an equation correspond to the solutions of the equation. [5-2]

■ Lines having positive slope slant upward to the right. Lines having negative slope slant downward to the right. The greater the absolute value of the slope, the steeper the line. [5-3, 5-4]

■ To write an equation for a line, it is enough to know the coordinates of two points of the line, or the coordinates of one point and the slope of the line. [5-4, 5-5]

PROCESSES

■ Match points in a plane with ordered pairs of real numbers. [5-1]

1. $(-2, 5)$ **2.** $(0, -3)$ **3.** $(5, -2)$ **4.** $(3, 0)$

■ Graph linear equations. [5-2]

5. $3x - 2y = 6$ **6.** $y = -4$ **7.** $\frac{1}{5}x - \frac{1}{2}y = 1$

■ Find the slope of a line. [5-3, 5-4]

8. the line containing $(4, -3)$ and $(2, -10)$ **9.** the line for $4x + 2y = 7$

■ Use the special forms of a linear equation. [5-5]

10. Give an equation for the line with slope $\frac{5}{4}$ containing point $(0, -3)$.

11. Give an equation for the line containing $(0, 7)$ and $\left(\frac{2}{5}, 3\right)$.

12. Graph $y = 4x - 6$ **13.** Graph $3x - 2y = 6$

OBJECTIVES: Identify and graph functions and relations, in particular those defined by linear equations and inequalities.
Solve problems involving linear and direct variation.

5-6 FUNCTIONS AND THEIR GRAPHS

A **function** is a set of ordered pairs, no two of which have the same first member.

EXAMPLE 1   Which set of ordered pairs is a function?   Which set is not a function?   Why?

$\{(1, 7), (2, 9), (1, 0)\}$ $\{(1, 3), (2, 2), (3, 2)\}$

SOLUTION   The first set is not a function.   Two ordered pairs, $(1, 7)$ and $(1, 0)$, have the same first member.

The second set is a function.   The first members of the ordered pairs are all different.

The set of first members of the ordered pairs of a function is the **domain** of the function.   The set of second members of the ordered pairs is the **range** of the function.   The **graph of a function** is the graph of the ordered pairs of the function.

A function may be defined by specifying its domain and a rule for forming its ordered pairs.

EXAMPLE 2   Describe the ordered pairs that belong to the function defined below.   Describe the range of the function. Draw the graph of the function.

> DOMAIN: The counting numbers
> RULE: $x \longrightarrow 2x - 1$

SOLUTION   The rule pairs each counting number with twice the number less one.

The pairs that belong to the function are $(1, 1)$, $(2, 3)$, $(3, 5)$, and so on.

The range of the function is the set $\{1, 3, 5, \ldots\}$ of *odd* counting numbers.

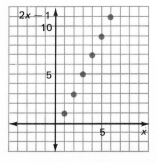

The solutions of an equation in two variables form a set of ordered pairs. If no two ordered pairs have the same first member, the solution set is a function. The equation may be used as the rule for defining the function.

Often the variables used in the equation for a function are x and y with x representing a member of the domain and y representing the corresponding member of the range. Sometimes the function itself is given a name like f or g, or some other symbol. Then, instead of y, a symbol such as $f(x)$ (read "f of x" or "f at x") or $g(x)$ is used for the member of the range that corresponds to x.

EXAMPLE 3   Find several ordered pairs of numbers that belong to the function defined below.

Plot the ordered pairs in the coordinate plane. Draw the graph of the function by drawing the curve suggested by the plotted points.

DOMAIN: The real numbers
RULE: $f(x) = x^2 + 1$, or $y = x^2 + 1$

SOLUTION $f(-3) = (-3)^2 + 1$, $f(-2) = (-2)^2 + 1$, $f(-1) = (-1)^2 + 1$
                    $= 10$ $= 5$ $= 2$

Also, $f(0) = 1$, $f(1) = 2$, $f(2) = 5$, $f(3) = 10$.

GRAPH

x	$f(x)$, or y
-3	10
-2	5
-1	2
0	1
1	2
2	5
3	10

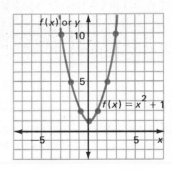

Graphically, it can be easy to test whether a set of ordered pairs of numbers is a function. Since two ordered pairs of a function cannot have the same first member, the graph should not have two points in any vertical line. This is called the *Vertical-Line Test*.

EXAMPLE 4   Which is the graph of a function?

a. 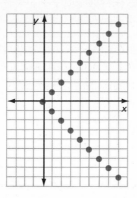   **b.**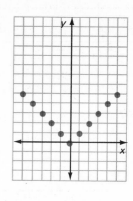

SOLUTION   The first graph shows many pairs of points in line vertically.   Their ordered pairs have the same first members.
This is not the graph of a function.

The second graph shows that no two ordered pairs have
the same first member.   This is the graph of a function.

EXAMPLE 5   Sketch a graph for each equation.

$$y^2 = x, \quad y = \sqrt{x}$$

Tell which equation cannot be used to define a function.

SOLUTION $y^2 = x$

x	y
0	0
1	± 1
4	± 2
9	± 3

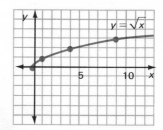

$y = \sqrt{x}$

x	y
0	0
1	1
4	2
9	3

There are many pairs of solutions of $y^2 = x$ that have the
same first member. $y^2 = x$ cannot define a function.
This is suggested graphically by the Vertical-Line Test. ⁻

CLASSROOM EXERCISES

Is the set of ordered pairs a function?

1. $\{(2, 1), (3, 7), (2, 4)\}$

2. $\{(1, 1), (3, 8), (-1, 4), (2, 8)\}$

3. The domain is the set of integers. The rule for a function pairs each integer x with the number $10x$. Describe the range.

Is the graph that of a function?

4.
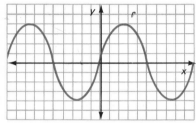

5.
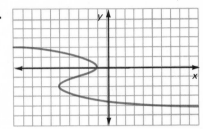

Sketch a graph and tell whether the equation can be used to define a function.

6. $x = -y^2$

7. $y = -\sqrt{x}$

Find five ordered pairs of numbers that belong to the function. Plot the ordered pairs. Then complete the graph of the function.

8. Domain: $\{-2, -1, 0, 1, 2\}$
Rule: $f(x) = x^2 - 1$, or $y = x^2 - 1$

9. Domain: the real numbers
Rule: $f(x) = x^2 - 1$, or $y = x^2 - 1$

EXERCISES

A Is the set of ordered pairs a function?

1. $\{(1, 2), (2, 2), (3, 2), (4, 2)\}$

2. $\{(2, 1), (2, 2), (2, 3), (2, 4)\}$

3. $\{(-2, 2), (3, 0), (-2, 1)\}$

4. $\{(2, 1), (-1, 1), (-1, 3)\}$

Is the graph that of a function?

5.
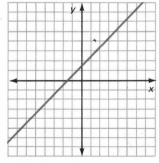

6.
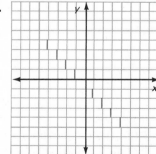

7.
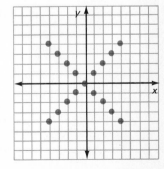

8. 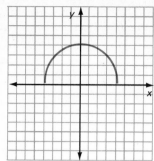 **9.** 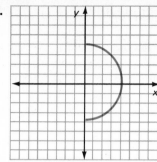 **10.**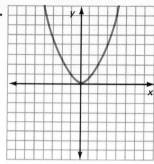

Draw the graph. Describe the range of the function.

11. Domain: the integers
Rule: $x \rightarrow 2x$

12. Domain: the integers
Rule: $x \rightarrow 5x$

13. Domain: the integers
Rule: $x \rightarrow 3x + 1$

Find seven ordered pairs of numbers that belong to the function. Plot the ordered pairs. Then complete the graph of the function.

14. Domain: $\{-1, 0, 1, 2, 3, 4, 5\}$
Rule: $f(x) = x^2 - 4x$ or $y = x^2 - 4x$

15. Domain: the real numbers
Rule: $f(x) = x^2 - 4x$ or $y = x^2 - 4x$

Sketch a graph and tell whether the equation may be used to define a function.

16. $y = 2$ **17.** $x = -1$ **18.** $x = 4y^2$ **19.** $y = 2\sqrt{x}$

For $f(x) = 4x - 1$, find

20. $f(3)$. **21.** $f(-5)$. **22.** $f(b)$. **23.** $f(k)$.

For $f(x) = 2x^2 + x - 1$, find

24. $f(2)$. **25.** $f(0.1)$.

For $f(x) = 2x^3 - x + 6$, find

26. $f(1) - f(-1)$.

[B] For $f(x) = a^2 - x^2$, find

For $f(x) = x^2 + 1$, find

27. $f(a)$. **28.** $f(-a)$. **29.** $f(1 - a)$. **30.** $f(f(2))$.

31. Let $f(x) = x^2 - 6x + 3$. When the domain is $\{0, 1, 2, 3\}$, does $f(x)$ increase or decrease as x increases from 0 to 3? When the domain is $\{3, 4, 5, 6\}$, does $f(x)$ increase or decrease as x increases from 3 to 6?

Graph.

32. $f(x) = |x|$ **33.** $f(x) = |x + 1|$ **34.** $f(x) = |2x - 4|$

[C] **35.** Let $f(x) = \sqrt{25 - x^2}$. Make a table showing $f(x)$ for the integral values of x from -5 to 5 inclusive. Sketch the graph.

5-7   LINEAR FUNCTIONS

The solution set of any linear equation, $Ax + By = C$, with $B \neq 0$, is a function. Such a function is a **linear function**. The replacements for x belong to the domain and the replacements for y belong to the range of a linear function.

A linear equation that defines a linear function may be written in the form $y = mx + b$. When the domain of the function is the set of real numbers, the graph of the function is a line with slope m and y-intercept b. When the domain is a subset of the real numbers, the graph will be a portion of this line.

EXAMPLE 1   Draw the graph of the function defined below.
Describe the range of the function.

> DOMAIN: The real numbers greater than zero.
> RULE: $y = \frac{1}{2}x + 3$

SOLUTION   The function is a linear function. Its domain is restricted to numbers for x that are greater than zero. Its graph is a portion of the line that has slope $\frac{1}{2}$ and y-intercept 3.

GRAPH

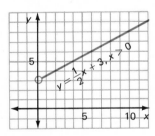

Since numbers for x must be greater than zero, numbers for y, as suggested by the graph, must be greater than 3. Thus, the range of this function is the set of real numbers greater than 3.

From now on we shall assume that the domain of a linear function is the set of real numbers unless we state otherwise.

EXAMPLE 2 Draw the graph of the function g defined by the equation $g(x) = 3x - 1$.

SOLUTION Recall that for a function named g, $g(x)$ is simply another way to represent the second member of the ordered pair whose first member is x. That is, $g(x) = 3x - 1$ is another form of the linear equation $y = 3x - 1$.

The graph is a line with slope 3 and y-intercept -1.

GRAPH

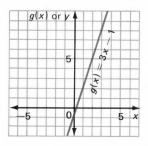

Linear functions may be applied to situations in which two unknowns are related by a linear equation. That is, the two unknowns *vary linearly*.

EXAMPLE 3 A pilot is flying an airplane at an altitude of 1000 meters and then begins climbing at the rate of 300 m/min. The altitude, $h(t)$, of the airplane is linearly related to the time, t, that elapses from the beginning of the climb.

$$h(t) = 300t + 1000$$

Graph the linear function defined by this equation.

SOLUTION The domain is restricted to $t \geq 0$. There is also a time, not given in the statement of the problem, beyond which the airplane stops climbing and, hence, beyond which the linear relationship does not apply. If you were preparing this graph for use by others, you would have to alert them to this fact, possibly by a note on the graph itself.

GRAPH

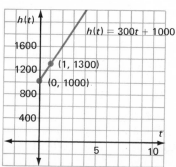

EXAMPLE 4 y and x are linearly related.   When x is 12, y is 2.   When x is 6, y is 0.   Find a linear function that describes this relationship.

SOLUTION   Use $y = mx + b$.

Replace x by 12 and y by 2.   Also, replace x by 6 and y by 0.   Solve the resulting system of equations for m and b.

$$2 = 12m + b$$
$$0 = 6m + b$$
Subtract. $2 = 6m$

$$\tfrac{1}{3} = m$$

Replace m by $\tfrac{1}{3}$ in $0 = 6m + b$
$$0 = 6\left(\tfrac{1}{3}\right) + b$$
$$-2 = b$$

CONCLUSION   The equation $y = \tfrac{1}{3}x - 2$ defines a function which contains $(6, 0)$ and $(12, 2)$.

CHECK $\begin{array}{l} y = \tfrac{1}{3}x - 2 \\ 0 \stackrel{?}{=} \tfrac{1}{3}(6) - 2 \\ 0 = 0 \ \checkmark \end{array}$ $\bigg|$ $\begin{array}{l} y = \tfrac{1}{3}x - 2 \\ 2 \stackrel{?}{=} \tfrac{1}{3}(12) - 2 \\ 2 = 2 \ \checkmark \end{array}$

Two unknowns *vary directly* when they are related by an equation of the form $y = mx$.   Since *linear variation* is described by an equation of the form $y = mx + b$, *direct variation* is a special case of linear variation in which $b = 0$.   The graph for a direct variation is a line containing the point $(0, 0)$.

CLASSROOM EXERCISES

Graph the function.

1. $y = 2x + 3$

2. $h(x) = -\tfrac{3}{5}x + 2$

3. Graph the function. Describe the range.
DOMAIN: the positive real numbers
RULE: $y = 2x - 1$ or $f(x) = 2x - 1$

4. y and x are linearly related.   When x is 5, y is 2.   When x is 7 y is 1.   Find a linear function that describes this relationship.

5. A tree is 5 meters high.   It grows at the rate of 0.25 m per year.   Express the height, $h(t)$, of the tree as a linear function of t, the time in years since the tree was 5 meters tall.   Graph this function.

6. The amount of paint needed to paint a house varies directly with the area covered.   In painting 38 m², 4 L of paint were used.   Give a linear function that relates area covered and the amount of paint used.   Graph the function.

EXERCISES

A Graph the function. Describe the range.

1. DOMAIN: the positive real numbers
   RULE: $y = 2x + 3$

2. DOMAIN: the positive real numbers
   RULE: $y = 4x - 2$

3. DOMAIN: the nonnegative real numbers
   RULE: $f(x) = \frac{1}{3}x + 4$

4. DOMAIN: the nonnegative real numbers
   RULE: $g(x) = \frac{1}{2}x + 3$

Graph the function.

5. $f(x) = -3x + 4$

6. $y = \frac{5}{3}x - 2$

y and x are linearly related. Find a linear function that describes each relationship.

7. For $x = 2$, $y = 0$, and
   for $x = 4$, $y = 5$.

8. For $x = 3$, $y = 0$, and
   for $x = 7$, $y = 2$.

9. For $x = 1$, $y = 5$, and
   for $x = 6$, $y = 3$.

10. A hawk is flying at an altitude of 40 meters. Then it begins climbing at the rate of 3 m/min. Express the altitude, $h(t)$, of the hawk as a linear function of time, t, in minutes elapsed from the start of the climb. Graph the function.

11. The current price of gasoline is $0.35 per liter. If the price increases at a rate of 3 cents per month, express the price of a liter, $p(t)$, as a linear function of the time, t, in months, elapsed from the time gasoline was $0.35 per liter.

12. After a rainstorm, there are 2 meters of water covering a road. The water recedes at the rate of 0.25 meter per hour. Express the depth of the water, $d(t)$, as a linear function of the time, t, elapsed from the end of the rainstorm.

13. From a budget of $10 000, an organization spends money at the rate of $400 per day. Express the amount of money, $a(t)$ retained by the organization as a function of the number of days after the money was budgeted.

B 14. Graph the function. Describe the range.
   DOMAIN: the real numbers such that
   $$0 \le x \le 6$$
   RULE: $f(x) = -2x + 12$

15. The Acme Calculator Company finds that the number of mini-calculators produced and the cost of producing them vary linearly. It costs $4000 to produce 250 calculators and $5000 to produce 450 calculators. Express cost as a function of the number of calculators produced.

16. The standard rental charge for a computer from the Acme Calculator Company is $70 plus $150 per hour. The standard rental charge from Ace Computer Company is $670 plus $50 per hour. Graph these functions. When would it be more advantageous to rent from Acme?

C 17. An electric company has proposed a new rate structure. There will be a monthly service charge of $10 for each customer. The consumer will pay 4 cents per kilowatt hour for the first 500 kilowatt hours and 5 cents/kW · h for each kilowatt hour above 500. Write the monthly cost as a function of the number of kilowatt hours used. Graph this function.

5-8 RELATIONS; LINEAR INEQUALITIES

A **relation** is any set of ordered pairs. Hence, any function is a relation. Unlike a function, however, two pairs that belong to a relation may have the same first member.

As with a function, the **domain of a relation** is the set of first members of the ordered pairs in the relation. The **range of a relation** is the set of second members of the ordered pairs.

A linear inequality is one that may be written in the standard form $Ax + By > C$ or $Ax + By < C$ with A and B not both zero. By definition, the solution set of any linear equation or inequality is a set of ordered pairs and, hence, a relation. For a linear *equation*, the relation is a function. For an *inequality*, it is not a function.

EXAMPLE 1   Show that the inequality $x + y > 0$ defines a relation that is not a function.

SOLUTION   The solution set of $x + y > 0$ includes (5,4) and (5, 3) since $5 + 4 > 0$ and $5 + 3 > 0$.

However, a function cannot contain two ordered pairs with the same first member. Therefore, the relation defined by $x + y > 0$ (its solution set) is not a function.

The graph of a linear inequality is the region on one side of a line in the coordinate plane. To graph a linear inequality, first find the line that is the boundary of the graph by writing the inequality in the form $y > mx + b$ or $y < mx + b$. The line for $y = mx + b$ is the boundary of the graph. Then determine on which side of the boundary line the points representing solutions of the inequality are located.

EXAMPLE 2   Graph the relation defined by the inequality $2y - 3x > 6$.

SOLUTION $2y - 3x > 6$
$$2y > 3x + 6$$
$$y > \tfrac{3}{2}x + 3$$

GRAPH

Since y *is greater than* $\tfrac{3}{2}x + 3$, the graph of the inequality is the region *above* the line $y = \tfrac{3}{2}x + 3$. The dashes show that the line for $y = \tfrac{3}{2}x + 3$, or $2y - 3x = 6$, is not part of the graph.

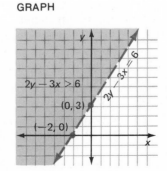

A sentence that uses the symbol $\geq$ or $\leq$ is a compound sentence formed from an equation and an inequality. For example, $y \leq 4x - 5$ is the compound sentence $y < 4x - 5$ *or* $y = 4x - 5$. Its graph is the region for $y < 4x - 5$ and the line for $y = 4x - 5$ combined.

EXAMPLE 3   Graph $y \leq 4x - 5$.

SOLUTION   Since $y \leq 4x - 5$, the graph is made up of the points in or below the line $y = 4x - 5$. We draw the line for $y = 4x - 5$ to include it as part of the graph.

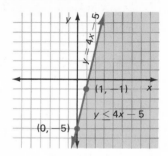

EXAMPLE 4   Graph $y > -3$.

SOLUTION

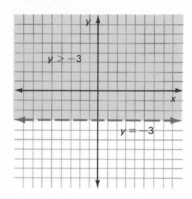

EXAMPLE 5   Graph $x \leq 4$.

SOLUTION

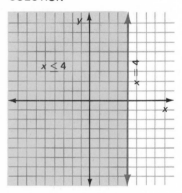

GRAPHING A LINEAR INEQUALITY

1. Write the inequality in the form $y < mx + b$, $y > mx + b$, $y \leq mx + b$, or $y \geq mx + b$.

2. Graph the linear equation $y = mx + b$. This line is the boundary of the graph desired. For $y < mx + b$ and $y > mx + b$, show a dashed line for the boundary. For $y \leq mx + b$ and $y \geq mx + b$, show the line for the boundary.

3. Shade one of the two regions to the side of the boundary line. For $y > mx + b$ or $y \geq mx + b$, shade the region *above* the boundary. For $y < mx + b$ or $y \leq mx + b$, shade the region *below* the boundary.

CLASSROOM EXERCISES

Show that each inequality defines a relation that is not a function.

1. $2x - y > 0$ **2.** $x + y + 1 > 0$

Graph.

3. $4y - 3x \geq 12$ **4.** $y < 2x - 1$ **5.** $y \geq 2$ **6.** $x < -1$

EXERCISES

Ⓐ Show that each inequality defines a relation that is not a function.

1. $3x + y \geq 3$ **2.** $-x + 4y < 7$ **3.** $y \leq 3x + 1$ **4.** $y \leq 3x - 1$

Graph.

5. $y > x$ **6.** $y < x$ **7.** $x + y + 2 \geq 0$ **8.** $2x + y + 5 \leq 0$

9. $3x + y + 1 < 0$ **10.** $x + 2y + 2 > 0$ **11.** $3x - 2y \geq 18$ **12.** $7x - 2y \geq 14$

13. $y > 2$ **14.** $y \leq -3$ **15.** $x > 1$ **16.** $x \geq 0$

Ⓑ **17.** $y \geq x$ and $x \geq 0$ **18.** $y > 3x - 4$ and $y > 2$ **19.** $x + 2y \geq 6$ or $x - 2y \leq 6$

20. $x \geq 0$ and $y < 0$ **21.** $y \geq |x|$ **22.** $y < |x - 1|$

Ⓒ **23.** $|x| = |y|$ **24.** $|x| > |y|$ **25.** $\dfrac{|x|}{|y|} > 1$

26. $y \geq |2x - 5|$ and $y \leq 4 - |2x - 5|$ **27.** $x + y \geq 6$, $2x + y \leq 12$, and $y < x + 6$

▮1.9980469▮ SUMS "APPROACHING" A NUMBER

For the sequence, $1, \frac{1}{2}, \frac{1}{4}, \frac{1}{8}, \frac{1}{16}, \ldots$, the sum of the first 5 terms is 1.9375. The sum of the first 10 terms is approximately 1.9980. The sum of the first 15 terms is approximately 1.9999.

The sums are said to "approach" the number 2.

For each sequence below, the sums of the terms "approach" some number. Find the number.

1. $1, \frac{1}{4}, \frac{1}{16}, \frac{1}{64}, \ldots$ **2.** $1, -\frac{1}{3}, \frac{1}{9}, -\frac{1}{27}, \ldots$ **3.** $1, -\frac{1}{4}, \frac{1}{16}, -\frac{1}{64}, \ldots$

4. $1, \frac{2}{3}, \frac{4}{9}, \frac{8}{27}, \ldots$ **5.** $1, -\frac{2}{3}, \frac{4}{9}, -\frac{8}{27}, \ldots$ **6.** $1, \frac{1}{3}, \frac{1}{9}, \frac{1}{27}, \ldots$

5-9 INVERSE RELATIONS AND INVERSE FUNCTIONS

The inverse of a relation is obtained by interchanging the two members of each ordered pair of the relation. Hence, the inverse of a relation is also a relation.

EXAMPLE 1 Graph the relation $\{(2, 1), (3, 1), (4, 1)\}$. Find its inverse. Graph the inverse.

SOLUTION The inverse of $\{(2, 1), (3, 1), (4, 1)\}$ is $\{(1, 2), (1, 3), (1, 4)\}$

The graph of the relation is shown in black.

The graph of the inverse relation is shown in red.

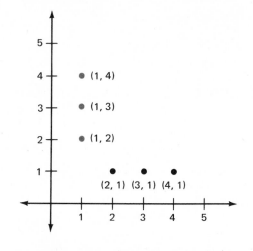

The ordered pairs that belong to a relation defined by an equation or an inequality in x and y are solutions of the equation or inequality. If we interchange the two members of each ordered pair, we have the solutions of the sentence formed by interchanging x and y. Therefore, the sentence formed by interchanging x and y defines the inverse of the original relation.

EXAMPLE 2 Graph $y = 2x - 3$. Find its inverse. Graph the inverse.

SOLUTION The inverse of
$$y = 2x - 3$$
is $x = 2y - 3$

In slope-intercept form, the inverse relation is

$$y = \tfrac{1}{2}x + \tfrac{3}{2}$$

The graph of the relation is shown in heavy black.

The graph of the inverse relation is shown in red.

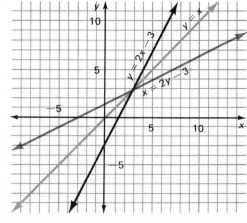

The graphs of a relation and its inverse are *symmetric* about the graph of $y = x$. In Example 2 the line for $y = x$ is shown in light gray.

An important type of function is one for which the inverse relation is also a function. Not all functions are of this type. When a function has two ordered pairs with the same second member, the inverse relation has two ordered pairs with the same first member. By definition, such a relation is not a function.

The only functions for which there are inverse functions are those that have no ordered pairs with the same second member. Each number in the range of the function corresponds to *exactly* one number in the domain.

EXAMPLE 3   For which function, f or g, is the inverse relation also a function?

$$f = \{(7, 1), (9, 2), (0, 1)\} \quad g = \{(3, 1), (2, 2), (1, 3)\}$$

SOLUTION   The inverse of f is $\{(1, 7), (2, 9), (1, 0)\}$ which is not a function.

The inverse of g is $\{(1, 3), (2, 2), (3, 1)\}$ which is a function.

By the Vertical-Line Test, we can tell graphically whether a relation is a function. A similar Horizontal-Line Test permits us to tell graphically whether the inverse of a function is also a function.

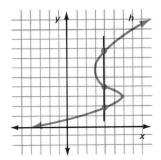

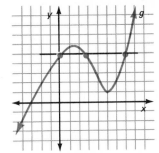

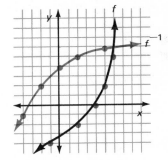

h is not a function. Three points of the graph have the same first coordinate.

g is a function, but its inverse is not. Three points of the graph have the same second coordinate.

f is a function. Its inverse, f^{-1}, also is a function.

As shown in the third graph, the symbol f^{-1} (read "f inverse") may be used to name the inverse of a function f. The -1 is part of the symbol. It is not an exponent.

CLASSROOM EXERCISES

Graph the relation. Find and graph the inverse of the relation.

1. $\{(1, 3), (2, 3), (4, 4)\}$ **2.** $y = 3x + 2$

3. For which function, f or g, is the inverse relation also a function?

$\quad f = \{(2, 0), (-1, 3), (6, 1), (3, 4)\} \quad g = \{(2, 1), (-1, 2), (0, 1), (1, 3)\}$

Apply the vertical and horizontal line tests to the graph of each equation. Does the equation define a function? Is its inverse a function?

4. $3x + y = 6$ **5.** $x = 2$ **6.** $y = -1$

EXERCISES

A Graph the relation. Find and graph the inverse of each relation.

1. $\{(2, 1), (0, 3), (1, 1)\}$ **2.** $\{(-1, 2), (3, 1), (0, 2)\}$

3. $\{(1, 2), (3, 4), (5, 6), (8, 1)\}$ **4.** $\{(0, -1), (-2, -3), (1, 2), (3, 0)\}$

5. $y = -2x + 3$ **6.** $y = -4x + 5$ **7.** $y = 3x + 5$

8. $y = 6x + 1$ **9.** $y = \frac{1}{2}x + \frac{3}{2}$ **10.** $y = \frac{1}{3}x + \frac{5}{3}$

For which function in each pair is the inverse relation also a function?

11. $f = \{(2, 1), (0, -1), (8, 4), (9, 2)\} \quad g = \{(1, 8), (2, 7), (0, 6), (3, 8)\}$

12. $h = \{(-8, 2), (9, 1), (0, 1), (2, 1)\} \quad k = \{(1, 2), (0, 4), (11, 3), (-1, 0)\}$

13. $h = \{(1, 1), (2, 3), (4, 3)\} \quad k = \{(3, 2), (4, 4), (1, 1)\}$

14. $f = \{(0, 0), (3, 6), (7, 1)\} \quad g = \{(1, 6), (3, 3), (2, 6)\}$

Apply the vertical and horizontal line tests to the graph of each equation. Does the equation define a function? Is its inverse a function?

15. $x = -2$ **16.** $y = 1$ **17.** $y = -3$

18. $x = 4$ **19.** $-2x + 5y = 10$ **20.** $y = 3x + 7$

B The graphs of f and f^{-1} are symmetric about the line $y = x$.

21. Graph $y = x$. On the same coordinate system, graph $f(x) = 3x + 1$ and its inverse.

Apply the vertical and horizontal line tests to the graph of each equation. Does the equation define a function? Is its inverse a function?

22. $y = |x|$ **23.** $y = \sqrt{x}$ **24.** $y = x^2, x \geq 0$

C For $f(x) = 3x + 2$, evaluate each expression.

25. $f^{-1}(f(3))$ **26.** $f(f^{-1}(11))$ **27.** $f^{-1}(f(a))$

28. Find all linear functions for which $f(x) = f^{-1}(x)$.

CHECKING YOUR UNDERSTANDING

WORDS AND SYMBOLS

function

domain of a function, of a relation

inverse of a function, f^{-1}

linear function

linear inequality

relation

range of a function, of a relation

inverse of a relation

linear variation

direct variation

CONCEPTS

■ Any rule that defines a function associates each member of the domain with one member of the range. In the graph of a function, no two points are in the same vertical line. When each member of the range is associated with only one member of the domain, the inverse of a function also is a function. In the graph of a function for which the inverse also is a function, no two points are in the same horizontal line [5-6, 5-9]

■ A function is a relation. A relation is not necessarily a function. Every relation has an inverse relation which may or may not be a function. The graphs of a relation and its inverse are symmetric with respect to the line for $y = x$. [5-8, 5-9]

■ The graph for a linear inequality in two variables is the region on one side of the graph for the linear equation. The line is the boundary line for the graph and may or may not belong to the graph. [5-8]

PROCESSES

■ Decide whether a relation is a function. Tell whether the inverse relation is a function. [5-6, 5-8, 5-9]

1. Is {(1, 2), (2, 1), (1, 3)} a function?   **2.** Is its inverse a function?

3. Does $y = 2x + 1$ define a function?   **4.** Is its inverse a function?

■ Identify ordered pairs that belong to a function. Sketch the graph of a function; of a linear inequality. [5-6 to 5-8]

5. For $f(x) = 2x - 3$, find $f(-2)$. Find two other ordered pairs of f.

6. Graph $f(x) = 2x - 3$.   **7.** Graph $y = 2x - 4$.   **8.** Graph $3y + 7x \geq -2$.

■ Solve problems involving linear variation or direct variation. [5-7]

9. y varies directly as x. y is 6 when x is 14. Find y when x is 35.

CHAPTER REVIEW

Determine which quadrant or axis contains each point. [5-1]

1. $A(5, 0)$ **2.** $B(-1, 7)$ **3.** $C\left(-8, -\frac{1}{2}\right)$ **4.** $D(9, -9)$ **5.** $E(0, -1)$

Graph each equation. [5-2]

6. $y = -2x + 1$ **7.** $4y - x = 20$ **8.** $3x = 7 - y$

Find the slope of the line for each equation. [5-3]

9. $y = 3x - 1$ **10.** $y = -\frac{1}{4}x - 1$ **11.** $5x - 2y = 6$

Find the slope and y-intercept. [5-4]

12. $y = -2x + 3$ **13.** $y = \frac{1}{2}x - 5$ **14.** $2y = -x + 10$

Find an equation for the line having slope m and containing the given point. [5-5]

15. $(5, 0)$, $m = 2$ **16.** $(-4, 0)$, $m = -3$ **17.** $(2, 6)$, $m = 3$ **18.** $(-2, -1)$, $m = 2$

Find an equation for the line containing each pair of points.

19. $(0, 6)$ and $(3, 0)$ **20.** $(0, 0)$ and $(2, -4)$ **21.** $(3, 8)$ and $(-1, -4)$ **22.** $(3, -1)$ and $(-2, -11)$

For each function draw the graph and describe the range. [5-6]

23. DOMAIN: real numbers   **24.** DOMAIN: $\{0, 1, 2, 3, \cdots\}$
       RULE: $x \rightarrow 2x + 1$ RULE: $x \rightarrow x^2$

In each of the following, x and y vary linearly. Find a linear equation that describes each variation. [5-7]

25. $x = 2$ when $y = 7$ and   **26.** $x = 4$ when $y = 0$ and
      $x = -1$ when $y = -2$ $x = -4$ when $y = 4$.

Graph. [5-8]

27. $y > 2x - 3$ **28.** $2y + 5x \leq 12$

Give the inverse of each relation. [5-9]

29. $\{(0, 1), (0, 3), (1, 5)\}$ **30.** $y = \frac{1}{2}x + 3$

CAPSULE REVIEW

Write the letter of the best response.

1. If a point has a negative abscissa and a positive ordinate, it must lie in

    a. Quadrant 1   **b.** Quadrant 2   **c.** Quadrant 3   **d.** Quadrant 4

2. Which of the following is not a solution of the equation $3x - 4y = 4$?

    a. $(3, 1)$ **b.** $(4, 2)$ **c.** $\left(1, -\frac{1}{4}\right)$ **d.** $\left(-2, -\frac{5}{2}\right)$

3. The slope of the graph of $2x + y = 6$ is

    a. -2 **b.** 2 **c.** $\frac{1}{2}$ **d.** $\frac{2}{3}$

4. An equation for the line whose slope is $\frac{2}{5}$ and whose y-intercept is 3 is

    a. $2x + 5y = 15$ **b.** $-15x + 5y = 2$ **c.** $5x - 2y = 15$ **d.** $-2x + 5y = 15$

5. An equation for the line whose x-intercept is -3 and whose y-intercept is 4 is

    a. $3x + 4y = 3$ **b.** $y = \frac{3}{4}x - 3$ **c.** $4x - 3y = -12$ **d.** $y = x + 7$

6. x and y are linearly related. When x is 0, y is 32. When x is 100, y is 212. An equation describing the linear relation is

    a. $x = \frac{9}{5}y + 32$ **b.** $y = \frac{9}{5}x + 32$ **c.** $x = \frac{5}{9}y - 32$ **d.** $y = \frac{5}{9}x - 32$

7. The relation graphed at right is defined by the linear inequality

    a. $y \le 2x - 4$

    b. $y < 2x - 4$

    c. $y \ge -2x - 4$

    d. $y > -2x + 4$

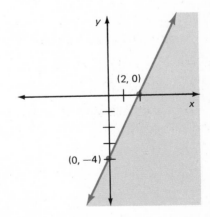

8. Which of these relations has an inverse which is *not* a function?

    a. $\{(2, 1), (2, 2), (2, 3), (2, 4)\}$ **b.** $\{(1, 2), (2, 4), (3, 3), (4, 2)\}$

    c. $\{(1, 1), (2, 2), (3, 3), (4, 4)\}$ **d.** $\{(1, -2), (-2, 1), (3, 5), (5, 3)\}$

CHAPTER TEST

1. Give the x-coordinate of point A.
2. Give the y-coordinate of point B.

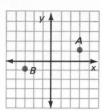

3. Complete.   A solution for $2x + 3y = 22$ is $(2, \underline{\ ?\ })$.
4. Complete.   A solution for $4x - 5y - 5 = 0$ is $(\underline{\ ?\ }, 3)$.

5. Give the slope of the line which contains the points $(2, 4)$ and $(3, 6)$.
6. Write an equation for a line with no slope.
7. Find the slope of the line $5x + 7y = 9$.
8. Find the y-intercept of the line $3x - 6y = 12$.
9. Write an equation for the line which contains the point $(1, 4)$ and has slope 5.

10. Write an equation for the line which contains the point $(3, 2)$ and has slope -1.

11. An electrician charges \$25 plus \$20 per hour for a service call.   Write an equation relating the total charge (C) to the number of hours (h).

12. Write an equation for the relation graphed at the right.

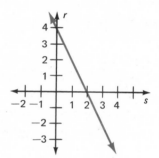

13. Is $\{(1, 2), (3, 4), (5, 4)\}$ a function?   Explain why or why not.

14. Give the domain of $\{(1, 1), (3, 9), (5, 25)\}$.

15. Sketch the graph of the function defined by $f(x) = x - 1$.
16. Sketch the graph of the function defined by $g(x) = -3x + 2$.
17. Sketch the graph of the relation $y < x + 2$.
18. Sketch the graph of the relation $y \geq 2x - 3$.

19. Give the inverse of $\left\{ \left(3, \frac{1}{3}\right), \left(2, \frac{1}{2}\right) \right\}$.

20. Sketch the graph of a function whose inverse is not a function.

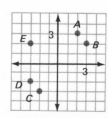

Write the letter of the best response.

21. Which point has coordinates $(-3, -2)$?
    a. A **b.** B **c.** C **d.** D **e.** E

22. Which of these number pairs is a solution of $4x + 8y = 56$?

    a. $(6, 2)$ **b.** $(6, 4)$ **c.** $(6, 9)$ **d.** $(6, 18)$ **e.** $(6, 26)$

23. What is the slope of the line containing points $(3, 1)$ and $(5, 2)$?

    a. -2 **b.** -1 **c.** $\frac{1}{2}$ **d.** 1 **e.** 2

24. What are the slope and y-intercept of the line $y = 2x - 8$?

    a. 2 and -8 **b.** 2 and 4 **c.** 2 and 8 **d.** $\frac{1}{2}$ and 4 **e.** $\frac{1}{2}$ and -4

25. Which of these is an equation for the line with slope 4 containing the point $(-2, 2)$?

    a. $y - 2 = 4(x + 2)$ **b.** $y + 2 = 4(x - 2)$ **c.** $y - 2 = \frac{1}{4}(x + 2)$

    d. $y + 2 = \frac{1}{4}(x - 2)$ **e.** $y - 2 = -4(x + 2)$

26. Which equation is graphed in Figure 1?

    a. $p = -3q + 6$

    b. $p = 3q + 6$

    c. $p = -2q - 3$

    d. $p = 2q + 6$

    e. $p = 6q - 3$

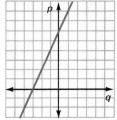

Figure 1

27. Which is the graph of a function in Figure 2?

    a. a **b.** b **c.** c **d.** d **e.** e

28. A salesperson drives 200 km and then drives at 80 km/h for another n hours. Which equation gives the *total distance* traveled?

    a. $f(n) = 80$

    b. $f(n) = 80n$

    c. $f(n) = 80n + 200$

    d. $f(n) = 200$

    e. $f(n) = 80n - 200$

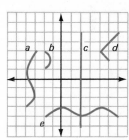

Figure 2

29. Which of these number pairs is a solution for the relation $y < 5x - 4$?

    a. $(0, 0)$ **b.** $(0, 4)$ **c.** $(0, 5)$ **d.** $(0, -4)$ **e.** $(0, -5)$

30. Which relation is the *inverse* of $\{(1, 2), (2, 4)\}$?

    a. $\{(1, -2), (2, -4)\}$ **b.** $\{(2, 1), (4, 2)\}$ **c.** $\left\{\left(1, \frac{1}{2}\right), \left(2, \frac{1}{4}\right)\right\}$

    d. $\{(-1, 2), (-2, 4)\}$ **e.** $\left\{(1, 2), \left(\frac{1}{2}, 4\right)\right\}$

CHAPTER 6
SYSTEMS
OF LINEAR EQUATIONS
AND INEQUALITIES

From parents, children adopt patterns they regard as worthwhile. Students do the same with respect to teachers as do young adults with respect to employers. In time, the circle is completed when a person becomes a model —parent, teacher, or employer, and often more than one—from whom children adopt patterns they regard as worthwhile. . . .

OBJECTIVE: Graph and solve systems of two linear equations.

6-1 SOLVING A SYSTEM OF LINEAR EQUATIONS BY GRAPHING

The graph for a linear equation in two variables is a line. A solution of the linear equation is given by the coordinates of any point in the line.

Two linear equations in two variables form a **system** of linear equations. A **solution of a system** is any common solution of the equations in the system. Graphically, such a solution is given by the coordinates of each point in the intersection of the graphs of the two equations.

EXAMPLE 1 Solve the system $\begin{array}{l} x + y = 5 \\ x - y = 1 \end{array}$ by graphing.

SOLUTION $\quad x + y = 5 \quad\quad\quad\quad\quad\quad\quad\quad\quad\quad\quad x - y = 1$

x	y
0	5
2	3
4	1

$y = -x + 5$
slope $= -1$

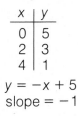

x	y
5	4
4	3
1	0

$y = x - 1$
slope $= 1$

The slopes are different. The lines intersect at $(3, 2)$ as shown by the graphs. The solution of the system is $(3, 2)$.

CHECK $\quad\quad x + y = 5 \quad\quad\quad\quad\quad x - y = 1$
$\quad\quad\quad\quad\quad 3 + 2 \stackrel{?}{=} 5 \quad\quad\quad\quad\quad 3 - 2 \stackrel{?}{=} 1$
$\quad\quad\quad\quad\quad\quad\quad 5 = 5 \quad✔ \quad\quad\quad\quad\quad 1 = 1 \quad✔$

As in Example 1, the graphs for two linear equations may have different slopes. The lines intersect at one point and the system has one solution. The equations in such a system are called **consistent equations**.

It is possible, however, that the graphs for two linear equations have the same slope. When the y-intercepts are different, the lines are parallel. They have no point in common. There is no solution of the system. The equations are called **inconsistent equations**.

EXAMPLE 2 Solve $\boxed{\begin{array}{c} x + y = 5 \\ x + y = 3 \end{array}}$ by graphing.

SOLUTION

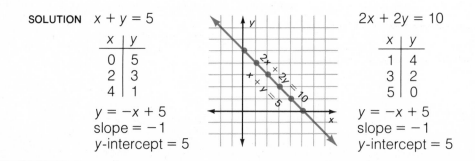

$x + y = 5$

x	y
0	5
2	3
4	1

$y = -x + 5$
slope = -1
y-intercept = 5

$x + y = 3$

x	y
0	3
2	1
4	-1

$y = -x + 3$
slope = -1
y-intercept = 3

The graphs are parallel lines. There is no solution of the system. The equations are inconsistent. The inconsistency may be seen from the equations themselves. The sum of the same pair of numbers cannot be both 5 and 3.

When two linear equations in a system have as their graph the same line (one slope, one y-intercept), the equations have all their solutions in common. The equations are consistent and there are infinitely many solutions of the system. The equations are called **equivalent**, or **dependent**, **equations**.

EXAMPLE 3 Solve $\boxed{\begin{array}{c} x + y = 5 \\ 2x + 2y = 10 \end{array}}$ by graphing.

SOLUTION

$x + y = 5$

x	y
0	5
2	3
4	1

$y = -x + 5$
slope = -1
y-intercept = 5

$2x + 2y = 10$

x	y
1	4
3	2
5	0

$y = -x + 5$
slope = -1
y-intercept = 5

The graph is the same for each equation. Each solution of either equation is a solution of the system. The equations are consistent and equivalent, or dependent.

CLASSROOM EXERCISES

Solve the system by graphing.

1. $x - y = 0$
$x + y = 0$

2. $x = -2$
$3x + y = 1$

3. $y = \frac{1}{2}x$
$x + 2y = 8$

EXERCISES

A Solve the system by graphing.

1. $y = -x$
$3x - 2y = 15$

2. $y = 2x$
$x - 2y = 6$

3. $x - y = 5$
$2x + 3y = 10$

4. $y - x = 1$
$3y - 2x = 0$

5. $3x + y = -3$
$2x - y = -7$

6. $2x + y = -9$
$3x - 2y = -3$

7. $4x + y = -3$
$8x + 2y = -6$

8. $-x + 3y = 7$
$-5x + 15y = 35$

9. $3x + 4y = 2$
$x - 2y = 9$

10. $3x + 2y = 5$
$2x - y = 8$

11. $-x + y = 6$
$2x + 3y = 18$

12. $y = 3$
$y = 5$

B **13.** $2x + y = 2$
$6x - 2y = 11$

14. $2y = 3x + 5$
$3x + 4y = 10$

15. $y = -\frac{1}{2}x + 3$
$2y + x = 6$

16. $2x + 2y = 9$
$5y + 4x = 16$

17. $\frac{1}{2}x + \frac{1}{3}y = 2$
$-x + \frac{1}{3}y = 4$

18. $5x + y = 3x + 2y + 3$
$2x + 7y = -x + 2y + 11$

C **19.** $y - x = -1$
$3y = -2x + 7$
$-2x + y = -3$

20. $3y - 2x = 12$
$4x + 7y = 28$
$y = -8x + 56$

21. $x + 2y = 6$
$y = |x|$

A RATIONAL PATTERN

It is clear that $\dfrac{1}{1 \cdot 2} = \dfrac{1}{2}$. Now simplify each of the following.

1. $\dfrac{1}{1 \cdot 2} + \dfrac{1}{2 \cdot 3}$

2. $\dfrac{1}{1 \cdot 2} + \dfrac{1}{2 \cdot 3} + \dfrac{1}{3 \cdot 4}$

3. $\dfrac{1}{1 \cdot 2} + \dfrac{1}{2 \cdot 3} + \dfrac{1}{3 \cdot 4} + \dfrac{1}{4 \cdot 5}$

4. Predict $\dfrac{1}{1 \cdot 2} + \dfrac{1}{2 \cdot 3} + \dfrac{1}{3 \cdot 4} + \dfrac{1}{4 \cdot 5} + \dfrac{1}{5 \cdot 6}$. Check with your calculator.

5. Write a general expression for $\dfrac{1}{1 \cdot 2} + \dfrac{1}{2 \cdot 3} + \dfrac{1}{3 \cdot 4} + \cdots + \dfrac{1}{n(n + 1)}$.

6-2   SOLVING A LINEAR SYSTEM ALGEBRAICALLY

The algebraic solution of a linear system of equations is faster and more accurate than the graphical solution. In carrying it out, we combine two equations of the system so as to eliminate one of the variables. One method commonly used involves writing both equations in the *standard form*, $Ax + By = C$, and then using addition or subtraction. Another involves substitution. The two methods are illustrated in the following two examples.

EXAMPLE 1   Solve

$$\begin{array}{l} \dfrac{7x}{3} = 4 - \dfrac{y}{2} \\[2mm] 3(x + 2) = 5(y + 9) \end{array}$$

SOLUTION   Simplify each equation.

$$\begin{array}{l} \dfrac{7x}{3} = 4 - \dfrac{y}{2} \\[2mm] 3(x + 2) = 5(y + 9) \end{array} \qquad M_6 \qquad \begin{array}{l} 14x = 24 - 3y \\[2mm] 3x + 6 = 5y + 45 \end{array}$$

Write each in standard form.   Find x by addition.

$$\begin{array}{ll} 14x + 3y = 24 & \qquad M_5 \quad 70x + 15y = 120 \\ 3x - 5y = 39 & \qquad M_3 \quad \underline{9x - 15y = 117} \\ & \qquad \text{Add.} \quad 79x = 237 \\ & \qquad\qquad\qquad\qquad x = 3 \end{array}$$

Find y by replacing x by 3 in $3x - 5y = 39$.

$$\begin{array}{l} 3x - 5y = 39 \\ 3(3) - 5y = 39 \\ -5y = 30 \\ y = -6 \end{array}$$

The solution is $(3, -6)$.

CHECK   Replace x by 3 and y by -6 in the original equations.

$$\begin{array}{l} \dfrac{7x}{3} = 4 - \dfrac{y}{2} \\[2mm] \dfrac{7(3)}{3} \stackrel{?}{=} 4 - \dfrac{-6}{2} \\[2mm] 7 \stackrel{?}{=} 4 + 3 \\ 7 = 7 \quad \text{✔} \end{array} \qquad\Bigg| \qquad \begin{array}{l} 3(x + 2) = 5(y + 9) \\[2mm] 3(3 + 2) \stackrel{?}{=} 5(-6 + 9) \\[2mm] 3(5) \stackrel{?}{=} 5(3) \\ 15 = 15 \quad \text{✔} \end{array}$$

EXAMPLE 2 Solve $\begin{array}{l} 3x - 7y = 5 \\ 2x + y = 9 \end{array}$.

SOLUTION Solve the second equation for y.

$$2x + y = 9$$
$$y = 9 - 2x$$

Find x by substitution.
Replace y by $9 - 2x$ in $3x - 7y = 5$.

$$3x - 7(9 - 2x) = 5$$
$$3x - 63 + 14x = 5$$
$$17x = 68$$
$$x = 4$$

Find y. Replace x by 4 in $y = 9 - 2x$.

$$y = 9 - 2(4)$$
$$y = 1$$

The solution is $(4, 1)$.

CHECK The check is left for the student.

Sometimes the coefficients of the variables in a system will have the appearance of variables themselves. The variables usually are represented by letters from the end of the alphabet, such as x, y, or z. The coefficients usually are represented by letters from the first of the alphabet, such as a, b, or c. Such coefficients are parameters that will be known for a specific situation.

EXAMPLE 3 Solve $\begin{array}{l} ax + by = a^2 \\ bx - ay = ab \end{array}$.

SOLUTION Find x by addition.

$$\begin{array}{l} ax + by = a^2 \\ bx - ay = ab \end{array}$$

M_a $\quad a^2x + aby = a^3$
M_b $\quad \dfrac{b^2x - aby = ab^2}{}$
Add. $\quad a^2x + b^2x = a^3 + ab^2$
$\quad (a^2 + b^2)x = a(a^2 + b^2)$
$\quad x = a$

Find y by replacing x by a in $ax + by = a^2$.

$$a(a) + by = a^2$$
$$by = 0$$
$$y = 0$$

The solution is $(a, 0)$.

CHECK The check is left for the student.

SOLVING A SYSTEM OF TWO LINEAR EQUATIONS

By Addition or Subtraction

1. Write the equations in standard form. Then, if necessary, multiply both members of one or both equations by such numbers as will make the coefficients of one of the variables equal in both equations.

2. Add or subtract the members of the resulting equations, eliminating one of the variables.

By Substitution

1. Solve one equation for one variable in terms of the other.

2. Replace this variable in the other equation by the expression found in Step 1.

3. Solve the new equation for the other variable.

4. Replace this variable by its number in either equation, and solve for the remaining variable.

5. Write the ordered pair that is the common solution. Check the solution in both equations.

Remember, for any system of linear equations, either method will lead to the solution when a solution exists. Addition or subtraction usually is easier to use if either variable has opposite or equal coefficients in the two equations. Substitution may be easier if the coefficient of one of the variables is 1.

CLASSROOM EXERCISES

Solve.

1. $x + y = 6$
$x - y = 4$

2. $2x + y = 7$
$x - y = 5$

3. $4x - y = 3$
$3x + 5y = 31$

4. $y = 3x - 7$
$-9x + 3y = 5$

5. $x - 1 = 2y + 1$
$-2(x + 3) + y - 1 = -2$

6. $x + y = a$
$x - y = b$

EXERCISES

[A] Solve.

1. $3x + 7y = 17$
$y = 2x$

2. $3x + 2y = 9$
$y = 3x$

3. $8x - 11y = -2$
$y = -2$

4. $2x + 3y = 3$
$x = -3$

5. $2x + 3y = 2$
$5x - y = -29$

6. $4x + y = -5$
$2x - 3y = -13$

7. $3x - 6y = 12$
$-2x + 4y = -8$

8. $2x - 4y = 6$
$-3x + 6y = 9$

9. $4x - 3y = 8$
$4x - 5y = 0$

10. $5x + 3y = 10$
$2x + 3y = 16$

11. $x + y = 2c$
$2x - y = 4c$

12. $x + y = a - b$
$x - y = a + b$

13. $x + y = 2a$
$3x - y = 2(a + b)$

14. $x + 1.5y = 4$
$0.9x + 2.1y = 2.1$

15. $2.3x - 4.1y = -8.6$
$5.1x + 3.25y = 24.125$

16. $ax + by = a^2 + b^2$
$x + y = 2a$

17. $5x + 2y = \dfrac{1}{2}$
$6x + 5y = 11$

18. $20x - 6y = 7$
$-5x + 8y = 11\dfrac{1}{4}$

B **19.** $x(y - 2) = y(x + 3)$
$\dfrac{3x + y + 1}{2x + 1} = \dfrac{5}{2}$

20. $\dfrac{5y}{3} + \dfrac{7x}{6} = 68$
$\dfrac{y}{4} + \dfrac{7x}{4} = 12$

21. $\dfrac{-27x + 2y + 4}{x - y - 3} = 3$
$\dfrac{x - \frac{3}{10}y + \frac{1}{5}}{-10x + y - \frac{9}{2}} = \dfrac{1}{5}$

22. $\dfrac{2}{5} = \dfrac{2x + y - 1}{-2x + 4y + 1}$
$\dfrac{7x - 2y + 1}{-7x + y + 6} = 1$

23. $\dfrac{x^2 + 2xy + y^2 - 1}{x + y + 1} = 2$
$2x - y = 4$

24. $\dfrac{3(x - 2) + y + 2}{2(x - 2) + ab + b^2} = 1$
$\dfrac{a}{b} = \dfrac{x}{y}$

C **25.** $(m + n)x - (m - n)y = 4mn$
$(m - n)x + (m + n)y = 2(m^2 - n^2)$

26. $ax + by = c$
$dx + ey = f$

27. If $ae - bd = 2$ and $b + d = 1$, find a, b, d, e so that
$\boxed{\begin{array}{l} ax + by = 3 \\ dx + ey = 4 \end{array}}$
has solution $(4, 5)$.
(HINT: Use the result of Exercise 26.)

28. Find a and b so that $\dfrac{3x + 1}{x^2 + 2x - 3} = \dfrac{a}{x - 1} + \dfrac{b}{x + 3}$ for all x, $x \neq 1$, $x \neq -3$.
(HINT: Write the right member with a common denominator.)

NO CALCULATOR ALLOWED

Which is larger, 2^{100} or 3^{75}?   Justify your answer.

OBJECTIVE: Solve other systems of equations using techniques developed for solving linear systems in two variables.

6-3 FIRST-DEGREE EQUATIONS HAVING MORE THAN TWO VARIABLES.

The standard form for a first-degree equation in three variables is

$$Ax + By + Cz = D.$$

Its solutions are ordered triples of numbers. An **ordered triple** is of the form (x, y, z). A solution of a *system* of such equations is any solution that is common to all equations in the system.

SYSTEMS OF THREE EQUATIONS IN THREE VARIABLES

$$x + y - z = 4 \qquad\qquad x - 2y + 3z = 9$$
$$3x - 5y + 4z = 3 \qquad\qquad 3x - y = -10$$
$$6x - 7y - 2z = 2 \qquad\qquad 5y + 4z = 2$$

To solve a system of three first-degree equations in three variables, combine one pair of equations to eliminate one variable. Then combine a second pair, if necessary, to eliminate the same variable. The result is a system of two linear equations in two variables which may be solved by methods already developed.

EXAMPLE 1 Solve
$$\begin{aligned} x + y - z &= 4 \\ 3x - 5y + 4z &= 3 \\ 6x - 7y - 2z &= 2 \end{aligned}$$.

SOLUTION Eliminate z from the first and second equations by addition.

M_4
$$\begin{aligned} 4x + 4y - 4z &= 16 \\ 3x - 5y + 4z &= 3 \end{aligned}$$

Add. $\quad 7x - y = 19$

Eliminate z from the first and third equations by subtraction.

M_2
$$\begin{aligned} 2x + 2y - 2z &= 8 \\ 6x - 7y - 2z &= 2 \end{aligned}$$

Subtract. $-4x + 9y = 6$

We now have the system
$$\begin{aligned} 7x - y &= 19 \\ -4x + 9y &= 6 \end{aligned}$$.

Find x by addition.

$$7x - y = 19$$
$$-4x + 9y = 6$$

M_9

$$63x - 9y = 171$$
$$-4x + 9y = 6$$

Add. $\quad 59x \qquad = 177$
$$x = 3$$

Find y by replacing x by 3 in $\quad 7x - y = 19$.

$$7(3) - y = 19$$
$$y = 2$$

Find z by replacing x by 3 and y by 2 in $x + y - z = 4$.

$$3 + 2 - z = 4$$
$$z = 1.$$

The solution is $(3, 2, 1)$.

CHECK

$x + y - z = 4$	$3x - 5y + 4z = 3$	$6x - 7y - 2z = 2$
$3 + 2 - 1 \overset{?}{=} 4$	$3(3) - 5(2) + 4(1) \overset{?}{=} 3$	$6(3) - 7(2) - 2(1) \overset{?}{=} 2$
$4 = 4 \quad ✔$	$3 = 3 \quad ✔$	$2 = 2 \quad ✔$

EXAMPLE 2 Solve

$$\begin{aligned} x - 2y + 3z &= 9 \\ 3x - y &= -10 \\ 5y + 4z &= 2 \end{aligned}$$

SOLUTION Eliminate z from the first and third equations by subtraction.

$M_4 \qquad 4x - 8y + 12z = 36$
$M_3 \qquad \qquad 15y + 12z = \ \ 6$

Subtract. $\quad 4x - 23y \qquad = 30$

We now have the system

$$\begin{aligned} 4x - 23y &= 30 \\ 3x - y &= -10 \end{aligned}$$

Solving this system, we find $x = -4$ and $y = -2$.
Replacing y by -2 in $5y + 4z = 2$ gives $z = 3$.
The solution is $(-4, -2, 3)$.

CHECK The check is left for the student.

In general, for any system of equations to have one solution, there must be as many equations as variables. The system may be solved by eliminating variables to reduce the size of the system. If during the process we discover inconsistent or dependent equations, we can conclude that there will be zero or infinitely many solutions, respectively.

CLASSROOM EXERCISES

Solve.

1. $x + y = 4$
$x + z = 5$
$x + y + z = 8$

2. $x + y + 5z = 16$
$-x + y - z = -6$
$x + 2y + 8z = 24$

3. $x - 2y + 3z = 9$
$3x - y = -10$
$5y + 4z = 2$

EXERCISES

A Solve.

1. $x + y + z = 6$
$x + y - z = 0$
$x - y - z = 2$

2. $x + y + z = 7$
$x - y - z = 3$
$x - y + z = 11$

3. $x + y = 3$
$y + z = 12$
$z + x = 7$

4. $x + y = 4$
$x + z = -2$
$y + z = 8$

5. $x + y = 7$
$x + z = 1$
$y + z = 4$

6. $x + 5y + 3z = 4$
$3x - 2y + 4z = 21$
$2x + 3y - z = -13$

7. $2x + 3y - z = 4$
$2x - y + 2z = 3$
$3x + 2y + z = 6$

8. $2x + 3y = 18$
$x - 4z = 7$
$y + z = 3$

9. $4x + 2y = 8$
$x - 3z = 7$
$y + z = -1$

10. $3x + y - 2z = 8$
$x + 2y - 3z = 6$
$2x - y + z = 1$

11. $x + y + 5z = 7$
$2x + 3y + 12z = 15$
$-x + y - z = -2$

12. $x + y + z = 5$
$3x + y - z = 6.4$
$2y - 4x + 3z = 0.3$

13. $6x - 14y + 6z = -0.8$
$5x - 5y - 5z = -4$
$2x + 2y - 5z = -1.8$

14. $\dfrac{x}{3} + \dfrac{y}{2} = \dfrac{5}{6} - z$

$x + 1 + \dfrac{y}{3} = \dfrac{z}{2}$

$\dfrac{x}{3} + 1 + \dfrac{z}{2} = y$

15. $\dfrac{x}{5} + \dfrac{6y}{5} + 2z = \dfrac{7}{5}$

$x - \dfrac{3y}{4} = z$

$\dfrac{x}{2} + z = \dfrac{1}{2}$

B **16.** $2y - 3(x - 1) = 1 + z$
$4x + z = 1$
$6x + 2(y + z) = 5(x + 1)$

17. $2x + 3y + 2z = -(3x + 17)$
$-3x + 4y - z = 2z - 7$
$4x + 5y - 40 = 5z - 2y$

18. $\dfrac{0.1 - x - y + 3z}{x + y - z} = 2$

$\dfrac{2.6 - x - 5z}{x - y + z} = 1$

$3x + 5y - 4z = -5.2$

C **19.** $x + 5y + 5z = 5b$
$2x - y - 2z = 15b$
$x + y + 3z = -5b$

20. $ax + by = 2$
$bx + z = 2$
$b^2y + az = 2$

21. $x + y + z = 3a + 2b$
$bx + 2ay = 8ab$
$ax - y = 2a^2 - 3b$

22. The graph of a first-degree equation in three variables is a plane in a *three-dimensional coordinate system*. Tell what it could mean graphically for a system of three first-degree equations in three variables to have 0 solutions, 1 solution, or more than one solution.

PUBLIC SERVICE

Federal, state, and local governments employ close to 14 million people in the "service" occupations. These include law enforcement, fire-fighting and prevention, postal service, environmental control, education, certain areas of medicine, and all areas of transportation.

Since most careers in government are classified under the Civil Service Section, vacancies are filled by competitive examination. These examinations consist of at least two sections—English skills and mathematical skills as these skills relate to the positions available. Generally, persons who have performed better in their school work will perform better on Civil Service examinations.

MATHEMATICAL SAMPLER

1. You are in the U.S. Army Corps of Engineers helping to plan a new government building. The building will have four floors underground. Each floor will have exterior dimensions of 30 m by 75 m by 3.1 m. The earth that must be excavated will be removed from the building site. Each 2.75-cubic meter truckload removed will cost the project $11.75. Compute the cost for removing the earth from the building site.

2. You are a transportation expeditor for the United States Department of the Interior. Your task is to ship 210-liter drums of a new fertilizer from Atlanta, Georgia, to Des Moines, Iowa, in the most economical way. Each drum has a diameter of 58 cm and a height of 88 cm. The drums are to be shipped upright by rail or by truck. The cost for each barrel shipped by truck is $3.50. The cost for each railroad freight car used is $710. The interior dimensions of the freight cars that would be used are length 15.4 m, width 2.8 m, and height 3.2 m. Find the number of barrels for which shipping by rail would cost less than shipping by truck.

6-4   SYSTEMS OF FRACTIONAL EQUATIONS

A system may involve fractional equations. Clearing the equations of fractions first may simplify the system to one that is linear.

EXAMPLE 1   Solve $\boxed{\dfrac{x+4}{y}=\dfrac{x}{y-2} \qquad \dfrac{x-4}{y}=\dfrac{x}{y+6}}$.

SOLUTION   First, clear each equation of fractions and simplify.

$$\frac{x+4}{y}=\frac{x}{y-2}$$

$M_{y(y-2)}$
$$(x+4)(y-2)=xy$$
$$xy+4y-2x-8=xy$$
$$4y-2x=8$$

$$\frac{x-4}{y}=\frac{x}{y+6}$$

$M_{y(y+6)}$
$$(x-4)(y+6)=xy$$
$$xy-4y+6x-24=xy$$
$$-4y+6x=24$$

We now have the system $\boxed{\begin{aligned}4y-2x&=8\\-4y+6x&=24\end{aligned}}$.

Find x by addition.

$$\begin{aligned}4y-2x&=8\\-4y+6x&=24\\\hline 4x&=32\\x&=8\end{aligned}$$

Find y by replacing x by 8 in $4y-2x=8$.

$$4y-2(8)=8$$
$$4y=24$$
$$y=6$$

The solution is $(8,6)$.

CHECK

$$\frac{x+4}{y}=\frac{x}{y-2}$$
$$\frac{8+4}{6}\overset{?}{=}\frac{8}{6-2}$$
$$2=2 \quad \checkmark$$

$$\frac{x-4}{y}=\frac{x}{y+6}$$
$$\frac{8-4}{6}\overset{?}{=}\frac{8}{6+6}$$
$$\frac{2}{3}=\frac{2}{3} \quad \checkmark$$

The equations in Example 2 below are not linear equations in x and y. Such a system may be solved, however, without clearing fractions.

EXAMPLE 2 Solve $\begin{cases} \dfrac{6}{x} + \dfrac{10}{y} = 5 \\ \dfrac{4}{x} - \dfrac{5}{y} = 1 \end{cases}$.

SOLUTION Find x by addition. First multiply both members of the second equation by 2.

$$\frac{6}{x} + \frac{10}{y} = 5$$

M_2 $$\frac{8}{x} - \frac{10}{y} = 2$$

Add. $$\frac{14}{x} \qquad = 7$$

$$14 = 7x$$
$$2 = x$$

Find y by replacing x by 2 in $\dfrac{6}{x} + \dfrac{10}{y} = 5$.

$$\frac{6}{2} + \frac{10}{y} = 5$$
$$\frac{10}{y} = 2$$
$$5 = y$$

The solution is $(2, 5)$.

CHECK The check is left for the student.

CLASSROOM EXERCISES

Solve.

1. $\dfrac{x+1}{y} = \dfrac{x-2}{y-1}$

$\dfrac{x}{y+8} = \dfrac{x-2}{y+4}$

2. $\dfrac{2x}{2y-7} = \dfrac{x-4}{y}$

$\dfrac{x+4}{3x} = \dfrac{y-7}{3y}$

3. $-\dfrac{7}{x} + \dfrac{2}{y} = \dfrac{15}{2}$

$\dfrac{5}{x} - \dfrac{2}{y} = -\dfrac{11}{2}$

EXERCISES

A Solve.

1. $\dfrac{2x + y}{5x - y} = \dfrac{1}{2}$

$\dfrac{x - 2y + 9}{4x + 3y} = \dfrac{2}{3}$

2. $\dfrac{12x + y - 4}{5x - 4y} = 2$

$\dfrac{5x + 2y}{3x - 2y + 8} = \dfrac{3}{2}$

3. $\dfrac{2}{x - 1} + \dfrac{3}{y - 1} = 0$

$\dfrac{1}{2x + 5} + \dfrac{1}{y} = 0$

4. $\dfrac{y + 4}{x - 4} - \dfrac{y}{x} = 0$

$\dfrac{y - 2}{x - 3} - \dfrac{y + 4}{x + 1} = 0$

5. $\dfrac{x + 9}{y - 8} = \dfrac{x + 6}{y - 4}$

$\dfrac{y + 4}{x - 3} = \dfrac{y - 4}{x + 1}$

6. $\dfrac{6x}{2x + 3} = \dfrac{3y - 12}{y}$

$\dfrac{4x - 3}{4x} = \dfrac{y}{y + 4}$

7. $\dfrac{1}{x} + \dfrac{1}{y} = \dfrac{5}{6}$

$\dfrac{1}{x} - \dfrac{1}{y} = \dfrac{1}{6}$

8. $\dfrac{3}{x} + \dfrac{2}{y} = 2$

$\dfrac{4}{x} - \dfrac{3}{y} = -\dfrac{1}{6}$

9. $\dfrac{2}{x} + \dfrac{1}{y} = 4$

$\dfrac{1}{x} - \dfrac{2}{y} = -1$

10. $\dfrac{5}{a} + \dfrac{1}{b} = 0$

$\dfrac{3}{a} - \dfrac{2}{b} = \dfrac{13}{10}$

11. $\dfrac{3}{m} + \dfrac{4}{n} = -\dfrac{1}{2}$

$\dfrac{7}{m} - \dfrac{11}{n} = 9$

12. $\dfrac{5}{x} - \dfrac{2}{y} = 16$

$\dfrac{3}{x} - \dfrac{4}{y} = 18$

13. $\dfrac{3}{x} + \dfrac{5}{y} = \dfrac{3}{2}$

$\dfrac{2}{x} - \dfrac{3}{y} = -\dfrac{4}{15}$

14. $\dfrac{4}{A} - \dfrac{3}{B} = 2$

$\dfrac{10}{A} - \dfrac{9}{B} = 3$

15. $\dfrac{1}{x} + \dfrac{1}{y} = \dfrac{1}{5}$

$\dfrac{1}{x} - \dfrac{1}{y} = 5$

B **16.** $\dfrac{x + 4}{x} = \dfrac{y}{y + 6}$

$\dfrac{x + 6}{x + 2} = \dfrac{y}{y - 2}$

17. $\dfrac{4x + 9}{3y} = \dfrac{8x - 3}{6y - 3}$

$\dfrac{2x + 7}{3y + 2} = \dfrac{4x - 6}{6y - 6}$

18. $\dfrac{5}{x} - \dfrac{3}{y} = 20$

$\dfrac{2}{x} + \dfrac{3}{y} = 8$

19. $\dfrac{5}{m} + \dfrac{6}{n} = 2$

$\dfrac{7}{m} + \dfrac{8}{n} = 2$

20. $\dfrac{1}{x - 2} + \dfrac{1}{y + 2} = 0$

$\dfrac{3}{x + 2} - \dfrac{4}{y - 2} = 0$

21. $\dfrac{4}{x + 3} - \dfrac{5}{y - 3} = 0$

$\dfrac{1}{x - 3} + \dfrac{1}{y + 3} = 0$

22. $\dfrac{1}{x} + \dfrac{1}{y} + \dfrac{1}{z} = 9$

$\dfrac{2}{x} - \dfrac{1}{y} + \dfrac{3}{z} = 13$

$\dfrac{3}{x} + \dfrac{2}{y} + 4 = \dfrac{4}{z}$

23. $\dfrac{1}{x} + \dfrac{2}{y} = a$

$\dfrac{3}{x} - \dfrac{4}{y} = 3a$

24. $\dfrac{2}{x} + \dfrac{3}{y} = 5a + b$

$\dfrac{4}{x} - \dfrac{1}{y} = 3a - 5b$

C **25.** $\dfrac{1}{x} + \dfrac{1}{y} = m, \quad \dfrac{1}{y} + \dfrac{1}{z} = p$

$\dfrac{1}{x} + \dfrac{1}{z} = n$

26. $\dfrac{x - 3}{y} = \dfrac{x}{y + a}$

$\dfrac{x - 2}{x} = \dfrac{y}{y - 2a}$

27. $\dfrac{x - 5}{y} = \dfrac{x}{y + 1}$

$3 = \dfrac{2x + 11y + 4}{x + 2y}$

Solve.

28. Beth and Angie run at constant rates. Beth's rate is four-fifths of Angie's. In a race, Angie gave Beth a 20-second headstart. Angie won by 200 meters. In a second race over the same course, Angie gave Beth a 150-meter headstart. Angie won by 30 seconds. How many meters are there in the course?

CHECKING YOUR UNDERSTANDING

WORDS AND SYMBOLS

consistent equations
dependent equations
inconsistent equations

solution of a system of linear equations
standard form of a linear equation in two variables, $Ax + By = C$
system of linear equations

CONCEPTS

■ A system of two linear equations in two variables has no solution, one solution, or infinitely many solutions. There are infinitely many solutions when the two equations have the same graph. There are no solutions when the two graphs are parallel. There is one solution when the two (distinct) graphs are not parallel. [6-1]

■ A system of equations may be solved algebraically by combining two equations at a time to eliminate variables. When it is clear that a resulting equation has no solution, there is no solution of the system. When it is clear that a resulting equation has infinitely many solutions, there are infinitely many solutions of the system. [6-2 to 6-4]

PROCESSES

■ Solve a system of linear equations in two variables graphically. [6-1]

1. $x + y = 6$
$2x - y = -3$

2. $y = 2x + 3$
$y = -3x - 2$

3. $x + 2y = 6$
$4y + 8 = -2x$

■ Solve a system of equations algebraically. [6-2 to 6-4]

4. $2x - 3y = 6$
$-x + 2y = -5$

5. $8x = 3y - 1$
$2y = 5x + 1$

6. $ax + 2by = 2(a^2 + b^2)$
$bx - ay = ab$

7. $x + y - 3 = 0$
$x - 3 = -4$
$2x + 3y + 3z = 1$

8. $\dfrac{x - 1}{y} = \dfrac{x}{y - 4}$

$\dfrac{2x + 1}{y} = \dfrac{4x - 3}{2y - 5}$

9. $\dfrac{21}{x} + \dfrac{3}{y} = 2$

$\dfrac{7}{x} - \dfrac{6}{y} = 3$

OBJECTIVE: Solve problems by solving systems of linear equations.

6-5 PROBLEM SOLVING: VALUE PROBLEMS

Knowing how to solve systems of equations allows you to use two or more variables for solving problems. The use of two or more variables should be considered whenever two or more results are called for.

One type of problem suited to the use of two variables is a "value problem". It involves a number of items having one value and a number of items having another value. One equation will relate the number of items. A second equation will relate their values.

EXAMPLE 1   50 coins, consisting of quarters and dimes, are worth $9.80. Find the number of each kind of coin.

 quarter   dime

SOLUTION   The number of quarters plus the number of dimes is 50. The value of the quarters plus the value of the dimes is $9.80.

Use $\left[\begin{array}{l} q \quad \text{for the number of quarters.} \\ d \quad \text{for the number of dimes.} \\ 25q \text{ for the value of the quarters in cents.} \\ 10d \text{ for the value of the dimes in cents.} \end{array}\right.$

$$\boxed{\begin{array}{l} q + d = 50 \\ 25q + 10d = 980 \end{array}}$$

Find q by subtraction.

$\left.\begin{array}{l} q + d = 50 \\ 25q + 10d = 980 \end{array}\right\} \longrightarrow M_{10}$

$$\begin{array}{rl} 10q + 10d &= 500 \\ 25q + 10d &= 980 \\ \hline \end{array}$$

Subtract. $-15q \quad\quad = -480$

$$q = 32$$

Find d by replacing q by 32 in $q + d = 50$.

$$32 + d = 50$$
$$d = 18$$

CONCLUSION   There are 32 quarters and 18 dimes.

CHECK   The value of 32 quarters is $8.00.
The value of 18 dimes is $1.80.
The value of the 50 coins is $9.80.   ✔

CLASSROOM EXERCISES

Solve.

1. 17 coins consisting of nickels and dimes, are worth $1.10. Find the number of each kind of coin.

2. 46 tickets, consisting of adults' and children's tickets, are valued at $68.75. The adult ticket price is $2.50. A child's ticket is one-half the adult price. Find the number of each kind of ticket.

3. A confectioner mixed pecans priced at $5.85 per kilogram with almonds priced at $4.93 per kilogram. How many kilograms of each kind of nut must be used to make a mixture of 40 kilograms to be sold at $5.62 per kilogram?

EXERCISES

A Solve.

1. 75 coins, consisting of nickels and dimes, are worth $5.95. Find the number of each kind of coin.

2. 27 coins, consisting of quarters and dimes, are worth $5.25. Find the number of each kind of coin.

3. Coffee priced at $7.50 per kilogram is mixed with coffee priced at $8.40 per kilogram. How many kilograms of each kind should be mixed to make 180 kg that would be priced at $7.75 per kilogram?

4. A telegram of 15 words costs $4.95. Another telegram of 37 words costs $8.25. The charge is based on a fixed fee for the first 15 words and a charge for each additional word. Find the charge for the first 15 words and for each additional word.

5. A grocer bought oranges at $1.44 a dozen and sold them at $1.68 a dozen. The grocer lost 30 oranges due to spoilage. The grocer earned $7.80 on the oranges. How many oranges were bought?

6. A store marks down the price of a television set by $10. It normally sells 20 of these sets. By reducing the price, it sells 25 sets and earns $1250 more than it normally earns. Find the regular price of one of these television sets.

7. A discount drugstore sold 3 bars of soap and 2 tubes of toothpaste to one customer for $3.52 and earned a profit of 31 cents. It sold 4 bars of the same soap and 1 tube of the same toothpaste to another customer for $3.11 and earned a profit of 28 cents. How much did a bar of soap and a tube of toothpaste cost the drugstore?

B 8. 30 coins, consisting of nickels, dimes and quarters, are valued at $3.50. The number of nickels is equal to the number of quarters plus twice the number of dimes. Find the number of each kind of coin.

9. A number of nickels and dimes has a value of v cents. There are t coins. Find the number of each kind of coin in terms of t and v.

10. The perimeter of a rectangle is 116 m. When the width is doubled, the perimeter is 152 m. Find the dimensions of the rectangle.

C 11. At Rocky's Cafe you can buy 13 egg salad sandwiches for the price of 11 hamburger sandwiches or 7 roast beef sandwiches. What is the most likely price for each kind of sandwich?

6-6 PROBLEM SOLVING: INVESTMENT PROBLEMS

When two amounts are invested at different interest rates, you may use two variables and a system of two equations. One equation will relate the two amounts. The other equation will relate the interest earned by each amount.

EXAMPLE 1 Mrs. Santini invested $5000, part at $7\frac{1}{2}\%$ interest per year and the rest at 5%. How much did she invest at each rate if the income from both investments was $330 per year?

SOLUTION The amount at $7\frac{1}{2}\%$ plus the amount at 5% is $5000.

The interest at $7\frac{1}{2}\%$ plus the interest at 5% is $330.

Use
$$\begin{bmatrix} s & \text{for the number of dollars invested at } 7\frac{1}{2}\%. \\ f & \text{for the number of dollars invested at 5\%.} \\ 0.075s & \text{for the income from the } 7\frac{1}{2}\% \text{ investment.} \\ 0.05f & \text{for the income from the 5\% investment.} \end{bmatrix}$$

$$\boxed{\begin{aligned} s + f &= 5000 \\ 0.075s + 0.05f &= 330 \end{aligned}}$$

Find *s* by subtraction.

$$\left.\begin{aligned} s + f &= 5000 \\ 0.075s + 0.05f &= 330 \end{aligned}\right\} \rightarrow \begin{matrix} M_{50} \\ M_{1000} \end{matrix} \quad \begin{aligned} 50s + 50f &= 250\,000 \\ \underline{75s + 50f} &= \underline{330\,000} \end{aligned}$$

$$\begin{aligned} \text{Subtract.} \qquad -25s &= -80\,000 \\ s &= 3200 \end{aligned}$$

Find *f* by replacing *s* by 3200 in $s + f = 5000.$
$$\begin{aligned} 3200 + f &= 5000 \\ f &= 1800 \end{aligned}$$

CONCLUSION Mrs. Santini invested $3200 at $7\frac{1}{2}\%$ and $1800 at 5%.

CHECK Investments of $3200 at $7\frac{1}{2}\%$ and $1800 at 5% make a total investment of $5000.

Is the total annual income $330?
$$\begin{aligned} 0.075(3200) + 0.05(1800) &\overset{?}{=} 330 \\ 240 + 90 &\overset{?}{=} 330 \\ 330 &= 330 \quad \checkmark \end{aligned}$$

CLASSROOM EXERCISES

Solve.

1. A banker invested $4500, part at 6% interest per year and the rest at 8.5%. The total interest for one year from both investments was $320. How much was invested at each rate?

2. An investment banker opened two accounts, one with $4000 and the second with $7600. The annual interest rate on the first investment was 1.5% more than on the second investment. The annual interest from both investments was $930. Find the annual interest rate for each investment.

3. The Franklins want to invest $60 000, part at 7% interest per year and the rest at 4%. How much should they invest at each rate to earn interest at the rate of 5% on the total investment?

EXERCISES

Solve.

1. Tomas invested $5000, part at 6.5% interest per year and the rest at 7%. How much was invested at each rate when the income from both investments was $340?

2. Virginia has invested $15 000, part at 6.5% interest per year and the rest at 9%. Her total yearly income from both investments is $1200. How much does she have invested at each rate?

3. Sylvia has three times as much money invested at 4% interest per year as she has invested at 7%. Her accountant tells her that if the amounts were interchanged, her annual income would increase by $240. How much does she have invested at each rate?

4. The Millers have $25 000 invested, part at 7% interest per year, part at 6%, and the rest at 5%. The total yearly income from their investments is $1540. The income from the 7% investment is $160 a year more than the income from the 6% investment. How much money have they invested at each rate?

5. Mr. Telford has some money invested in bonds. He receives 1% more interest per year on an investment of $3600 than he does on a second investment of $2800. He receives $452 annually from the two investments. What is the annual rate of interest on each investment?

B 6. One investment is made at 5% yearly interest. A larger amount is invested at 7%. The difference of the investments is $2500. The total interest is 6.2% of the total investment. At the end of a year, how much are both investments together worth?

7. Mrs. Hernandez has some money invested, part at 5% interest per year and the rest at 8%. The annual income is equal to the interest that would be earned by investing all of her money at an annual interest rate of 7%. If she were to decrease the amount invested at 5% by $1000 and reinvest the $1000 at 8%, her annual income would be 7.2% of the amount invested. Find the amounts Mrs. Hernandez has invested at 5% and at 8%.

C 8. One investment lost 5% of its worth in a year. Another investment earned 7% in a year. The resulting gain was 3% of the total investment. The investments and gain together were worth $7725 at the end of the year. How much was each investment?

6-7 PROBLEM SOLVING: DIGIT PROBLEMS

In digit problems, you are asked to find a number by finding the digits in its numeral. For a numeral having two digits, use two variables. For a numeral having three digits, use three variables.

When u is used for the units digit, t for the tens digit, and h for the hundreds digit, the expression $100h + 10t + u$ represents the number. When the digits for the number are reversed, the expression $100u + 10t + h$ represents the new number.

EXAMPLE 1 The sum of the digits of a two digit numeral is 10. When the digits are reversed, the new number is 36 less than the original number. What is the original number?

SOLUTION The sum for the digits is 10.

The number for the digits in reverse order equals the original number less 36.

$$\text{Use} \begin{cases} u & \text{for the units digit.} \\ t & \text{for the tens digit.} \\ 10t + u & \text{for the original number.} \\ 10u + t & \text{for the second number.} \end{cases}$$

$$\boxed{\begin{array}{l} t + u = 10 \\ 10u + t = 10t + u - 36 \end{array}}$$

Simplify the second equation and solve by addition.

$$\begin{array}{l} t + u = 10 \\ 10u + t = 10t + u - 36 \end{array} \longrightarrow \qquad \begin{array}{r} t + u = 10 \\ -t + u = -4 \\ \hline \text{Add.} \quad 2u = 6 \\ u = 3 \end{array}$$

Find t. Replace u by 3 in $t + u = 10$.
$$t + 3 = 10$$
$$t = 7$$

CONCLUSION The original number is 73.

CHECK The sum of 7 and 3 is 10. Is 37 equal to 73 less 36?
$$37 \stackrel{?}{=} 73 - 36$$
$$37 = 37 \qquad ✔$$

CLASSROOM EXERCISES

Solve.

1. The sum of the digits of a two-digit number is 14. The units digit exceeds the tens digit by 4. Find the number.

2. A two-digit number is one more than nine times the sum of its digits. The tens digit exceeds the units digit by 8. Find the number.

3. The sum of the digits of a two-digit number is 12. When the digits of the number are reversed, the new number exceeds the original number by 36. Find the original number.

4. The sum of the digits of a two-digit number is 11. When the number is increased by 27, the digits will be reversed. Find the number.

EXERCISES

A Solve.

1. The sum of the digits of a two-digit number is 6. When 18 is subtracted from the number, the digits will be reversed. Find the number.

2. The sum of the digits of a two-digit number is 7. When 45 is added to the number, the digits will be reversed. Find the number.

3. The difference of the digits of a two-digit number is 3. When the digits are reversed, the sum of the new number and the original number is 121. Find the original number.

4. A two-digit number is 2 more than 8 times the sum of its digits. When 8 is added to the number, the result is 9 times the sum of the digits. Find the number.

5. A two-digit number is divided by the sum of its digits. The quotient is 5. The remainder is 1. Twice the tens digit of the number plus the units digit is 16. Find the number.

6. A two-digit number is divided by 1 less than the sum of its digits. The quotient is 3. When the digits are reversed, the new number is 6 more than 3 times the original number. Find the original number.

7. The sum of the digits of a two-digit number is 9. When the digits are reversed, the ratio of the original number to the new number is 3 to 8. Find the original number.

8. The sum of the digits of a three-digit number is 9. When the digits are reversed, the new number is 198 less than the original number. When the units and tens digits are interchanged, the result is a number that is 9 less than the original number. Find the original number.

B 9. The difference of two two-digit numbers is 10. The sum of the units digits is 4. The difference of the units digits is 0. The sum of the tens digits is 7. Find the numbers.

10. The sum of the digits of a two-digit number is 5. The absolute value of their difference is 3. Find all such two-digit numbers.

C 11. The sum of the digits of a four-digit number is 15. The hundreds digit is one more than the units digit. The sum of the thousands and units digits is 4. The sum of twice the hundreds digit and the tens digit is 14. Find the number.

OBJECTIVE: Show the solution set graphically for a system of linear inequalities.

6-8   GRAPHICAL SOLUTION OF A SYSTEM OF LINEAR INEQUALITIES

As we saw in Chapter 5, the solutions of a linear inequality have as their graph the points on one side of a line in the coordinate plane.   The solutions of a *system* of linear inequalities are the common solutions of the inequalities in the system.   Graphically, the solution set for the system corresponds to the intersection of the graphs for the inequalities.

EXAMPLE 1   Solve $\begin{array}{c} y > x + 2 \\ y > 4 - x \end{array}$ graphically.

SOLUTION   The deeply-shaded region shows the common solutions of both inequalities. Hence, it is the graph of the solution set of the system.

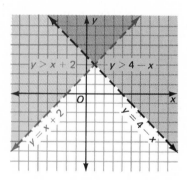

EXAMPLE 2   Solve $\begin{array}{c} x + y \geq 6 \\ y \leq 2x - 4 \\ x < 6 \end{array}$ graphically.

SOLUTION   The solutions of this system of three inequalities correspond to the points that are in the intersection of the three graphs.   The deeply-shaded region shows the solution set of the system.

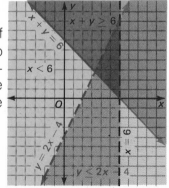

For each of the Examples 1 and 2, checking that points in the deeply-shaded region correspond to solutions of the system is left for the student. It also serves as a check to test whether the coordinates of points that are *not* in the deeply-shaded region give a false sentence for at least one inequality in the system.

CLASSROOM EXERCISES

Solve the system by graphing.

1. $y > 9 - x$
$y \geq x + 3$

2. $x + y \leq 4$
$y \geq 2x - 4$
$x < 4$

3. $y \leq -x + 1$
$y > x + 2$

EXERCISES

A Solve the system by graphing.

1. $x + y > 2$
$y \leq x - 7$

2. $x + y \leq 5$
$y > x + 1$

3. $y \geq 3x - 1$
$y < 5 - 2x$

4. $y > 2x - 3$
$y \leq 6 - 2x$

5. $x + 5y \geq 10$
$y \geq 2$

6. $2x + 3y \leq 6$
$x \leq 3$

7. $x + 7 > y$
$y < -2x - 7$

8. $x + 11 \geq y$
$y \leq -2x - 11$

9. $x + y \geq -6$
$x + 8 < -y$

10. $x + y \geq 10$
$x < 5$
$y \geq x + 10$

11. $x < 6$
$x + y \geq 18$
$y \geq x + 6$

12. $5y + 2x \geq 10$
$y \leq 2$
$x - y \leq 3$

B **13.** $-5 < x < 1$
$x + 2y \leq 8$

14. $0 \leq x \leq 5$
$-3 \leq y \leq 0$

15. $x \leq y \leq -x + 2$

16. $3x - 7y \leq 21$
$x + y \leq 7$
$0 < x < 8$

17. $x \geq 0$
$5x + 2y \leq 10$
$y > 6$

18. $-9 \leq x \leq 2$
$18 < -4x + 9y < 36$

C **19.** $|x| < 4$
$y \geq -3$
$y \leq |x|$

20. $-2 \leq y < |x|$
$3y - 5x \geq -6$
$3y + 5x \geq -6$

21. $x + y \leq 10$
$2x + y \geq 10$
$x + 2y \geq 10$
$x < 8$

22. At Wizard Wire Company, it takes 4 hours of process A to produce 1 km of #8 wire and 7 hours of process B to produce 1 km of #8 wire. For #6 wire the production time per kilometer is 5 hours for each of the two processes. Each week the company must produce at least 2 km of #6 wire. Processes A and B are available for at most 70 and 100 hours per week respectively. How many kilometers of each wire can the company produce each week? Draw a graph to show all possible solutions.

CHAPTER REVIEW

Solve each linear system by graphing. [6-1]

1. $x + y = 6$
$2x - y = 9$

2. $y = -3x - 4$
$6x + 2y = 9$

3. $y = -3x - 7$
$y = \frac{1}{3}x + 1$

Solve and check. [6-2, 6-3]

4. $5y = -2x - 8$
$x + 2y = -3$

5. $3y = x + 2$
$7y - 5x = 6$

6. $mx + ny = 1$
$mx - ny = 1$

7. $x + y - z = -2$
$2x - y + z = 6$
$x - 3y + 3z = 14$

8. $2x - y - 4z = 0$
$3x + y \qquad = 11$
$4y - 3z = 5$

Solve. [6-4 to 6-7]

9. $\dfrac{x + 2}{y} = \dfrac{x}{y - 1}$
$\dfrac{3 - x}{-y} = \dfrac{x}{y + 3}$

10. $\dfrac{3}{x} + \dfrac{2}{y} = \dfrac{4}{3}$
$\dfrac{9}{x} - \dfrac{12}{y} = 1$

11. $\dfrac{x + 2}{x} = \dfrac{y + 3}{y}$
$\dfrac{x + y}{y - 1} = 1$

12. Number 10 nails cost 90 cents a box. Number 8 nails cost 75 cents a box. A carpenter needs twice as many boxes of number 10 nails as number 8 nails. How many boxes of each kind of nails can be bought for $15.30?

13. Mr. Garcia invested $17 000, part at 9% and the rest at $7\frac{1}{2}$%. The annual income from both investments was $1455. How much was invested at each rate?

14. The tens digit of a two-digit number is two more than twice the units digit. The sum of the number and the number with the digits reversed is 121. Find the number.

Solve each system of inequalities by graphing. [6-8]

15. $y > 2x - 1$
$y < -x + 3$

16. $3x - 2y \le 12$
$2y + x > -10$

17. $x - 2y \ge 6$
$3x + y > 5$

CAPSULE REVIEW

Write the letter of the best response.

1. Which two equations are inconsistent?

a. $y = \frac{1}{2}x - 6$
$y = \frac{1}{3}x + 2$

b. $y = 3x + 1$
$y = 3x + 4$

c. $y = \frac{5}{2}x - 3$
$5x - 2y = 6$

d. $y = 6$
$x = 7$

2. The system $\begin{array}{l} 5x + 2y = 4 \\ 3x - y = 9 \end{array}$ has the solution

   a. $\left(3, \dfrac{1}{2}\right)$ **b.** $(2, -3)$ **c.** $(2, 4)$ **d.** $\left(\dfrac{1}{3}, 4\right)$

3. The system $\begin{array}{l} x + y + z = 9 \\ x - y - z = 1 \\ 2x + 3y - z = 6 \end{array}$ has the solution

   a. $(5, 3, 1)$ **b.** $(-3, 0, 7)$ **c.** $(5, 0, 4)$ **d.** $(-3, -2, -2)$

4. If two linear equations are dependent, their graphs

   a. intersect at one point   **b.** are the same line
   c. are parallel lines   **d.** intersect at two or more points.

5. The system of fractional equations $\begin{array}{l} \dfrac{x-5}{y} = \dfrac{x}{y+15} \\[2mm] \dfrac{x+2}{y} = \dfrac{x}{y+1} \end{array}$ simplifies to which
system of linear equations?

   a. $\begin{array}{l} 15x - 5y = 75 \\ x + 2y = -2 \end{array}$ **b.** $\begin{array}{l} 15x - 5y = 75 \\ 5x + 2y = -10 \end{array}$

   c. $\begin{array}{l} 7x - 5y = 60 \\ x + 2y = -2 \end{array}$ **d.** $\begin{array}{l} 7x - 5y = 60 \\ 5x + 2y = -10 \end{array}$

6. Shelagh has four fewer dimes than she has nickels. The value of her
dimes and nickels is $1.70. She has

   a. 12 dimes   **b.** 14 dimes   **c.** 10 nickels   **d.** 14 nickels

7. The sum of the digits of a two-digit number is eight. Interchanging the
digits gives a number which is three greater than four times the original
number. Which system of equations correctly represents this information?
(Assume the original number has t as its tens digit and u as its units digit.)

   a. $\begin{array}{l} t + u = 8 \\ 4t - 3u = 3 \end{array}$ **b.** $\begin{array}{l} t + u = 8 \\ 6t + 5u = 41 \end{array}$

   c. $\begin{array}{l} t + u = 8 \\ 39t - 6u = -3 \end{array}$ **d.** $\begin{array}{l} t - u = -8 \\ 13t + 5u = -1 \end{array}$

CHAPTER TEST

1. How many solutions does this system of equations have?
$$\begin{array}{l} x + y = 3 \\ x + y = 5 \end{array}$$

2. Solve this system of equations by graphing.
$$\begin{array}{l} x + y = 7 \\ x - y = 5 \end{array}$$

Solve.

3. $2x + 3y = 1$
$x - 3y = 5$

4. $3x + y = 1$
$y = x + 5$

5. $x + y + z = 7$
$x - y + z = 3$
$x - y + 2z = 4$

6. $x + y + z = 4$
$2x + y + z = 6$
$3x + y + 2z = 7$

7. $\dfrac{x + 2}{y} = \dfrac{x + 6}{y + 1}$

$\dfrac{x - 3}{y} = \dfrac{x - 1}{y - 2}$

8. $\dfrac{3}{x} + \dfrac{3}{y} = 2$

$\dfrac{4}{x} - \dfrac{6}{y} = 3$

9. Ten coins consisting of nickels and dimes are worth 65¢. How many of the coins are nickels?

10. Twenty coins consisting of dimes and quarters are worth $4.25. How many of the coins are dimes?

11. $10 000 is invested, part at 7% per year and part at 8% per year. Find the amount invested at each interest rate if the annual income from the investments is $720.

12. $5000 is invested, part at 6% per year and part at $8\frac{1}{2}$% per year. Find the amount invested at each interest rate if the annual income from the investments is $412.50.

13. The sum of the digits in a two-digit number is 12. If the digits are interchanged the new number is 18 larger than the original number. Find the original number.

14. The sum of the digits in a two-digit number is 15. If the digits are interchanged the new number is 27 less than the original number. Find the original number.

Solve each system of inequalities by graphing.

15. $x + y < 6$
$y > x - 1$

16. $y > x - 3$
$y < x + 3$
$x < 3$

Write the letter of the best response.

17. In which system are the equations equivalent?

   a. $x + 2y = 3$
       $x - 2y = 3$

   b. $x + 2y = 3$
       $x + 2y = 6$

   c. $x + 2y = 3$
      $2x + 4y = 3$

   d. $x + 2y = 3$
      $2x + 4y = 6$

   e. $x + 2y = 3$
      $2x - 4y = 6$

18. What does x equal in the solution of the system $\begin{array}{l} 2x + y = 5 \\ 3x - 2y = 11 \end{array}$?

   a. 1   **b.** $2\dfrac{1}{2}$ **c.** 3   **d.** $3\dfrac{1}{5}$ **e.** -1

19. What does x equal in the solution of the system $\begin{array}{l} 2x - y + z = 6 \\ x + y + z = 6 \\ 2x + y + z = 8 \end{array}$?

   a. 1   **b.** 2   **c.** 3   **d.** 4   **e.** 5

20. What does x equal in the solution of the system $\begin{array}{l} \dfrac{3}{x} + \dfrac{4}{y} = 1 \\[2mm] \dfrac{8}{x} - \dfrac{6}{y} = 1 \end{array}$?

   a. 1   **b.** 2   **c.** 3   **d.** 4   **e.** 5

21. Twenty-four coins consisting of nickels and quarters are worth $2.00. How many of the coins are nickels?

   a. 4   **b.** 8   **c.** 12   **d.** 16   **e.** 20

22. $8000 is invested, part at $6\frac{1}{2}$% per year and part at 7% per year. How much is invested at $6\frac{1}{2}$% if the annual income from the investments is $530?

   a. $2000   **b.** $4000   **c.** $5000   **d.** $6000   **e.** $7000

23. The sum of the digits of a two-digit number is 8. If the digits are interchanged, the new number is 54 less than the original number. What is the original number?

   a. 71   **b.** 62   **c.** 83   **d.** 93   **e.** 17

24. What is the shape of the region which is the graphical solution for this system? $\begin{array}{l} x < 1 \\ y < 3 \\ x + y > 1 \end{array}$

   a. half-plane   **b.** triangular   **c.** square   **d.** a point   **e.** a line

CHAPTER 7
EXPONENTS, RADICALS, AND COMPLEX NUMBERS

Suppose two aircraft are five kilometers apart. Each is traveling 600 kilometers per hour and heading toward the other. The air traffic controller and the aircraft pilots have just 15 seconds to react to avoid a collision. This requires cooperation, confidence, trust in both humans and machines, ability to withstand pressure, and ability to make good, sound decisions quickly. It has taken you about 15 seconds to read this.

> **OBJECTIVES:** Evaluate numerical expressions involving exponents and radicals.   Use the rules for operating with exponents.

7-1   RULES OF EXPONENTS

Rational number exponents in fraction form, including negative exponents and the exponent zero, are used in many applications of mathematics.   We shall define such exponents so that the rules for their use are the same as the rules for operating with positive integral exponents which follow.

> ### RULE OF MULTIPLICATION
>
> For any real number x and positive integers m and n,
>
> $$x^m \cdot x^n = x^{m+n}$$

EXAMPLE 1   Multiply x^3 and x^2.

   SOLUTION   Not using the rule,

$$x^3 \cdot x^2 = (x \cdot x \cdot x)(x \cdot x)$$
$$= x^5$$

Using the rule,

$$x^3 \cdot x^2 = x^{3+2}$$
$$= x^5$$

EXAMPLE 2   Simplify $(x + y)^2(x + y)$.

   SOLUTION $(x + y)^2(x + y) = (x + y)^{2+1}$, or $(x + y)^3$

> ### RULE OF DIVISION
>
> For any real number x, $x \neq 0$, and positive integers m and n, with $m > n$,
>
> $$\frac{x^m}{x^n} = x^{m-n} \qquad \Big| \qquad \frac{x^n}{x^m} = \frac{1}{x^{m-n}}$$

EXAMPLE 3   Divide x^5 by x^2.

   SOLUTION   Not using the rule,

$$\frac{x^5}{x^2} = \frac{x \cdot x \cdot x \cdot \overset{1}{\cancel{x}} \cdot \overset{1}{\cancel{x}}}{\underset{1}{\cancel{x}} \cdot \underset{1}{\cancel{x}}}$$
$$= x^3$$

Using the rule,

$$\frac{x^5}{x^2} = x^{5-2}$$
$$= x^3$$

EXAMPLE 4 Divide x^4 by x^6.

SOLUTION Not using the rule,

$$\frac{x^4}{x^6} = \frac{\overset{1\cdot1\cdot1\cdot1}{\cancel{x}\cdot\cancel{x}\cdot\cancel{x}\cdot\cancel{x}}}{\underset{1\cdot1\cdot1\cdot1}{\cancel{x}\cdot\cancel{x}\cdot\cancel{x}\cdot\cancel{x}\cdot x\cdot x}}$$

$$= \frac{1}{x^2}$$

Using the rule,

$$\frac{x^4}{x^6} = \frac{1}{x^{6-4}}$$

$$= \frac{1}{x^2}$$

EXAMPLE 5 Simplify $\dfrac{(x-y)^3}{x-y}$.

SOLUTION $\dfrac{(x-y)^3}{x-y} = (x-y)^{3-1}$

$$= (x-y)^2$$

EXAMPLE 6 Simplify $\dfrac{x^2\cdot x^6}{x^5}$, $x \neq 0$.

SOLUTION $\dfrac{x^2\cdot x^6}{x^5} = x^{(2+6)-5}$

$$= x^3$$

RULE OF A POWER OF A POWER

For any real number x and positive integers m and n,

$$(x^m)^n = x^{mn}$$

EXAMPLE 7 Simplify $(x^3)^2$.

SOLUTION Not using the rule,
$$(x^3)^2 = x^3 \cdot x^3$$
$$= x^{3+3}, \text{ or } x^6$$

Using the rule,
$$(x^3)^2 = x^{3\cdot2}$$
$$= x^6$$

RULE OF A POWER OF A PRODUCT

For any real numbers x and y and positive integer n,

$$(xy)^n = x^n y^n$$

EXAMPLE 8 Simplify $(2y)^4$.

SOLUTION Not using the rule,
$$(2y)^4 = 2y \cdot 2y \cdot 2y \cdot 2y$$
$$= 16y^4$$

Using the rule,
$$(2y)^4 = 2^4 y^4$$
$$= 16y^4$$

EXAMPLE 9 Simplify $(2x^2)^3$.

SOLUTION $(2x^2)^3 = 2^3(x^2)^3$
$$= 8x^6$$

RULE OF A POWER OF A QUOTIENT

For any real numbers x and y, $y \neq 0$, and positive integer n,

$$\left(\frac{x}{y}\right)^n = \frac{x^n}{y^n}$$

EXAMPLE 10 Simplify $\left(\frac{x}{4}\right)^3$.

SOLUTION Not using the rule,

$$\left(\frac{x}{4}\right)^3 = \frac{x}{4} \cdot \frac{x}{4} \cdot \frac{x}{4}$$

$$= \frac{x \cdot x \cdot x}{4 \cdot 4 \cdot 4}$$

$$= \frac{x^3}{64}$$

Using the rule,

$$\left(\frac{x}{4}\right)^3 = \frac{x^3}{4^3}$$

$$= \frac{x^3}{64}$$

EXAMPLE 11 Simplify $\left(\frac{2x^5}{x^2 y^m}\right)^3$ for $x \neq 0$, $y \neq 0$, and m an integer.

SOLUTION $\left(\dfrac{2x^5}{x^2 y^m}\right)^3 = \dfrac{(2x^5)^3}{(x^2 y^m)^3}$

$$= \frac{8x^{15}}{x^6 y^{3m}}$$

$$= \frac{8x^9}{y^{3m}}$$

CLASSROOM EXERCISES

Simplify. Use the rules of exponents.

1. $a^4 \cdot a^2$ **2.** $(a^5)^3$ **3.** $(2y)^3$ **4.** $(5x^4)^2$

5. $\dfrac{a^6}{a^2}$ **6.** $\left(\dfrac{x}{y}\right)^5$ **7.** $\dfrac{y^7 \cdot y^3}{y^5}$ **8.** $\dfrac{(c+d)^5}{(c+d)^3}$

EXERCISES

A Simplify. Use the rules of exponents.

1. $a^6 \cdot a^2$ **2.** $x^3 \cdot x^5$ **3.** $a^6 \div a^2$ **4.** $b^5 \div b^4$

5. $(a^6)^2$ **6.** $(b^5)^3$ **7.** $(xy)^5$ **8.** $(cd)^7$

9. $\dfrac{m^7}{m^4}$

10. $\dfrac{x^5}{x^2}$

11. $\left(\dfrac{-2}{5}\right)^3$

12. $\left(\dfrac{3}{4}\right)^2$

13. $2a^3 \cdot a^2$

14. $3b^2 \cdot b$

15. $(x^2 y^3)^3$

16. $(ab^2)^4$

17. $\left(\dfrac{2c^2}{b^3}\right)^2$

18. $\left(\dfrac{3a^3}{b}\right)^3$

19. $\dfrac{(4ab)^2}{2a}$

20. $\dfrac{(3mn)^2}{3n}$

21. $x^2 \cdot y^3 \cdot x \cdot y$

22. $a^3 \cdot b \cdot a^2 \cdot b^4$

23. $(x^2 \cdot x^3)^4$

24. $(a^3 \cdot a^4)^2$

25. $(x - y)^3 (x - y)^2$

26. $(a + b)^7 (a + b)^4$

27. $(a^2 b^3)^n$

28. $(x^3 y^3)^n$

29. $\dfrac{(x + y)^5}{x + y}$

30. $\dfrac{(c - d)^7}{(c - d)^4}$

31. $\dfrac{2z^3 \cdot z^2}{z^4}$

32. $\dfrac{10w^5 \cdot w^4}{w^8}$

33. $\dfrac{b^{5n}}{b^{2n}}$

34. $\dfrac{x^{3n}}{x^n}$

35. $\dfrac{a^{3m} b^n}{a^m b^2}$

36. $\dfrac{x^{2n} y^{3m}}{x^n y^m}$

B 37. $[(a - 2)(a - 2)]^3$

38. $(c^m d^m)^{2m}$

39. $(2x^3 y^2)^2 \cdot (xy^2)$

40. $\dfrac{a^{x+5}}{a^{5-x}}$

41. $\left(\dfrac{x^2 + 2xy + y^2}{x + y}\right)^2$

42. $\left(\dfrac{3m}{5n}\right)^2 \left(\dfrac{3n}{5m}\right)^3$

43. $\left(\dfrac{9a^2 b^3}{3a^3 b}\right)^2$

44. $\left(\dfrac{25a^4 b^n}{5a^3 b^2}\right)^m$

45. $\left(\dfrac{b^{x-y} \cdot b^{2y-x}}{b^{y-1}}\right)^{10}$

46. $\dfrac{x^{n+3} y^2}{x^2 y}$

47. $(a^{x+2})^{x-2}$

48. $\left(\dfrac{c^4 + 4c^2 + 4}{c^2 + 2}\right)^2$

C 49. For $x = 3a^4$, $y = \dfrac{(2xz)^3}{x^2}$ and $z = a^5$, express y in terms of a.

50. Find n when $(16)^n = 2^{32}$.

51. Arrange these numbers from smallest to largest by first expressing each as a power of 2: 8^3, 4^6, 2^{10}, 16^2.

Show why, in general,

52. $x^a + x^b \neq x^{ab}$.

53. $x^a + y^a \neq (x + y)^a$.

54. $x^{(a^b)} \neq (x^a)^b$.

AUDREY'S LIBRARY

Audrey has started a mathematics and science library. Quite a few of her books, 22 in fact, are paperback reprints of famous works. However, Audrey's main interest is mathematics. Therefore, exactly 60% of her books are on various phases of that subject. There are also two books on biology. Of the remainder, two-thirds are on physics and one-third on chemistry. Audrey hopes to increase the size of her library to 50 volumes by the time school is out. How many books are in Audrey's library now?

7-2 ROOTS AND RADICALS

Any positive real number may be expressed as the product of two *equal* factors. The factor is a **square root** of the number. Any real number may be expressed as the product of three equal factors. Such a factor is a **cube root** of the number. In general, when a number is the product of n equal factors, that factor is an **nth root** of the number.

EXAMPLE 1 Find two square roots of 9.

SOLUTION $9 = (3)(3)$ and $9 = (-3)(-3)$.
Each of 3 and -3 is a square root of 9.

EXAMPLE 2 Find a cube root of -27.

SOLUTION $-27 = (-3)(-3)(-3)$
-3 is a cube root of -27.

There are two other cube roots of -27. However, they are numbers of a type that we shall study later in this chapter.

EXAMPLE 3 Find two fourth roots of 16.

SOLUTION $16 = 2 \cdot 2 \cdot 2 \cdot 2$ and $16 = (-2)^4$.
2 and -2 are fourth roots of 16.

A **radical** is an indicated root of a number. Recall that the symbol $\sqrt{}$ is the radical sign. The number shown "inside" the radical sign is the **radicand**. The **index** of the radical indicates which root is to be taken. However, the index 2 for square roots usually is not shown.

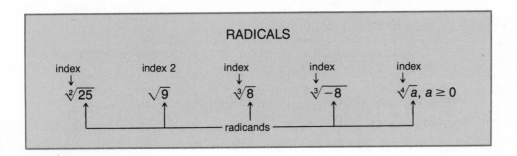

To avoid confusion, mathematicians have agreed that $\sqrt[n]{a}$ should have just one meaning for each integral index. In general, $\sqrt[n]{a}$ will refer to the **principal nth root** of the real number a as follows:

THE PRINCIPAL nth ROOT

For any real number a and integer n, $n > 1$,

■ $\sqrt[n]{a}$ is a positive real number or 0 when a is positive or 0.

■ $\sqrt[n]{a}$ is a negative real number when a is negative and n is odd.

When a is negative and n is even, $\sqrt[n]{a}$ does not represent a real number. Instead, it represents an *imaginary* number, a type of number that we shall study later in this chapter. In such a case, we do not speak of $\sqrt[n]{a}$ as indicating a principal root.

EXAMPLE 4 Find $\sqrt{25}$.

SOLUTION $25 = 5^2$ and $25 = (-5)^2$.
However, since $\sqrt{25}$ represents the principal square root, $\sqrt{25} = 5$.

EXAMPLE 5 Find $\sqrt[5]{-32}$.

SOLUTION $-32 = (-2)^5$
Thus, $\sqrt[5]{-32} = -2$.

EXAMPLE 6 Find $-\sqrt{49}$.

SOLUTION $\sqrt{49} = 7$, the principal square root.
Therefore, $-\sqrt{49} = -7$.
$-\sqrt{49}$ represents the negative square root of 49.

EXAMPLE 7 Find $\sqrt{-16}$.

SOLUTION $-16 = (?)^2$. There is no real number whose square is -16 since the square of any real number is greater than or equal to zero. Therefore, $\sqrt{-16}$ does not represent a real number. There is no *principal* square root of -16.

The symbol $\pm\sqrt{a}$ may be used to represent both the principal square root and the negative square root of a positive real number.

EXAMPLE 8 Find $\pm\sqrt{64}$.

SOLUTION Since $\sqrt{64} = 8$, $\pm\sqrt{64} = \pm 8$.
± 8 represents the two square roots of 64, 8 and -8.

We often need to simplify a radical that has an algebraic expression for its radicand. To be correct in simplifying a radical such as $\sqrt{a^2}$, we should say

$$\left.\begin{array}{l} \sqrt{a^2} = a \text{ for } a \geq 0. \\ \sqrt{a^2} = -a \text{ for } a < 0. \end{array}\right\} \text{ That is, } \sqrt{a^2} = |a|.$$

EXAMPLE 9 Find $\sqrt{4x^2}$.

SOLUTION $\sqrt{4x^2} = \sqrt{(2x)^2}$
$= 2|x|$

In general,

$$\sqrt[n]{a^n} = |a|, \text{ when } n \text{ is even.}$$

When n is odd, however, $\sqrt[n]{a}$ represents a positive or negative number to agree with the positive or negative nature of a. Therefore, we may write

$$\sqrt[n]{a^n} = a, \text{ when } n \text{ is odd.}$$

EXAMPLE 10. Find $\sqrt[3]{-27y^6}$

SOLUTION $\sqrt[3]{-27y^6} = \sqrt[3]{(-3y^2)^3}$
$= -3y^2$

EXAMPLE 11 Find $\sqrt[4]{256a^4}$.

SOLUTION $\sqrt[4]{256a^4} = \sqrt[4]{(4a)^4}$
$= 4|a|$

CLASSROOM EXERCISES

1. Find two square roots of 4.

2. Find a cube root of -8.

Find the indicated root.

3. $\sqrt{9}$

4. $-\sqrt{25}$

5. $\pm\sqrt{81}$

6. $\sqrt{x^2}$

7. $\sqrt{y^6}$

8. $-\sqrt{49x^4}$

9. $\sqrt[3]{-1728y^3}$

10. $\sqrt[6]{64a^{12}}$

EXERCISES

Ⓐ **1.** Find two square roots of 25.

2. Find two square roots of 49.

3. Find a cube root of 27.

4. Find a cube root of -125.

5. Find two fourth roots of 81.

6. Find two sixth roots of 64.

Find the indicated root. If no real root exists, then state this.

7. $\sqrt{16}$

8. $\sqrt{100}$

9. $-\sqrt{49}$

10. $-\sqrt{121}$

11. $\pm\sqrt{169}$

12. $\pm\sqrt{256}$

13. $\sqrt[3]{729}$

14. $\sqrt[3]{216}$

15. $\sqrt[3]{-64}$ **16.** $\sqrt[3]{-216}$ **17.** $\sqrt[5]{-1}$ **18.** $\sqrt[5]{32}$

19. $\sqrt{-25}$ **20.** $\sqrt{-36}$ **21.** $-\sqrt[3]{-1000}$ **22.** $-\sqrt[3]{-64}$

23. $-\sqrt{-9}$ **24.** $-\sqrt{-100}$ **25.** $\sqrt{9y^4}$ **26.** $\sqrt{16b^4}$

27. $\sqrt{x^2y^4}$ **28.** $\sqrt{a^6b^4}$ **29.** $\sqrt[3]{8x^3}$ **30.** $\sqrt[3]{64y^3}$

31. $\sqrt[3]{-27x^9}$ **32.** $\sqrt[3]{-125a^{12}}$ **33.** $-\sqrt{4a^6b^{10}}$ **34.** $-\sqrt{64x^8y^2}$

35. $\sqrt[4]{16x^8y^4}$ **36.** $\sqrt[4]{81a^{12}b^4}$ **37.** $-\sqrt{1.44p^4}$ **38.** $-\sqrt{1.96q^8}$

39. $\sqrt[3]{0.008a^3}$ **40.** $\sqrt[3]{0.027b^6}$ **41.** $\sqrt[4]{x^{12}y^{32}}$ **42.** $\sqrt[4]{c^{20}d^8}$

43. $-\sqrt{10\,000x^{16}y^4}$ **44.** $-\sqrt{2500a^{10}b^6}$ **45.** $\sqrt[4]{625x^8y^4}$ **46.** $\sqrt[4]{256a^8b^4}$

B **47.** $\sqrt{(x+2)^2}$ **48.** $\sqrt{4(a-b)^2}$ **49.** $\sqrt{x^2-6x+9}$

50. $\sqrt[3]{-8(x+y)^3}$ **51.** $\sqrt[3]{-27(a-b)^{12}}$ **52.** $\sqrt[n]{x^n}$

53. $\sqrt[n]{a^{2n}}$ **54.** $\sqrt[5]{32(x-y)^{10}}$ **55.** $\sqrt{9x^2+18x+9}$

56. $\sqrt{100k^2+40k+4}$ **57.** $\sqrt{(x+y)^2(a+b)^4}$ **58.** $\sqrt[3]{(m-n)^6(x+y)^9}$

C **59.** $\sqrt[n]{4^n \cdot x^{3n}}$ **60.** $\sqrt[k]{2^k \cdot 3^{2k}m^{5k}}$ **61.** $\sqrt[4]{\dfrac{16}{5} \cdot \left(\dfrac{5x^{12}y^9}{x^4y^5}\right)^5}$

62. $\sqrt[4]{625x^4}$ **63.** $\sqrt{81x^2+54xy+9y^2}$ **64.** $\sqrt[6]{64x^{12}y^6}$

65. $\sqrt{\sqrt{625x^4}}$ **66.** $\sqrt[3]{\sqrt{64x^{12}y^6}}$ **67.** $\sqrt{\sqrt[3]{64x^{12}y^6}}$

$\boxed{1.4142136}$ CONTINUED FRACTIONS

Simplify. Do you know a simple name for a number that is approximately equal to the result shown by the calculator display?

1. $1 + \dfrac{3}{1 + \dfrac{2}{1 + \dfrac{2}{1 + \dfrac{1}{3}}}}$

2. $1 + \dfrac{5}{3 + \dfrac{5}{3 + \dfrac{5}{5 + \dfrac{5}{8}}}}$

3. $1 + \dfrac{1}{2 + \dfrac{1}{2 + \dfrac{1}{2 + \dfrac{1}{2 + \dfrac{1}{2 + \dfrac{1}{2}}}}}}$

4. $1 + \dfrac{2}{2 + \dfrac{2}{2 + \dfrac{2}{2 + \dfrac{2}{2 + \dfrac{2}{2 + 2}}}}}$

7-3 POSITIVE RATIONAL EXPONENTS

We extend the definitions of exponents now to include positive rational exponents. We do this in a way that allows us also to extend the rules for operating with exponents to include exponents of this type. For example, we would like $a^{\frac{1}{3}}$ to have a meaning that will let us say

$$a^{\frac{1}{3}} \cdot a^{\frac{1}{3}} \cdot a^{\frac{1}{3}} = a^{\frac{1}{3}+\frac{1}{3}+\frac{1}{3}}$$
$$= a^1, \text{ or } a.$$

This suggests that each of three equal factors whose product is a may be represented by $a^{\frac{1}{3}}$. Therefore, $a^{\frac{1}{3}}$ should represent $\sqrt[3]{a}$, the principal cube root of a. In general, we define $a^{\frac{1}{n}}$ as follows.

$$a^{\frac{1}{n}} = \sqrt[n]{a}$$

when $\sqrt[n]{a}$ represents a real number.

EXAMPLE 1 Simplify $81^{\frac{1}{2}}$.

SOLUTION $81^{\frac{1}{2}} = \sqrt{81}$
$= 9$

EXAMPLE 2 Simplify $\left(-\dfrac{a^3}{8}\right)^{\frac{1}{3}}$.

SOLUTION $\left(-\dfrac{a^3}{8}\right)^{\frac{1}{3}} = \sqrt[3]{-\dfrac{a^3}{8}}$
$= -\dfrac{a}{2}$

We would like $a^{\frac{m}{n}}$, m and n positive integers, to have a meaning that would allow us to write, for example,

$$a^{\frac{2}{3}} = \left(a^{\frac{1}{3}}\right)^2, \text{ or } (\sqrt[3]{a})^2$$

In general we would like to have

$$a^{\frac{m}{n}} = \left(a^{\frac{1}{n}}\right)^m, \text{ or } (\sqrt[n]{a})^m.$$

Therefore, we define $a^{\frac{m}{n}}$ as follows.

$$a^{\frac{m}{n}} = (\sqrt[n]{a})^m$$

when $\sqrt[n]{a}$ represents a real number.

EXAMPLE 3 Simplify $8^{\frac{2}{3}}$.

SOLUTION $8^{\frac{2}{3}} = (\sqrt[3]{8})^2$
$= (2)^2$, or 4

EXAMPLE 4 Simplify $\left(\frac{9}{16}\right)^{\frac{3}{2}}$.

SOLUTION $\left(\frac{9}{16}\right)^{\frac{3}{2}} = \left(\sqrt{\frac{9}{16}}\right)^3$
$= \left(\frac{3}{4}\right)^3$, or $\frac{27}{64}$.

The rules for exponents suggest that $a^{\frac{m}{n}}$ could be thought of either as $\left(a^{\frac{1}{n}}\right)^m$, as defined, or as $(a^m)^{\frac{1}{n}}$. Indeed, either form may be used as long as we remain aware of any necessary restrictions on a and n.

EXAMPLE 5 Simplify $8^{\frac{2}{3}}$.

SOLUTION $8^{\frac{2}{3}} = \sqrt[3]{8^2}$
$= \sqrt[3]{64}$, or 4. Compare this result with Example 3.

EXAMPLE 6 Simplify $125^{\frac{5}{3}}$.

SOLUTION 1

$125^{\frac{5}{3}} = (\sqrt[3]{125})^5$
$= 5^5$, or 3125.

SOLUTION 2

$125^{\frac{5}{3}} = \sqrt[3]{125^5}$
The computation suggested by $\sqrt[3]{125^5}$ is too tedious to be useful.

The following examples illustrate the rules for operating with positive rational exponents.

EXAMPLE 7 Multiply $a^{\frac{1}{2}}$ by $a^{\frac{1}{2}}$, $a \geq 0$.

SOLUTION 1

$a^{\frac{1}{2}} \cdot a^{\frac{1}{2}} = a^{\frac{1}{2} + \frac{1}{2}}$
$= a^1$, or a.

SOLUTION 2

$\left(a^{\frac{1}{2}}\right)^2 = a^{\frac{1}{2} \cdot 2}$
$= a^{\frac{2}{2}}$, or a.

EXAMPLE 8 Multiply $m^{\frac{1}{2}}$ and $m^{\frac{1}{3}}$, $m \geq 0$.

SOLUTION $m^{\frac{1}{2}} \cdot m^{\frac{1}{3}} = m^{\frac{1}{2} + \frac{1}{3}}$
$= m^{\frac{3}{6} + \frac{2}{6}}$, or $m^{\frac{5}{6}}$

EXAMPLE 9 Divide $b^{\frac{4}{5}}$ by $b^{\frac{3}{5}}$.

SOLUTION $\dfrac{b^{\frac{4}{5}}}{b^{\frac{3}{5}}} = b^{\frac{4}{5} - \frac{3}{5}}$, or $b^{\frac{1}{5}}$

EXAMPLE 10 Simplify $\left(r^{\frac{2}{3}}\right)^{\frac{1}{2}}$, $r \geq 0$.

SOLUTION $\left(r^{\frac{2}{3}}\right)^{\frac{1}{2}} = r^{\frac{2}{3} \cdot \frac{1}{2}}$, or $r^{\frac{1}{3}}$

EXAMPLE 11 Simplify $(8y^6)^{\frac{1}{3}}$.

SOLUTION $(8y^6)^{\frac{1}{3}} = 8^{\frac{1}{3}}(y^6)^{\frac{1}{3}}$
$= 2y^{\frac{6}{3}}$, or $2y^2$

EXAMPLE 12 Simplify $\left(\dfrac{36x^3}{y^4}\right)^{\frac{1}{2}}$, $x \geq 0$.

SOLUTION $\left(\dfrac{36x^3}{y^4}\right)^{\frac{1}{2}} = \dfrac{36^{\frac{1}{2}}(x^3)^{\frac{1}{2}}}{(y^4)^{\frac{1}{2}}}$, or $\dfrac{6x^{\frac{3}{2}}}{y^2}$

CLASSROOM EXERCISES

Simplify.

1. $27^{\frac{1}{3}}$

2. $\left(\dfrac{4}{9}\right)^{\frac{3}{2}}$

3. $(64)^{\frac{2}{3}}$

4. $\left(\dfrac{27}{125}\right)^{\frac{2}{3}}$

5. $\left(x^{\frac{3}{4}}\right)^2$

6. $\left(\dfrac{a^3}{27}\right)^{\frac{1}{3}}$

7. $\left(\dfrac{25y^5}{x^8}\right)^{\frac{1}{2}}$

8. $(16y^8)^{\frac{1}{4}}$

9. $(-8)^{\frac{5}{3}}$

10. $a^{\frac{2}{3}} \cdot a^{\frac{1}{2}}$

EXERCISES

A Simplify.

1. $25^{\frac{1}{2}}$

2. $(-27)^{\frac{1}{3}}$

3. $(-64)^{\frac{1}{3}}$

4. $4^{\frac{3}{2}}$

5. $9^{\frac{5}{2}}$

6. $125^{\frac{2}{3}}$

7. $\left(\dfrac{1}{16}\right)^{\frac{1}{2}}$

8. $\left(\dfrac{27}{64}\right)^{\frac{4}{3}}$

9. $\left(\dfrac{4}{9}\right)^{\frac{3}{2}}$

10. $(0.027)^{\frac{1}{3}}$

11. $(1.21)^{\frac{1}{2}}$

12. $\left(a^{\frac{2}{3}}\right)^3$

13. $\left(b^{\frac{3}{2}}\right)^2$

14. $\left(\dfrac{16x^6}{y^2}\right)^{\frac{1}{2}}$

15. $\left(\dfrac{9a^4}{b^8}\right)^{\frac{1}{2}}$

Perform the indicated operations.

16. $a^{\frac{2}{3}} \cdot a^{\frac{1}{3}}$

17. $a^{\frac{3}{5}} \cdot a^{\frac{1}{5}}$

18. $b^{\frac{1}{2}} \cdot b^{\frac{1}{4}}$

19. $b^{\frac{1}{3}} \cdot b^{\frac{1}{2}}$

20. $x^{\frac{1}{2}} \cdot x^{\frac{1}{5}}$ **21.** $c^{\frac{1}{3}} \cdot c^{\frac{1}{4}}$ **22.** $m^{0.5} \cdot m^{0.25}$ **23.** $y^{0.75} \cdot y^{0.50}$

24. $a \cdot a^{\frac{1}{2}}$ **25.** $b^{\frac{1}{3}} \cdot b$ **26.** $a \cdot a^{\frac{2}{3}} \cdot a^{\frac{1}{3}}$ **27.** $n^{\frac{1}{2}} \cdot n^{\frac{1}{2}} \cdot n^{\frac{1}{4}}$

28. $\dfrac{a^{\frac{3}{4}}}{a^{\frac{1}{4}}}$ **29.** $\dfrac{x^{\frac{1}{2}}}{x^{\frac{1}{3}}}$ **30.** $\dfrac{y^{\frac{2}{3}}}{y^{\frac{1}{4}}}$ **31.** $\left(\dfrac{x^2}{y^2}\right)^{\frac{1}{3}}$ **32.** $\left(\dfrac{x^{\frac{1}{2}}}{y^{\frac{1}{3}}}\right)^3$ **33.** $\left(\dfrac{x^{\frac{1}{2}}}{y^{\frac{1}{3}}}\right)^{\frac{3}{4}}$

B   **34.** $\dfrac{x^{\frac{n}{3}}}{x^{\frac{1}{3}}}$ **35.** $\dfrac{b^{\frac{2n}{3}}}{b^{\frac{n}{2}}}$ **36.** $\dfrac{a^{\frac{2}{3}}b^{\frac{1}{2}}}{b^{\frac{1}{3}}}$ **37.** $\left(\dfrac{x^{\frac{3}{4}}y^{\frac{2}{3}}}{x^{\frac{1}{3}}y^{\frac{1}{2}}}\right)^{\frac{1}{3}}$

38. $\left(3a^{\frac{1}{3}} \cdot b^{\frac{2}{3}} \cdot c\right)\left(2ab^{\frac{1}{4}}c^2\right)$ **39.** $((a + b)^2)^{\frac{3}{2}}$ **40.** $((c - d)^n)^{\frac{2}{n}}$

41. $(x^{3n} \cdot y^n \cdot z^n)^{\frac{1}{n}}$ **42.** $(m^{x+2} \cdot m^{2x+1})^{\frac{1}{3}}$ **43.** $(4x^6)^{\frac{1}{2}}(27x^3y^9)^{\frac{1}{3}}$

44. $\left(\dfrac{(a - b)^{10}}{(b - a)^8}\right)^{\frac{n}{2}}$ **45.** $\left(\dfrac{x^{a+b}}{x^{a-b}}\right)^{\frac{1}{2}}$ **46.** $\left(\dfrac{49x^4y^2}{z^6}\right)^{\frac{1}{2}}$ **47.** $\left(\dfrac{27x^9y^{12}}{64x^3}\right)^{\frac{1}{3}}$

C   **48.** $(m - n) \div \left(m^{\frac{1}{2}} + n^{\frac{1}{2}}\right)$ **49.** $\left(a^{\frac{1}{2}} + b^{\frac{1}{2}}\right)\left(a^{\frac{1}{2}} - b^{\frac{1}{2}}\right)$

50. $(a + b) \div \left(a^{\frac{1}{3}} + b^{\frac{1}{3}}\right)$

51. Find the value of x for which $((125)^{\frac{1}{3}}(128)^{\frac{1}{x}})^2 = 1600$.
(Hint: if $a^n = a^m$ then $n = m$, for $a \neq 0$, $a \neq 1$.)

SCIENTIFIC NOTATION

For convenience, very large or very small numbers often are expressed in *scientific notation*. They are shown as the product of a number between 1 and 10 and a power of 10.

8 places

$150\ 000\ 000 = 1.5 \times 10^8$

5 places

$0.0000666 = 6.66 \times 10^{-5}$

Expressing a number in scientific notation is simple if you note the relationship between the exponent of 10 and the number of places over which the decimal point is moved for the new numeral. Try it.

1. 37 000 000 000 000   **2.** 0.0000014   **3.** 5 030 000 000

4. 0.00000000030   **5.** 70 700 000 000   **6.** 0.000702

Write without exponents.

7. 1.770×10^6 **8.** 3.6×10^{-5} **9.** 1.025×10^4 **10.** 7.2×10^{-12}

7-4   ZERO AND NEGATIVE EXPONENTS

For the multiplication rule $x^m \cdot x^n = x^{m+n}$ to hold for a zero exponent, we must define x^0 so that

$$\boxed{x^0} \cdot x^n = x^{0+n}$$
$$= x^n$$

Since $\boxed{1} \cdot x^n = x^n$, it is reasonable to make the following definition for x^0.

> $x^0 = 1$ when $x \neq 0$.
>
> The zero power of any number, except 0, is 1.

EXAMPLE 1 Simplify $2^0 + 4^0$.

   SOLUTION $2^0 + 4^0 = 1 + 1$, or 2.

EXAMPLE 2 Simplify $\dfrac{a^0}{3x^0}$.

   SOLUTION $\dfrac{a^0}{3x^0} = \dfrac{1}{3 \cdot 1}$, or $\dfrac{1}{3}$.

If the multiplication law is to hold for negative exponents, we must define x^{-m} so that

$$x^m \cdot \boxed{x^{-m}} = x^{m+(-m)}$$
$$= x^0$$
$$= 1$$

Since $x^m \cdot \boxed{\dfrac{1}{x^m}} = 1$, it is reasonable to define x^{-m} to be the reciprocal of x^m.

> $x^{-m} = \dfrac{1}{x^m}$ when $x \neq 0$.

In general, an expression with positive exponents is said to be *simpler* than an expression with negative exponents.

EXAMPLE 3 Simplify 3^{-2}.

   SOLUTION $3^{-2} = \dfrac{1}{3^2}$, or $\dfrac{1}{9}$.

EXAMPLE 4 Simplify $16^{-\frac{1}{2}}$

SOLUTION $16^{-\frac{1}{2}} = \dfrac{1}{16^{\frac{1}{2}}}$

$= \dfrac{1}{\sqrt{16}}$, or $\dfrac{1}{4}$.

EXAMPLE 5 Simplify $\dfrac{x^2 y^{-3}}{2z^{-4}}$.

SOLUTION $\dfrac{x^2 y^{-3}}{2z^{-4}} = \dfrac{x^2}{2} \cdot \dfrac{y^{-3}}{1} \cdot \dfrac{1}{z^{-4}}$

$= \dfrac{x^2}{2} \cdot \dfrac{1}{y^3} \cdot \dfrac{z^4}{1}$

$= \dfrac{x^2 z^4}{2y^3}$

EXAMPLE 6 Multiply x^2 and x^{-3}.

SOLUTION 1

$x^2 \cdot x^{-3} = \overset{1}{\cancel{x^2}} \cdot \dfrac{1}{\underset{x}{\cancel{x^3}}}$

$= \dfrac{1}{x}$

SOLUTION 2

$x^2 \cdot x^{-3} = x^{2+(-3)}$

$= x^{-1}$

$= \dfrac{1}{x}$

EXAMPLE 7 Divide $\dfrac{y^{-1}}{y^{-4}}$.

SOLUTION 1

$\dfrac{y^{-1}}{y^{-4}} = \dfrac{\frac{1}{y}}{\frac{1}{y^4}}$

$= \dfrac{1}{y} \cdot \dfrac{y^4}{1}$

$= y^3$

SOLUTION 2

$\dfrac{y^{-1}}{y^{-4}} = y^{-1-(-4)}$

$= y^{-1+4}$

$= y^3$

EXAMPLE 8 Simplify $(x^{-2})^3$.

SOLUTION 1

$(x^{-2})^3 = \left(\dfrac{1}{x^2}\right)^3$

$= \dfrac{1}{x^6}$

SOLUTION 2

$(x^{-2})^3 = x^{-6}$

$= \dfrac{1}{x^6}$

EXAMPLE 9 Represent $x^{-2}(x^2 + 1 + x^{-2})$ using positive exponents.

SOLUTION $x^{-2}(x^2 + 1 + x^{-2}) = x^{-2} \cdot x^2 + x^{-2} \cdot 1 + x^{-2} \cdot x^{-2}$

$= x^0 + x^{-2} + x^{-4}$

$= 1 + \dfrac{1}{x^2} + \dfrac{1}{x^4}$

EXAMPLE 10 Simplify $(xy^{-2})^{-1}$.

SOLUTION 1	SOLUTION 2	SOLUTION 3
$(xy^{-2})^{-1}$	$(xy^{-2})^{-1}$	$(xy^{-2})^{-1}$
$= \dfrac{1}{xy^{-2}}$	$= \left(\dfrac{x}{y^2}\right)^{-1}$	$= x^{-1}y^2$
$= \dfrac{y^2}{x}$	$= \dfrac{1}{\frac{x}{y^2}}$	$= \dfrac{y^2}{x}$
	$= \dfrac{y^2}{x}$	

CLASSROOM EXERCISES

Simplify.   Show only positive exponents in your result.

1. 12^0
2. 4^{-3}
3. $49^{-\frac{1}{2}}$
4. $(k^{-1})^4$
5. $y^{-1}(y^3 + 1 + y^{-2})$

6. $y^3 \cdot y^{-4}$
7. $(2x^{-3})^{-1}$
8. $\dfrac{16x^0}{y^3}$
9. $\dfrac{x^{-3}}{x^{-5}}$
10. $\dfrac{1}{x^{-2}} - \dfrac{1}{2^{-2}}$

EXERCISES

Ⓐ Simplify.   Show only positive exponents in your result.

1. $5^0 + 3^0$
2. $6^0 - 2^0$
3. $3^0 \cdot 4$
4. $5^0 \cdot 3$
5. 2^{-1}

6. 4^{-1}
7. $4^{-\frac{1}{2}}$
8. $9^{-\frac{1}{2}}$
9. $(-4)^{-3}$
10. $(-3)^{-4}$

11. $\dfrac{4}{2x^0}$
12. $\dfrac{12}{3x^0}$
13. $\dfrac{4}{3^{-1}}$
14. $\dfrac{2}{4^{-1}}$
15. $x^{-6} \cdot x^9$

16. $y^{-8} \cdot y^{10}$
17. $\dfrac{1}{3b^{-2}}$
18. $\dfrac{4}{3a^{-6}}$
19. $b^5 \div b^{-2}$
20. $c^4 \div c^{-3}$

21. $\dfrac{a^{-6}}{a^{-7}}$
22. $\dfrac{x^{-3}}{x^{-4}}$
23. $\dfrac{x^{-6}}{x^2}$
24. $\dfrac{x^{-9}}{x^5}$
25. $\dfrac{n^{-2}}{n^3}$

26. $\dfrac{x^{-3}}{x^5}$
27. $(m^{-3})^3$
28. $(x^{-2})^4$
29. $(x^{-2}y)^{-1}$
30. $(cd^{-3})^{-1}$

31. $\left(\dfrac{x^2}{y}\right)^{-1}$
32. $\left(\dfrac{c^3}{d^2}\right)^{-1}$
33. $\left(\dfrac{x^2}{y^3}\right)^{-3}$
34. $\left(\dfrac{a^5}{b^2}\right)^{-2}$
35. $(x^{-3}y^{-2})^{-3}$

Ⓑ **36.** $\dfrac{4a^{-2}b^3}{8a^{-3}b}$
37. $\dfrac{9c^{-3}d^5}{12c^{-4}d^{-6}}$
38. $\dfrac{2^0 + 3}{1 - 2^{-1}}$
39. $\dfrac{3 + 4^0}{1 - 3^{-1}}$

40. $((a - b)^3)^{-\frac{2}{3}}$
41. $((x + y)^{-2})^{\frac{3}{2}}$
42. $x(x - x^{-1})$
43. $y^2(y^2 - y^{-2})$

44. $b^{\frac{1}{2}}\left(b^2 + b^{\frac{2}{3}} - b\right)$
45. $x^{\frac{1}{3}}\left(x^2 - x^{\frac{1}{2}} - x\right)$
46. $(x^2 + 2xy + y^2)^{-\frac{1}{2}}$
47. $\dfrac{(x + 2y)^{-3}(x - 2y)}{(x + 2y)^{-4}}$

Ⓒ Perform the indicated operation and simplify.

48. $(a + b)(a^{-1} - b^{-1})$ **49.** $(x^{-2} + y^{-2})(x^{-2} - y^{-2})$ **50.** $(m^{-1} - n^{-1})(m^{-2} + m^{-1}n^{-1} + n^{-2})$

51. $\dfrac{a^{-2} - b^{-2}}{a^{-1} - b^{-1}}$ **52.** $\dfrac{m^{-3} + n^{-3}}{m^{-1} + n^{-1}}$ **53.** $\dfrac{a^{-1} - b^{-1}}{a^{-\frac{1}{2}} + b^{-\frac{1}{2}}}$

CHECKING YOUR UNDERSTANDING

WORDS AND SYMBOLS

negative exponent   rational exponent, $a^{\frac{m}{n}}$ zero exponent, a^0

Rules for Operating with Exponents

Multiplication   Division   Power of a Power   Power of a Product   Power of a Quotient

CONCEPTS

■ Zero, rational, and negative exponents are defined in such a way that the rules for operating with integral exponents also apply to them. [7-1, 7-3, 7-4]

■ The principal nth root, $\sqrt[n]{a}$, is a real number when a is a real number and n is an odd positive integer or when a is a non-negative real number and n is an even positive integer. [7-2]

■ Numbers with the same base and opposite exponents are reciprocals. [7-4]

PROCESSES

■ Use the definitions of exponents and the rules for operating with exponents to simplify expressions. [7-1, 7-3, 7-4]

1. $\dfrac{x^7 y}{y^3} \cdot \dfrac{xy^5}{x^2}$ **2.** $\dfrac{(x^2 z^3)^3}{xz}$ **3.** $\left(\dfrac{3(a-4)^n}{(a-4)}\right)^2$ **4.** $9^{\frac{3}{2}}$

5. $\left(-\dfrac{27}{8}\right)^{\frac{5}{3}}$ **6.** $\left(\dfrac{z^{\frac{2}{3}}}{z^{\frac{1}{6}}}\right)^2$ **7.** $\left(m^{\frac{7}{8}}\right)^{\frac{4}{7}}$ **8.** $\left(\dfrac{x^0}{3}\right)^{-2}$

9. $\dfrac{4^{-3}}{4^{\frac{1}{2}}}$ **10.** $(8a^{-3})^{-\frac{1}{3}}$ **11.** $\dfrac{(xy)^5}{x^{-3}}$ **12.** $\left(\dfrac{a^{\frac{2}{3}} b^{\frac{1}{2}}}{c^{\frac{3}{4}}}\right)^{-6}$

■ Find the principal nth root. [7-2]

13. $-\sqrt[4]{81}$ **14.** $\sqrt[7]{-1}$ **15.** $\sqrt[3]{27a^3 b^3}$ **16.** $\sqrt[4]{256a^8 b^4}$

> **OBJECTIVES:** Simplify radicals. Add, subtract, multiply, and divide with radicals. Solve radical equations.

7-5 PRODUCTS INVOLVING RADICALS

Each term in the equation

$$a^{\frac{1}{n}} \cdot b^{\frac{1}{n}} = (ab)^{\frac{1}{n}}$$

may be replaced by the corresponding term that uses a radical.

$$\sqrt[n]{a} \cdot \sqrt[n]{b} = \sqrt[n]{ab}$$

This new equation may be used both to multiply and to simplify radicals.

EXAMPLE 1 Multiply $\sqrt{3}$ and $\sqrt{5}$.

SOLUTION $\sqrt{3}\sqrt{5} = \sqrt{15}$

To simplify a square-root radical, factor the radicand to show as many perfect-square factors as possible. Then find the square root of each such factor.

EXAMPLE 2 Simplify $\sqrt{20}$.

SOLUTION $\begin{aligned}\sqrt{20} &= \sqrt{4 \cdot 5}\\ &= \sqrt{4}\sqrt{5}\\ &= 2\sqrt{5}\end{aligned}$

EXAMPLE 3 Simplify $5x\sqrt{18(x + y)^3}$, for $x + y \geq 0$.

SOLUTION $\begin{aligned}5x\sqrt{18(x + y)^3} &= 5x\sqrt{9(x + y)^2 \cdot 2(x + y)}\\ &= 5x\sqrt{9(x + y)^2}\sqrt{2(x + y)}\\ &= 5x \cdot 3(x + y)\sqrt{2(x + y)},\\ &= 15x(x + y)\sqrt{2(x + y)}\end{aligned}$

To simplify a radical that is a cube root, factor the radicand to show as many perfect-cube factors as possible. Then find the cube root of each such factor.

EXAMPLE 4 Simplify $\sqrt[3]{24x^4}$.

SOLUTION $\begin{aligned}\sqrt[3]{24x^4} &= \sqrt[3]{8x^3 \cdot 3x}\\ &= \sqrt[3]{8x^3}\sqrt[3]{3x}\\ &= 2x\sqrt[3]{3x}\end{aligned}$

EXAMPLE 5   Multiply $2\sqrt{6}$ and $3\sqrt{2}$.   Then simplify.

SOLUTION $2\sqrt{6} \cdot 3\sqrt{2} = 2 \cdot 3\sqrt{6}\sqrt{2}$
$= 6\sqrt{12}$
$= 6\sqrt{4 \cdot 3}$
$= 6\sqrt{4}\sqrt{3}$
$= 6 \cdot 2\sqrt{3}$, or $12\sqrt{3}$

EXAMPLE 6   Multiply $\sqrt[3]{6}$ and $\sqrt[3]{72}$.   Then simplify.

SOLUTION $\sqrt[3]{6}\sqrt[3]{72} = \sqrt[3]{6}\sqrt[3]{6 \cdot 6 \cdot 2}$
$= \sqrt[3]{6 \cdot 6 \cdot 6 \cdot 2}$
$= \sqrt[3]{6^3}\sqrt[3]{2}$, or $6\sqrt[3]{2}$

EXAMPLE 7   Multiply $\sqrt{2x}$ and $(\sqrt{5x})^3$ for $x \geq 0$.   Then simplify.

SOLUTION $\sqrt{2x}(\sqrt{5x})^3 = \sqrt{2x}\sqrt{5x}(\sqrt{5x})^2$
$= \sqrt{10x^2}(5x)$
$= \sqrt{10}\,x\,(5x)$
$= 5x^2\sqrt{10}$

Some computations with radicals may be made easier by reversing the simplifying process.

EXAMPLE 8   Complete: $2\sqrt{110} = \sqrt{?}$

SOLUTION $2\sqrt{110} = \sqrt{4}\sqrt{110}$
$= \sqrt{440}$

EXAMPLE 9   Complete: $3\sqrt[3]{18} = \sqrt[3]{?}$.

SOLUTION $3\sqrt[3]{18} = \sqrt[3]{27} \cdot \sqrt[3]{18}$
$= \sqrt[3]{27 \cdot 18}$, or $\sqrt[3]{486}$

CLASSROOM EXERCISES

Perform the indicated operations and simplify.

1. $\sqrt{27}$
2. $\sqrt[3]{16x^5}$
3. $3x\sqrt{12(x + y)^5}$
4. $\sqrt{2} \cdot \sqrt{5}$

5. $\sqrt{2} \cdot \sqrt{6}$
6. $4\sqrt{2} \cdot 2\sqrt{10}$
7. $\sqrt[3]{2}\sqrt[3]{4}$
8. $\sqrt[3]{4}\sqrt[3]{32}$

9. $\sqrt{3x} \cdot \sqrt{7x}$
10. $(\sqrt{7x})^3$
11. $3\sqrt{10} = \sqrt{?}$
12. $2\sqrt[3]{20} = \sqrt[3]{?}$

EXERCISES

A Simplify.

1. $\sqrt{8}$ 2. $\sqrt{12}$ 3. $\sqrt{24}$ 4. $\sqrt{18}$

5. $\sqrt[3]{24}$ 6. $\sqrt[3]{54}$ 7. $\sqrt{50a}$ 8. $\sqrt{54b}$

9. $\sqrt[3]{54x^4}$ 10. $\sqrt[3]{24y^5}$ 11. $\sqrt{48xy^2}$ 12. $\sqrt{24x^2y}$

13. $\sqrt{98a^4b^3}$ 14. $\sqrt{200x^3y^2}$ 15. $\sqrt[3]{40x^4y}$ 16. $\sqrt[5]{64x^6y}$

17. $3\sqrt{12x^5}$ 18. $5\sqrt{15y^7}$ 19. $5a\sqrt[3]{8a^4}$ 20. $5x\sqrt[3]{16x^4}$

Multiply as indicated. Then simplify.

21. $\sqrt{5}\cdot\sqrt{2}$ 22. $\sqrt{3}\cdot\sqrt{7}$ 23. $\sqrt{2}\sqrt{18}$ 24. $\sqrt{3}\sqrt{27}$

25. $\sqrt[3]{2}\sqrt[3]{3}$ 26. $\sqrt[3]{4}\sqrt[3]{5}$ 27. $\sqrt{3}\sqrt{18}$ 28. $\sqrt{3}\sqrt{8}$

29. $\sqrt{ab}\sqrt{ac}$ 30. $\sqrt{a}\sqrt{abc}$ 31. $\sqrt{\frac{4}{3}}\cdot\sqrt{\frac{3}{4}}$ 32. $\sqrt{\frac{7}{6}}\sqrt{\frac{6}{7}}$

33. $(\sqrt[3]{5})^3$ 34. $(\sqrt[3]{4})^3$ 35. $\sqrt{3y}\sqrt{2y}$ 36. $\sqrt{5z}\sqrt{3z}$

Complete.

37. $5\sqrt{6}=\sqrt{?}$ 38. $5\sqrt{15}=\sqrt{?}$ 39. $2\sqrt[3]{30}=\sqrt[3]{?}$ 40. $3\sqrt[3]{10}=\sqrt[3]{?}$

B Simplify

41. $3\sqrt{250(x-y)^3}$ 42. $a\sqrt{169(a+b)^3}$ 43. $x\sqrt[3]{16(x-y)^5}$ 44. $\sqrt[5]{243a^6}$

45. $\sqrt{8}\sqrt{3}\sqrt{18}$ 46. $\sqrt[3]{16}\sqrt[3]{12}\sqrt[3]{45}$ 47. $\sqrt[4]{32}\sqrt[4]{24}\sqrt[4]{27}$ 48. $\sqrt[4]{144a^6b^3c^2}$

49. $\sqrt[7]{128x^8y^{12}z^{21}}$ 50. $\sqrt{3}(\sqrt{2}-3\sqrt{6})$ 51. $\sqrt{5}(\sqrt{2}-\sqrt{15})$ 52. $\sqrt[6]{64x^7}$

Complete.

53. $2x\sqrt{140y}=\sqrt{?}$ 54. $3x^2\sqrt[3]{5}=\sqrt[3]{?}$ 55. $4y\sqrt[3]{xy}=\sqrt[3]{?}$

C Simplify.

56. $\sqrt[n]{a^n}\cdot\sqrt[n]{a^{2n}}$ 57. $\sqrt{a^{2n+2}}\cdot\sqrt[3]{a^{3n-3}}$ 58. $\sqrt[n]{x^{n+1}}\cdot\sqrt[n]{x^{n+2}}$ 59. $\sqrt[n]{x^{n-2}}\cdot\sqrt[n]{x^3}$

60. $(\sqrt[3]{2x+1})^6$ 61. $(\sqrt[8]{x+1})^{16}$ 62. $(\sqrt{2x}+\sqrt{x+1})^2$

63. $(x\sqrt[n]{x})^n$ 64. $(x^a\sqrt[n]{x^a})^n$ 65. $(2x\sqrt[3]{x^2y^4})(xy\sqrt[3]{x^4y})^2$

Simplify. Think of the radicand as a trinomial of the form $a^2+2ab+b^2$ with the second term of the radicand as the $2ab$ term.

66. $\sqrt{7+4\sqrt{3}}$ 67. $\sqrt{175+26\sqrt{6}}$ 68. $\sqrt{86+18\sqrt{5}}$

7-6 DIVISION INVOLVING RADICALS

Each term in the equation

$$\frac{a^{\frac{1}{n}}}{b^{\frac{1}{n}}} = \left(\frac{a}{b}\right)^{\frac{1}{n}}, \; b \neq 0,$$

may be replaced by the corresponding term that uses a radical.

$$\frac{\sqrt[n]{a}}{\sqrt[n]{b}} = \sqrt[n]{\frac{a}{b}}, \; b \neq 0$$

This new equation may be used to simplify both radicals and quotients involving radicals. A "simplified" quotient has no radicals in a denominator.

EXAMPLE 1 Divide $\sqrt{18}$ by $\sqrt{3}$. Simplify the quotient.

SOLUTION 1	SOLUTION 2
$\dfrac{\sqrt{18}}{\sqrt{3}} = \sqrt{\dfrac{18}{3}}$, or $\sqrt{6}$	$\dfrac{\sqrt{18}}{\sqrt{3}} = \dfrac{\sqrt{3}\sqrt{6}}{\sqrt{3}}$, or $\sqrt{6}$

EXAMPLE 2 Divide $\sqrt[3]{24a^7}$ by $\sqrt[3]{3a}$, $a \neq 0$. Then simplify.

SOLUTION 1	SOLUTION 2
$\dfrac{\sqrt[3]{24a^7}}{\sqrt[3]{3a}} = \sqrt[3]{\dfrac{24a^7}{3a}}$ $= \sqrt[3]{8a^6}$, or $2a^2$	$\dfrac{\sqrt[3]{24a^7}}{\sqrt[3]{3a}} = \dfrac{\sqrt[3]{3a}\,\sqrt[3]{8a^6}}{\sqrt[3]{3a}}$ $= \sqrt[3]{8a^6}$, or $2a^2$

EXAMPLE 3 Divide $\sqrt{54r^3s}$ by $\sqrt{3s^3}$, $r > 0$, $s > 0$. Then simplify.

SOLUTION 1	SOLUTION 2
$\dfrac{\sqrt{54r^3s}}{\sqrt{3s^3}} = \sqrt{\dfrac{54r^3s}{3s^3}}$ $= \sqrt{\dfrac{18r^3}{s^2}}$ $= \dfrac{\sqrt{9r^2}\sqrt{2r}}{\sqrt{s^2}}$ $= \dfrac{3r\sqrt{2r}}{s}$	$\dfrac{\sqrt{54r^3s}}{\sqrt{3s^3}} = \dfrac{\sqrt{9r^2}\sqrt{6rs}}{\sqrt{s^2}\sqrt{3s}}$ $= \dfrac{3r\sqrt{2r}\sqrt{3s}}{s\sqrt{3s}}$ $= \dfrac{3r\sqrt{2r}}{s}$

A radical in simplest form has no fractions in its radicand.   To simplify a radical so that the radicand contains no fractions, use the Multiplication Property of One.

EXAMPLE 4   Simplify $\sqrt{\frac{1}{8}}$.

SOLUTION   First, multiply the radicand by $\frac{2}{2}$ to change the denominator to a perfect square.

$$\sqrt{\frac{1}{8}} = \sqrt{\frac{1}{8} \cdot \frac{2}{2}}$$

$$= \sqrt{\frac{2}{16}}$$

$$= \frac{\sqrt{2}}{4}, \text{ or } \frac{1}{4}\sqrt{2}$$

EXAMPLE 5   Divide $\sqrt{3x}$ by $\sqrt{2x^3y}$, $x > 0$, $y > 0$.   Then simplify.

SOLUTION $\dfrac{\sqrt{3x}}{\sqrt{2x^3y}} = \sqrt{\dfrac{3x}{2x^3y}}$

$$= \sqrt{\frac{3}{2x^2y} \cdot \frac{2y}{2y}}$$

$$= \sqrt{\frac{6y}{(2xy)^2}}$$

$$= \frac{\sqrt{6y}}{2xy}, \text{ or } \frac{1}{2xy}\sqrt{6y}$$

To simplify a radical having index 3, use the Multiplication Property of One to change the denominator of the radicand to a perfect cube. Also find all perfect-cube factors of the numerator.

EXAMPLE 6   Simplify $\sqrt[3]{\dfrac{8}{3a^2}}$, $a \neq 0$.

SOLUTION $\sqrt[3]{\dfrac{8}{3a^2}} = \sqrt[3]{\dfrac{8}{3a^2} \cdot \dfrac{9a}{9a}}$

$$= \sqrt[3]{\frac{8}{(3a)^3} \cdot 9a}$$

$$= \frac{\sqrt[3]{8}}{\sqrt[3]{(3a)^3}} \cdot \sqrt[3]{9a}$$

$$= \frac{2}{3a}\sqrt[3]{9a}, \text{ or } \frac{2\sqrt[3]{9a}}{3a}$$

CLASSROOM EXERCISES

Simplify.

1. $\dfrac{\sqrt{15}}{\sqrt{5}}$ **2.** $\dfrac{\sqrt[3]{81b^2}}{\sqrt[3]{3b^2}}$ **3.** $\dfrac{\sqrt[4]{x^{11}}}{\sqrt[4]{x^3}}$ **4.** $\dfrac{\sqrt{12a^2b}}{\sqrt{3ab^3}}$ **5.** $\sqrt{\dfrac{25}{7b}}$

6. $\sqrt[3]{\dfrac{27}{5b}}$ **7.** $\dfrac{\sqrt{7y}}{\sqrt{3xy^5}}$ **8.** $\sqrt{\dfrac{2}{3}}$ **9.** $\sqrt[3]{\dfrac{ac}{b^2}}$ **10.** $\dfrac{\sqrt{24x^3y^2}}{\sqrt{18x^2y}}$

EXERCISES

A Simplify.

1. $\dfrac{\sqrt{12}}{\sqrt{3}}$ **2.** $\dfrac{\sqrt{20}}{\sqrt{5}}$ **3.** $\dfrac{\sqrt{30x}}{\sqrt{3x}}$ **4.** $\dfrac{\sqrt{30y}}{\sqrt{6y}}$ **5.** $\dfrac{\sqrt{2}}{\sqrt{\frac{1}{2}}}$

6. $\dfrac{\sqrt{3}}{\sqrt{\frac{1}{3}}}$ **7.** $\dfrac{\sqrt{45}}{\sqrt{9}}$ **8.** $\dfrac{\sqrt{60}}{\sqrt{10}}$ **9.** $\dfrac{\sqrt[3]{36}}{\sqrt[3]{9}}$ **10.** $\dfrac{\sqrt[3]{28}}{\sqrt[3]{7}}$

11. $\dfrac{\sqrt[3]{24a^2b^2}}{\sqrt[3]{3ab}}$ **12.** $\dfrac{\sqrt[3]{75b^2}}{\sqrt[3]{25b^2}}$ **13.** $\sqrt{\dfrac{4}{5}}$ **14.** $\sqrt{\dfrac{8}{3}}$ **15.** $\dfrac{\sqrt{6x^3y}}{\sqrt{2xy^3}}$

16. $\dfrac{\sqrt{15ba^3}}{\sqrt{5b^2a}}$ **17.** $\sqrt{\dfrac{20}{3}}$ **18.** $\sqrt{\dfrac{8}{5}}$ **19.** $\sqrt{\dfrac{2x}{7}}$ **20.** $\sqrt{\dfrac{3a}{5}}$

21. $\sqrt[3]{\dfrac{3}{4}}$ **22.** $\sqrt[3]{\dfrac{2}{9}}$ **23.** $\sqrt{\dfrac{5}{12}}$ **24.** $\sqrt{\dfrac{3}{50}}$ **25.** $\sqrt{\dfrac{a}{b}}$

26. $\sqrt{\dfrac{a}{5b}}$ **27.** $\sqrt[3]{\dfrac{125}{3x^2}}$ **28.** $\sqrt[3]{\dfrac{64}{5y^2}}$ **29.** $\sqrt[3]{\dfrac{ac}{b^2}}$ **30.** $\sqrt[3]{\dfrac{5m^3}{8n^2}}$

31. $\dfrac{\sqrt{5x}}{\sqrt{2x^3y}}$ **32.** $\dfrac{\sqrt{2y^3}}{\sqrt{7y^5x}}$ **33.** $\dfrac{\sqrt{2x^3y}}{\sqrt{5x}}$ **34.** $\dfrac{\sqrt{7y^5x}}{\sqrt{2y^3}}$ **35.** $\dfrac{1}{2}\sqrt{\dfrac{5y}{18x}}$

B **36.** $\dfrac{a}{b}\sqrt{\dfrac{3b^2}{8a^3}}$ **37.** $\sqrt{\dfrac{a^{m+1}}{a^{m-1}}}$ **38.** $\dfrac{\sqrt{6x-6}}{\sqrt{3x-3}}$ **39.** $\dfrac{\sqrt[4]{x^{13}}}{\sqrt[4]{x^5}}$ **40.** $\dfrac{\sqrt[4]{y^{15}}}{\sqrt[4]{y^7}}$

41. $\dfrac{\sqrt[3]{72a^7}}{\sqrt[3]{9a}}$ **42.** $\dfrac{\sqrt[3]{16b^8}}{\sqrt[3]{2b^2}}$ **43.** $\dfrac{\sqrt{27x^5}}{\sqrt{\frac{1}{3}x^4}}$ **44.** $\sqrt[4]{\dfrac{27}{36a}}$ **45.** $\sqrt[5]{\dfrac{2x}{25}}$

46. $\sqrt{x+\dfrac{y^2}{x}}$ **47.** $\sqrt{c^2-\left(\dfrac{c}{2}\right)^2}$ **48.** $\dfrac{\sqrt[4]{(xy)^{15n}}}{\sqrt[4]{x^{3n}}}$ **49.** $\sqrt{\dfrac{1}{x-y}}$

C **50.** $\sqrt{\dfrac{4x^{2n}}{9y}}$ **51.** $\sqrt[n]{\dfrac{1}{x^n}}$ **52.** $\sqrt[n]{\dfrac{x^{2n}}{x}}$ **53.** $\sqrt[k]{\dfrac{x}{x^{2k}}}$ **54.** $\sqrt[k]{\dfrac{x^{2k+1}}{y^{4k-3}}}$

7-7 RATIONALIZING DENOMINATORS

A fraction with a radical in its denominator is not considered to be in simplest form. The process of simplifying fractions by finding rational denominators is called *rationalizing the denominator*. To do this, use the Multiplication Property of One to change the fraction so that the denominator is "made rational."

EXAMPLE 1 Simplify $\dfrac{3}{\sqrt{5}}$, $\dfrac{\sqrt{2}}{\sqrt{27}}$, and $\dfrac{1}{\sqrt{6x}}$, $x > 0$, by rationalizing the denominators.

SOLUTION

$$\dfrac{3}{\sqrt{5}}$$

$$= \dfrac{3}{\sqrt{5}} \cdot \dfrac{\sqrt{5}}{\sqrt{5}}$$

$$= \dfrac{3\sqrt{5}}{5}, \text{ or } \dfrac{3}{5}\sqrt{5}$$

$$\dfrac{\sqrt{2}}{\sqrt{27}}$$

$$= \dfrac{\sqrt{2}}{3\sqrt{3}} \cdot \dfrac{\sqrt{3}}{\sqrt{3}}$$

$$= \dfrac{\sqrt{6}}{9}, \text{ or } \dfrac{1}{9}\sqrt{6}$$

$$\dfrac{1}{\sqrt{6x}}$$

$$= \dfrac{1}{\sqrt{6x}} \cdot \dfrac{\sqrt{6x}}{\sqrt{6x}}$$

$$= \dfrac{\sqrt{6x}}{6x}, \text{ or } \dfrac{1}{6x}\sqrt{6x}$$

EXAMPLE 2 Simplify $\dfrac{1}{\sqrt[3]{12}}$.

SOLUTION $\dfrac{1}{\sqrt[3]{12}} = \dfrac{1}{\sqrt[3]{2^2 \cdot 3}} \cdot \dfrac{\sqrt[3]{2 \cdot 3^2}}{\sqrt[3]{2 \cdot 3^2}}$

$$= \dfrac{\sqrt[3]{18}}{\sqrt[3]{2^3 \cdot 3^3}}$$

$$= \dfrac{\sqrt[3]{18}}{6}, \text{ or } \dfrac{1}{6}\sqrt[3]{18}$$

EXAMPLE 3 Give a decimal approximation for $\dfrac{3}{\sqrt{2}}$. Use $\sqrt{2} \doteq 1.414$.

SOLUTION 1

$$\dfrac{3}{\sqrt{2}} = \dfrac{3}{\sqrt{2}} \cdot \dfrac{\sqrt{2}}{\sqrt{2}}$$

$$= \dfrac{3\sqrt{2}}{2}$$

$$\doteq \dfrac{3(1.414)}{2}$$

$$\doteq 2.121$$

SOLUTION 2

$$\dfrac{3}{\sqrt{2}} \doteq \dfrac{3}{1.414}$$

The division is left for the student.

CLASSROOM EXERCISES

Simplify by rationalizing the denominator.

1. $\dfrac{\sqrt{2}}{\sqrt{7}}$ **2.** $\dfrac{1}{\sqrt{5y}}$ **3.** $\dfrac{\sqrt[3]{3}}{\sqrt[3]{4}}$ **4.** $\dfrac{1}{\sqrt[3]{18}}$ **5.** $\dfrac{\sqrt{3}}{\sqrt{8}}$

6. Give a decimal approximation for $\dfrac{2}{\sqrt{3}}$. Use 1.732 for $\sqrt{3}$. Tell why the computation is easier when you rationalize the denominator first.

EXERCISES

A Simplify by rationalizing the denominator.

1. $\dfrac{\sqrt{5}}{\sqrt{3}}$ **2.** $\dfrac{\sqrt{5}}{\sqrt{7}}$ **3.** $\dfrac{3}{\sqrt{2}}$ **4.** $\dfrac{2}{\sqrt{3}}$ **5.** $\dfrac{6}{2\sqrt{3}}$

6. $\dfrac{2}{\sqrt[4]{3}}$ **7.** $\dfrac{3}{\sqrt[3]{2}}$ **8.** $\dfrac{\sqrt{45}}{\sqrt{8}}$ **9.** $\dfrac{5\sqrt{2}}{3\sqrt{75}}$ **10.** $\dfrac{2\sqrt{3}}{5\sqrt{20}}$

11. $\dfrac{2}{\sqrt[3]{4}}$ **12.** $\dfrac{7}{\sqrt[3]{25}}$ **13.** $\dfrac{5}{3\sqrt[3]{5}}$ **14.** $\dfrac{1}{\sqrt[3]{xy^2}}$ **15.** $\dfrac{1}{\sqrt[3]{a^2b}}$

Approximate. Use 1.414 for $\sqrt{2}$, 1.732 for $\sqrt{3}$, and 2.449 for $\sqrt{6}$.

16. $\dfrac{10}{\sqrt{2}}$ **17.** $\dfrac{1}{\sqrt{3}}$ **18.** $\dfrac{6}{\sqrt{6}}$ **19.** $\dfrac{\sqrt{2}}{\sqrt{3}}$ **20.** $\dfrac{\sqrt{3}}{\sqrt{2}}$

B Simplify.

21. $\dfrac{\sqrt[3]{2x^2y}}{\sqrt[3]{12xy^2}}$ **22.** $\sqrt[3]{\dfrac{3a^2b^3}{27ab^4}}$ **23.** $\sqrt{(x+y)^{-3}}$ **24.** $\dfrac{1}{\sqrt[10]{x^2y^8z^3}}$

C **25.** $\sqrt[n]{\dfrac{1}{x^{n-3}}}$ **26.** $\sqrt[n]{\dfrac{a}{x^{2n-1}}}$ **27.** $\dfrac{1}{2^{\frac{3}{2}}-1}$ **28.** $\sqrt[m]{\dfrac{2x^2y^{3m}}{9x^5y^{4m-1}}}$

EXPONENTS WITH EXPONENTS

When exponents have exponents, "work down". For example, $6^{2^3} = 6^8$, not 36^3.

Which is greater?

1. 2^{3^4} or 4^{3^2} **2.** 4^{3^2} or $(4^3)^2$ **3.** 2^{4^0} or 2^{0^4} **4.** $0.5^{2^{0.5}}$ or $0.5^{0.5^2}$

7-8   CHANGING THE INDEX OF A RADICAL

Sometimes a radical can be replaced by a radical with a smaller index. To do this, first replace the radical by the corresponding expression having a fraction exponent. Work with the rules for operations involving exponents. Reduce the fraction if possible. Then replace the expression having a fraction exponent by the corresponding expression having a radical.

EXAMPLE 1   Simplify $\sqrt[4]{4}$.

SOLUTION $\sqrt[4]{4} = \sqrt[4]{2^2}$

$\quad\quad = 2^{\frac{2}{4}}$

$\quad\quad = 2^{\frac{1}{2}}$

$\quad\quad = \sqrt{2}$

EXAMPLE 2   Simplify $\sqrt[4]{16x^6}$, $x \geq 0$.

SOLUTION $\sqrt[4]{16x^6} = \sqrt[4]{2^4 x^4 x^2}$

$\quad\quad = 2x \cdot x^{\frac{2}{4}}$

$\quad\quad = 2x \cdot x^{\frac{1}{2}}$

$\quad\quad = 2x\sqrt{x}$

EXAMPLE 3   Simplify $\sqrt[6]{25x^4}$.

SOLUTION $\sqrt[6]{25x^4} = \sqrt[6]{5^2 x^4}$

$\quad\quad = (5^2 x^4)^{\frac{1}{6}}$

$\quad\quad = 5^{\frac{2}{6}} x^{\frac{4}{6}}$

$\quad\quad = 5^{\frac{1}{3}} x^{\frac{2}{3}}$

$\quad\quad = (5x^2)^{\frac{1}{3}}$

$\quad\quad = \sqrt[3]{5x^2}$

EXAMPLE 4   Simplify $\sqrt[4]{\dfrac{4x^{10}}{y^2}}$, $x \geq 0$, $y > 0$.

SOLUTION $\sqrt[4]{\dfrac{4x^{10}}{y^2}} = \sqrt[4]{\dfrac{4x^{10}}{y^2} \cdot \dfrac{y^2}{y^2}}$

$\quad\quad = \sqrt[4]{\dfrac{x^8}{y^4} \cdot 2^2 x^2 y^2}$

$\quad\quad = \dfrac{x^2}{y}(2^2 x^2 y^2)^{\frac{1}{4}}$

$\quad\quad = \dfrac{x^2}{y}(2xy)^{\frac{1}{2}}$

$\quad\quad = \dfrac{x^2}{y}\sqrt{2xy}$

Each term in the equation

$$a^{\frac{1}{mn}} = \left(a^{\frac{1}{m}}\right)^{\frac{1}{n}}$$

may be replaced by the corresponding term that uses a radical.

$$\sqrt[mn]{a} = \sqrt[n]{\sqrt[m]{a}}$$

This equation may be used to simplify radicals.

EXAMPLE 5   Simplify $\sqrt[9]{64}$.

SOLUTION $\sqrt[9]{64} = \sqrt[3]{\sqrt[3]{4^3}}$

$\quad\quad = \sqrt[3]{4}$

EXAMPLE 6   Simplify $\sqrt[6]{27a^3}$, $a > 0$.

SOLUTION $\sqrt[6]{27a^3} = \sqrt[2]{\sqrt[3]{(3a)^3}}$

$\quad\quad = \sqrt{3a}$

CLASSROOM EXERCISES

Simplify.

1. $\sqrt[4]{9}$ **2.** $\sqrt[6]{4a^2}$ **3.** $\sqrt[8]{64}$ **4.** $\sqrt[4]{625x^{10}}$ **5.** $\sqrt[4]{\dfrac{8a^3}{b^2}}$

EXERCISES

A Simplify.

1. $\sqrt[4]{25}$ **2.** $\sqrt[4]{49}$ **3.** $\sqrt[4]{a^2}$ **4.** $\sqrt[4]{36a^2}$ **5.** $\sqrt[6]{27}$

6. $\sqrt[6]{64x^2}$ **7.** $\sqrt[6]{x^3y^3}$ **8.** $\sqrt[6]{125c^3}$ **9.** $\sqrt[4]{81y^6}$ **10.** $\sqrt[4]{625x^{14}}$

11. $\sqrt[10]{32}$ **12.** $\sqrt[10]{243}$ **13.** $\sqrt[4]{16x^2y^2}$ **14.** $\sqrt[4]{144a^2b^2}$ **15.** $\sqrt[12]{64x^3y^6}$

16. $\sqrt[12]{64a^2b^6}$ **17.** $\sqrt[10]{a^4b^2c^8}$ **18.** $\sqrt[10]{x^5y^{10}z^5}$ **19.** $\sqrt[9]{\dfrac{27}{x^3}}$ **20.** $\sqrt[6]{\dfrac{a^2}{25}}$

B **21.** $\sqrt[4]{\dfrac{243a^{12}y^{-4}}{27a^{-4}}}$ **22.** $\sqrt[4]{\dfrac{16a^8x^{-4}}{a^{-8}}}$ **23.** $\sqrt[4]{\dfrac{3125x^{10}y^{-2}}{125x^{-2}}}$ **24.** $\sqrt[4]{9x^2 - 30xy + 25y^2}$

25. $\sqrt[4]{\dfrac{8a^2b^{-6}}{2b^4}}$ **26.** $\sqrt[4]{x^6} \cdot \sqrt{x}$ **27.** $\sqrt[10m]{3^{10}x^{10n}y^{5k}}$ **28.** $\sqrt[6]{4x^{-2} + 8x^{-1} + 4}$

C **29.** $\sqrt[3]{\sqrt[4]{64z^{18}w^6}}$ **30.** $\sqrt[2n]{2^{4n}a^{6n}b^{8n}}$ **31.** $\sqrt[4]{100a^2 + 300ab + 225b^2}$

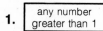 ## ROOTS "APPROACHING" A NUMBER

Use a calculator that has the $\boxed{\sqrt{x}}$ key. Follow the sequence of key strokes shown. Find whether the sequence of numbers displayed by the calculator "approaches" a number.

1.

2.

7-9   ADDITION AND SUBTRACTION INVOLVING RADICALS

Just as we can combine two *like* terms,

$$5x + 2x = 7x,$$

or two fractions with *like* denominators,

$$\frac{5}{8} + \frac{2}{8} = \frac{7}{8},$$

so we can combine two *like* radicals.

$$5\sqrt{3} + 2\sqrt{3} = 7\sqrt{3}$$

Like radicals have identical indexes and radicands.

Like Radicals	Unlike Radicals
$5\sqrt{3}$ and $2\sqrt{3}$	$5\sqrt{3}$ and $3\sqrt{2}$
$\sqrt{a}$ and $-\dfrac{5\sqrt{a}}{2}$	$\sqrt{a}$ and $\sqrt{\dfrac{a}{2}}$
$3\sqrt[3]{4x}$ and $\frac{1}{2}\sqrt[3]{4x}$	$\sqrt[3]{4x}$ and $\sqrt{4x}$

EXAMPLE 1   Simplify $2\sqrt{5} + 6\sqrt{5} - 3\sqrt{5}$.

SOLUTION $2\sqrt{5} + 6\sqrt{5} - 3\sqrt{5} = 8\sqrt{5} - 3\sqrt{5}$
$$= 5\sqrt{5}$$

EXAMPLE 2   Simplify $5\sqrt{a} + 3\sqrt{b} - 2\sqrt{a} - \sqrt{b}$.

SOLUTION $5\sqrt{a} + 3\sqrt{b} - 2\sqrt{a} - \sqrt{b} = 5\sqrt{a} - 2\sqrt{a} + 3\sqrt{b} - 1\sqrt{b}$
$$= 3\sqrt{a} + 2\sqrt{b}$$

Sometimes we can simplify unlike radicals to obtain like radicals.

EXAMPLE 3   Simplify $\sqrt{75} + 3\sqrt{27} - 2\sqrt{48}$.

SOLUTION $\sqrt{75} + 3\sqrt{27} - 2\sqrt{48} = \sqrt{25 \cdot 3} + 3\sqrt{9 \cdot 3} - 2\sqrt{16 \cdot 3}$
$$= 5\sqrt{3} + 9\sqrt{3} - 8\sqrt{3}$$
$$= 6\sqrt{3}$$

EXAMPLE 4 Simplify $\sqrt{\frac{1}{2}} + \sqrt{\frac{9}{8}} - \sqrt{\frac{1}{32}}$.

SOLUTION $\sqrt{\frac{1}{2}} + \sqrt{\frac{9}{8}} - \sqrt{\frac{1}{32}} = \sqrt{\frac{1}{4} \cdot 2} + \sqrt{\frac{9}{16} \cdot 2} - \sqrt{\frac{1}{64} \cdot 2}$

$$= \frac{1}{2}\sqrt{2} + \frac{3}{4}\sqrt{2} - \frac{1}{8}\sqrt{2}$$

$$= \frac{9}{8}\sqrt{2}$$

To *rationalize* a binomial denominator, we use the fact that the product of the sum and difference of two terms is the difference of their squares.

$$(\sqrt{a} + \sqrt{b})(\sqrt{a} - \sqrt{b}) = a - b$$

EXAMPLE 5 Simplify $\dfrac{6}{\sqrt{5} - \sqrt{2}}$ by rationalizing the denominator.

SOLUTION $\dfrac{6}{\sqrt{5} - \sqrt{2}} = \dfrac{6}{\sqrt{5} - \sqrt{2}} \cdot \dfrac{\sqrt{5} + \sqrt{2}}{\sqrt{5} + \sqrt{2}}$

$$= \frac{6(\sqrt{5} + \sqrt{2})}{5 - 2}$$

$$= \frac{6(\sqrt{5} + \sqrt{2})}{3}, \text{ or } 2(\sqrt{5} + \sqrt{2})$$

EXAMPLE 6 Simplify $\dfrac{3\sqrt{2} - \sqrt{3}}{3\sqrt{2} + 2\sqrt{3}}$.

SOLUTION $\dfrac{3\sqrt{2} - \sqrt{3}}{3\sqrt{2} + 2\sqrt{3}} = \dfrac{3\sqrt{2} - \sqrt{3}}{3\sqrt{2} + 2\sqrt{3}} \cdot \dfrac{3\sqrt{2} - 2\sqrt{3}}{3\sqrt{2} - 2\sqrt{3}}$

$$= \frac{18 - 6\sqrt{6} - 3\sqrt{6} + 6}{18 - 12}$$

$$= \frac{24 - 9\sqrt{6}}{6}$$

$$= \frac{8 - 3\sqrt{6}}{2}, \text{ or } 4 - \frac{3}{2}\sqrt{6}$$

The factor we use to rationalize a binomial denominator of the form $\sqrt{a} + \sqrt{b}$ is its *conjugate*, $\sqrt{a} - \sqrt{b}$. In Example 5, $\sqrt{5} - \sqrt{2}$ and $\sqrt{5} + \sqrt{2}$ are conjugates. In Example 6, $3\sqrt{2} + 2\sqrt{3}$ and $3\sqrt{2} - 2\sqrt{3}$ are conjugates.

CLASSROOM EXERCISES

Simplify.

1. $8\sqrt{2} - 6\sqrt{2} + 5\sqrt{2}$ **2.** $6\sqrt{c} - 3\sqrt{d} + 4\sqrt{c} + 8\sqrt{d}$ **3.** $3\sqrt{5} - 5\sqrt{7} + 2\sqrt{7} - \sqrt{5}$

4. $\sqrt{12} + \sqrt{80} + \sqrt{27} + \sqrt{5}$ **5.** $\sqrt{\frac{1}{3}} + \sqrt{\frac{12}{25}} - \sqrt{\frac{1}{27}}$ **6.** $(\sqrt{3} + \sqrt{2})(\sqrt{3} - \sqrt{2})$

Simplify by rationalizing the denominator.

7. $\dfrac{5}{\sqrt{7} - \sqrt{3}}$ **8.** $\dfrac{3}{\sqrt{3} + \sqrt{5}}$ **9.** $\dfrac{2\sqrt{3} + 3\sqrt{2}}{2\sqrt{3} - \sqrt{2}}$

EXERCISES

[A] Simplify.

1. $8\sqrt{3} + 2\sqrt{3} - 4\sqrt{3}$ **2.** $\sqrt{20} + \sqrt{45} - 4\sqrt{5}$ **3.** $\sqrt{3} - 5\sqrt{3} + 9\sqrt{3}$

4. $7\sqrt{5} + 3\sqrt{5} - \sqrt{5}$ **5.** $\sqrt{12} + \sqrt{27} + \sqrt{48}$ **6.** $\sqrt{28} - \sqrt{63} + \sqrt{7}$

7. $\sqrt{4x} - \sqrt{x} + \sqrt{25x}$ **8.** $\sqrt{9y} + \sqrt{y} - \sqrt{36y}$ **9.** $\sqrt[3]{54} + \sqrt[3]{128} - 3\sqrt[3]{16}$

10. $\sqrt{\frac{1}{2}} + \sqrt{\frac{2}{3}} + \sqrt{\frac{1}{6}}$ **11.** $\sqrt{\frac{25}{3}} - 2\sqrt{\frac{16}{3}} + \sqrt{\frac{1}{6}}$ **12.** $3\sqrt{\frac{1}{12}} - \sqrt{\frac{1}{15}} + 5\sqrt{\frac{3}{5}}$

13. $4\sqrt{7} - 6\sqrt{11} + 3\sqrt{11} - 3\sqrt{7}$ **14.** $2\sqrt{5} - 4\sqrt{7} + 3\sqrt{5} - 5\sqrt{7}$

15. $(\sqrt{2} + \sqrt{5})(\sqrt{2} + \sqrt{5})$ **16.** $(\sqrt{7} + 1)(\sqrt{7} - 1)$ **17.** $(\sqrt{2} + \sqrt{3})^2$

18. $(2\sqrt{3} - 1)^2$ **19.** $\dfrac{1}{2 - \sqrt{3}}$ **20.** $\dfrac{1}{3 + \sqrt{2}}$

21. $\dfrac{6}{\sqrt{6} - \sqrt{2}}$ **22.** $\dfrac{\sqrt{3} - \sqrt{2}}{\sqrt{3} + \sqrt{2}}$ **23.** $\dfrac{\sqrt{7} - \sqrt{6}}{\sqrt{7} + \sqrt{6}}$

[B] **24.** $\dfrac{x}{\sqrt{x} - \sqrt{y}}$ **25.** $\dfrac{a}{\sqrt{a} + \sqrt{b}}$ **26.** $\dfrac{\sqrt{x} - \sqrt{y}}{\sqrt{x} + \sqrt{y}}$

27. $\sqrt{\frac{x}{y}} + \sqrt{\frac{y}{x}} - \sqrt{\frac{1}{xy}}$ **28.** $\sqrt{\frac{a}{b}} - \sqrt{\frac{b}{a}} + \sqrt{\frac{4}{ab}}$ **29.** $(\sqrt[3]{2} + \sqrt[3]{3})^2$

30. $(\sqrt{x} + \sqrt{x - y})(\sqrt{x} - \sqrt{x - y})$ **31.** $\sqrt{(a + b)^2 x} - \sqrt{(a - b)^2 x}$

32. $\sqrt{(x + y)^3} + \sqrt{4(x + y)} - 3\sqrt{x + y}$ **33.** $(\sqrt{x - 2} + \sqrt{x + 2})(\sqrt{x - 2} - \sqrt{x + 2})$

34. $\sqrt[3]{8ab^3 + 8b^4} + \sqrt[3]{27a^4 + 27a^3b} + \sqrt[3]{(a + b)^4}$

[C] **35.** $\sqrt{\frac{x + 1}{x - 1}} + \sqrt{\frac{x - 1}{x + 1}} - \sqrt{\frac{1}{x^2 - 1}}$ **36.** $\sqrt{1 + \sqrt{9\sqrt[16]{x^{32}} + 16\sqrt[3]{x^6}}}$ **37.** $\dfrac{x\sqrt{x + 1} - \sqrt{x}}{\sqrt{x + 1} + \sqrt{x}}$

38. $(\sqrt{a + b} + \sqrt{a - b})(\sqrt{a + b} - \sqrt{a - b})$ **39.** $(\sqrt{t + 1} - 3t)(\sqrt{t + 1} + 3t)$

7-10 OTHER EXPRESSIONS INVOLVING RADICALS AND EXPONENTS (OPTIONAL)

To simplify more difficult expressions involving radicals, it is helpful to replace the radicals by the corresponding expressions having fraction exponents. Then use the rules for operations involving exponents.

EXAMPLE 1 Simplify the products $\sqrt{3} \cdot \sqrt[3]{5}$ and $\sqrt{32} \cdot \sqrt[3]{32}$.

SOLUTION
$$\sqrt{3} \cdot \sqrt[3]{5} = 3^{\frac{1}{2}} \cdot 5^{\frac{1}{3}}$$
$$= 3^{\frac{3}{6}} \cdot 5^{\frac{2}{6}}$$
$$= (3^3 \cdot 5^2)^{\frac{1}{6}}$$
$$= 675^{\frac{1}{6}}$$
$$= \sqrt[6]{675}$$

$$\sqrt{32} \cdot \sqrt[3]{32} = \sqrt{2^5} \cdot \sqrt[3]{2^5}$$
$$= 2^{\frac{5}{2}} \cdot 2^{\frac{5}{3}}$$
$$= 2^{\frac{25}{6}}$$
$$= 2^4 \cdot 2^{\frac{1}{6}}$$
$$= 16 \sqrt[6]{2}$$

EXAMPLE 2 Simplify the product $\sqrt[3]{3a^2} \cdot \sqrt[4]{4a^3}$, $a \geq 0$.

SOLUTION
$$\sqrt[3]{3a^2} \cdot \sqrt[4]{4a^3} = (3a^2)^{\frac{1}{3}} (4a^3)^{\frac{1}{4}}$$
$$= 3^{\frac{1}{3}} a^{\frac{2}{3}} 4^{\frac{1}{4}} a^{\frac{3}{4}}$$
$$= 3^{\frac{4}{12}} a^{\frac{8}{12}} 4^{\frac{3}{12}} a^{\frac{9}{12}}$$
$$= (3^4 a^8 4^3 a^9)^{\frac{1}{12}}$$
$$= \sqrt[12]{5184a^{17}}$$
$$= a \sqrt[12]{5184a^5}$$

EXAMPLE 3 Simplify $\sqrt[3]{\sqrt{x^7}}$, $x \geq 0$.

SOLUTION
$$\sqrt[3]{\sqrt{x^7}} = ((x^7)^{\frac{1}{2}})^{\frac{1}{3}}$$
$$= (x^7)^{\frac{1}{6}}$$
$$= \sqrt[6]{x^7}$$
$$= x \sqrt[6]{x}$$

EXAMPLE 4 Simplify $\dfrac{\sqrt[4]{x}}{\sqrt[3]{y}} \left(\dfrac{x^{\frac{1}{4}}}{y^{\frac{1}{3}}} \right)^2 \left(\dfrac{x^{-\frac{1}{2}}}{y^{-\frac{1}{2}}} \right)$, $x > 0$, $y > 0$.

SOLUTION $\dfrac{\sqrt[4]{x}}{\sqrt[3]{y}}\left(\dfrac{x^{\frac{1}{4}}}{y^{\frac{1}{3}}}\right)^2\left(\dfrac{x^{-\frac{1}{2}}}{y^{-\frac{1}{2}}}\right) = \dfrac{x^{\frac{1}{4}}}{y^{\frac{1}{3}}}\cdot\dfrac{\overset{1}{\cancel{x^{\frac{2}{4}}}}}{y^{\frac{2}{3}}}\cdot\dfrac{y^{\frac{1}{2}}}{\underset{1}{\cancel{x^{\frac{1}{2}}}}}$

$$= \dfrac{x^{\frac{1}{4}}y^{\frac{1}{2}}}{y}$$

$$= \dfrac{x^{\frac{1}{4}}y^{\frac{2}{4}}}{y}$$

$$= \dfrac{(xy^2)^{\frac{1}{4}}}{y}$$

$$= \dfrac{\sqrt[4]{xy^2}}{y}$$

CLASSROOM EXERCISES

Simplify.

1. $\sqrt{7}\cdot\sqrt[3]{4}$

2. $\sqrt[4]{9b^5}\cdot\sqrt[3]{b^2}$

3. $\sqrt[4]{\sqrt{a^9}}$

4. $\dfrac{\sqrt[3]{4}}{\sqrt{2}}$

EXERCISES

[A] Simplify.

1. $\sqrt{2}\cdot\sqrt[3]{5}$

2. $\sqrt[3]{4}\cdot\sqrt{5}$

3. $\sqrt{a}\cdot\sqrt[3]{a^2}$

4. $2\sqrt{c}\cdot\sqrt[3]{c}$

5. $\sqrt[3]{x^2}\cdot\sqrt{xy}$

6. $5\sqrt{2}\sqrt[3]{12}$

7. $a\sqrt{b}\cdot b\sqrt[3]{a}$

8. $2\sqrt{2}\cdot\sqrt[4]{3}$

9. $\sqrt{2xy^2}\cdot\sqrt[6]{4x^2y}$

10. $a\sqrt{ab}\cdot\sqrt[4]{2a^2b^2}$

11. $\sqrt[3]{\sqrt[4]{x^{17}}}$

12. $\sqrt[4]{\sqrt[3]{y^{13}}}$

13. $\sqrt[6]{\sqrt[3]{2^{36}x^{35}}}$

14. $\sqrt[4]{\sqrt[5]{3^{40}x^{23}}}$

15. $\dfrac{\sqrt[3]{2}}{\sqrt{3}}$

16. $\dfrac{\sqrt{6}}{\sqrt[3]{9}}$

[B] **17.** $\sqrt{a-b}\cdot\sqrt[4]{(a-b)^3}$

18. $(2-\sqrt[3]{4})(2+\sqrt[3]{4})$

19. $(\sqrt[3]{2}+\sqrt{3})^2$

20. $\sqrt[4]{\left(\dfrac{b^{\frac{3}{4}}a^{-2}}{a}\right)^{-1}}$

21. $\sqrt[5]{\left(\dfrac{y^{\frac{12}{5}}x^{-2}}{x^2}\right)^{-1}}$

22. $\dfrac{a^{\frac{1}{5}}\sqrt[3]{b^{-\frac{1}{3}}}}{b^{\frac{2}{3}}\sqrt[4]{a^{-2}}}$

[C] **23.** $\left(\dfrac{a^2b}{64a^{-3}b^{\frac{1}{3}}}\right)^{\frac{1}{3}}$

24. $\sqrt{\dfrac{\sqrt[5]{32}\cdot\sqrt{4}}{2^{-2}-2^{-3}}}$

25. $\dfrac{\sqrt[4]{x}}{\sqrt[5]{y}}\left(\dfrac{x^{\frac{1}{2}}}{y^{\frac{1}{3}}}\right)^2\cdot\left(\dfrac{x^{\frac{1}{2}}}{y^{-\frac{1}{2}}}\right)$

7-11 SOLVING RADICAL EQUATIONS

A **radical equation** is one in which the variable appears in a radicand. To solve an equation having a radical as one member, raise both members of the equation to the same power as the index of the radical.

EXAMPLE 1 Solve $\sqrt{2x^2 + 17} = x + 3$.

SOLUTION

$\sqrt{2x^2 + 17} = x + 3$

Square both members.

$(\sqrt{2x^2 + 17})^2 = (x + 3)^2$

$2x^2 + 17 = x^2 + 6x + 9$

$x^2 - 6x + 8 = 0$

$(x - 2)(x - 4) = 0$

Therefore, $x - 2 = 0$ or $x - 4 = 0$

$x = 2$ | $x = 4$

CHECK

$\sqrt{2x^2 + 17} = x + 3$

$\sqrt{2(2)^2 + 17} \stackrel{?}{=} 2 + 3$

$\sqrt{25} \stackrel{?}{=} 5$

$5 = 5$ ✔

$\sqrt{2x^2 + 17} = x + 3$

$\sqrt{2(4)^2 + 17} \stackrel{?}{=} 4 + 3$

$\sqrt{49} \stackrel{?}{=} 7$

$7 = 7$ ✔

The process of raising both members of an equation to the same power may introduce roots of the new equation, called the *derived equation*, that are not roots of the original equation. Thus, it is important to check your results in the original equation. A solution of the derived equation that is not a solution for the given equation is called an *extraneous solution*.

EXAMPLE 2 Solve $\sqrt{x - 1} = -4$.

SOLUTION

$\sqrt{x - 1} = -4$

$x - 1 = 16$

$x = 17$

CHECK

$\sqrt{x - 1} = -4$

$\sqrt{17 - 1} \stackrel{?}{=} -4$

$\sqrt{16} \stackrel{?}{=} -4$

$4 \neq -4$

CONCLUSION

The equation has no solution.
17 is an extraneous solution.

Sometimes the first step in solving a radical equation involves isolating the radical as one member.

EXAMPLE 3 Solve $\sqrt{25 - x^2} + x + 1 = 0$.

SOLUTION

$$\sqrt{25 - x^2} + x + 1 = 0$$
$$\sqrt{25 - x^2} = -x - 1$$
$$25 - x^2 = (-x - 1)^2$$
$$25 - x^2 = x^2 + 2x + 1$$
$$0 = 2x^2 + 2x - 24$$
$$0 = 2(x + 4)(x - 3)$$

Therefore, $x + 4 = 0 \quad$ or $\quad x - 3 = 0$
$$x = -4 \quad\quad\quad x = 3$$

CHECK

$$\sqrt{25 - x^2} + x + 1 = 0$$
$$\sqrt{25 - (-4)^2} + (-4) + 1 \stackrel{?}{=} 0$$
$$\sqrt{25 - 16} - 4 + 1 \stackrel{?}{=} 0$$
$$\sqrt{9} - 3 \stackrel{?}{=} 0$$
$$0 = 0 \quad \text{✓}$$

$$\sqrt{25 - x^2} + x + 1 = 0$$
$$\sqrt{25 - (3)^2} + (3) + 1 \stackrel{?}{=} 0$$
$$\sqrt{25 - 9} + 3 + 1 \stackrel{?}{=} 0$$
$$\sqrt{16} + 4 \stackrel{?}{=} 0$$
$$8 \neq 0$$

CONCLUSION $\quad$ −4 is a solution of the equation. 3 is not a solution. 3 is an extraneous solution.

When an equation includes two radicals, it sometimes is not possible to isolate each radical as one of the members. In such a case it may be necessary to follow the procedure for squaring a binomial. One of the terms of the "binomial" will be one of the radicals.

EXAMPLE 4 Solve $\sqrt{x - 5} + \sqrt{x} = 5$.

SOLUTION

$$\sqrt{x - 5} + \sqrt{x} = 5$$
$$\sqrt{x - 5} = 5 - \sqrt{x}$$

Square both members.

$$x - 5 = 25 - 10\sqrt{x} + x$$
$$10\sqrt{x} = 30$$
$$\sqrt{x} = 3$$

Square both members.

$$x = 9$$

CHECK

$$\sqrt{x - 5} + \sqrt{x} = 5$$
$$\sqrt{9 - 5} + \sqrt{9} \stackrel{?}{=} 5$$
$$5 = 5 \quad \text{✓}$$

EXAMPLE 5 Solve $\sqrt[3]{x+5} = 4$.

SOLUTION $\sqrt[3]{x+5} = 4$

Cube both members.

$x + 5 = 64$

$x = 59$

CHECK $\sqrt[3]{x+5} = 4$

$\sqrt[3]{59+5} \overset{?}{=} 4$

$\sqrt[3]{64} \overset{?}{=} 4$

$4 = 4$ ✔

CLASSROOM EXERCISES

Solve and check.

1. $\sqrt{x} = 2$

2. $\sqrt{2x^2 + 28} = x + 4$

3. $\sqrt{3x - 2} - 2\sqrt{x} = 1$

4. $\sqrt{x^2 + 9} + x - 5 = 0$

5. $\sqrt[3]{x-6} = 5$

6. $(y - 2)^{\frac{1}{2}} = 4 - y$

EXERCISES

A   Solve and check.

1. $x^{\frac{1}{2}} = 4$

2. $x^{\frac{1}{2}} = 9$

3. $\sqrt{x+1} = -3$

4. $\sqrt{x-2} = -5$

5. $(x - 3)^{\frac{1}{2}} = 6$

6. $(x + 2)^{\frac{1}{2}} = 4$

7. $\sqrt[3]{x-2} = 3$

8. $\sqrt[3]{x+1} = 5$

9. $\sqrt{x^2 + 5} - 5 = -x$

10. $\sqrt{y^2 - 11} + 1 = y$

11. $\sqrt{x} + 1 = \sqrt{x+5}$

12. $\sqrt{x} + 2 = \sqrt{x+8}$

13. $\sqrt{x} - 4 = 5 - 2\sqrt{x}$

14. $\sqrt{2x^2 + 49} = x + 5$

15. $\sqrt{2x^2 + 41} = x + 5$

16. $\sqrt{2x^2 + 49} - x + 5 = 0$

17. $\sqrt{2y + 6} = \sqrt{2y - 5}$

18. $\sqrt{2x^2 + 7} = x + 2$

19. $\sqrt{2x^2 + 31} = x + 4$

20. $\sqrt{y + 7} + 4 = 0$

21. $\sqrt[3]{\dfrac{x}{3}} - 3 = 0$

22. $\sqrt[3]{\dfrac{y}{2}} - 2 = 0$

23. $\sqrt{5x - 7} = \sqrt{x + 10}$

24. $\sqrt{12x - 3} = \sqrt{5x + 2}$

B   Solve.

25. The formula $t = \sqrt{\dfrac{2s}{g}}$ gives the time, t, in seconds that it takes a body starting at rest to fall a distance of s meters. Solve the formula for s. Then find the distance a body, starting at rest, will fall in 3 seconds. Use $g \doteq 9.81$.

Solve and check.

26. $\sqrt{x + 5} + \sqrt{x} = 5$

27. $\sqrt{x + 4} + \sqrt{x - 4} = 4$

28. $\sqrt{5y + 4} = \sqrt{5y - 9} + 1$

Solve for x.

29. $\sqrt{3x - a} - \sqrt{x + a} = 0$

Solve for y.

30. $\sqrt{y^2 + a^2 + b^2 - 2ay} = y + a$

C Solve and check.

31. $\sqrt{x + 4} + \sqrt{x - 4} = 2\sqrt{x - 1}$

32. $\sqrt{4x + 5} - \sqrt{x + 4} = \sqrt{x - 1}$

33. $\sqrt[4]{(2x + 1)^2} = \sqrt{x} + 1$

34. $(\sqrt{3} + \sqrt{3 - x})(\sqrt{3} - \sqrt{3 - x}) + 1 = \sqrt{2x^2 + 1}$

35. $\dfrac{\sqrt{x}}{\sqrt{x} - 2} = \dfrac{1 - 2x}{x - 4}$

36. $\sqrt{x^2 - \dfrac{1}{9}} + \sqrt{x^2 + \dfrac{1}{9}} = \dfrac{\sqrt{18x^2 + 8\sqrt{5}}}{3}$

CHECKING YOUR UNDERSTANDING

WORDS AND SYMBOLS

conjugate of $\sqrt{a} + \sqrt{b}$, $\sqrt{a} - \sqrt{b}$
like radicals

radical equation
rationalize a denominator

CONCEPTS

■ Since $(\sqrt[n]{a})^m = a^{\frac{m}{n}}$, the rules for operating with exponents may be used to multiply, divide, and simplify radicals. [7-5 to 7-10]

■ Squaring both members of an equation may lead to an extraneous solution. [7-11]

PROCESSES

■ Add, subtract, multiply, divide, and simplify radicals. [7-5 to 7-10]

1. $\sqrt{250}$ **2.** $\sqrt{27z^5}$ **3.** $\sqrt[4]{\dfrac{81}{4a^3}}$ **4.** $\sqrt[8]{81b^4}$

5. $\sqrt[3]{12x}\,\sqrt[3]{36x^2}$ **6.** $\sqrt{126s^4t} \div \sqrt{2st^3}$ **7.** $\sqrt{27} - \sqrt{\dfrac{243}{4}} + \sqrt{\dfrac{300}{64}}$

■ Rationalize a denominator. [7-7, 7-9]

8. $\dfrac{2}{\sqrt[3]{50}}$ **9.** $\dfrac{4}{2 - \sqrt{6}}$ **10.** $\dfrac{2\sqrt{5} - \sqrt{3}}{\sqrt{5} + 2\sqrt{3}}$

■ Solve radical equations. [7-11]

11. $\sqrt{x - 3} = x - 5$ **12.** $\sqrt{x + 3} - \sqrt{2x - 1} = 1$

OBJECTIVES: Identify and graph complex numbers. Add, subtract, multiply, and divide complex numbers.

7-12 COMPLEX NUMBERS

We know that the square of a real number is never a negative number. Thus, we cannot find a real number that is a solution of the equation $x^2 = -1$. Since no real number is a solution, we create a solution by defining a number, named i, having the property that $i^2 = -1$. Hence, the number i is a solution of the equation $x^2 = -1$.

Remember, however, that i is not a real number. It is called an *imaginary number*. We can write $i = \sqrt{-1}$ to indicate that $i^2 = -1$. With i, we shall require also that most of the familiar number properties hold. This allows us to define other imaginary numbers.

IMAGINARY NUMBERS

$$\sqrt{-1} = i \qquad \sqrt{-2} = \sqrt{-1 \cdot 2} \qquad \sqrt{-3} = \sqrt{-1 \cdot 3} \qquad \sqrt{-4} = \sqrt{-1 \cdot 4}$$
$$= \sqrt{-1}\sqrt{2} \qquad\qquad = \sqrt{-1}\sqrt{3} \qquad\qquad = \sqrt{-1}\sqrt{4}$$
$$= i\sqrt{2} \qquad\qquad = i\sqrt{3} \qquad\qquad = 2i$$

$$-\sqrt{-1} = -i \qquad -\sqrt{-2} = -i\sqrt{2} \qquad -\sqrt{-3} = -i\sqrt{3} \qquad -\sqrt{-4} = -2i$$

... and so on

EXAMPLE 1 Represent $\sqrt{-9}$ using i.

SOLUTION
$$\sqrt{-9} = \sqrt{-1 \cdot 9}$$
$$= \sqrt{-1}\sqrt{9}$$
$$= 3i$$

EXAMPLE 2 Represent $-\sqrt{-8}$ using i.

SOLUTION
$$-\sqrt{-8} = -\sqrt{-1 \cdot 8}$$
$$= -\sqrt{-1}\sqrt{8}$$
$$= -i\sqrt{4 \cdot 2}$$
$$= -2i\sqrt{2}$$

EXAMPLE 3 Simplify i^3.

SOLUTION
$$i^3 = i^2 \cdot i$$
$$= -1 \cdot i$$
$$= -i$$

EXAMPLE 4 Simplify $(-i)^2$.

SOLUTION
$$(-i)^2 = i^2$$
$$= -1$$

When a and b represent real numbers, the imaginary number bi may be paired with a to form a **complex number**. This number often is shown as $a + bi$. The set of all numbers that may be represented by using pairs of real numbers in this way is the set of complex numbers.

Note that since either *a* or *b* could be zero, both the imaginary numbers of the form *bi* and the real numbers themselves are complex numbers.

COMPLEX NUMBERS

Real	Imaginary	
3	i	$3 + i$
$14\sqrt{2}$	$-6i$	$14\sqrt{2} - 6i$
$-\frac{3}{8}$	$\frac{2}{3}i$	$-\frac{3}{8} + \frac{2}{3}i$
π	$\sqrt{7}i$	$\pi + \sqrt{7}i$
a	$bi, b \neq 0$	$a + bi, b \neq 0$

EXAMPLE 5 Represent $2 - \sqrt{-9}$ using i.

SOLUTION
$$2 - \sqrt{-9}$$
$$= 2 - i\sqrt{9}$$
$$= 2 - 3i$$

EXAMPLE 6 Represent $\dfrac{-9 + \sqrt{-36}}{3}$ using i.

SOLUTION
$$\frac{-9 + \sqrt{-36}}{3}$$
$$= \frac{-9 + i\sqrt{36}}{3}$$
$$= \frac{-9 + 6i}{3}$$
$$= -3 + 2i$$

The complex numbers have allowed us to define $\sqrt{a}$ for *any* real number *a*. A necessary result of our definition is that we must modify a property of radicals as follows.

$$\sqrt{ab} = \begin{cases} \sqrt{a}\,\sqrt{b} & \text{when either of } a \text{ or } b \text{ is non-negative.} \\ -\sqrt{a}\,\sqrt{b} & \text{when both } a \text{ and } b \text{ are negative.} \end{cases}$$

EXAMPLE 7 Simplify $\sqrt{-2}\sqrt{-2}$.

SOLUTION 1
$$\sqrt{-2} \cdot \sqrt{-2} = i\sqrt{2}\,i\sqrt{2}$$
$$= i^2 \cdot 2$$
$$= -2$$

SOLUTION 2
$$\sqrt{-2} \cdot \sqrt{-2} = -\sqrt{(-2)(-2)}$$
$$= -\sqrt{4}$$
$$= -2$$

CLASSROOM EXERCISES

Simplify. Represent each imaginary number using i.

1. $\sqrt{-4}$ **2.** $-\sqrt{-12}$ **3.** i^2 **4.** $(-i)^3$

5. i^4 **6.** $\sqrt{-2}\sqrt{-3}$ **7.** $3 - \sqrt{-25}$ **8.** $\dfrac{-25 + \sqrt{-625}}{5}$

EXERCISES

A   Simplify. Represent each imaginary number using i.

1. $\sqrt{-1}$ **2.** $\sqrt{-25}$ **3.** $\sqrt{-6}$ **4.** $\sqrt{-7}$

5. $\sqrt{-49}$ **6.** $\sqrt{-100}$ **7.** $\sqrt{-\dfrac{1}{16}}$ **8.** $\sqrt{-\dfrac{1}{25}}$

9. $\sqrt{-3}$ **10.** $\sqrt{-15}$ **11.** $2\sqrt{-8}$ **12.** $3\sqrt{-24}$

13. $\sqrt{\dfrac{-4}{9}}$ **14.** $\sqrt{\dfrac{-16}{81}}$ **15.** $\sqrt{-28}$ **16.** $\sqrt{-32}$

17. $\sqrt[3]{-8}$ **18.** $\sqrt[5]{-32}$ **19.** i^5 **20.** i^6

21. $1.45 - \sqrt{-0.36}$ **22.** $2.23 - \sqrt{-0.04}$ **23.** $2 - \sqrt{-4}$ **24.** $10 - \sqrt{-49}$

25. $\dfrac{4 + \sqrt{-4}}{2}$ **26.** $\dfrac{6 + \sqrt{-9}}{3}$ **27.** $\dfrac{18 - \sqrt{-63}}{12}$ **28.** $\dfrac{40 - \sqrt{-80}}{10}$

29. $\sqrt{-5}\sqrt{-4}$ **30.** $\sqrt{-3}\sqrt{5}$ **31.** $\sqrt{-2}\sqrt{11}$ **32.** $\sqrt{-4}\sqrt{-16}$

B   Replace a, b, and c in $\dfrac{-b + \sqrt{b^2 - 4ac}}{2a}$ by the given values. Simplify the result.

33. $a = 1, b = 2, c = 15$ **34.** $a = 3, b = -5, c = 9$ **35.** $a = -2, b = 4, c = -4$

Simplify.

36. $2 + \sqrt{-\dfrac{1}{2}}$ **37.** $3 - \sqrt{-\dfrac{2}{5}}$ **38.** $\sqrt{2^{-3} - 2^3}$

C   Simplify the radical. Begin by factoring -1 from each term of the radicand. Then transform the remaining binomial into the trinomial form $a^2 + 2ab + b^2$.

39. $\sqrt{-18 - 8\sqrt{2}}$ **40.** $\sqrt{-14 - 6\sqrt{5}}$ **41.** $\sqrt{-55 - 14\sqrt{6}}$

Find all values of x for which the radical represents an imaginary number.

Simplify. Write each quotient in the form $a + bi$.

42. $\sqrt{(5 - 4x)^3}$ **43.** $\sqrt{(2x - 7)^3}$ **44.** $\dfrac{1}{1 + \sqrt{-3}}$ **45.** $\dfrac{1}{1 - \sqrt{-2}}$

7-13 OPERATIONS WITH COMPLEX NUMBERS

We want the rules for operating with complex numbers to allow us to use the real numbers as we always have used them. The following definitions involving complex numbers make this possible.

> Equality: $a + bi = c + di$, if and only if $a = c$ and $b = d$.
>
> Addition: $(a + bi) + (c + di) = (a + c) + (b + d)i$.
>
> Multiplication: $(a + bi)(c + di) = (ac - bd) + (ad + bc)i$.

For the complex numbers, zero may be represented as $0 + 0i$, one as $1 + 0i$, and $-(c + di)$ as $-c - di$. To subtract $c + di$ from $a + bi$, we add $-(c + di)$ to $a + bi$.

$$(a + bi) - (c + di) = (a + bi) + [-(c + di)]$$
$$= (a + bi) + (-c - di)$$
$$= (a - c) + (b - d)i$$

When complex numbers are shown in the form $a + bi$, performing the operations for complex numbers is similar to performing the operations for real-number polynomials.

EXAMPLE 1 Add $4 + 3i$ and $-6 - i$.

SOLUTION $(4 + 3i) + (-6 - i) = 4 - 6 + 3i - i$
$$= -2 + 2i$$

EXAMPLE 2 Subtract $5 - 6i$ from $3 + 2i$.

SOLUTION $(3 + 2i) - (5 - 6i) = 3 + 2i - 5 + 6i$
$$= 3 - 5 + 2i + 6i$$
$$= -2 + 8i$$

EXAMPLE 3 Multiply $3 - 4i$ and $2 + 3i$.

SOLUTION $(3 - 4i)(2 + 3i) = 3 \cdot 2 + 3 \cdot 3i - 4i \cdot 2 - 4i \cdot 3i$
$$= 6 + 9i - 8i - 12i^2$$
$$= 6 + i - 12(-1)$$
$$= 18 + i$$

EXAMPLE 4 Multiply $\sqrt{-12}$ and $\sqrt{-3}$.

SOLUTION $\sqrt{-12} \cdot \sqrt{-3} = i\sqrt{12}\, i\sqrt{3}$
$$= i^2\sqrt{36}$$
$$= (-1)6$$
$$= -6$$

EXAMPLE 5   Divide $\sqrt{12}$ by $\sqrt{-6}$.

SOLUTION $\dfrac{\sqrt{12}}{\sqrt{-6}} = \dfrac{\sqrt{12}}{i\sqrt{6}}$

$$= \dfrac{\sqrt{2}}{i} \cdot \dfrac{i}{i}$$

$$= \dfrac{i\sqrt{2}}{-1}$$

$$= -i\sqrt{2}$$

The **conjugate** of the complex number $a + bi$ is the complex number $a - bi$.

EXAMPLE 6   Multiply $5 - 3i$ and its conjugate.

SOLUTION   The conjugate of $5 - 3i$ is $5 + 3i$.
$$(5 - 3i)(5 + 3i) = 25 - 9i^2$$
$$= 25 - 9(-1)$$
$$= 34$$

The product of any non-zero complex number and its conjugate is a positive real number.   Note that the two imaginary terms of the product are additive inverses with sum 0.
$$(a + bi)(a - bi) = a^2 + abi - abi - b^2i^2$$
$$= a^2 \qquad\qquad - b^2(-1)$$
$$= a^2 + b^2$$

We use this fact to simplify the quotient of two complex numbers. With it we may write any such quotient in the form $a + bi$.

EXAMPLE 7   Simplify $\dfrac{4 - 2i}{1 + 3i}$.

SOLUTION   To obtain a real number for the denominator, use its conjugate and multiply by $\dfrac{1 - 3i}{1 - 3i}$

$$\dfrac{4 - 2i}{1 + 3i} = \dfrac{4 - 2i}{1 + 3i} \cdot \dfrac{1 - 3i}{1 - 3i}$$

$$= \dfrac{4 - 12i - 2i - 6}{1 + 9}$$

$$= \dfrac{-2 - 14i}{10}$$

$$= \dfrac{-1 - 7i}{5}, \text{ or } = -\dfrac{1}{5} - \dfrac{7}{5}i$$

CLASSROOM EXERCISES

Write the complex number in $a + bi$ form.

1. $(2 + 4i) + (-3 + 6i)$ **2.** $(-2 + 4i) - (6 + 3i)$ **3.** $(2 - 5i)(1 + 4i)$

4. $\sqrt{-9} \cdot \sqrt{-4}$ **5.** $3 \div 2i$ **6.** $(2 + 3i) \div (5 - 2i)$ **7.** $\sqrt{21} \div \sqrt{-7}$

EXERCISES

A   Write the complex number in $a + bi$ form.

1. $2\sqrt{-2} \cdot 3\sqrt{-5}$ **2.** $4\sqrt{-3} \cdot 2\sqrt{-7}$ **3.** $2i\sqrt{5} \cdot i\sqrt{5}$ **4.** $3i\sqrt{2} \cdot i\sqrt{2}$

5. $\sqrt{-6} \div \sqrt{2}$ **6.** $\sqrt{-25} \div \sqrt{5}$ **7.** $\sqrt{-4} \div \sqrt{-8}$ **8.** $\sqrt{-12} \div \sqrt{-3}$

9. $6\sqrt{7} \div 2\sqrt{-3}$ **10.** $\sqrt{15} \div \sqrt{-5}$ **11.** $\sqrt{6} \div \sqrt{-30}$ **12.** $\sqrt{45} \div \sqrt{-5}$

13. $3 + (7 - 2i)$ **14.** $-5 + (-3 + 6i)$ **15.** $(-5 + 3i) + 6i$ **16.** $(4 - 7i) + 3i$

17. $(7 + 3i) - (2 + 2i)$ **18.** $(8 + 5i) - (5 + i)$ **19.** $-8(2 - i)$ **20.** $5(7 + 3i)$

21. $(5 - i)(5 + i)$ **22.** $(a + bi)(a - bi)$ **23.** $(3 - 7i)^2$ **24.** $(3 - 4i) \div (3 + 4i)$

25. $\dfrac{1}{3 - 5i}$ **26.** $\dfrac{1}{2 + 4i}$ **27.** $\dfrac{5 - 4i}{5 + 4i}$ **28.** $\dfrac{10 - i}{10 + i}$ **29.** $\dfrac{4 + 5i}{5 - 3i}$

Multiply the number by its conjugate.

30. $3 - 4i$ **31.** $5 - 12i$ **32.** $2 + 3i$ **33.** $4 + 3i$

Simplify. n represents a positive integer.

34. i^{12} **35.** i^{13} **36.** i^{14} **37.** i^{15} **38.** $3 + 4i^5$

39. $2 + 3i^9$ **40.** $1 \div i^{19}$ **41.** $1 \div i^{37}$ **42.** $3 \div i^{42}$ **43.** $5 \div i^{80}$

B   **44.** i^{4n} **45.** i^{4n+1} **46.** i^{4n+2} **47.** i^{4n+3} **48.** i^{4n+4}

Write the complex number in $a + bi$ form.

49. $(c + 2di) + (2c + 3di)$ **50.** $(3m + ni) - (2m - 4ni)$ **51.** $(2x + 3yi)(-4x - yi)$

52. $(a + bi) \div (a - bi)$ **53.** $(3x - 2yi)^2$ **54.** $\left(-\dfrac{1}{2} + \dfrac{\sqrt{3}}{2}i\right)^3$

55. $\left((x - 1)^{\frac{3}{2}} - (x + 1)^{\frac{3}{2}}i\right) \cdot \left((x - 1)^{\frac{3}{2}} + (x + 1)^{\frac{3}{2}}i\right)$ **56.** $(\sqrt{18} + \sqrt{27}i) + (\sqrt{50} - \sqrt{12}i)$

C   **57.** Find a and b so that $\dfrac{7 - 4i}{a + bi} = 0.85 - 0.95i$.

58. For $a \neq 0$ and $b \neq 0$, find x and y so that $(a + bi)(x + yi) = 1$.

ANOTHER FORM FOR COMPLEX NUMBERS

Complex numbers often are given in the form $a + bi$. In this *rectangular form*, operations such as addition and multiplication are carried out by treating the two complex numbers as binomials, keeping in mind that i^2 may be replaced by -1.

Some people consider the i in $a + bi$ as the distinguishing characteristic of a complex number. The presence of i helps them remember that these are not the familiar real numbers commonly used in everyday life. The actual distinguishing characteristic of a complex number, however, is the ordered pair of real numbers a and b, whether they be given in the form $a + bi$ or simply as (a, b). In fact, some people prefer the *ordered-pair form* (a, b) for a complex number instead of the rectangular form $a + bi$.

Here are the definitions for the operations on complex numbers when the numbers are given in ordered-pair form.

Ordered-Pair Form

$$(a, b) + (c, d) = (a + c, b + d)$$
$$(a, b) - (c, d) = (a - c, b - d)$$
$$(a, b)(c, d) = (ac - bd, ad + bc)$$
$$\frac{(a, b)}{(c, d)} = \left(\frac{ac + bd}{c^2 + d^2}, \frac{bc - ad}{c^2 + d^2} \right)$$

Simplify. Use the operations as they are defined above. Check by using the operations as they are defined for numbers shown in rectangular form. These are reviewed following the exercises.

1. $(3, 1) + (2, 4)$ **2.** $(-1.5, 0.7) + (0, -2.3)$ **3.** $(\sqrt{3}, -1) + (\sqrt{3}, 1)$

4. $(3, 1) - (2, 4)$ **5.** $(-1.5, 0.7) - (0, -2.3)$ **6.** $(\sqrt{3}, -1) - (\sqrt{3}, 1)$

7. $(3, 1) \cdot (2, 4)$ **8.** $(-1.5, 0.7)(0, -2.3)$ **9.** $(\sqrt{3}, -1) \cdot (\sqrt{3}, 1)$

10. $\dfrac{(3, 1)}{(2, 4)}$ **11.** $\dfrac{(-1.5, 0.7)}{(0, -2.3)}$ **12.** $\dfrac{(\sqrt{3}, -1)}{(\sqrt{3}, 1)}$

Rectangular Form

$$(a + bi) + (c + di) = (a + c) + (b + d)i$$
$$(a + bi) - (c + di) = (a - c) + (b - d)i$$
$$(a + bi)(c + di) = (ac - bd) + (ad + bc)i$$
$$\frac{a + bi}{c + di} = \left(\frac{ac + bd}{c^2 + d^2} \right) + \left(\frac{bc - ad}{c^2 + d^2} \right)i$$

7-14 GRAPHING COMPLEX NUMBERS

A complex number, $a + bi$, involves an ordered pair (a, b) of real numbers. Therefore, we may represent the complex number graphically in the same way that we represent the ordered pair of real numbers.

<table>
<tr>
<td align="center">Graph of the Ordered Pair
(a, b) of Real Numbers</td>
<td align="center">Graph of the
Complex Number $a + bi$</td>
</tr>
<tr>
<td>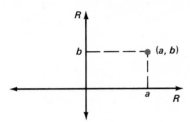</td>
<td>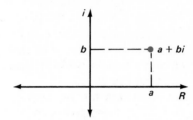</td>
</tr>
<tr>
<td align="center">The Real-Number Plane</td>
<td align="center">The Complex-Number Plane</td>
</tr>
</table>

In the complex plane, the *real part*, a, of each complex number $a + bi$ corresponds to a point of the horizontal axis. Therefore, we call this axis *the axis of reals*. The *imaginary part*, b, of each complex number $a + bi$ corresponds to a point of the vertical axis, or the *axis of imaginaries*.

EXAMPLE 1 Graph the complex numbers $5 + 0i$, or 5, $0 + 3i$, or $3i$, $5 + 3i$, $-5 - 3i$, $-5 + 3i$, and $3 - 5i$.

SOLUTION

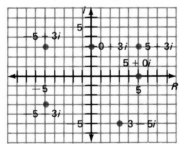

EXAMPLE 2 Name the complex numbers whose graphs are shown.

SOLUTION Point A is the graph of $3 + 2i$. B is the graph of $0 - 3i$, or $-3i$. C is the graph of $6 + 0i$, or 6. D is the graph of $-1 + 4i$. E is the graph of $-3 - 2i$.

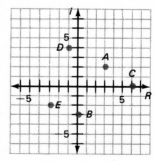

It is possible to give a graphical or geometric representation in the complex plane for the sum of two complex numbers.

EXAMPLE 3 Add $4 + 3i$ and $2 - i$ algebraically and geometrically.

SOLUTION 1 $(4 + 3i) + (2 - i) = (4 + 2) + (3i - i)$
$$= 6 + 2i$$

SOLUTION 2 Graph $4 + 3i$, $2 - i$, and $0 + 0i$.

Complete the parallelogram.

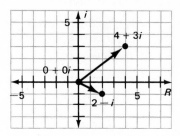 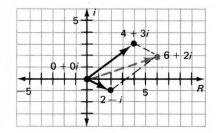

CONCLUSION The sum is $6 + 2i$.

Recall that a complex number is subtracted by adding its opposite. Thus, it is possible also to represent graphically the difference of two complex numbers in the complex plane by completing a parallelogram.

EXAMPLE 4 Subtract $4 - 2i$ from $1 + 3i$ algebraically and geometrically.

SOLUTION 1 $(1 + 3i) - (4 - 2i) = (1 + 3i) + [-(4 - 2i)]$
$$= 1 + 3i - 4 + 2i$$
$$= -3 + 5i$$

SOLUTION 2 Think of $(1 + 3i) - (4 - 2i)$ as $(1 + 3i) + (-4 + 2i)$.

Graph $1 + 3i$, $-4 + 2i$, and $0 + 0i$.

Complete the parallelogram.

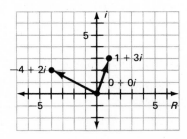 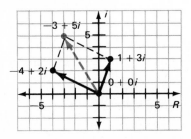

CONCLUSION The difference is $-3 + 5i$.

ADDING AND SUBTRACTING COMPLEX NUMBERS GRAPHICALLY

To add two complex numbers graphically,

1. Graph each number in the complex plane.
2. Complete a parallelogram having the two plotted points and the origin as three of its vertices.
3. Graphically determine the complex number for the fourth vertex. This number is the desired sum.

To find the difference of two complex numbers, use the opposite of the number subtracted and proceed as in Steps 1 and 2. The coordinate of the fourth vertex is the difference.

CLASSROOM EXERCISES

Graph the complex number.

1. $8 + 0i$ **2.** $0 - 5i$ **3.** $-3 + 6i$ **4.** $2i$ **5.** 4

Use graph paper. Perform the indicated operation geometrically, then algebraically.

6. $(2 + 5i) + (3 + 2i)$ **7.** $(7 + 10i) - (6 - 2i)$

EXERCISES

A Graph the complex number.

1. $0 + 7i$ **2.** $5 + 0i$ **3.** $3i$ **4.** -2 **5.** $1 - 2i$
6. $2 - 3i$ **7.** $4 + 3i$ **8.** $3 + 4i$ **9.** $-2 + 5i$ **10.** $-5 - 12i$

Use graph paper. Perform the indicated operation geometrically, then algebraically.

11. $(2 - i) + 4i$ **12.** $4 + (2 - 4i)$ **13.** $(1 + 2i) + (3 + i)$
14. $(2 + i) + (-3 + 2i)$ **15.** $(-3 + 2i) - (4 + i)$ **16.** $(3 + 2i) - (2 + i)$
B **17.** $[(1 + 2i) + (3 - 5i)] + (1 + 4i)$ **18.** $(1 + 2i) + [(3 - 5i) + (1 + 4i)]$

C The absolute value, $|a + bi|$, of a complex number is defined to be $\sqrt{a^2 + b^2}$.

19. Tell how this is similar to $|n|$, for n a real number.
20. Show that $(a + bi) \cdot (a - bi) = |a + bi|^2$
21. Show that $|(a + bi) \cdot (c + di)| = |a + bi| \cdot |c + di|$
22. Add $a + bi$ and $c + di$ geometrically to show why $|(a + bi) + (c + di)| \leq |a + bi| + |c + di|$ is called the "triangle inequality".

CHECKING YOUR UNDERSTANDING

WORDS AND SYMBOLS

axis of imaginaries

axis of reals

complex number, $a + bi$

conjugate of $a + bi$, $a - bi$

complex plane

imaginary number

CONCEPTS

■ Every pair of real numbers corresponds to a complex number and every complex number corresponds to a pair of real numbers. The real numbers themselves are a subset of the complex numbers. [7-12, 7-14]

■ Every real number has a square root among the complex numbers. [7-12]

■ The operations on the complex numbers in the form $a + bi$ may be performed in a way similar to the way in which operations on polynomials are performed. [7-13]

PROCESSES

■ Represent complex numbers in the form $a + bi$, a and b real numbers. [7-12]

1. $-\sqrt{-12}$ **2.** i^{11} **3.** $\dfrac{8 + i\sqrt{-24}}{4}$ **4.** $3 - i\sqrt{-9}$

■ Add, subtract, multiply, and divide complex numbers. [7-13]

5. $(17 - 6i) + (4 - 2i)$ **6.** $(-3 + 3i) - (4 - 4i)$ **7.** $\sqrt{-4}\,\sqrt{-25}$

8. $(4 - 2i)(7 + 3i)$ **9.** $\dfrac{-6 + 3i}{5 - 2i}$ **10.** $(2 + i) \div (3 - 7i)$

■ Graph, add, and subtract using the complex plane. [7-14]

11. Graph $4 - i$, $8 + 3i$, and $5i$.   **12.** Show $(3 + 3i) + (5 + 4i)$ geometrically.

!

1. The standard numeral for the product

$$100 \cdot 99 \cdot 98 \cdot 97 \cdot 96 \cdot \cdots \cdot 5 \cdot 4 \cdot 3 \cdot 2 \cdot 1$$

ends in how many zeros?

2. Find the greatest power of 2 that is a factor of

$$100 \cdot 99 \cdot 98 \cdot 97 \cdot 96 \cdot \cdots \cdot 5 \cdot 4 \cdot 3 \cdot 2 \cdot 1.$$

CHAPTER REVIEW

Perform the indicated operation and simplify. [7-1]

1. $x^3 \cdot x^7$ **2.** $y^{10} \div y^2$ **3.** $(x^3)^4$ **4.** $(-2b^2)^3$

5. $\dfrac{4x^9}{8x^3}$ **6.** $a^5 \cdot b \cdot a \cdot b^3$ **7.** $(2c^2d)^2 \cdot (cd^2)$ **8.** $\left(\dfrac{a^3}{b}\right)^2$

Find the indicated root. [7-2]

9. $\sqrt[3]{64}$ **10.** $-\sqrt{121}$ **11.** $\sqrt[3]{-27y^3}$

Simplify. [7-3 to 7-10]

12. $36^{\frac{1}{2}}$ **13.** $(-64)^{\frac{2}{3}}$ **14.** $(0.0016)^{\frac{5}{4}}$ **15.** $y^{\frac{1}{3}} \cdot y^{\frac{1}{2}}$ **16.** $4y^{\frac{2}{3}} \div 2y^{\frac{1}{2}}$

17. $5^0 \cdot 4$ **18.** 2^{-2} **19.** $\left(\dfrac{2}{3}\right)^4$ **20.** $\dfrac{x^4}{x^{-2}}$ **21.** $\dfrac{a^{-2}b^3}{a^3b^{-1}}$ **22.** $\dfrac{6xy^{-2}}{3x^2y^{-4}}$

23. $\sqrt{5} \cdot \sqrt{10}$ **24.** $2\sqrt{7} \cdot 3\sqrt{14}$ **25.** $\sqrt{6} \cdot \sqrt{3b}$ **26.** $\sqrt{\dfrac{2}{3}}\,\sqrt{\dfrac{2}{3}}$

27. $\dfrac{\sqrt{27}}{\sqrt{3}}$ **28.** $\dfrac{\sqrt{40}}{\sqrt{5}}$ **29.** $\dfrac{\sqrt[3]{3x^3y^4}}{\sqrt[3]{x^3y}}$ **30.** $\sqrt{\dfrac{1}{7}}$

31. $\sqrt[6]{9x^4}$ **32.** $\sqrt[10]{n^4m^2p^8}$ **33.** $\sqrt[4]{25(a-b)^2c^6}$

34. $8\sqrt{5} - 2\sqrt{5} + 3\sqrt{5}$ **35.** $\sqrt{9x} - \sqrt{x} - \sqrt{25x}$ **36.** $\sqrt{\dfrac{2}{3}} - \sqrt{24} + \sqrt{\dfrac{1}{54}}$

37. $\dfrac{3}{2 - \sqrt{3}}$ **38.** $\dfrac{4}{2\sqrt{3} + 2\sqrt{5}}$ **39.** $\dfrac{3\sqrt{2} - 2\sqrt{3}}{5\sqrt{2} + \sqrt{3}}$

40. $\dfrac{a^{\frac{2}{3}}\sqrt[3]{b^{-\frac{5}{3}}}}{b^{\frac{4}{9}}\sqrt[3]{a^{-5}}}$ **41.** $\sqrt{\left(\dfrac{x^2y^3}{x^4}\right)^{-1}}$

Solve and check. [7-11]

42. $\sqrt{2x - 4} = 8$ **43.** $\sqrt{4x^2 + 3} + 2x = 3$ **44.** $\sqrt[3]{4 - 2x} - 5 = 0$

Simplify. [7-12, 7-13]

45. $5 - \sqrt{-4}$ **46.** $\sqrt{36} + 2\sqrt{-9}$ **47.** $9 - \sqrt{-27}$ **48.** $-5 - \sqrt{-75}$

49. $(3 + 5i) + (6 - i)$ **50.** $\dfrac{3}{4 - 2i}$ **51.** $2\sqrt{-5} \cdot 3\sqrt{-2}$

52. Use graph paper.   Find $(8 + 3i) - (2 - i)$ geometrically.   Check algebraically. [7-14]

CAPSULE REVIEW

Write the letter of the best response.

1. Which of these is the simplified form of $(3x^4y)^2(2xy^3)$?

   a. $18x^7y^5$ **b.** $18x^{16}y^6$ **c.** $18x^9y^5$ **d.** $6x^9y^5$

2. Which of these is the simplified form of $\sqrt{18} + \sqrt{50} - \sqrt{98}$?

   a. $\sqrt{2}$ **b.** $\sqrt{-30}$ **c.** $-13\sqrt{2}$ **d.** $8\sqrt{2}$

3. Which of these is the simplified form of $(-3 + 5i)^2$?

   a. $34 - 30i$ **b.** $-16 - 30i$ **c.** -16 **d.** $-14 - 30i$

4. The simplified form of $\dfrac{6 - 6i}{2 + 3i}$ has denominator

   a. 4   **b.** 5   **c.** -5 **d.** 13

5. The simplified form of the expression $7i^{126}$ is

   a. $-7i$ **b.** $7i$ **c.** -1 **d.** -7

6. The simplified form of $\dfrac{\sqrt{5} - 2\sqrt{3}}{\sqrt{5} + 2\sqrt{3}}$ is

   a. $\dfrac{-17 + 4\sqrt{15}}{7}$ **b.** $-\dfrac{17}{7}$ **c.** $-17 + 20\sqrt{3}$ **d.** $-\dfrac{5\sqrt{3}}{3}$

7. The sum $(-3 - 4i) + (3 + 8i)$ equals

   a. -12 **b.** 12 **c.** $0 - 4i$ **d.** $4i$ **e.** $-3 + 4i$

8. Which of these is the solution of the equation $\sqrt{3x - 2} - 2\sqrt{x} = 1$?

   a. 9   **b.** 1   **c.** 0   **d.** the equation has no solution

9. Which of these is the simplest form of $\sqrt[6]{16x^{12}y^{20}}$?

   a. $x^2y^3\sqrt[6]{16y^2}$ **b.** $x^6y^3\sqrt[6]{16y^2}$ **c.** $x^2y^3\sqrt[3]{4y}$ **d.** $x^2y^6\sqrt[3]{4y}$

CHAPTER TEST

Solve.

1. $3^4 \cdot 3^5 = 3^x$ **2.** $(3^4)^3 = 3^x$

3. Give the square roots of 36.   **4.** Find $\sqrt[3]{8a^6}$ where a is positive.

Simplify.

5. $27^{\frac{1}{3}}$ **6.** $(a^6b^{12})^{\frac{2}{3}}$ **7.** $9^{-\frac{1}{2}}$ **8.** a^{-3} **9.** $\sqrt[3]{24}$

10. $(\sqrt{6})(\sqrt{10})$ **11.** $\sqrt[6]{4}$ **12.** $\sqrt[4]{16a^2}$ **13.** $5\sqrt{3} + 2\sqrt{3} - \sqrt{3}$ **14.** $\sqrt{18} + \sqrt{32}$

15. $\sqrt{\dfrac{a^3}{8}}$ **16.** $\dfrac{\sqrt{6a}}{\sqrt{2a^3}}$ **17.** $\dfrac{\sqrt{2}}{\sqrt{3}}$ **18.** $\dfrac{2}{\sqrt{5} + \sqrt{3}}$

Solve.

19. $\sqrt{x + 5} = x + 3$

20. $\sqrt{x + 26} - x + 4 = 0$

21. Simplify i^5.

22. Simplify $\sqrt{-9} + \sqrt{-16}$.

23. Subtract $4 + i$ from $2 + 3i$.

24. Add $-3 - 2i$ and $-2 + 7i$.

25. Multiply $\sqrt{-2}$ and $\sqrt{-18}$.

26. Graph the numbers 4, $2i$, and $4 + 2i$.

Write the letter of the best response.

27. What does $(x^2y^3)^4$ equal?

    a. x^2y^7 **b.** x^6y^7 **c.** x^8y^{12} **d.** x^2y^{12} **e.** $x^{16}y^{81}$

28. What is the index in the expression $\sqrt[4]{2^3 - 5}$?

    a. 1   **b.** 2   **c.** 3   **d.** 4   **e.** 5

29. How may $x^{\frac{3}{4}}$ be written as a radical?

    a. $\sqrt{x^{\frac{3}{4}}}$ **b.** $\sqrt[3]{x^4}$ **c.** $\sqrt[4]{3x}$ **d.** $\dfrac{x^3}{4}$ **e.** $\sqrt[4]{x^3}$

30. What does 4^0 equal?

    a. 0   **b.** 1   **c.** 2   **d.** 3   **e.** 4

31. What is the product of $\sqrt{6}$ and $\sqrt{15}$ simplified?

    a. $\sqrt{21}$ **b.** 90   **c.** $9\sqrt{10}$ **d.** $6\sqrt{10}$ **e.** $3\sqrt{10}$

32. What is $\sqrt{\dfrac{9x^3}{8x^2}}$ simplified?

    a. $\sqrt{x}$ **b.** $\dfrac{3}{2}\sqrt{2x}$ **c.** $\dfrac{3}{4}\sqrt{2x}$ **d.** $\dfrac{\sqrt{6x}}{4}$ **e.** $\dfrac{3}{2}\sqrt{x}$

33. What is $\sqrt[6]{9x^2}$ simplified?

    a. $\sqrt[4]{3x}$ **b.** $\sqrt[3]{3x}$ **c.** $\sqrt{3x}$ **d.** $3x$ **e.** $\dfrac{x}{2}$

34. What is $\sqrt{12} + \sqrt{48}$ simplified?

    a. $\sqrt{60}$ **b.** $30\sqrt{3}$ **c.** $20\sqrt{3}$ **d.** $16\sqrt{3}$ **e.** $6\sqrt{3}$

35. What is $\dfrac{\sqrt[3]{2}}{\sqrt[3]{5}}$ simplified?

    a. $\dfrac{\sqrt[3]{7}}{5}$ **b.** $\dfrac{\sqrt[3]{10}}{5}$ **c.** $\dfrac{\sqrt[3]{12}}{5}$ **d.** $\dfrac{\sqrt[3]{50}}{5}$ **e.** $\dfrac{\sqrt[3]{250}}{5}$

36. What does x equal if $\sqrt{x + 14} = x + 2$?

    a. 2   **b.** -5 **c.** 2 or -5 **d.** -2 or 5   **e.** -12

37. Which of these is an imaginary number?

    a. $\sqrt{-6}$ **b.** $-\sqrt{6}$ **c.** $\dfrac{1}{\sqrt{6}}$ **d.** $\sqrt{6}$ **e.** $-\dfrac{1}{\sqrt{6}}$

CHAPTER 8
QUADRATIC FUNCTIONS AND
QUADRATIC EQUATIONS

Why? . . . How? . . . The questions remain the same but the answers become more complex as we proceed from grade school through high school to trade school, college, or a training program. We become involved with the questions that interest us. We leave the rest for others. Our interests become better defined. We learn what we can do and what we do not want to do. We see more clearly where we are heading.

OBJECTIVES: Graph quadratic functions by plotting points. Solve quadratic equations. Use the discriminant to determine the nature of the solutions of a quadratic equation.

8-1 QUADRATIC FUNCTIONS AND QUADRATIC EQUATIONS

A **quadratic function** is a function that is defined by an equation of the form $y = ax^2 + bx + c$, or $f(x) = ax^2 + bx + c$, when $a \neq 0$. The graph of a quadratic function is a **parabola**.

EXAMPLE 1 Graph the quadratic function defined by the equation $y = x^2 - x + 2$, or $f(x) = x^2 - x + 2$.

SOLUTION First, find several ordered pairs of the function.

For $x = -2$	For $x = -1$	$(x, f(x))$
$f(-2) = (-2)^2 - (-2) + 2$	$f(-1) = (-1)^2 - (-1) + 2$	or
$= 8$	$= 4$	(x, y)
For $x = 0$	For $x = 1$	$(-2, 8)$
$f(0) = 0^2 - 0 + 2$	$f(1) = 1^2 - 1 + 2$	$(-1, 4)$
$= 2$	$= 2$	$(0, 2)$
For $x = 2$	For $x = 3$	$(1, 2)$
$f(2) = 2^2 - 2 + 2$	$f(3) = 3^2 - 3 + 2$	$(2, 4)$
$= 4$	$= 8$	$(3, 8)$

Graph these ordered pairs. Then draw a smooth curve containing these points. If the location of the curve is anywhere in doubt, calculate more ordered pairs of the function to guide you. For example, $\left(\frac{1}{2}, \frac{7}{4}\right)$ is another ordered pair of this function. It suggests the part of the graph from $(0, 2)$ to $(1, 2)$.

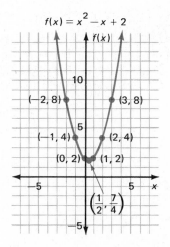

$$f(x) = x^2 - x + 2$$

The equation that defines a quadratic *function* can have the form
$$f(x) = ax^2 + bx + c.$$
To find numbers for x for which $f(x) = 0$, we find solutions, or **roots**, of the quadratic *equation*
$$0 = ax^2 + bx + c.$$
These numbers are called **zeros of the function**.

Graphically, we find the x-coordinate of each point of the parabola for which the y-coordinate is zero. In general, there are three cases.

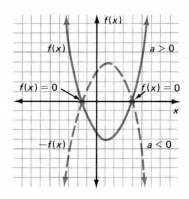

1. There may be two numbers for x for which $f(x)$ is 0. Thus, the equation $ax^2 + bx + c = 0$ could have two real-number solutions.

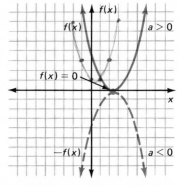

2. There may be one number for x for which $f(x)$ is 0. Thus, the equation $ax^2 + bx + c = 0$ could have only one real-number solution.

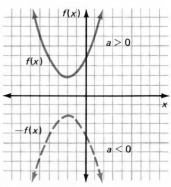

3. There may be no real numbers for x for which $f(x)$ is 0. Thus, the equation $ax^2 + bx + c = 0$ could have no real-number solutions.

EXAMPLE 3 Approximate the solutions (roots) of $-2x^2 + x + 28 = 0$ graphically.

SOLUTION Draw the graph for $f(x) = -2x^2 + x + 28$.

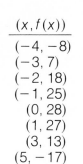

$(x, f(x))$
$(-4, -8)$
$(-3, 7)$
$(-2, 18)$
$(-1, 25)$
$(0, 28)$
$(1, 27)$
$(3, 13)$
$(5, -17)$

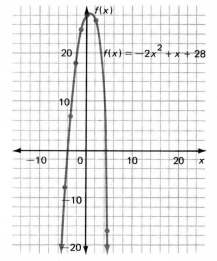

From the graph, it appears that $f(x)$ is 0 for $x = 4$ and $x = -3\frac{1}{2}$.

CHECK

$-2x^2 + x + 28 = 0$
$-2(4)^2 + 4 + 28 \overset{?}{=} 0$
$-32 + 4 + 28 \overset{?}{=} 0$
$0 = 0$ ✔

$-2x^2 + x + 28 = 0$
$-2\left(-3\frac{1}{2}\right)^2 + \left(-3\frac{1}{2}\right) + 28 \overset{?}{=} 0$
$-\frac{49}{2} - \frac{7}{2} + 28 \overset{?}{=} 0$
$0 = 0$ ✔

CONCLUSION The solutions (roots) of the quadratic equation $-2x^2 + x + 28 = 0$ are 4 and $-3\frac{1}{2}$.

Graphing the Quadratic Function Defined by $f(x) = ax^2 + bx + c$

1. Find several ordered pairs of the function.
2. Graph these ordered pairs.
3. Draw a smooth curve through these points.

Solving the Quadratic Equation $ax^2 + bx + c = 0$ Graphically

1. Draw the graph for $f(x) = ax^2 + bx + c$.
2. Approximate the x-coordinate of each point of the graph for which the y-coordinate is zero.
3. Check your approximations. Replace x in the original equation by each number found in Step 2.

CLASSROOM EXERCISES

Graph the function.

1. $f(x) = x^2 - x + 1$ **2.** $f(x) = x^2 + 6x + 8$ **3.** $f(x) = x^2 - 7x + 10$

Solve the equation graphically.

4. $x^2 + 2x - 3 = 0$ **5.** $2x^2 - 7x - 4 = 0$ **6.** $x^2 - 6x + 9 = 0$

EXERCISES

[A] Graph the function.

1. $f(x) = x^2 + x - 6$ **2.** $f(x) = x^2 - x - 12$ **3.** $f(x) = 2x^2$

4. $f(x) = -6x^2$ **5.** $f(x) = -x^2$ **6.** $f(x) = x^2 - 9$

7. $f(x) = 8 - x - x^2$ **8.** $f(x) = 10 - 2x - x^2$ **9.** $f(x) = 2x^2 + 3x - 5$

10. $f(x) = x^2 - 3x - 2$ **11.** $f(x) = 2x^2 - 7x + 4$ **12.** $f(x) = -x^2 - 3x + 10$

Solve the equation graphically.

13. $x^2 - x - 2 = 0$ **14.** $x^2 + x - 2 = 0$ **15.** $x^2 - 3x + 2 = 0$

16. $x^2 - 4 = 0$ **17.** $x^2 - 25 = 0$ **18.** $x^2 - 3x = 0$

19. $4x^2 - 20x + 25 = 0$ **20.** $x^2 + 4 = 0$ **21.** $x^2 + 6 = 0$

22. $3x^2 + 5x = 2$ **23.** $2x^2 - 3x = 5$ **24.** $x^2 - x + \frac{1}{4} = 0$

[B] Graph the function.

25. $f(x) = 3(x - 1)^2 + 1$ **26.** $f(x) = 5\left(x + \frac{3}{2}\right)^2 - 2$ **27.** $f(x) = -(2x + 1)^2 - 3$

Solve the equation graphically.

28. $(x - 2)^2 - \frac{9}{4} = 0$ **29.** $4x(x - 9) + 81 = 0$ **30.** $-(2x + 1)^2 = 3$

31. On the same set of axes graph the functions defined by $f(x) = x^2 - 2x - 3$ and $f(x) = -x^2 + 2x + 3$. Give the coordinates of the intersection of the graphs. What do you know about the solutions of the equations $x^2 - 2x - 3 = 0$ and $-x^2 + 2x + 3 = 0$?

32. On the same set of axes graph the functions $f(x) = x^2 - 3x$, and $f(x) = x^2 - 3x + 3$. Choose any value for x. For this value of x, how much greater is $x^2 - 3x + 3$ than $x^2 - 3x$?

[C] **33.** Graph $f(x) = x^2 - 25$ and $f(x) = x + 5$ on the same set of coordinate axes. Use the graphs to find the solutions for the non-linear system.

34. Determine the coefficients a, b, c of the parabola $y = ax^2 + bx + c$ which contains the points $(0, 10)$, $(1, 6)$, and $(3, 16)$.

8-2 SOLVING INCOMPLETE QUADRATIC EQUATIONS

An **incomplete quadratic equation** is one having the form $ax^2 + c = 0$. This type can be solved by finding square roots.

EXAMPLE 1   Solve $x^2 - 16 = 0$.

SOLUTION
$$x^2 - 16 = 0$$
$$x^2 = 16$$
$$\sqrt{x^2} = \sqrt{16}$$
$$|x| = 4$$

Therefore, $x = 4$ or $x = -4$.   This may be written $x = \pm 4$.

CHECK
$$x^2 - 16 = 0$$
$$4^2 - 16 \overset{?}{=} 0$$
$$0 = 0 \quad \checkmark$$

$$x^2 - 16 \overset{?}{=} 0$$
$$(-4)^2 - 16 \overset{?}{=} 0$$
$$0 = 0 \quad \checkmark$$

Finding square roots is easiest when the coefficient of the second-degree term is 1.

EXAMPLE 2   Solve $7x^2 - 252 = 0$.

SOLUTION
$$7x^2 - 252 = 0$$
$$7x^2 = 252$$
$D_7 \qquad \qquad x^2 = 36$
$$\sqrt{x^2} = \sqrt{36}$$
$$|x| = 6$$

Therefore, $x = 6$ or $x = -6$.   This may be written $x = \pm 6$.

CHECK
$$7x^2 - 252 = 0$$
$$7(6)^2 - 252 \overset{?}{=} 0$$
$$0 = 0 \quad \checkmark$$

$$7x^2 - 252 = 0$$
$$7(-6)^2 - 252 \overset{?}{=} 0$$
$$0 = 0 \quad \checkmark$$

EXAMPLE 3   Solve $x^2 - 25 = 25$.

SOLUTION
$$x^2 - 25 = 25$$
$$x^2 = 50$$
$$|x| = \sqrt{50}$$

Therefore, $x = 5\sqrt{2}$ or $x = -5\sqrt{2}$.
$$x = \pm 5\sqrt{2}$$

CHECK
$$x^2 - 25 = 25$$
$$(5\sqrt{2})^2 - 25 \overset{?}{=} 25$$
$$50 - 25 \overset{?}{=} 25$$
$$25 = 25 \quad \checkmark$$

$$x^2 - 25 = 25$$
$$(-5\sqrt{2})^2 - 25 \overset{?}{=} 25$$
$$50 - 25 \overset{?}{=} 25$$
$$25 = 25 \quad \checkmark$$

When an incomplete quadratic equation is written in the form $x^2 = -b$ and $-b < 0$, there are no real-number solutions. There are two imaginary-number solutions, however. They are $i\sqrt{b}$ and $-i\sqrt{b}$. These two solutions may be represented by $\pm i\sqrt{b}$.

EXAMPLE 4   Solve $5y^2 + 12 = 0$.

SOLUTION $5y^2 + 12 = 0$

$$5y^2 = -12$$

$$y^2 = -\frac{12}{5}$$

$$y = \pm i\sqrt{\frac{12}{5}}$$

$$= \pm i\sqrt{\frac{4 \cdot 3}{5} \cdot \frac{5}{5}}$$

$$= \pm \frac{2}{5}i\sqrt{15}$$

Therefore, $y = \frac{2}{5}i\sqrt{15}$ or $y = -\frac{2}{5}i\sqrt{15}$

CHECK

$$5y^2 + 12 = 0$$

$$5\left(\frac{2}{5}i\sqrt{15}\right)^2 + 12 \stackrel{?}{=} 0$$

$$5\left(\frac{4}{25}(-1)(15)\right) + 12 \stackrel{?}{=} 0$$

$$5\left(-\frac{12}{5}\right) + 12 \stackrel{?}{=} 0$$

$$0 = 0 \quad \checkmark$$

The check for $y = -\frac{2}{5}i\sqrt{15}$ is left for the student.

Solving an Incomplete Quadratic Equation, $ax^2 + c = 0$

1. Write the equation in the form $x^2 = -\frac{c}{a}$.

2. Find square roots of each member.

3. Check your results by replacing x in the original equation.

CLASSROOM EXERCISES

Solve. Give irrational-number solutions in simplest radical form.

1. $x^2 - 4 = 0$

2. $y^2 - \frac{1}{9} = 0$

3. $5c^2 - 245 = 0$

4. $x^2 - 36 = 36$

5. $2c^2 - \frac{1}{8} = 0$

6. $9x^2 + 8 = 2x^2 + 6$

EXERCISES

Ⓐ Solve. Give irrational-number solutions in simplest radical form.

1. $c^2 - 49 = 0$ **2.** $x^2 - 81 = 0$ **3.** $4x^2 - 100 = 0$

4. $5y^2 - 20 = 0$ **5.** $2y^2 - 36 = 0$ **6.** $5x^2 - 40 = 0$

7. $x^2 - 6.25 = 0$ **8.** $x^2 - 0.64 = 0$ **9.** $3n^2 + 9 = 57$

10. $p^2 - 6 = 30$ **11.** $x^2 - 49 = 49$ **12.** $y^2 - 1 = 1$

13. $x^2 + 5 = 0$ **14.** $x^2 + 17 = 0$ **15.** $\frac{1}{3}x^2 = 1$

16. $\frac{1}{5}y^2 = 2$ **17.** $3x^2 + 2 = x^2 - 8$ **18.** $7x^2 = 3x^2 - 2$

19. $12x^2 = 7x^2 - 3$ **20.** $3x^2 - 100 = -19$ **21.** $3x^2 + 100 = 124$

Ⓑ **22.** $\frac{x}{9} = \frac{36}{4x}$ **23.** $\frac{4}{x-3} = \frac{1}{3} + \frac{4}{x+3}$ **24.** $(2x-1)(3x+2) = x + 292$

25. $4(x-1)^2 = 9$ **26.** $-3(x+1)^2 = 27$ **27.** $-2(x-1)^2 = 8$

28. $2(3x-1)^2 = 7$ **29.** $3(2x+3)^2 = -6$ **30.** $\sqrt{x^2 + 1} = \sqrt{82}$

Solve for the indicated variable.

31. $V = \pi r^2 h$, for r **32.** $mx^2 = 1$, for x **33.** $s = \frac{1}{2}gt^2$, for t

Ⓒ Give each solution in simplest form.

34. $5x^2 = \sqrt{13}$ **35.** $(x^2 - 4)^2 = 12$ **36.** $(2x - 1)^3 = -\frac{16}{9}$

37. The Frozen Fantasy is a tasty snack having a spherical shape. It consists of an extremely crunchy outer spherical shell, an inner spherical shell of carob and a sphere of yogurt at the center having radius of 1 unit. The radius of the yogurt sphere plus the thickness of the carob inner shell is one-third the radius of the whole snack. When the volume of the crunchy outer shell exceeds the volume of the carob inner shell by 268π cubic units, how many units thick is the carob inner shell?

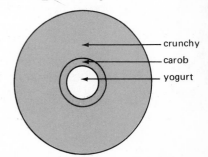

crunchy

carob

yogurt

8-3 SOLVING QUADRATIC EQUATIONS BY COMPLETING THE SQUARE

Being able to recognize perfect-square trinomials can be helpful in solving quadratic equations. Recall that a perfect-square trinomial has two terms that are perfect squares. Its other term is twice the product of the square roots of the perfect-square terms.

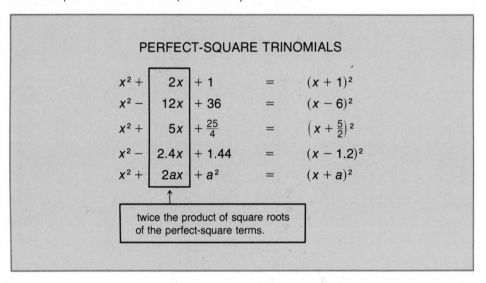

PERFECT-SQUARE TRINOMIALS

$$x^2 + \boxed{2x} + 1 = (x + 1)^2$$
$$x^2 - \boxed{12x} + 36 = (x - 6)^2$$
$$x^2 + \boxed{5x} + \frac{25}{4} = \left(x + \frac{5}{2}\right)^2$$
$$x^2 - \boxed{2.4x} + 1.44 = (x - 1.2)^2$$
$$x^2 + \boxed{2ax} + a^2 = (x + a)^2$$

twice the product of square roots of the perfect-square terms.

Note that in the examples above the constant (third) term of each trinomial is the square of one-half the coefficient of x in the second term.

EXAMPLE 1   Complete each member to show a perfect-square trinomial.

$$x^2 + 6x + ? = (x + ?)^2$$

SOLUTION   The coefficient of x in the second term is 6. One-half the coefficient is 3. The square of 3 is 9. Thus, 9 is the constant term of the perfect-square trinomial.

$$x^2 + 6x + 9 = (x + 3)^2$$

To solve a quadratic equation by *completing the square*, collect in the left member the terms with the variable, and in the right member the constant terms. Complete a perfect-square for the left member and add the same number to the right member. Then find square roots of each member and complete any necessary steps that may remain.

EXAMPLE 2 Solve $x^2 + 6x = 27$ by completing the square.

SOLUTION
$$x^2 + 6x = 27$$

Complete the perfect square for the left member and add the same number to the right member.

A_9 $x^2 + 6x + 9 = 27 + 9$
$$(x + 3)^2 = 36$$
$$\sqrt{(x + 3)^2} = \sqrt{36}$$
$$|x + 3| = 6$$

Therefore, $x + 3 = 6$ or $x + 3 = -6$.
$$x = 3 \qquad\qquad x = -9$$

CHECK
$$x^2 + 6x = 27 \qquad\qquad x^2 + 6x = 27$$
$$3^2 + 6(3) \stackrel{?}{=} 27 \qquad (-9)^2 + 6(-9) \stackrel{?}{=} 27$$
$$27 = 27 ✔ \qquad\qquad 27 = 27 ✔$$

Completing the square is easiest when the coefficient of the second-degree term is 1. When it is different from 1, divide both members of the equation by that coefficient before completing the square.

EXAMPLE 3 Solve $-3y^2 + 5y = 2$ by completing the square.

SOLUTION
$$-3y^2 + 5y = 2$$

D_{-3}
$$y^2 - \frac{5}{3}y = -\frac{2}{3}$$
$$y^2 - \frac{5}{3}y + \left(\frac{5}{6}\right)^2 = -\frac{2}{3} + \frac{25}{36}$$
$$\left(y - \frac{5}{6}\right)^2 = \frac{1}{36}$$
$$\left|y - \frac{5}{6}\right| = \frac{1}{6}$$

$$y - \frac{5}{6} = \frac{1}{6} \quad \text{or} \quad y - \frac{5}{6} = -\frac{1}{6}$$
$$y = 1 \qquad\qquad y = \frac{2}{3}$$

CHECK
The check is left for the student.

EXAMPLE 4 Solve $x^2 - 3x = 2$ by completing the square.

SOLUTION
$$x^2 - 3x = 2$$
$$x^2 - 3x + \left(\frac{3}{2}\right)^2 = 2 + \left(\frac{3}{2}\right)^2$$
$$\left(x - \frac{3}{2}\right)^2 = \frac{17}{4}$$
$$x - \frac{3}{2} = \pm \frac{\sqrt{17}}{2}$$
$$x = \frac{3 + \sqrt{17}}{2} \quad \text{or} \quad x = \frac{3 - \sqrt{17}}{2}$$

CHECK
The check is left for the student.

When completing the square gives a quadratic equation in the form $(x - a)^2 = -b$ and $-b < 0$, there are no real-number solutions for the equation. There are two complex-number solutions, however. They are $a + i\sqrt{b}$ and $a - i\sqrt{b}$. These two solutions may be represented by $a \pm i\sqrt{b}$.

EXAMPLE 5 Solve $x^2 + x + 1 = 0$.

SOLUTION
$$x^2 + x + 1 = 0$$
$$x^2 + x \qquad = -1$$
$$x^2 + x + \left(\frac{1}{2}\right)^2 = -1 + \left(\frac{1}{2}\right)^2$$
$$\left(x + \frac{1}{2}\right)^2 = -\frac{3}{4}$$
$$x + \frac{1}{2} = \pm\sqrt{-\frac{3}{4}}$$
$$x = -\frac{1}{2} + \frac{\sqrt{3}}{2}i \quad \text{or} \quad x = -\frac{1}{2} - \frac{\sqrt{3}}{2}i$$

CHECK
$$x^2 + x + 1 = 0$$
$$\left(-\frac{1}{2} + \frac{\sqrt{3}}{2}i\right)^2 + \left(-\frac{1}{2} + \frac{\sqrt{3}}{2}i\right) + 1 \overset{?}{=} 0$$
$$\frac{1}{4} - \frac{\sqrt{3}}{2}i - \frac{3}{4} - \frac{1}{2} + \frac{\sqrt{3}}{2}i + 1 \overset{?}{=} 0$$
$$0 = 0 \quad \checkmark$$

The check for $x = -\frac{1}{2} - \frac{\sqrt{3}}{2}i$ is left for the student.

SOLVING A QUADRATIC EQUATION BY COMPLETING THE SQUARE

1. Write the equation $ax^2 + bx + c = 0$ in the form $x^2 + \frac{b}{a}x = -\frac{c}{a}$.

2. Add to each member the square of one-half the coefficient of x.

3. Find square roots of each member.

4. Solve the resulting linear equations.

5. Check your results by replacing the variable in the original equation.

CLASSROOM EXERCISES

Give the term needed to complete a perfect-square trinomial.

1. $x^2 - 12x + ?$ **2.** $x^2 + 14x + ?$ **3.** $x^2 - 5x + ?$

Solve by completing the square.

4. $x^2 - 2x = 8$ **5.** $x^2 - 12x + 11 = 0$ **6.** $x^2 - 5x - 14 = 0$

7. $-2x^2 - 13x + 7 = 0$ **8.** $x^2 - 5x - 3 = 0$ **9.** $x^2 + 2x + 10 = 0$

EXERCISES

A Give the term needed to complete a perfect-square trinomial.

1. $c^2 - 3c + ?$ **2.** $x^2 - 11x + ?$ **3.** $x^2 + \frac{2}{3}x + ?$

4. $x^2 + \frac{2}{5}x + ?$ **5.** $x^2 + 0.1x + ?$ **6.** $y^2 + 0.01y + ?$

Solve by completing the square.

7. $x^2 + 4x = -3$ **8.** $x^2 - 12x = -27$ **9.** $y^2 - 2y = 35$

10. $c^2 - 5c - 14 = 0$ **11.** $y^2 - 3y - 54 = 0$ **12.** $c^2 - 8 = 26$

13. $y^2 + 48 = -14y$ **14.** $k^2 + 5k - 14 = 0$ **15.** $x^2 - 9x + 8 = 0$

16. $4x^2 + 11x = 3$ **17.** $-3h^2 + 5h = 2$ **18.** $2x^2 - 22x = -28$

19. $5x^2 + 16x = -6$ **20.** $6x^2 + 5x - 3 = 0$ **21.** $-x^2 - x + 1 = 0$

22. $m^2 - 35 = 2m$ **23.** $5y^2 + 2y - 2 = 0$ **24.** $2k^2 - 8k + 5 = 0$

25. $3x^2 - 6x + 15 = 0$ **26.** $-4x^2 + 16x - 25 = 0$ **27.** $x^2 - x + 1 = 0$

28. $4x^2 + x + 2 = 0$ **29.** $6x^2 - 8x + 1 = 0$ **30.** $x^2 - x - 10 = 0$

Solve for x.

31. $x^2 + 3ax + 2a^2 = 0$ **32.** $x^2 + 6kx = 7k^2$ **33.** $x^2 - 2cx = 35c^2$

B Give the term needed to complete a perfect-square trinomial.

34. $x^{-2} + 2x^{-1} + ?$ **35.** $x^{\frac{1}{2}} - 3x^{\frac{1}{4}} + ?$ **36.** $x^2 + 5\sqrt{3}x + ?$

Solve for x by completing the square.

37. $x^2 + \sqrt{3}x + 5 = 0$ **38.** $\frac{1}{x^2} + \frac{3}{x} + 5 = 0$ **39.** $dx^2 - ex - f = 0$

C **40.** $x^4 + 4x^2 - 3 = 4\sqrt{3}$ **41.** $\dfrac{\sqrt[4]{(x-1)(2x-1)}}{\sqrt{x-1}} = \sqrt[4]{x}$

8-4 SOLVING QUADRATIC EQUATIONS BY USING THE QUADRATIC FORMULA

Any quadratic equation may be solved by completing the square. When the general quadratic equation, $ax^2 + bx + c = 0$, $a \neq 0$, is solved in this way, the result is the **quadratic formula**.

$$ax^2 + bx + c = 0$$
$$ax^2 + bx \qquad = -c$$
$$D_a \qquad x^2 + \frac{b}{a}x \qquad = -\frac{c}{a}$$

Complete the square for the left member and add the same number to the right member.

$$x^2 + \frac{b}{a}x + \left(\frac{b}{2a}\right)^2 = \left(\frac{b}{2a}\right)^2 - \frac{c}{a}$$

$$x^2 + \frac{b}{a}x + \frac{b^2}{4a^2} = \frac{b^2}{4a^2} - \frac{c}{a}$$

$$\left(x + \frac{b}{2a}\right)^2 = \frac{b^2 - 4ac}{4a^2}$$

$$x + \frac{b}{2a} = \pm \frac{\sqrt{b^2 - 4ac}}{2a}$$

$$x + \frac{b}{2a} = \frac{\sqrt{b^2 - 4ac}}{2a} \qquad \text{or} \quad x + \frac{b}{2a} = -\frac{\sqrt{b^2 - 4ac}}{2a}$$

$$x = -\frac{b}{2a} + \frac{\sqrt{b^2 - 4ac}}{2a} \qquad\qquad x = -\frac{b}{2a} - \frac{\sqrt{b^2 - 4ac}}{2a}$$

$$x = \frac{-b + \sqrt{b^2 - 4ac}}{2a} \qquad\qquad x = \frac{-b - \sqrt{b^2 - 4ac}}{2a}$$

THE QUADRATIC FORMULA

For the quadratic equation $ax^2 + bx + c = 0$, $a \neq 0$, the solutions are

$$x = \frac{-b \pm \sqrt{b^2 - 4ac}}{2a} .$$

To use the quadratic formula for solving a quadratic equation, replace a, b, and c in the formula by the corresponding coefficients from the equation.

EXAMPLE 1 Solve $x^2 + 2x - 3 = 0$. Use the quadratic formula.

SOLUTION Comparing the equations

$ax^2 + bx + c = 0$ and
$x^2 + 2x - 3 = 0$,

we see that $a = 1$, $b = 2$, and $c = -3$.

Replacing a, b, and c by these numbers in the quadratic

formula gives $x = \dfrac{-2 \pm \sqrt{2^2 - 4(1)(-3)}}{2(1)}$

$= \dfrac{-2 \pm \sqrt{16}}{2}$

$= \dfrac{-2 \pm 4}{2}$

$= -1 \pm 2$

$x = -1 + 2 \quad$ or $\quad x = -1 - 2$
$x = 1 \qquad\qquad \mid \quad x = -3$

CHECK
The check is left
for the student.

EXAMPLE 2 Solve $3x^2 - 4x - 2 = 0$.

SOLUTION $3x^2 - 4x - 2 = 0$, $a = 3$, $b = -4$, $c = -2$

By the formula, $x = \dfrac{-(-4) \pm \sqrt{(-4)^2 - 4(3)(-2)}}{2 \cdot 3}$

$= \dfrac{4 \pm \sqrt{40}}{6}$

$= \dfrac{4 \pm 2\sqrt{10}}{6}$

$= \dfrac{2 \pm \sqrt{10}}{3}$

$x = \dfrac{2}{3} + \dfrac{\sqrt{10}}{3}$ or $x = \dfrac{2}{3} - \dfrac{\sqrt{10}}{3}$

CHECK

$3x^2 - 4x - 2 = 0$

$3\left(\dfrac{2}{3} + \dfrac{\sqrt{10}}{3}\right)^2 - 4\left(\dfrac{2}{3} + \dfrac{\sqrt{10}}{3}\right) - 2 \overset{?}{=} 0$

$3\left(\dfrac{4}{9} + \dfrac{4\sqrt{10}}{9} + \dfrac{10}{9}\right) - 4\left(\dfrac{2}{3} + \dfrac{\sqrt{10}}{3}\right) - 2 \overset{?}{=} 0$

$\dfrac{4}{3} + \dfrac{4\sqrt{10}}{3} + \dfrac{10}{3} - \dfrac{8}{3} - \dfrac{4\sqrt{10}}{3} - 2 \overset{?}{=} 0$

$0 = 0 \ ✔$

The check for $x = \dfrac{2}{3} - \dfrac{\sqrt{10}}{3}$ is left for the student.

EXAMPLE 3 Solve $x^2 + x + 2 = 0$.

SOLUTION $x^2 + x + 2 = 0, \quad a = 1, b = 1, c = 2$

By the formula, $x = \dfrac{-1 \pm \sqrt{1^2 - 4(1)(2)}}{2(1)}$

$$= \dfrac{-1 \pm \sqrt{-7}}{2}$$

$$= \dfrac{-1 \pm i\sqrt{7}}{2}$$

$$x = -\dfrac{1}{2} + \dfrac{\sqrt{7}}{2}i \text{ or } x = -\dfrac{1}{2} - \dfrac{\sqrt{7}}{2}i$$

CHECK The check is left for the student.

SOLVING A QUADRATIC EQUATION USING THE QUADRATIC FORMULA

1. Write the equation in the form $ax^2 + bx + c = 0$.
2. Replace a, b, and c in the quadratic formula

$$x = \dfrac{-b \pm \sqrt{b^2 - 4ac}}{2a}$$

by the corresponding coefficients from the equation.
3. Simplify the right member.
4. Check your results by replacing x in the original equation.

CLASSROOM EXERCISES

Solve. Use the quadratic formula.

1. $x^2 + x - 6 = 0$ **2.** $2x^2 - x - 3 = 0$ **3.** $3x^2 + 2x + 5 = 0$

EXERCISES

Ⓐ Solve. Use the quadratic formula.

1. $3x^2 + 8x + 5 = 0$ **2.** $5x^2 + 26x + 5 = 0$ **3.** $2x^2 + 2x - 24 = 0$

4. $y^2 + 6y = 55$ **5.** $8x^2 - 2x = 1$ **6.** $7x^2 - 11x = -4$

7. $x^2 + x - 2 = 0$ **8.** $x^2 + 2x - 8 = 0$ **9.** $2x^2 = 1 - 3x$

10. $3x = 2 - 9x^2$

11. $x^2 + x + 1 = 0$

12. $x^2 + x + 5 = 0$

13. $8x^2 = 1 - 4x$

14. $3x^2 = 6 - 4x$

15. $x^2 + 6x + 9 = 0$

16. $x^2 - 10x + 25 = 0$

17. $x^2 - 81 = 0$

18. $x^2 - 121 = 0$

19. $11x^2 - 12x = -3$

20. $13x^2 - 14x = -4$

21. $x^2 + 0.7x = 0.12$

22. $6x^2 - 0.7x + 0.02 = 0$

23. $3x^2 - x + 5 = 0$

24. $5x^2 - x + 6 = 0$

Solve for x. Use the quadratic formula.

25. $2x^2 + 4bx - c = 0$

26. $x^2 + cx + d = 0$

27. $ax^2 + x + 1 = 0$

B Solve. Use the quadratic formula.

28. $(x - 3)^2 + 2(x + 5)^2 = 40$

29. $x(x - 2) = 7$

30. $\dfrac{m^2 - 3}{2} + \dfrac{m}{4} = 1$

31. $\dfrac{x - 1}{2} - \dfrac{3x + 1}{3} + \dfrac{4x^2}{3} = 0$

32. $3x^2 + 4 = \sqrt{5}x$

33. $3\sqrt{6}x^2 + \sqrt{24} = 13x$

Solve for x. Use the quadratic formula.

34. $ax^2 + 2bx - 1 = 0$

35. $x^2 + (\sqrt{4a^2 + 1})x + a^2 = 0$

C **36.** Find the three cube roots of 1. (Hint: Begin by factoring $x^3 - 1$ in $x^3 - 1 = 0$.)

37. Solve $(y - 3)^{\frac{1}{2}} + (y - 3)^{\frac{1}{4}} - 12 = 0$. (Hint: Replace $(y - 3)^{\frac{1}{4}}$ by x.)

PROPERTIES OF ABSOLUTE VALUE

Absolute value is used frequently in advanced mathematics courses, especially in calculus. In addition to the definition and the number-line interpretation, there are four important properties of absolute value.

In each of the following, which of the symbols, $=$, $<$, $\leq$, $>$, $\geq$, should replace the ? symbol? Use various combinations of positive and negative replacements for a and b to help you decide.

1. $|a| \cdot |b|$? $|ab|$

2. $\left|\dfrac{a}{b}\right|$? $\dfrac{|a|}{|b|}$

3. $|a + b|$? $|a| + |b|$

4. $|a - b|$? $|a| - |b|$

5. Can you think of ways to *prove* your conjectures?

8-5 THE DISCRIMINANT

The solutions (roots) of the quadratic equation $ax^2 + bx + c = 0$ are given by the quadratic formula,

$$x = \frac{-b \pm \sqrt{b^2 - 4ac}}{2a}.$$

The radicand $b^2 - 4ac$ is called the **discriminant** of the equation because it can tell us so much about the solutions of the equation.

When the coefficients a, b, and c are real numbers, for example, a positive discriminant tells us that there are two real solutions. A discriminant equal to zero tells us that there is one real solution. A negative discriminant tells us that there are two imaginary solutions.

The discriminant provides even more information when the coefficients a, b, and c are integers as is shown in the following examples.

EXAMPLE 1 Solve $2x^2 - 5x - 3 = 0$. Relate the discriminant to the nature of the solutions.

SOLUTION $2x^2 - 5x - 3 = 0$, $a = 2, b = -5, c = -3$

$$x = \frac{-(-5) \pm \sqrt{\text{the discriminant}}}{2(2)}$$

$$= \frac{5 \pm \sqrt{49}}{4}$$

$$x = \frac{5 + 7}{4} \quad \text{or} \quad x = \frac{5 - 7}{4}$$

$$x = 3 \qquad \qquad x = -\tfrac{1}{2}$$

> The discriminant:
> $$b^2 - 4ac$$
> $$= (-5)^2 - 4(2)(-3)$$
> $$= 25 + 24$$
> $$= 49$$

The discriminant, $b^2 - 4ac$, is positive and the square of an integer. There are two rational-number solutions.

CHECK The check is left for the student.

EXAMPLE 2 Solve $x^2 + 5x + 3 = 0$. Relate the discriminant to the nature of the solutions.

SOLUTION $x^2 + 5x + c = 0$, $a = 1, b = 5, c = 3$

$$x = \frac{-5 \pm \sqrt{\text{the discriminant}}}{2(1)}$$

$$x = \frac{-5 + \sqrt{13}}{2} \text{ or } x = \frac{-5 - \sqrt{13}}{2}$$

> The discriminant:
> $$b^2 - 4ac$$
> $$= 5^2 - 4(1)(3)$$
> $$= 13$$

The discriminant is positive, but not the square of an integer. There are two irrational-number solutions.

CHECK The check is left for the student.

EXAMPLE 3 Solve $x^2 - 8x + 16 = 0$. Relate the discriminant to the nature of the solutions.

SOLUTION $x^2 - 8x + 16 = 0$, $a = 1$, $b = -8$, $c = 16$

$$x = \frac{-(-8) \pm \sqrt{\text{the discriminant}}}{2(1)}$$

$$= \frac{8 \pm \sqrt{0}}{2}$$

$x = 4$

> The discriminant:
> $b^2 - 4ac$
> $= (-8)^2 - 4(1)(16)$
> $= 0$

The discriminant is zero. There is one rational-number solution. Such a solution often is called a *double root*.

CHECK The check is left for the student.

EXAMPLE 4 Solve $x^2 - x + 2 = 0$. Relate the discriminant to the nature of the solutions.

SOLUTION $x^2 - x + 2 = 0$, $a = 1$, $b = -1$, $c = 2$

$$x = \frac{-(-1) \pm \sqrt{\text{the discriminant}}}{2(1)}$$

$$= \frac{1 \pm \sqrt{-7}}{2}$$

$x = \frac{1}{2} + \frac{\sqrt{7}}{2}i$ or $x = \frac{1}{2} - \frac{\sqrt{7}}{2}i$

> The discriminant:
> $b^2 - 4ac$
> $= (-1)^2 - 4(1)(2)$
> $= -7$

The discriminant is negative. There are two complex-number solutions. The numbers are conjugates.

CHECK The check is left for the student.

THE NATURE OF THE SOLUTIONS OF A QUADRATIC EQUATION		
Discriminant	Real-Number Coefficients	Integral Coefficients
positive	two real-number solutions	two real-number solutions
the square of an integer		two rational-number solutions
not the square of an integer		two irrational-number solutions
zero	one real-number solution	one rational-number solution
negative	two complex-number solutions	

CLASSROOM EXERCISES $b^2 - 4ac$

Determine the nature of the solutions of each equation.

1. $15x^2 - x - 2 = 0$ **2.** $3x^2 - 7x + 5 = 0$ **3.** $-2x^2 + 5x + 2 = 0$

4. $49x^2 - 28x + 4 = 0$ **5.** $-3x^2 + 7x - 4 = 0$ **6.** $4x^2 - 12x + 25 = 0$

EXERCISES

A   Determine the nature of the solutions of each equation.

1. $\overset{a}{x^2} + \overset{b}{5x} - \overset{c}{3} = 0$ **2.** $\overset{a}{x^2} - \overset{b}{5x} - \overset{c}{4} = 0$ **3.** $\overset{a}{x^2} + \overset{b}{9x} + \overset{c}{14} = 0$

4. $4x^2 + 3x = 0$ **5.** $x^2 - 6x = -9$ **6.** $x^2 - 10x = -25$

7. $6y^2 + 6 = -10y$ **8.** $2m^2 + 3 = m$ **9.** $x^2 + x + \frac{1}{2} = 0$

10. $x^2 - \frac{1}{3}x + 2 = 0$ **11.** $4x^2 + 1 = 4x$ **12.** $25x^2 + 1 = -10x$

13. $6y^2 + 13y + 6 = 0$ **14.** $14x^2 - x - 3 = 0$ **15.** $x^2 - x - 1 = 0$

16. $2x^2 - 2x - 1 = 0$ **17.** $x^2 - x + 1 = 0$ **18.** $x^2 - 3x + 7 = 0$

B   **19.** $\sqrt{3}x^2 - 5x + 2\sqrt{3} = 0$ **20.** $2x^2 - \sqrt{7}x + \sqrt{7} = 0$

21. $x^2 + 2\sqrt[4]{3}x + \sqrt{2} = 0$ **22.** $3x^2 - 17.4 = 0$

Find the value of k for which each equation will have just one solution.

23. $4x^2 - 20kx + 25 = 0$ **24.** $9y^2 - 6y + k = 0$ **25.** $2m^2 + km + 32 = 0$

26. $kx^2 - 12x + 2k + 1 = 0$ **27.** $4x^2 + kx + k + 5 = 0$ **28.** $(2k + 5)y^2 - ky + 1 = 0$

29. For what numbers m are the solutions of $x^2 + 6x + m = 0$ imaginary?

30. For what numbers k does the graph of $y = 6x^2 + kx + 15$ intersect the x-axis?

31. For what numbers k are the solutions of $kx^2 + 4x + 10 = 0$ real?

32. One solution to a quadratic equation is $1 + i$. Give the other solution.

C   The quadratic formula gives the two solutions of a quadratic equation.

33. Show that the sum of the solutions is $-\frac{b}{a}$.

34. Show that the product of the solutions is $\frac{c}{a}$.

Use the results from Exercises 33 and 34 to find the sum and product of the solutions of each equation below. Check by solving the equation and adding and multiplying the solutions.

35. $x^2 - 5x + 6 = 0$ **36.** $2y^2 - 3y + 2 = 0$ **37.** $3y^2 - 7y = 2$

8-6 EQUATIONS THAT ARE QUADRATIC IN FORM

Sometimes an equation that is not of the second degree can be written to be quadratic in form.   Then it can be solved by one of the methods used for solving a quadratic equation.

EXAMPLE 1 Solve $5x^4 - 125 = 0$.

SOLUTION $5x^4 - 125 = 0$
$$5x^4 = 125$$
$$x^4 = 25$$
$$x^2 = \pm 5$$

$$x^2 = 5 \qquad\qquad \text{or} \quad x^2 = -5$$
$$x = \pm\sqrt{5} \qquad\qquad\qquad x = \pm\sqrt{-5}$$
$$x = \sqrt{5} \quad \text{or} \quad x = -\sqrt{5} \quad\Big|\quad x = i\sqrt{5} \quad \text{or} \quad x = -i\sqrt{5}$$

CHECK
$$5x^4 - 125 = 0 \qquad\qquad 5x^4 - 125 = 0$$
$$5(\pm\sqrt{5})^4 - 125 \overset{?}{=} 0 \qquad 5(\pm i\sqrt{5})^4 - 125 \overset{?}{=} 0$$
$$5(25) - 125 \overset{?}{=} 0 \qquad\qquad 5(25) - 125 \overset{?}{=} 0$$
$$0 = 0 \; \checkmark \qquad\qquad\qquad 0 = 0 \; \checkmark$$

EXAMPLE 2 Solve $x^4 - 2x^2 - 24 = 0$.

SOLUTION $x^4 - 2x^2 - 24 = 0$ can be replaced by
$(x^2)^2 - 2(x^2) - 24 = 0$ which is quadratic in x^2.
$$(x^2 - 6)(x^2 + 4) = 0$$
Therefore, $x^2 - 6 = 0 \qquad$ or $\quad x^2 + 4 = 0$
$$x^2 = 6 \qquad\qquad\qquad x^2 = -4$$
$$x = \pm\sqrt{6} \qquad\qquad\qquad x = \pm\sqrt{-4}$$
$$x = \sqrt{6} \quad \text{or} \quad x = -\sqrt{6} \quad\Big|\quad x = 2i \quad \text{or} \quad x = -2i$$

CHECK The check is left for the student.

EXAMPLE 3 Solve $(x^2 - x)^2 - (x^2 - x) - 30 = 0$.

SOLUTION This is quadratic in $(x^2 - x)$.
$$(x^2 - x)^2 - (x^2 - x) - 30 = 0$$
$$[(x^2 - x) - 6][(x^2 - x) + 5] = 0$$
Therefore,
$$x^2 - x - 6 = 0 \quad \text{or } x^2 - x + 5 = 0$$
$$(x - 3)(x + 2) = 0 \qquad\qquad\qquad x = \frac{1 \pm \sqrt{-19}}{2}$$
$$x - 3 = 0 \text{ or } x + 2 = 0$$
$$x = 3 \; \Big| \quad x = -2$$
$$x = \frac{1}{2} + \frac{\sqrt{19}}{2}i \text{ or } x = \frac{1}{2} - \frac{\sqrt{19}}{2}i$$

CHECK The check is left for the student.

EXAMPLE 4 Solve $x^{\frac{1}{2}} - 5x^{\frac{1}{4}} + 6 = 0$.

SOLUTION $x^{\frac{1}{2}} - 5x^{\frac{1}{4}} + 6 = 0$ can be replaced by

$(x^{\frac{1}{4}})^2 - 5(x^{\frac{1}{4}}) + 6 = 0$ which is quadratic in $x^{\frac{1}{4}}$.

$(x^{\frac{1}{4}} - 3)(x^{\frac{1}{4}} - 2) = 0$

Therefore, $x^{\frac{1}{4}} - 3 = 0$ or $x^{\frac{1}{4}} - 2 = 0$

$$x^{\frac{1}{4}} = 3 \qquad\qquad x^{\frac{1}{4}} = 2$$
$$x = 3^4 \qquad\qquad x = 2^4$$
$$x = 81 \qquad\qquad x = 16$$

CHECK $x^{\frac{1}{2}} - 5x^{\frac{1}{4}} + 6 = 0$ $\qquad$ $x^{\frac{1}{2}} - 5x^{\frac{1}{4}} + 6 = 0$

$81^{\frac{1}{2}} - 5(81)^{\frac{1}{4}} + 6 \overset{?}{=} 0$ $\qquad$ $16^{\frac{1}{2}} - 5(16)^{\frac{1}{4}} + 6 \overset{?}{=} 0$

$9 - 5(3) + 6 \overset{?}{=} 0$ $\qquad\qquad$ $4 - 5(2) + 6 \overset{?}{=} 0$

$0 = 0$ ✔ $\qquad\qquad\qquad$ $0 = 0$ ✔

EXAMPLE 5 Solve $\left(\dfrac{x^2 + 4}{x}\right)^2 - 9\left(\dfrac{x^2 + 4}{x}\right) + 20 = 0$, $x \neq 0$.

SOLTUION This is quadratic in $\dfrac{x^2 + 4}{x}$.

$$\left(\frac{x^2 + 4}{x}\right)^2 - 9\left(\frac{x^2 + 4}{x}\right) + 20 = 0$$

$$\left(\frac{x^2 + 4}{x} - 5\right)\left(\frac{x^2 + 4}{x} - 4\right) = 0$$

Therefore, $\dfrac{x^2 + 4}{x} - 5 = 0$ or $\dfrac{x^2 + 4}{x} - 4 = 0$

$$x^2 - 5x + 4 = 0 \qquad\qquad x^2 - 4x + 4 = 0$$
$$(x - 4)(x - 1) = 0 \qquad\qquad (x - 2)(x - 2) = 0$$
$$x - 4 = 0 \quad\text{or}\quad x - 1 = 0 \qquad\qquad x - 2 = 0$$
$$x = 4 \quad | \quad x = 1 \qquad\qquad\qquad x = 2$$

CHECK $\left(\dfrac{x^2 + 4}{x}\right)^2 - 9\left(\dfrac{x^2 + 4}{x}\right) + 20 = 0$

$$\left(\frac{4^2 + 4}{4}\right)^2 - 9\left(\frac{4^2 + 4}{4}\right) + 20 \overset{?}{=} 0$$

$$25 - 45 + 20 \overset{?}{=} 0$$
$$0 = 0 \text{ ✔}$$

The checks for $x = 1$ and $x = 2$ are left for the student.

CLASSROOM EXERCISES

Solve.

1. $4x^4 - 64 = 0$ **2.** $7x^4 - 343 = 0$ **3.** $x^4 + 3x^2 - 4 = 0$

4. $x^6 - 28x^3 + 27 = 0$ **5.** $2x^{\frac{1}{2}} + x^{\frac{1}{4}} - 6 = 0$ **6.** $6x^{-2} = x^{-1} + 1$

7. $(y^2 - 1)^2 - 11(y^2 - 1) + 24 = 0$ **8.** $6\left(\dfrac{1}{x+1}\right)^2 - \left(\dfrac{1}{x+1}\right) = 1$

EXERCISES

A Solve.

1. $2x^4 - 18 = 0$ **2.** $3x^4 - 75 = 0$ **3.** $y^4 - 256 = 0$

4. $x^4 - 192 = 0$ **5.** $x^4 + 9x^2 + 18 = 0$ **6.** $x^4 - 13x^2 + 36 = 0$

7. $y^4 = 13y^2 - 40$ **8.** $6x^4 = 8x^2 - 2$ **9.** $x^4 - 5x^2 + 4 = 0$

10. $x^4 - 64 = 12x^2$ **11.** $y^4 - 10y^2 + 9 = 0$ **12.** $5x^4 + 4x^2 - 1 = 0$

13. $3m^4 = 5m^2 + 2$ **14.** $y^4 - 6y^2 + 5 = 0$ **15.** $m^4 - 7m^2 + 6 = 0$

16. $(x + 1)^2 - 3(x + 1) = 40$ **17.** $(y - 3)^2 + 4(y - 3) = 21$ **18.** $x^4 - 40x^2 + 144 = 0$

19. $(x^2 - x)^2 - 8(x^2 - x) = 9$ **20.** $x^{\frac{1}{2}} + 3x^{\frac{1}{4}} - 10 = 0$ **21.** $x^{\frac{1}{3}} - 3x^{\frac{1}{6}} + 2 = 0$

22. $\left(\dfrac{1}{x}\right)^2 - 9 = 0$ **23.** $\left(\dfrac{x + 2}{x}\right)^2 + \left(\dfrac{x + 2}{x}\right) = 6$ **24.** $49\left(\dfrac{x}{x^2 - 2}\right)^2 + 6 = 35\left(\dfrac{x}{x^2 - 2}\right)$

B Solve.

25. $(2x^2 - 1)^2 - 8(2x^2 - 1) + 7 = 0$ **26.** $(a^2 - 2a)^2 + 6 = 5(a^2 - 2a)$

27. $(x + 3)^{\frac{1}{2}} + 4 = 4(x + 3)^{\frac{1}{4}}$ **28.** $(x^2 + 4x)^2 + 8 = 6(x^2 + 4x)$

C **29.** $9(9x^2 - 25)^2 - 25 = 0$ **30.** $x^{\frac{2}{5}} - 11x^{\frac{1}{5}} + 30 = 0$ **31.** $x^{-\frac{4}{3}} - 8x^{-\frac{2}{3}} + 15 = 0$

STANDARD PAPER SIZES

Standard metric sizes that have a special property now exist for paper. Cut a sheet of any such size in half across the width. The two resulting pieces will be similar to the original piece. For such a sheet, how is length related to width? What are the sheet dimensions when the area is 1 m²?

8-7 SOLVING EQUATIONS THAT LEAD TO QUADRATIC EQUATIONS

Quadratic equations may arise when you are solving fractional or radical equations.

EXAMPLE 1 Solve $\dfrac{x-4}{x-5} - \dfrac{2x-1}{x+4} = \dfrac{1-2x}{x^2-x-20}$, $x \neq -4$, $x \neq 5$.

SOLUTION

$$\frac{x-4}{x-5} - \frac{2x-1}{x+4} = \frac{1-2x}{x^2-x-20}$$

$$\frac{x-4}{x-5} - \frac{2x-1}{x+4} = \frac{1-2x}{(x-5)(x+4)}$$

Multiply both members by $(x-5)(x+4)$.

$$(x+4)(x-4) - (x-5)(2x-1) = 1-2x$$
$$(x^2-16) - (2x^2-11x+5) = 1-2x$$
$$x^2-16-2x^2+11x-5 = 1-2x$$
$$-x^2+13x-22 = 0$$

Use the quadratic formula.

$$x = \frac{-13 \pm \sqrt{13^2 - 4(-1)(-22)}}{2(-1)}$$

$$= \frac{-13 \pm \sqrt{81}}{-2}$$

$$= \frac{-13 \pm 9}{-2}$$

Therefore, $x = \dfrac{-13+9}{-2}$ or $x = \dfrac{-13-9}{-2}$

$$x = 2 \qquad\qquad x = 11$$

CHECK

$$\frac{x-4}{x-5} - \frac{2x-1}{x+4} = \frac{1-2x}{x^2-x-20}$$

$$\frac{2-4}{2-5} - \frac{2(2)-1}{2+4} \overset{?}{=} \frac{1-2(2)}{2^2-2-20}$$

$$\frac{-2}{-3} - \frac{3}{6} \overset{?}{=} \frac{-3}{-18}$$

$$\frac{4}{6} - \frac{3}{6} \overset{?}{=} \frac{1}{6}$$

$$\frac{1}{6} = \frac{1}{6} \quad \blacktriangleright$$

The check for $x = 11$ is left for the student.

Remember, when you solve fractional or radical equations, it is possible to introduce extraneous solutions. Therefore it is important that you check your results by replacing the variable in the *original equation*. *Do not* use for your check any equation that was derived from the original equation.

EXAMPLE 2   Solve $2\sqrt{x^2 + 7} - 3x = 1$.

SOLUTION $2\sqrt{x^2 + 7} - 3x = 1$

$\quad\quad 2\sqrt{x^2 + 7} = 3x + 1$

Square both members.

$$4(x^2 + 7) = 9x^2 + 6x + 1$$
$$4x^2 + 28 = 9x^2 + 6x + 1$$
$$-5x^2 - 6x + 27 = 0$$

Use the quadratic formula.

$$x = \frac{-(-6) \pm \sqrt{(-6)^2 - 4(-5)(27)}}{2(-5)}$$

$$= \frac{6 \pm \sqrt{576}}{-10}$$

$$= \frac{6 \pm 24}{-10}$$

Therefore, $x = \dfrac{6 + 24}{-10}$ or $x = \dfrac{6 - 24}{-10}$

$\quad\quad\quad\quad x = -3$ $\quad\quad$ $x = \dfrac{9}{5}$

CHECK $\quad\quad 2\sqrt{x^2 + 7} - 3x = 1$

$2\sqrt{(-3)^2 + 7} - 3(-3) \overset{?}{=} 1$

$\quad\quad 2\sqrt{16} + 9 \overset{?}{=} 1$

$\quad\quad\quad\quad 8 + 9 \overset{?}{=} 1$

$\quad\quad\quad\quad\quad 17 \neq 1$ ✗

$\quad\quad 2\sqrt{x^2 + 7} - 3x = 1$

$2\sqrt{\left(\frac{9}{5}\right)^2 + 7} - 3\left(\frac{9}{5}\right) \overset{?}{=} 1$

$\quad\quad 2\sqrt{\frac{256}{25}} - \frac{27}{5} \overset{?}{=} 1$

$\quad\quad\quad \frac{32}{5} - \frac{27}{5} \overset{?}{=} 1$

$\quad\quad\quad\quad\quad 1 = 1$ ✓

Therefore, -3 is not a solution.

CONCLUSION   The solution of the equation is $\dfrac{9}{5}$.

EXAMPLE 3   Solve $\dfrac{1}{1+x} + \dfrac{1+x}{2-x} = \dfrac{3x^2}{2+x-x^2}$.

SOLUTION

$$\frac{1}{1+x} + \frac{1+x}{2-x} = \frac{3x^2}{2+x-x^2}$$

$$\frac{1}{1+x} + \frac{1+x}{2-x} = \frac{3x^2}{(1+x)(2-x)}$$

$$(2-x) + (1+x)(1+x) = 3x^2$$

$$2 - x + 1 + 2x + x^2 = 3x^2$$

$$-2x^2 + x + 3 = 0$$

Use the quadratic formula.

$$x = \frac{-1 \pm \sqrt{1 - 4(-2)(3)}}{2(-2)}$$

$$= \frac{-1 \pm \sqrt{25}}{-4}$$

$$= \frac{-1 \pm 5}{-4}$$

Therefore, $x = \dfrac{-1+5}{-4}$ or $x = \dfrac{-1-5}{-4}$

$$x = -1 \qquad\qquad x = \frac{3}{2}$$

CHECK   Replacing x by -1 in $\dfrac{1}{1+x}$ will give $\dfrac{1}{0}$, which is meaningless.   Therefore, -1 is an extraneous solution.   It is not a solution of the original equation.

$$\frac{1}{1+x} + \frac{1+x}{2-x} = \frac{3x^2}{2+x-x^2}$$

$$\frac{1}{1+\frac{3}{2}} + \frac{1+\frac{3}{2}}{2-\frac{3}{2}} \stackrel{?}{=} \frac{3\left(\frac{3}{2}\right)^2}{2+\frac{3}{2}-\left(\frac{3}{2}\right)^2}$$

$$\frac{2}{5} + 5 \stackrel{?}{=} \frac{\frac{27}{4}}{\frac{5}{4}}$$

$$\frac{27}{5} = \frac{27}{5} \quad \blacktriangleright$$

CONCLUSION   The solution of the equation is $\dfrac{3}{2}$.

CLASSROOM EXERCISES

Solve.

1. $\dfrac{x+2}{x+3} - \dfrac{6}{x-2} = \dfrac{-4x-14}{x^2+x-6}$

2. $\dfrac{x+3}{x-2} + \dfrac{3}{x-3} = \dfrac{2x-3}{x^2-5x+6}$

3. $1-x = \sqrt{x+11}$

4. $\sqrt{2-x} = x+4$

EXERCISES

Ⓐ Solve.

1. $\dfrac{x-1}{2x} = \dfrac{2}{x+3}$

2. $\dfrac{2x+1}{1-2x} = \dfrac{5x-38}{14}$

3. $x + \dfrac{5}{2x} + \dfrac{7}{2} = 0$

4. $\dfrac{x-1}{2} - \dfrac{5}{2} = \dfrac{2}{1-x}$

5. $\dfrac{3}{x-6} - \dfrac{1}{2} = \dfrac{2}{x-5}$

6. $\dfrac{5x+1}{2} = \dfrac{3}{2-x}$

7. $\dfrac{2x-1}{x-1} + \dfrac{x}{x+1} = \dfrac{1}{x^2-1}$

8. $\dfrac{8}{x-1} - \dfrac{4}{3x+1} = 1$

9. $\dfrac{3}{x-2} - \dfrac{5}{x+2} = 4$

10. $\dfrac{2y-4}{3y-1} = y+2$

11. $\dfrac{3x-5}{9x} - \dfrac{1}{3} = x$

12. $\dfrac{2}{x-1} - \dfrac{3}{x+2} = 1$

13. $\dfrac{3x}{2x+3} - \dfrac{2}{x-4} = \dfrac{x^2-11x+6}{2x^2-5x-12}$

14. $\dfrac{2m}{m-1} - \dfrac{m+3}{m+1} = \dfrac{19}{m^2-1}$

15. $1-x = \sqrt{x+5}$

16. $x-8 = -\sqrt{x+4}$

17. $\sqrt{3x-2} = 5x-8$

18. $\sqrt{x+4} = x-8$

19. $2x = 3 + \sqrt{7x-3}$

20. $\sqrt{y+4} + 20 = 2y$

21. $\sqrt{x+3} - \sqrt{x-2} = 1$

22. $\sqrt{2x-1} = 6 - \sqrt{x+4}$

23. $\sqrt{2x+2} - \sqrt{x+9} = 0$

24. $\sqrt{2x+3} - 2\sqrt{x+1} = -1$

25. $\left(\dfrac{x^2+6}{x}\right)^2 - 12\left(\dfrac{x^2+6}{x}\right) + 35 = 0$

26. $\left(\dfrac{x^2+8}{x}\right)^2 - 15\left(\dfrac{x^2+8}{x}\right) + 54 = 0$

Ⓑ **27.** $\dfrac{2}{x-1} - \dfrac{3}{x-2} = \dfrac{2}{x+4}$

28. $\dfrac{2}{1+\dfrac{1}{x-1}} + \dfrac{3}{x+1} = 1$

29. $\dfrac{12}{\sqrt{5x+6}} = \sqrt{2x+5}$

30. $\sqrt{x+3} = \dfrac{8}{\sqrt{x-9}}$

Ⓒ Find all real-number solutions.

31. $5(\sqrt{x-6})^2 - 6x\sqrt{x-6} + x^2 = 0$

32. $(x-5)^{-4} - 25(x-5)^{-2} + 144 = 0$

33. Find all pairs of real numbers (x, y) with $y - x = 1$ such that the sum of their principal square roots equals the reciprocal of the principal square root of their sum.

8-8 FORMING QUADRATIC EQUATIONS WHEN THE SOLUTIONS ARE GIVEN

We have studied the process for finding the solutions of an equation by factoring. By reversing the process we can find an equation whose solutions are given.

EXAMPLE 1 Find a quadratic equation which has solutions 3 and $-\frac{1}{2}$.

SOLUTION

$$x = 3 \qquad\qquad x = -\frac{1}{2}$$
$$x - 3 = 0 \qquad\qquad x + \frac{1}{2} = 0$$
$$2x + 1 = 0$$

Therefore, $(x - 3)(2x + 1) = 0$
$$2x^2 - 5x - 3 = 0$$

CHECK

$$2x^2 - 5x - 3 = 0 \qquad\qquad 2x^2 - 5x - 3 = 0$$
$$2(3)^2 - 5(3) - 3 \stackrel{?}{=} 0 \qquad\qquad 2\left(-\frac{1}{2}\right)^2 - 5\left(-\frac{1}{2}\right) - 3 \stackrel{?}{=} 0$$
$$0 = 0 \quad\checkmark \qquad\qquad 0 = 0 \quad\checkmark$$

EXAMPLE 2 Find an equation which has solutions $\sqrt{29}$ and $-\sqrt{29}$.

SOLUTION

$$x = \sqrt{29} \qquad\qquad x = -\sqrt{29}$$
$$x - \sqrt{29} = 0 \qquad\qquad x + \sqrt{29} = 0$$

Therefore, $(x - \sqrt{29})(x + \sqrt{29}) = 0$
$$x^2 - 29 = 0$$

CHECK

$$x^2 - 29 = 0$$
$$(\pm\sqrt{29})^2 - 29 \stackrel{?}{=} 0$$
$$0 = 0 \quad\checkmark$$

EXAMPLE 3 Find an equation which has solutions $4 - 2i$ and $4 + 2i$.

SOLUTION

$$x = 4 - 2i \qquad\qquad x = 4 + 2i$$
$$x - 4 + 2i = 0 \qquad\qquad x - 4 - 2i = 0$$

Therefore, $(x - 4 + 2i)(x - 4 - 2i) = 0$
$$(x - 4)^2 - (2i)^2 = 0$$
$$x^2 - 8x + 16 - (-4) = 0$$
$$x^2 - 8x + 20 = 0$$

CHECK

$$x^2 - 8x + 20 = 0$$
$$(4 + 2i)^2 - 8(4 + 2i) + 20 \stackrel{?}{=} 0$$
$$16 + 16i - 4 - 32 - 16i + 20 \stackrel{?}{=} 0$$
$$0 = 0 \quad\checkmark$$

The check for $x = 4 - 2i$ is left for the student.

EXAMPLE 4 Find a quadratic equation which has -3 as its only solution.

SOLUTION
$$x = -3$$
$$x + 3 = 0$$
Therefore, $(x + 3)(x + 3) = 0$
$$x^2 + 6x + 9 = 0$$

CHECK

$$x^2 + 6x + 9 = 0$$
$$(-3)^2 + 6(-3) + 9 \overset{?}{=} 0$$
$$0 = 0$$

The discriminant of $x^2 + 6x + 9 = 0$ is $36 - 4(9)$, or 0. Therefore, the quadratic equation has only one solution.

CLASSROOM EXERCISES

Write a quadratic equation for the given solutions.

1. -3 and 6

2. $\sqrt{7}$ and $-\sqrt{7}$

3. Only one solution, -4

4. $3 - i$ and $3 + i$

5. $2 - \sqrt{2}$ and $2 + \sqrt{2}$

6. $2i$ and $-2i$

EXERCISES

A Write a quadratic equation for the given solutions.

1. 3 and -4

2. 5 and -7

3. -1 and -3

4. -2 and -5

5. 3 and 0

6. 0 and -6

7. $\frac{2}{3}$ and -1

8. $\frac{3}{4}$ and -4

9. $\frac{1}{4}$ and $\frac{-3}{2}$

10. $\frac{-5}{2}$ and $\frac{1}{7}$

11. $\sqrt{11}$ and $-\sqrt{11}$

12. $\sqrt{23}$ and $-\sqrt{23}$

13. $5 - i$ and $5 + i$

14. $7 - i$ and $7 + i$

15. $3 - \sqrt{2}$ and $3 + \sqrt{2}$

16. $4 - \sqrt{3}$ and $4 + \sqrt{3}$

17. Only one solution, $\sqrt{5}$

18. $\sqrt{2}$ and $\sqrt{3}$

B Find an equation whose solutions are given.

19. 2, 1, and 3

20. i and $2i$

21. -1, 2, and -5

22. 3, 0, and -4

C **23.** The equation $x^2 + bx + c = 0$ has solutions r_1 and r_2 such that $r_1 - r_2 = 1$. Find r_1 and r_2.

24. Find the equation satisfied by r_1, r_2, and r_3 when $r_1 + r_2 + r_3 = 6$, $r_1 r_2 + r_1 r_3 + r_2 r_3 = 11$, and $r_1 r_2 r_3 = 6$.

CHECKING YOUR UNDERSTANDING

WORDS AND SYMBOLS

completing the square

discriminant, $b^2 - 4ac$

incomplete quadratic equation

parabola

quadratic equation

quadratic function

quadratic formula: $x = \dfrac{-b \pm \sqrt{b^2 - 4ac}}{2a}$

CONCEPTS

■ The graph of a quadratic function $f(x) = ax^2 + bx + c$ is a parabola. The x-coordinates of the points of intersection of the graph and the x-axis are solutions of the quadratic equation $ax^2 + bx + c = 0$. There may be zero, one, or two solutions of the quadratic equation. [8-1]

■ Any quadratic equation may be solved using the quadratic formula. [8-4]

■ For a quadratic equation with integral coefficients, the discriminant indicates whether the solutions are rational, irrational, or complex. It also tells whether there are 1 or 2 solutions. [8-5]

PROCESSES

■ Solve quadratic equations graphically. [8-1]

1. $x^2 - 2x - 8 = 0$ **2.** $-2x^2 - 9x + 5 = 0$

■ Solve quadratic equations algebraically. [8-2 to 8-4]

3. $4x^2 - 81 = 0$ **4.** $7x^2 - 5 = \frac{1}{7}$ **5.** $-5y^2 = 12$ **6.** $x^2 - 8x = 9$

7. $3x^2 - 2x - 2 = 0$ **8.** $x^2 - 3 = 3x$ **9.** $2x^2 + 2x = 2$ **10.** $5x^2 = x - 2$

■ Use the discriminant to determine the number and nature of the solutions of a quadratic equation without solving. [8-5]

11. $4x^2 - 4x + 1 = 0$ **12.** $x^2 - 2x + 3 = 0$ **13.** $\frac{3}{28}x^2 + \frac{3}{7}x - \frac{16}{21} = 0$

■ Solve equations that are quadratic in form or that lead to quadratic equations. [8-6, 8-7]

14. $3x^4 = 48$ **15.** $(x^2 - 3)^2 + 6(x^2 - 3) + 8 = 0$

16. $\dfrac{x + 2}{x + 3} = \dfrac{2x + 1}{x - 7} - \dfrac{3x}{x^2 - 4x - 21}$ **17.** $\sqrt{4x^2 - 2x - 17} = x - 2$

■ Find quadratic equations having given solutions. [8-8]

18. The solutions are 3 and $\frac{5}{3}$.   **19.** The solutions are $3 - 4i$ and $3 + 4i$.

OBJECTIVES: Graph quadratic functions. Use the defining quadratic expression to identify characteristics of the graph.

8-9 GRAPHING QUADRATIC FUNCTIONS; TERMS ASSOCIATED WITH THE GRAPHS

At the beginning of this chapter we drew the graphs of quadratic functions by plotting points. To help us draw the graphs more quickly and efficiently, we can use information provided by the coefficients in the defining equation,

$$f(x) = ax^2 + bx + c, \text{ or } y = ax^2 + bx + c, a \neq 0.$$

For example, when $x = 0$, $f(x) = c$. The graph of the function contains $(0, c)$. The y-intercept of the graph is the third term in $ax^2 + bx + c$.

Also, the numbers a and b help us locate the **vertex** of the parabola that is the graph of the function. The vertex is important because it is the point for which the function has a maximum or minimum value.

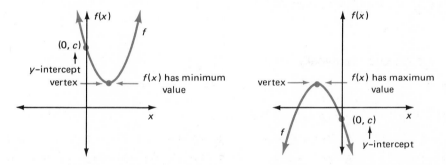

The x-coordinate of the vertex is always $-\dfrac{b}{2a}$. Completing a square helps us see why this is so.

$$f(x) = ax^2 + bx + c$$

$$= a\left(x^2 + \frac{b}{a}x\right) + c$$

Add a number to and subtract a number from the right member to complete the square inside the parentheses.

$$f(x) = a\left(x^2 + \frac{b}{a}x + \frac{b^2}{4a^2}\right) + c - a\left(\frac{b^2}{4a^2}\right)$$

$$= a\left(x + \frac{b}{2a}\right)^2 + c - \frac{b^2}{4a}$$

$$f(x) = a\left(x + \frac{b}{2a}\right)^2 - \frac{b^2 - 4ac}{4a}$$

Now, study this form for a quadratic-function equation.

$$f(x) = a\left(x + \frac{b}{2a}\right)^2 - \frac{b^2 - 4ac}{4a}$$

variable ↓

constant ⏞

a positive or a negative number

The expression $\left(x + \frac{b}{2a}\right)^2$ is always greater than or equal to zero. In fact, it has its smallest value, zero, when $x = -\frac{b}{2a}$. Thus, $f(x)$ has its smallest or greatest value, and the parabola for f has its vertex, for $x = -\frac{b}{2a}$. The parabola "opens" upward or downward from the vertex, depending upon whether a is positive or negative. If $a > 0$, the parabola "opens" upward and $f(x)$ has a minimum value for $x = -\frac{b}{2a}$. If $a < 0$, the parabola "opens" downward and $f(x)$ has a maximum value for $x = -\frac{b}{2a}$.

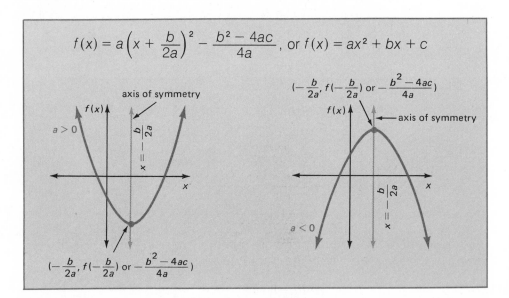

$$f(x) = a\left(x + \frac{b}{2a}\right)^2 - \frac{b^2 - 4ac}{4a}, \text{ or } f(x) = ax^2 + bx + c$$

The graph of a quadratic function is symmetric with respect to the vertical line containing the vertex. The equation of this line is $x = -\frac{b}{2a}$. It is called the **axis of symmetry** of the parabola.

EXAMPLE 1 Find the maximum or minimum value for $f(x)$ when $f(x) = -x^2 + 2x - 4$. Sketch the graph for f. Give the coordinates of the vertex. Give the y-intercept. Give the equation of the axis of symmetry.

SOLUTION $f(x) = -x^2 + 2x - 4$. $a = -1, b = 2, c = -4$.

The y-intercept is -4. The graph contains the point $(0, -4)$.

Since $a < 0$, the parabola for f opens downward and $f(x)$ has a *maximum* value when $x = -\dfrac{b}{2a}$

$$x = -\frac{b}{2a} \qquad\qquad f(x) = -x^2 + 2x - 4$$

$$= -\frac{2}{2(-1)} \qquad\quad f(1) = -(1)^2 + 2(1) - 4$$

$$x = 1 \qquad\qquad\qquad f(1) = -3$$

The maximum value for $f(x)$ is $f(1)$, or -3. The coordinates of the vertex are $\left(-\dfrac{b}{2a}, f\left(-\dfrac{b}{2a}\right)\right)$ or, $(1, -3)$. The equation of the axis of symmetry is $x = -\dfrac{b}{2a}$, or $x = 1$.

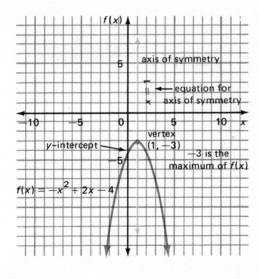

For the quadratic function defined by $f(x) = ax^2 + bx + c$, the coefficients a, b, and c, tell us

1. The y-intercept, c.

2. The x-coordinate of the vertex, $-\dfrac{b}{2a}$.

3. The equation of the axis of symmetry, $x = -\dfrac{b}{2a}$.

4. Whether the graph "opens" upward ($a > 0$) or downward ($a < 0$).

5. Whether $f(x)$ has a minimum value ($a > 0$), or a maximum value ($a < 0$). In either case, the *extreme* value is $f\left(-\dfrac{b}{2a}\right)$.

CLASSROOM EXERCISES

Find the y-intercept and the coordinates of the vertex for the graph of $f(x)$. Draw the graph. Give the equation of the axis of symmetry.

1. $f(x) = 5x^2$ **2.** $f(x) = -3x^2 + 2x + 5$ **3.** $f(x) = -x^2 - 6$

EXERCISES

A Find the y-intercept and the coordinates of the vertex for the graph of $f(x)$. Draw the graph. Give the equation of the axis of symmetry.

1. $f(x) = -3x^2 + 2x - 3$ **2.** $f(x) = -6x^2 + 4x - 5$ **3.** $f(x) = x^2 + x$

4. $f(x) = 7 - x - x^2$ **5.** $f(x) = 3 + 2x - x^2$ **6.** $f(x) = 5 - x^2$

7. $f(x) = 2x^2 - 8x - 4$ **8.** $f(x) = 1 - 3x + x^2$ **9.** $f(x) = 2 - 5x + x^2$

10. $f(x) = -2 + 7x^2$ **11.** $f(x) = x^2 - 4x$ **12.** $f(x) = x^2 + 2x$

13. $f(x) = -2x^2 + 6x$ **14.** $f(x) = x^2 + 4$ **15.** $f(x) = x^2 + 6$

16. $f(x) = 4 - 3x - x^2$ **17.** $f(x) = 5 - 2x - x^2$ **18.** $f(x) = 6x^2 - 8x + 1$

19. $f(x) = -2x^2 + 3$ **20.** $f(x) = 4 - 5x^2$ **21.** $f(x) = 1 - x^2$

B **22.** $f(x) = -3(x + 4)^2 + 7$ **23.** $f(x) = -\frac{1}{2}x^2 + x - \frac{1}{2}$ **24.** $f(x) = -\sqrt{2}x^2 + x - 1$

C **25.** Show that the x-intercept of the axis of symmetry for $f(x) = ax^2 + bx + c$ is the midpoint of the line segment connecting the x-intercepts of $f(x) = ax^2 + bx + c$ when the discriminant is non-negative.

26. Find the equation for the axis of symmetry of $f(x) = a(x - h)^2 + k$. What is the maximum or minimum value of $f(x)$?

ENVIRONMENT

A most serious concern today is how to safeguard our environment and how to restore the elements of the environment that we already have damaged. The majority of environmental careers center around control of air pollution, water pollution, noise pollution, radiation, and solid waste disposal. Even though much on-the-job training is necessary for careers related to the environment, formal training is required for most entry-level jobs.

Geologist is an example of a career that involves studying the earth as an environmental unit. Geologists study the structure and composition of the earth's crust. Their findings help in predicting earthquakes, determining where oil deposits may be located, and aiding in the construction of bridges, dams, and buildings.

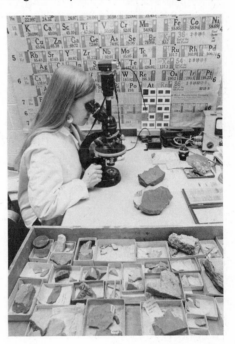

Their tasks may include:

1. examining the chemical and physical property of an earth specimen.
2. studying fossil remains.
3. experimenting with the flow of water and oil through rock structures.
4. advising where a dam should be built.
5. studying the flow of lava from an erupting volcano.
6. studying landforms and the forces that cause them to change.

High school courses that an individual considering a career in geology should pursue include algebra, geometry, trigonometry, biology, chemistry, and physics.

MATHEMATICAL SAMPLER

1. Granite begins to break apart under a pressure of 2×10^3 kPa. Granite has a density of 2.65 g/cm³ $\left(\text{density} = \dfrac{\text{mass}}{\text{volume}}\right)$. How tall could a column of granite be built before its weight would crush its base?

2. As a geologist technician, you have to compare the salinity of two water samples. $S(\text{salinity}) = 1.805 \times C(\text{chlorinity}) + 0.03$. Sample I has a chlorinity of 25 parts per 10^3. Sample II has a chlorinity of 3.7%. Which sample has the greater salinity? by how much?

8-10 HOW THE CONSTANTS OF THE FUNCTION AFFECT THE GRAPH

Further study of the equation

$$f(x) = ax^2 + bx + c$$

when it is written in the form

$$f(x) = a\left(x + \frac{b}{2a}\right)^2 - \frac{b^2 - 4ac}{4a}$$

will tell us more about its graph.

Because a is the coefficient of the second-degree term it determines the *shape* of the parabola as well as whether the parabola "opens" upward or downward. When $|a|$ is "small", the parabola is "wide". When $|a|$ is "large" the parabola is "narrow".

EXAMPLE 1 Draw the graphs of $f(x) = x^2$, $f(x) = 2x^2$, and $f(x) = \frac{1}{2}x^2$.

SOLUTION

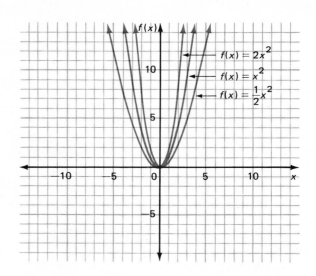

Since the vertex of the graph of

$$f(x) = ax^2 + bx + c, \text{ or } f(x) = a\left(x + \frac{b}{2a}\right)^2 - \frac{b^2 - 4ac}{4a}$$

is $\left(-\dfrac{b}{2a}, f\left(-\dfrac{b}{2a}\right)\right)$, the numbers a and b help determine both coordinates of the vertex and, hence, the location of the graph. The number c, however, helps determine only the second coordinate of the vertex. Therefore, c helps determine only the "vertical location" of the graph.

EXAMPLE 2 Draw the graphs of $f(x) = x^2 - 4x$,
$f(x) = x^2 - 4x + 3$, and $f(x) = x^2 - 4x + 7$.

SOLUTION

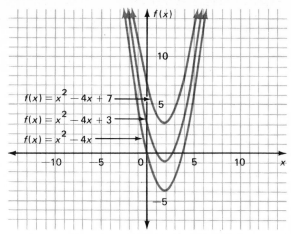

$f(x) = x^2 - 4x + 7$
$f(x) = x^2 - 4x + 3$
$f(x) = x^2 - 4x$

Note that the graph of $f(x) = x^2 - 4x + 3$ is 3 units above the graph of $f(x) = x^2 - 4x$. Similarly, the graph of $f(x) = x^2 - 4x + 7$ is 7 units above the graph of $f(x) = x^2 - 4x$.

How the Constants a, b, and c Affect the Graph of the Quadratic Function Defined by $f(x) = ax^2 + bx + c$

1. For $a > 0$, the graph "opens" upward. The function has a minimum $f(x)$-value at the vertex.

2. For $a < 0$, the graph "opens" downward. The function has a maximum $f(x)$-value at the vertex.

3. $|a|$ is "related inversely" to the width of the graph. That is, for larger $|a|$, the graphs are narrower; for smaller $|a|$, the graphs are wider.

4. The values of a, b, and c all affect the location of the vertex $\left(-\dfrac{b}{2a}, f\left(-\dfrac{b}{2a}\right)\right)$. However, c affects the y-coordinate only. If c increases, the graph shifts in the positive direction parallel to the y-axis. If c decreases, the graph shifts in the negative direction, parallel to the y-axis.

CLASSROOM EXERCISES

Graph the functions in each exercise using one pair of coordinate axes.

1. $f(x) = x^2$, $f(x) = 3x^2$, $f(x) = \frac{1}{3}x^2$
    2. $f(x) = -x^2$, $f(x) = -3x^2$, $f(x) = -\frac{1}{3}x^2$

3. $y = x^2$, $y = x^2 + 1$, $y = x^2 + 3$
    4. $y = -x^2$, $y = -x^2 + 1$, $y = -x^2 + 3$

5. $f(x) = x^2 - 9x$, $f(x) = x^2 - 9x + 2$, $f(x) = x^2 - 9x + 6$

EXERCISES

Graph the functions in each exercise using one pair of coordinate axes.

A **1.** $y = x^2$, $y = 4x^2$, $y = \frac{1}{4}x^2$
    2. $y = x^2$, $y = 5x^2$, $y = \frac{1}{5}x^2$

3. $f(x) = -x^2$, $f(x) = -2x^2$, $f(x) = -3x^2$
    4. $f(x) = -x^2$, $f(x) = -4x^2$, $f(x) = -5x^2$

5. $f(x) = x^2 - 6x$, $f(x) = x^2 - 6x + 3$, $f(x) = x^2 - 6x - 3$

6. $f(x) = x^2 - 8x$, $f(x) = x^2 - 8x + 4$, $f(x) = x^2 - 8x - 4$

7. $y = 5x - x^2$, $y = 2 + 5x - x^2$, $y = 6 + 5x - x^2$

8. $y = 7x - x^2$, $y = 3 + 7x - x^2$, $y = 7 + 7x - x^2$

9. $f(x) = x^2$, $f(x) = x^2 + 2$, $f(x) = x^2 - 2$
    10. $f(x) = x^2$, $f(x) = x^2 + 3$, $f(x) = x^2 - 3$

11. $y = -x^2$, $y = -x^2 + 1$, $y = -x^2 + 4$
    12. $y = -x^2$, $y = -x^2 + 6$, $y = -x^2 + 9$

13. $y = -x^2 - 1$, $y = -x^2 - 2$, $y = -x^2 + 3$
    14. $y = -x^2 - 2$, $y = -x^2 - 4$, $y = -x^2 + 5$

15. $f(x) = x^2 + 1$, $f(x) = 3x^2 + 1$, $f(x) = 9x^2 + 1$

16. $f(x) = x^2 - 2$, $f(x) = 4x^2 - 2$, $f(x) = 8x^2 - 2$

17. $y = \frac{1}{4}x^2$, $y = \frac{1}{16}x^2$, $y = \frac{1}{32}x^2$
    18. $y = -\frac{1}{4}x^2$, $y = -\frac{1}{16}x^2$, $y = -\frac{1}{32}x^2$

B **19.** $y = x^2 - 4x$, $y = 2x^2 - 8x$, $y = \frac{1}{2}x^2 - 2x$

20. $f(x) = 11 + 10x - x^2$, $f(x) = 22 + 20x - 2x^2$, $f(x) = \frac{11}{2} + 5x - \frac{1}{2}x^2$

21. $f(x) = x^2 - 2x + 1$, $f(x) = 2x^2 - 4x + 1$, $f(x) = 3x^2 - 6x + 1$

22. $y = -1 + 5x - x^2$, $y = -1 + 10x - 2x^2$, $y = -1 + 15x - 3x^2$

23. $y = (x - 1)^2 + 5$, $y = 2(x - 1)^2 + 5$, $y = 3(x - 1)^2 + 5$

24. $y = -(x - 1)^2 + 5$, $y = -2(x - 1)^2 + 5$, $y = -\frac{1}{2}(x - 1)^2 + 5$

25. $y = (x - 1)^2$, $y = (x + 1)^2$, $y = (x - 3)^2$

26. $f(x) = -(x - 3)^2$, $f(x) = -(x + 3)^2$, $f(x) = -(x - 5)^2$

C **27.** Find the equation of a parabola having the same x-intercepts as $y = 2x^2 + x - 21$ and having a minimum of -338.

28. Find the equation of a parabola with maximum y value 48 having the same y-intercept and axis of symmetry as $y = -x^2 + 6x + 3$.

OBJECTIVE: Solve problems using quadratic equations.

8-11 PROBLEM SOLVING: USING QUADRATIC EQUATIONS

When you use a quadratic equation to solve a problem, you may obtain two numbers for the variable in the equation. Either number, however, may not be useful as a solution for the problem. Each must be checked against the information given for the problem. Any solution of the equation that does not give a solution for the problem must be discarded.

EXAMPLE 1 The product of two consecutive positive even integers is 168. Find the integers.

SOLUTION Use $\begin{bmatrix} s & \text{for the smaller even integer.} \\ s+2 & \text{for the next larger even integer.} \end{bmatrix}$

$$s(s+2) = 168$$
$$s^2 + 2s = 168$$
$$s^2 + 2s - 168 = 0$$

Use the quadratic formula.

$$s = \frac{-2 \pm \sqrt{4 - 4(1)(-168)}}{2}$$

$$= \frac{-2 \pm \sqrt{676}}{2}$$

$$= \frac{-2 \pm 26}{2}$$

Therefore, $s = \dfrac{-2+26}{2}$ or $s = \dfrac{-2-26}{2}$

$$s = 12 \qquad\qquad s = -14$$
Also, $s + 2 = 14$ $\qquad$ Also, $s + 2 = -12$

Although the product of the consecutive even integers -14 and -12 is 168, they are not positive. Hence they are not solutions for the problem.

CONCLUSION The two integers are 12 and 14.

CHECK 12 and 14 are consecutive positive even integers.
$$12 \cdot 14 \overset{?}{=} 168$$
$$168 = 168 \quad ✔$$

Quadratic equations can arise from geometry problems. These may involve area or the Pythagorean Theorem, with the unknown being the length of a side. Since length cannot be negative, we can discard any negative solution of the quadratic equation.

THE PYTHAGOREAN THEOREM

For a right triangle with legs of lengths a and b and hypotenuse of length c,

$$a^2 + b^2 = c^2.$$

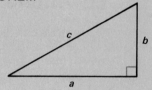

EXAMPLE 2   The hypotenuse of a right triangle is 1 centimeter longer than one leg. It is 8 centimeters longer than the other leg. How long is each side of the triangle?

SOLUTION   Use $\begin{bmatrix} h & \text{for the hypotenuse length in centimeters.} \\ h-1 & \text{for the length of one leg in centimeters.} \\ h-8 & \text{for the length of the other leg in centimeters.} \end{bmatrix}$

$$(h-1)^2 + (h-8)^2 = h^2$$
$$h^2 - 2h + 1 + h^2 - 16h + 64 = h^2$$
$$h^2 - 18h + 65 = 0$$
$$(h-13)(h-5) = 0$$

$h-13 = 0$	or	$h-5 = 0$
$h = 13$		$h = 5$
Also, $h-1 = 12$		Also, $h-1 = 4$
and $h-8 = 5$.		and $h-8 = -3$.
		Since negative length has no meaning here, this solution of the equation is discarded as a solution for the problem.

CONCLUSION   The sides are 5, 12, and 13 centimeters long.

CHECK
$$5^2 + 12^2 \overset{?}{=} 13^2$$
$$25 + 144 \overset{?}{=} 169$$
$$169 = 169 \quad ✓$$

Quadratic equations are also useful for solving motion problems involving distance, rate, and time. The formula $d = rt$ gives the distance, d, a person travels at rate r for time t.

EXAMPLE 3 The time it took to travel 540 kilometers in one direction was 1 hour greater than the time it took to return. The rate returning was 6 kilometers per hour faster than the rate going. Find the rate and time in each direction.

SOLUTION Distance equals rate times time in each direction.

Use $\begin{bmatrix} r \text{ for the rate going in kilometers per hour.} \\ t \text{ for the number of hours spent going.} \end{bmatrix}$

Make a chart.

	distance =	rate ·	time
Going	540	r	t
Returning	540	$r + 6$	$t - 1$

From the chart, we have this system.

$$\begin{array}{l} 540 = rt \\ 540 = (r + 6)(t - 1) \end{array}$$

Find r. Replace t by $\dfrac{540}{r}$ in $540 = (r + 6)(t - 1)$.

$$540 = (r + 6)\left(\frac{540}{r} - 1\right)$$

$$540 = 540 - r + \frac{3240}{r} - 6$$

$$r^2 + 6r - 3240 = 0$$
$$(r - 54)(r + 60) = 0$$

Therefore, $r - 54 = 0$ or $r + 60 = 0$
$\qquad\qquad\qquad r = 54 \qquad\qquad\qquad r = -60$
Also, $r + 6 = 60$.   Since r cannot be negative, -60 is discarded as a solution for the problem.

CONCLUSION 1 The rates were 54 km/h going and 60 km/h returning.

Find t. Replace r by 54.
$$540 = rt$$
$$540 = 54t$$
$$10 = t \qquad \text{Also, } t - 1 = 9.$$

CONCLUSION 2 It took 10 hours to go one way and 9 hours to return.

CHECK The check is left for the student.

EXAMPLE 4   Two hikers, Kelly and Leah, start from the intersection of two straight roads that are perpendicular. Kelly walks 3 km/h on one of the roads. Two hours later Leah begins walking on the other road at 4 km/h. How long must they walk before they are 8 km apart?

SOLUTION   Use $\begin{bmatrix} t & \text{for the number of hours Kelly walks.} \\ t-2 & \text{for the number of hours Leah walks.} \\ 3t & \text{for the number of kilometers Kelly walks.} \\ 4(t-2) & \text{for the number of kilometers Leah walks.} \end{bmatrix}$

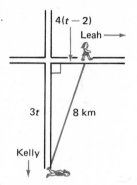

Make a diagram to show the distances. Then, use the Pythagorean Theorem.

$$(3t)^2 + (4(t-2))^2 = 8^2$$
$$9t^2 + 16(t^2 - 4t + 4) = 64$$
$$9t^2 + 16t^2 - 64t + 64 = 64$$
$$25t^2 - 64t = 0$$
$$t(25t - 64) = 0$$

$25t - 64 = 0$ or	$t = 0$
$25t = 64$	Also, $t - 2 = -2$
$t = 2.56$	Since time cannot be negative
Also, $t - 2 = 0.56$	here, -2 is discarded as a
	solution for the problem.

CONCLUSION   Kelly must walk for 2.56 hours and Leah for 0.56 hours (33 minutes 36 seconds) to be 8 kilometers apart.

CHECK $d_{\text{Kelly}} = r_{\text{Kelly}} \cdot t_{\text{Kelly}}$ $d_{\text{Leah}} = r_{\text{Leah}} \cdot t_{\text{Leah}}$
$\doteq 3(2.56)$ $\doteq 4(0.56)$
$\doteq 7.68$ $\doteq 2.24$

$$7.68^2 + 2.24^2 \overset{?}{=} 8^2$$
$$64 = 64 \quad ✔$$

CLASSROOM EXERCISES

Solve.

1. The square of a number is decreased by five. The result is 44. Find the number.

2. The perimeter of a rectangular garden is 80 meters. The area is 351 square meters. Find the dimensions of the garden.

3. The length of the hypotenuse of a right triangle exceeds the length of one leg by 9 cm and the length of the other by 2 cm. Find the lengths of the 3 sides.

4. The time it took to travel 280 kilometers one way was 1 hour less than the time it took to return. The rate returning was 14 kilometers per hour less than the rate going. Find the rate and time in each direction.

5. A walker and a jogger start from the intersection of two straight roads that are perpendicular. The walker travels 2 kilometers per hour along one of the roads. Leaving one hour later, the jogger travels down the other road at 8 kilometers per hour. How long after the jogger starts will they be 50 kilometers apart?

EXERCISES

Ⓐ Solve.   **NUMBER PROBLEMS**

1. The square of a number is increased by 19. The result is 100. Find the number.

2. The square of a number is decreased by 25. The result is 144. Find the number.

3. A number is 6 greater than another number. Their product is 135. Find the numbers.

4. The product of two numbers is 299. One number is 10 more than the other. Find the numbers.

5. Find two consecutive positive integers whose product is 1722.

6. Find two consecutive positive integers whose product is 6162.

7. A number increased by twice its square equals 300. Find the number.

8. Twice the square of a number is decreased by five times the number. The remainder is 150. Find the number.

9. One number exceeds another by 6. When the larger is divided by the smaller, the quotient is the same as when the smaller is divided by 25. Find the numbers.

GEOMETRY PROBLEMS

10. A rectangular field has area 1800 m² and perimeter 180 m. Find the dimensions of the field.

11. A rectangular plot of land contains 19 200 square meters. The length exceeds the width by 40 meters. Find the dimensions of the plot.

12. One side of a box is a rectangle having area 90 cm² and perimeter 46 cm. Find the dimensions of the side.

13. The number of units of area of an isosceles right triangle is equal to the number of units of length of its perimeter. Find the length of each side of the triangle.

14. The base of a ladder is set 6 meters from the base of a wall. The top of the ladder rests at a point 8 meters above the base of the wall. Find the length of the ladder.

15. The length of the hypotenuse of a right triangle is 117 centimeters and the length of one leg exceeds twice that of the other by 18 centimeters. Find the length of each leg.

Solve.   **MOTION PROBLEMS**

16. The time required to travel 180 kilometers in one direction was 1 hour more than the time required to return. Find the rate in each direction when the rate returning was 15 km/h faster than the rate going.

17. Two back-packers, Eva and Inez, start from the point of intersection of two straight roads which cross at right angles. Eva walks 2 kilometers per hour on one of the roads. Two hours later, Inez begins walking at 3 kilometers per hour on the other road. How long after Inez starts will they be 10 kilometers apart?

18. To fly 2025 kilometers, one airplane needs 0.5 hour more than a second airplane needs for flying 2795 kilometers. The speed of the second airplane is 320 kilometers per hour greater than that of the first. Find the speed of the first airplane.

19. On a non-stop flight from Chicago to London (6400 kilometers), an airplane flew against winds that reduced its rate by 24 kilometers per hour and caused the flight to require 12 minutes more than the usual time. Find the usual speed of the plane.

20. On a 900-kilometer trip, the weather reduced the average speed of a tractor-trailer by 5 kilometers per hour. The trip took 0.75 hour longer than usual. Find the average speed usually traveled by the truck.

[B] **21.** The sum of three numbers is 100. The product of the first two is 72. The third is 56 more than the sum of the first two. Find the numbers.

22. The sum of the perimeters of two squares is 80 centimeters and the area of one is three times the area of the other. Find in simplest radical form the length of a side of each square.

23. Find the length of the diagonal of a cube whose edge has length e.

24. Air is being pumped into two balloons. The first one had radius 4 meters initially, and its radius is increasing at 2 meters per minute. The radius of the second one was 3 meters initially and it is increasing at the rate of 4 meters per minute. The pumping started at the same time for each balloon. Find the radius of the larger balloon at the instant their total surface area is 265π square meters.

[C] **25.** Rectangle $ABCD$ is inscribed in a circle. PQ is a diameter of the circle and BQ has length 2 centimeters. AB has length 6 centimeters. Find the area of the circle.

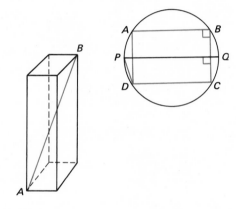

26. The height of a rectangular box is three times its length. Its volume is 288 cubic meters. The length of the diagonal from corner A to corner B is four times the width of the box. Find the dimensions of the box.

27. Point O is in a circle with radius length 29 centimeters. Particles A and B start at O and move in opposite directions around the circle. Particle A starts 2 seconds before B and the length of line segment OA increases at a rate of 6 centimeters per second. The length of line segment OB increases at a rate of 8 centimeters per second. Find the lengths OA and OB when A and B first become endpoints of a diameter.

A MATTER OF GRAVITY

Gravity is the significant force acting on a projectile after it is launched. The displacement of a projectile from a reference altitude may be given by the formula

$$s = \frac{1}{2}a_g t^2 + v_0 t + s_0.$$

The variables have the meanings given below. Positive numbers for the variables may, in general, be related to upward movement, negative numbers to downward movement.

s_0 = initial displacement in meters from the reference altitude

v_0 = initial velocity in meters per second

t = time, in seconds, elapsed from the launch time

a_g = acceleration due to Earth's gravitational force, approximately -9.8 meters per second per second (-9.8 m/s²).

The diagram below shows several ways to launch a projectile with respect to the reference altitude.

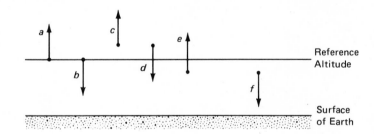

For Exercises 1-9, match the equation with a launch condition from the diagram.

1. $s = -4.9t^2$ **2.** $s = -4.9t^2 - 10$ **3.** $s = -4.9t^2 + 490$

4. $s = -4.9t^2 + 441t$ **5.** $s = -4.9t^2 - 441t$ **6.** $s = -4.9t^2 + 125t - 20$

7. $s = -4.9t^2 - 125t + 20$ **8.** $s = -4.9t^2 - 125t - 20$

9. $s = -4.9t^2 + 14.6t + 1.3$, describing the vertical motion of a football after one particular kick.

10. Describe the launch condition for each equation above. Use the numerical coefficients to do this.

11. Replace t by 1 in each equation. Evaluate s. Interpret the result.

12. Replace s by zero in each equation. Solve the equation. Interpret the solutions.

OBJECTIVES: Graph higher-degree polynomial functions. Solve higher-degree polynomial equations graphically and algebraically.

8-12 HIGHER-DEGREE POLYNOMIAL FUNCTIONS AND EQUATIONS

The quadratic functions and equations studied so far are of degree 2. The general **polynomial function of degree n** is defined by an equation of the form

$$f(x) = a_0 x^n + a_1 x^{n-1} + a_2 x^{n-2} + \cdots + a_{n-1} x + a_n$$

where $a_0, a_1, a_2, \cdots, a_n$ are constants, $a_0 \neq 0$, and n is a non-negative integer. The domain of a polynomial function is the set of real numbers.

When we draw the graph of a quadratic function defined by

$$f(x) = a_0 x^2 + a_1 x + a_2,$$

we change direction once. Therefore, a quadratic function has a maximum (or minimum) value. Its range is the set of real numbers that are no greater than its maximum value (or no less than its minimum value).

Third-Degree Polynomial Functions
$$f(x) = a_0 x^3 + a_1 x^2 + a_2 x^1 + a_3$$

When we draw the graph of a third-degree polynomial function, we change direction two times or not at all. The range is the set of real numbers.

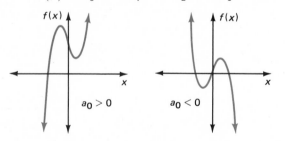

Fourth-Degree Polynomial Functions
$$f(x) = a_0 x^4 + a_1 x^3 + a_2 x^2 + a_3 x + a_4$$

When we draw the graph of a fourth-degree polynomial function, we change direction one or three times. The range is determined by the minimum value of the function or the maximum value of the function.

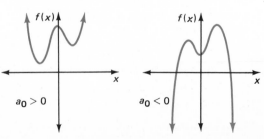

Fifth-Degree Polynomial Functions

$$f(x) = a_0x^5 + a_1x^4 + a_2x^3 + a_3x^2 + a_4x + a_5$$

When we draw the graph of a fifth degree polynomial function, we change direction zero, two, or four times. The range is the set of real numbers.

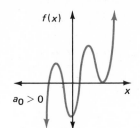

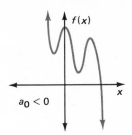

In general, when we draw the graph of a polynomial function of degree n we change direction an even or an odd number of times depending on whether $n - 1$ is even or odd. If the number of changes in direction is even (the degree of the polynomial is odd), the range of the function is the set of real numbers. If the number of changes in direction is odd (the degree of the polynomial is even), the function and its range have a maximum or minimum value.

EXAMPLE 1   Graph $f(x) = x^3 - 2x$.

SOLUTION   Since the function is of degree 3, we know that the graph changes direction either twice or not at all. The range is the set of real numbers.

$(x, f(x))$
$(-2, -4)$
$(-\sqrt{2}, 0)$
$(-1, 1)$
$(0, 0)$
$(1, -1)$
$(\sqrt{2}, 0)$
$(2, 4)$

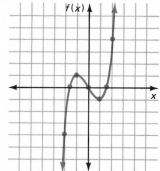

For each point of intersection of the x-axis and the graph of the *polynomial function*,

$$f(x) = a_0x^n + a_1x^{n-1} + a_2x^{n-2} + \cdots + a_{n-1}x + a_n,$$

the y-coordinate is 0. The x-coordinates of the points of intersection are zeroes of the polynomial function. They also are solutions of the *polynomial equation*

$$a_0x^n + a_1x^{n-1} + a_2x^{n-2} + \cdots + a_{n-1}x + a_n = 0.$$

The graph of a third-degree polynomial function always intersects the x-axis in at least 1 point. It can intersect the x-axis in as many as 3 points. Therefore, a third-degree polynomial equation always has one real-number solution, although it could have two or three. The graph of a fourth-degree polynomial function can intersect the x-axis in zero, one, two, three, or four points. A fourth-degree polynomial equation can have from zero to four real-number solutions.

EXAMPLE 2 Approximate the real-number solutions for $x^3 - 3x^2 + 3 = 0$ graphically.

SOLUTION

$(x, f(x))$
$(-1, -1)$
$(0, 3)$
$(1, 1)$
$(2, -1)$
$(3, 3)$

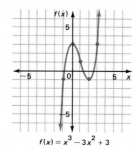

$f(x) = x^3 - 3x^2 + 3$

From the graph, it appears that $f(x)$ is 0 when x is approximately -0.9, 1.3, and 2.5.

CHECK

$$x^3 - 3x^2 + 3 = 0$$
$$(-0.9)^3 - 3(-0.9)^2 + 3 \stackrel{?}{=} 0$$
$$-0.729 - 2.43 + 3 \stackrel{?}{=} 0$$
$$-0.159 \doteq 0 \quad \vee$$

$$x^3 - 3x^2 + 3 = 0$$
$$(1.3)^3 - 3(1.3)^2 + 3 \stackrel{?}{=} 0$$
$$2.197 - 5.07 + 3 \stackrel{?}{=} 0$$
$$0.127 \doteq 0 \quad \vee$$

The check for $x \doteq 2.5$ is left for the student.

CLASSROOM EXERCISES

Graph.

Solve graphically.

1. $f(x) = -x^3$ **2.** $f(x) = x^3 - x$ **3.** $x^4 - 4 = 0$ **4.** $x^3 - 2x - 1 = 0$

5. Sketch the graph of a fourth-degree polynomial function for which there are no zeroes.

EXERCISES

A Graph.

1. $f(x) = x^4 - x^2$ **2.** $f(x) = x^4 - 4x^2$ **3.** $f(x) = x^3 - 3x$

4. $f(x) = x^3 - 5x$ **5.** $f(x) = -x^4$ **6.** $f(x) = x^5 + x$

Solve graphically. Approximate the real-number solutions.

7. $2x^3 - 3x^2 + 2x + 3 = 0$ **8.** $x^3 - 4x^2 + 7x - 3 = 0$

9. $x^3 - 3x - 3 = 0$ **10.** $x^3 - x^2 + 5 = 0$

11. $x^4 - 4x^2 + 2x - 2 = 0$ **12.** $9x^4 + 8x^2 - 1 = 0$

13. Sketch a graph of a fifth-degree polynomial function for which there are five zeroes.

14. Sketch the graph of a fourth-degree polynomial function for which there are three zeroes.

15. Sketch the graph of a third-degree polynomial function for which there are two zeroes.

B Graph.

16. $x = y^3 - y$ **17.** $x = y^2 - y^4$ **18.** $y = |x^3 - 25x|$

19. Find the real solutions to $x^5 - 5x^4 - 10x^3 + 50x^2 + 9x - 45 = 0$ graphically.

C Solve the system graphically.

20. $f(x) = x^4 - x^2$
$f(x) = 24 - 12\,|x - 1|$

21. $f(x) = -x^3 + 4x^2 - 3x$
$f(x) = 2x^4 - 2$

$\boxed{14623832}$ **CONTINUED RADICALS**

Simplify. Do you know a simple name for a number that is approximately equal to the result shown by the calculator display?

1. $\sqrt{2 + \sqrt{2 + \sqrt{2 + \sqrt{2 + \sqrt{2}}}}}$

2. $\sqrt{6 - \sqrt{6 - \sqrt{6 - \sqrt{6 - \sqrt{6}}}}}$

3. $\sqrt{6 + \sqrt{6 + \sqrt{6 + \sqrt{6 + \sqrt{6}}}}}$

4. $\sqrt{\frac{3}{4} + \sqrt{\frac{3}{4} + \sqrt{\frac{3}{4} + \sqrt{\frac{3}{4} + \sqrt{\frac{3}{4}}}}}}$

5. $\sqrt{7 - \sqrt{7 + \sqrt{7 - \sqrt{7 + \sqrt{7}}}}}$

6. $\sqrt{2\frac{1}{9} + \sqrt{2\frac{1}{9} - \sqrt{2\frac{1}{9} + \sqrt{2\frac{1}{9} - \sqrt{2\frac{1}{9}}}}}}$

8-13 ALGEBRAIC SOLUTION OF HIGHER-DEGREE POLYNOMIAL EQUATIONS

The graph of a polynomial *function* of degree *n* can intersect the *x*-axis in at most *n* points. Therefore, a polynomial *equation* of degree *n* can have *at most n* real-number solutions. It can be proved using advanced mathematics that there are *exactly n* solutions when the replacement set for the variable is the set of complex numbers.

We can find the two solutions of a second-degree polynomial equation, whether they are real or imaginary, by using the quadratic formula. There are formulas that give the solutions for all third-degree and fourth-degree equations also. However, the formulas are complicated and it is easier to find the solutions using other methods. It has been proved impossible to derive a formula for finding the solutions if the degree of the equation is greater than four.

The factoring techniques of Section 3-7 can help us solve equations that involve the sum or difference of two cubes.

EXAMPLE 1   Find the three cube roots of 27.

SOLUTION   We must solve the equation $x^3 = 27$.

$$x^3 = 27$$
$$x^3 - 27 = 0$$
$$(x - 3)(x^2 + 3x + 9) = 0$$

Therefore, $x - 3 = 0$ or $x^2 + 3x + 9 = 0$

$$x = 3 \qquad\qquad x = \frac{-3 \pm 3i\sqrt{3}}{2}$$

$$x = -\frac{3}{2} + \frac{3\sqrt{3}}{2}i$$

$$\text{or }\; x = -\frac{3}{2} - \frac{3\sqrt{3}}{2}i$$

CONCLUSION   The 3 cube roots of 27 are 3, $-\dfrac{3}{2} + \dfrac{3\sqrt{3}}{2}i$, and $-\dfrac{3}{2} - \dfrac{3\sqrt{3}}{2}i$.

CHECK   Checking that each of 3^3, $\left(-\dfrac{3}{2} + \dfrac{3\sqrt{3}}{2}i\right)^3$, and $\left(-\dfrac{3}{2} - \dfrac{3\sqrt{3}}{2}i\right)^3$ equals 27 is left for the student.

The Remainder and Factor Theorems that were introduced in Section 3-9 suggest a method for searching for the solutions of a polynomial equation.

THE REMAINDER THEOREM

If a polynomial in x is divided by $x - a$, then the remainder equals the value of the polynomial for $x = a$.

THE FACTOR THEOREM

If the value of a polynomial in x is zero for $x = a$, then $x - a$ is a factor of the polynomial.

EXAMPLE 2 Find which of $x - 1$, $x + 2$, and $x - 3$ is a factor of $x^3 - x^2 - 10x + 12$.   Then, solve $x^3 - x^2 - 10x + 12 = 0$.

SOLUTION   First, use the Factor Theorem. Replace x by 1.

$$x^3 - x^2 - 10x + 12 = (1)^3 - (1)^2 - 10(1) + 12$$
$$= 2$$
$$\neq 0$$

Therefore, $x - 1$ is not a factor of $x^3 - x^2 - 10x + 12$.

Replace x by -2.
$$x^3 - x^2 - 10x + 12 = (-2)^3 - (-2)^2 - 10(-2) + 12$$
$$= 20$$
$$\neq 0$$

Therefore, $x + 2$ is not a factor of $x^3 - x^2 - 10x + 12$.

Replace x by 3.
$$x^3 - x^2 - 10x + 12 = (3)^3 - (3)^2 - 10(3) + 12$$
$$= 0$$

Therefore, $x - 3$ *is* a factor of $x^3 - x^2 - 10x + 12$.

Now, solve the equation.
$$x^3 - x^2 - 10x + 12 = 0$$
$$(x - 3)(x^2 + 2x - 4) = 0$$

Therefore, $x - 3 = 0$ or $x^2 + 2x - 4 = 0$

$$x = 3 \qquad\qquad x = \frac{-2 \pm \sqrt{20}}{2}$$
$$x = -1 \pm \sqrt{5}$$
$$x = -1 + \sqrt{5} \text{ or } x = -1 - \sqrt{5}$$

CHECK   The check is left for the student.

When using the Factor Theorem, we essentially try to guess one solution for an equation. When we find one solution we have simplified the problem to that of solving a polynomial of one less degree. There is a theorem, the Rational Root Theorem, that tells us how to limit the number of our guesses as we look for rational-number solutions.

THE RATIONAL ROOT THEOREM

Suppose $\dfrac{p}{q}$ is a rational number in lowest terms (p and q are both integers, $q \neq 0$). Also, suppose it is a root (solution) of the polynomial equation

$$a_0 x^n + a_1 x^{n-1} + a_2 x^{n-2} + \cdots + a_{n-1} x + a_n = 0$$

in which $a_0, a_1, a_2, \cdots, a_{n-1}$, and a_n are integers. Then, p is a factor of a_n and q is a factor of a_0.

EXAMPLE 3 What are the only rational solutions possible for
$$2x^3 - 9x^2 + 14x - 5 = 0?$$
Solve the equation.

SOLUTION $a_0 = 2$, $a_3 = -5$.

The factors of 2 are ± 1 and ± 2. The factors of -5 are ± 1 and ± 5. By the Rational Root Theorem, the only rational solutions possible are ± 1, ± 5, $\pm \frac{1}{2}$, and $\pm \frac{5}{2}$.

Replacing x, we find that for $x = \frac{1}{2}$,
$$2x^3 - 9x^2 + 14x - 5 = 0.$$
Thus, by the Factor Theorem,

$\left(x - \frac{1}{2}\right)$ is a factor of the trinomial.

$$2x^3 - 9x^2 + 14x - 5 = 0$$
$$\left(x - \tfrac{1}{2}\right)(2x^2 - 8x + 10) = 0$$

Therefore, $x - \frac{1}{2} = 0$ or $2x^2 - 8x + 10 = 0$

$$x = \frac{1}{2} \qquad\qquad x^2 - 4x + 5 = 0$$

$$x = \frac{4 \pm \sqrt{-4}}{2}$$

$$x = 2 \pm i$$
$$x = 2 + i$$
$$\text{or } x = 2 - i$$

CHECK The check is left for the student.

CLASSROOM EXERCISES

Find

1. three cube roots of 125.

2. four fourth roots of 81.

3. Which of $(x - 1)$, $(x - 2)$, and $(x - 3)$ is a factor of $x^3 + 5x^2 - 12x + 6$?

4. Solve $x^3 + 5x^2 - 12x + 6 = 0$. Use the result from Exercise 3.

Solve. Use the Rational Root Theorem.

5. $x^3 - 3x + 2 = 0$

6. $3x^3 - 13x + 2 = 0$

EXERCISES

A Find

1. four fourth roots of 16.

2. four fourth roots of 1.

3. Which of $(x - 4)$, $(x + 2)$, and $(x - 2)$, is a factor of $x^3 + 2x^2 - 12x + 8$?

4. Which of $(x + 1)$, $(x - 3)$, and $(x - 6)$ is a factor of $x^3 - 11x^2 + 31x - 6$?

Solve. Use the results from Exercises 3 and 4.

5. $x^3 + 2x^2 - 12x + 8 = 0$.

6. $x^3 - 11x^2 + 31x - 6 = 0$.

List the only rational solutions possible for each equation.

7. $3x^3 + 2x^2 + 5x - 2 = 0$

8. $5x^3 - 16x^2 + 18x - 3 = 0$

9. $3x^3 + 2x^2 - 7x + 2 = 0$

10. $5x^3 - 9x^2 - 17x - 3 = 0$

Solve.

11. $x^3 - 3x - 2 = 0$

12. $x^3 - 3x + 2 = 0$

13. $6x^3 + x^2 - 2x = 0$

14. $6x^3 + 7x^2 - 3x = 0$

15. $x^3 - 8x^2 + 8x + 8 = 0$

16. $x^3 + 5x^2 + 2x + 10 = 0$

17. $5x^3 - 29x^2 + 21x - 5 = 0$

18. $6x^3 - 11x^2 - 3x + 2 = 0$

19. $5x^3 + 4x^2 - 31x + 6 = 0$

20. $3x^3 - 11x^2 + 5x + 8 = 0$

21. $x^4 - 4x^3 + x^2 + 6x = 0$

22. $x^4 + x^3 - 10x^2 - 12x = 0$

B **23.** Find six sixth roots of 1.

24. Find six sixth roots of 27.

25. A rectangular box has a volume of 350 cubic centimeters. The length is 3 centimeters more than the width. The height is 9 centimeters less than twice the width. Find the dimensions.

26. Find the value of k so that $x - 3$ is a factor of $2x^3 - 6x^2 + kx + 9$.

C **27.** Find the coordinates of all points of intersection of $y = 2x^4 - 162$ and $y = 6x^3 - 81x^2 + 73x$.

28. Find all numbers h and k for which $(x - 3)$ and $(x + 4)$ are factors of $2x^3 + hx^2 + kx + 12$.

CHECKING YOUR UNDERSTANDING

WORDS

axis of symmetry
maximum value

minimum value
polynomial equation

polynomial function
vertex of a parabola

CONCEPTS

▪ The graph of a quadratic function $f(x) = ax^2 + bx + c$ is a parabola. The vertex has x-coordinate $-\dfrac{b}{2a}$. The axis of symmetry is the graph for $x = -\dfrac{b}{2a}$. A maximum value for $f(x)$ occurs at the vertex when $a < 0$, that is, when the parabola opens downward. A minimum value for $f(x)$ occurs at the vertex when $a > 0$, that is, when the parabola opens upward. When $|a|$ is "small" the parabola is "wide." When $|a|$ is "large" the parabola is "narrow." [8-9, 8-10]

▪ The graph of a polynomial function of degree n "changes direction" an even or odd number of times depending on whether $n - 1$ is even or odd. It intersects the x-axis at most n times. A polynomial equation of degree n has at most n real-number solutions. [8-12]

PROCESSES

▪ Describe characteristics of the graph of a quadratic function by referring to the constants in $f(x) = ax^2 + bx + c$. [8-9, 8-10]

1. $y = 4x^2 + 12x - 27$ **2.** $y = -x^2 - 8x - 3$ **3.** $y = 2x^2 + 3x$

▪ Solve problems by solving quadratic equations. [8-11]

4. When a certain positive number is multiplied by 3 less than twice the number, the result is 252. Find this positive number.

5. In a right triangle, one leg is 4 cm longer than the other. The hypotenuse is $\sqrt{5}$ times as long as the shorter leg. Find the length of each side.

6. On a 450-kilometer trip, John can save $2\frac{1}{2}$ hours of travel time by using the expressway rather than the scenic route. John's average speed on the scenic route would be 15 km/h less than his average highway speed. Find his average speed and travel time for each route.

▪ Sketch the graph of a polynomial function of degree n. [8-12]

7. Sketch $y = 2x^3 + 3x$.   **8.** Sketch $f(x) = x^4 + x^3 - 5x^2 + x - 6$.

▪ Solve certain polynomial equations of degree n. [8-12, 8-13]

9. $2x^3 + 3x = 0$ **10.** $x^4 + x^3 - 5x^2 + x - 6 = 0$

11. $x^3 + x^2 - 5x - 2 = 0$ **12.** Find the three cube roots of -8.

CHAPTER REVIEW

Draw the graph of the function defined by the given equation. [8-1]

1. $y = 2x^2 + 2x + 3$

2. $f(x) = -x^2 - x + 7$

Find all real solutions of the equation by drawing a graph.

3. $x^2 + x - 12 = 0$

4. $x^2 - 2x + 3 = 0$

Solve. [8-2]

5. $x^2 - 72 = 0$

6. $9x^2 - 225 = 0$

7. $6 - 4x^2 = 18 - 3x^2$

Complete the perfect square. [8-3]

8. $x^2 - 18x + \underline{\quad?\quad} = (x - \underline{\quad?\quad})^2$

9. $x^2 + 2\sqrt{3}x + \underline{\quad?\quad} = (x + \underline{\quad?\quad})^2$

Solve by completing the square.

10. $x^2 - 6x + 7 = 0$

11. $y^2 - 2y + 2 = 0$

Solve by using the quadratic formula. [8-4]

12. $x^2 - 3x = 28$

13. $4x^2 - 12x + 25 = 0$

Find the discriminant of each equation. [8-5]

14. $7x^2 - 8x + 1 = 0$

15. $x^2 - 22x + 121 = 0$

16. $x^2 - 3x + 3 = 0$

17. Use the discriminant of $16x^2 - 16x - 1 = 0$. Describe the solutions of the equation.

Solve each equation. [8-6, 8-7]

18. $7x^4 - 63 = 0$

19. $x^{\frac{2}{7}} + 4x^{\frac{1}{7}} = -4$

20. $(y + 1)^2 - 3(y + 1) - 10 = 0$

21. $\dfrac{2x - 1}{x + 2} + \dfrac{x + 1}{x - 5} = \dfrac{2x - 4}{x - 5}$

22. $\sqrt{2x^2 - x + 30} = x + 4$

Find the quadratic equation having the given solutions. [8-8]

23. -8 and 1

24. $\dfrac{3}{2} + \dfrac{\sqrt{2}}{2}$ and $\dfrac{3}{2} - \dfrac{\sqrt{2}}{2}$

25. $1 + \dfrac{1}{2}i$ and $1 - \dfrac{1}{2}i$

Find the y-intercept of the graph for each function. [8-9]

26. $f(x) = 4x^2 - 7x + 3$

27. $y = -6x^2 + x - 5$

Find the maximum or minimum value of $f(x)$ for each function.

28. $f(x) = x^2 + 6x - 4$ **29.** $f(x) = -2x^2 + 3x + 4$

Use one set of coordinate axes. Draw the graph for each function. [8-10]

30. $f(x) = x^2 + x + \dfrac{1}{2}$ **31.** $f(x) = 2x^2 + 2x + 5$ **32.** $f(x) = 2x^2 + 2x + 1$

33. A number is 12 less than another number. Their product is 85. Find the numbers. [8-11]

34. The base of a triangle is 2 cm longer than its altitude. The area of the triangle is 2 cm². Find the length of the base.

35. Draw a graph of the function $f(x) = 2x^3 + 3$. [8-12]

36. Find the real number solutions for $2x^3 + 5x^2 - 4x - 3 = 0$ graphically.

37. Find all possible rational solutions of the equation $x^3 + 6x^2 + 10x + 3 = 0$. [8-13]

38. Solve the equation in Exercise 37.

CAPSULE REVIEW

Write the letter of the best response.

1. The graph of a function $f(x) = ax^2 + bx + c$ is shown at the right. How many real number solutions does the equation $ax^2 + bx + c = 0$ have?

  a. 0   **b.** 2

  c. 1   **d.** infinitely many

2. Which of the following sentences is not equivalent to $x^2 = b^2$?

  a. $x = b$ or $x = -b$ **b.** $x = \sqrt{b^2}$ or $x = -\sqrt{b^2}$

  c. $x = b$ or $-x = b$ **d.** $x = \sqrt{b^2}$ or $x = \sqrt{-b^2}$

3. What term must be added to $x^2 + \dfrac{4}{3}x$ to complete a perfect-square trinomial?

  a. $\dfrac{64}{9}$ **b.** $\dfrac{4}{9}$ **c.** $\dfrac{4}{3}$ **d.** $\dfrac{2}{3}$

4. Two quadratic equations have discriminants which are non-zero opposites. Both equations have solutions that are

  a. real   **b.** rational   **c.** imaginary   **d.** complex

5. The discriminant of a quadratic equation is 6. The solutions of that equation are

  a. rational   **b.** real but irrational   **c.** imaginary   **d.** non-negative

6. Which of these equations is quadratic in form?

  a. $x^{\frac{2}{5}} + 3x^{\frac{1}{5}} + 2 = 0$ **b.** $x^{\frac{3}{7}} + x^{\frac{2}{7}} + \dfrac{3}{2} = 0$ **c.** $(x + 1)^2 + 2x = 0$ **d.** $4x^8 + 7x = 0$

7. Which of these equations does not have $2 + i$ and $2 - i$ as its solutions?

a. $(x - (2 + i))(x - (2 - i)) = 0$

b. $(x - 2)^2 - i^2 = 0$

c. $(x - 2 - i)(x - 2 + i) = 0$

d. $(x - 2)^2 + i^2 = 0$

8. The graph of the function $y = 2x^2 + 8x + 3$ has

a. a minimum at $(-2, 5)$

b. a minimum at $(-2, -5)$

c. a maximum at $(-2, 5)$

d. a maximum at $(-2, -5)$

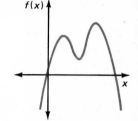

9. A polynomial function is graphed at the right. The degree of the polynomial which defines this function must be

a. less than 4

b. even

c. greater than 4

d. odd

10. Use the Rational Root Theorem to determine which of these could not be a solution of the equation $6x^4 + 3x^3 + 2x + 15 = 0$.

a. $\dfrac{5}{2}$

b. $\dfrac{3}{8}$

c. 15

d. $\dfrac{\sqrt{3}}{2}$

CHAPTER TEST

1. Draw the graph of $f(x) = x^2 + 4x + 4$.

2. Solve $x^2 - 5x + 6 = 0$ by graphing.

3. Solve $x^2 - 5 = 0$.

4. Solve $(x + 3)^2 = 6x$.

5. Complete a perfect-square trinomial. $x^2 + 8x + \underline{\quad ? \quad}$

6. Solve $x^2 + 10x + 20 = 4$ by completing the square.

7. Solve $x^2 + 4x - 1 = 0$ by using the quadratic formula.

8. Solve $x^2 + 2x - 2 = 0$ by using the quadratic formula.

9. What is the discriminant for the equation $2x^2 + 4x - 5 = 0$?

10. How many real-number solutions does a quadratic equation have if its discriminant is 0?

Solve for x.

11. $x^2 - 3dx + 2d^2 = 0$

12. $x^4 - 17x^2 = -16$

13. $2x^{\frac{1}{2}} - 3x^{\frac{1}{4}} = 9$

14. $1 = \dfrac{2}{x - 3} + \dfrac{3}{x - 1}$

15. $\sqrt{x + 5} = x + 3$

16. Write an equation whose solutions are 3 and 4.

17. Write an equation whose solutions are $2 + i$ and $2 - i$.

18. Find the y-intercept of the graph of $y = 2x^2 - 7x + 4$.

19. Find the vertex of the graph of $f(x) = x^2 - 6x + 10$.

20. Write an equation for a parabola which opens downward and whose axis of symmetry is to the right of the y-axis.

21. What effect does increasing c have on the graph of $y = ax^2 + bx + c$?

22. The product of two consecutive odd numbers is 399. Find the numbers.

23. If twice a number is increased by 8, the result equals the square of the number. Find the number.

24. A rectangle is 7 cm longer than it is wide. Its area is 120 cm². Find its length.

25. Ramon hiked west and then north. He traveled 1 km/h slower and 2 hours longer hiking north than he did hiking west. He hiked for 4 hours, finishing 13 km from his starting point. How fast did he travel hiking north?

26. The area of a rectangle is 44 m² and its perimeter is 27 m. Find its length and width.

27. The hypotenuse of a right triangle is 2 cm longer than one side and 9 cm longer than the other. Find the length of each side.

28. To travel 280 kilometers, a driver found it would take 0.5 hour less if the speed was 10 km/h faster than the usual rate. What was the usual rate?

29. Starting from the same place, one cyclist goes north at 24 km/h and another cyclist goes east at 18 km/h. How many hours must they travel to be 75 km apart?

Write the letter of the best response.

30. Which of these number pairs is a member of the function
$f(x) = x^2 + 2x + 1$?

    a. $(1, -2)$ **b.** $(1, 0)$ **c.** $(1, 2)$ **d.** $(1, 4)$ **e.** $(1, 5)$

31. What are the solutions of $x^2 + 9 = 0$?

    a. -9 and 9 **b.** -3 and 3 **c.** 3 and $3i$ **d.** $-3i$ and $3i$ **e.** no solutions

32. What is needed to complete the perfect-square trinomial $x^2 + $ ___?___ $ + 16$?

    a. $4x$ **b.** $8x$ **c.** $16x$ **d.** $32x$ **e.** $256x$

33. In using the quadratic formula to solve $2x^2 + 3x - 1 = 0$, what is $b^2 - 4ac$?

    a. 1 **b.** 8 **c.** 10 **d.** 14 **e.** 17

34. What are the solutions of $x^2 - kx - 2k^2 = 0$?

    a. $-k$ and $2k$ **b.** $-2k$ and k **c.** $-2k$ and $-k$ **d.** k and $2k$ **e.** $-2k$ and $3k$

35. What are the solutions of $4 + \sqrt{x + 26} = x$?

    a. -26 only   **b.** -1 only   **c.** 10 only   **d.** -1 and 10 **e.** $-26, -1$ and 10

36. What is the nature of the solutions of a quadratic equation if its discriminant equals -4?

    a. 1 rational number   **b.** 2 rational numbers   **c.** 1 irrational number

    d. 2 irrational numbers   **e.** 2 imaginary numbers

37. The length of the hypotenuse of a right triangle is 74 cm and its shortest side is 24 cm. What is the length of its other side?

   a. 70 cm   **b.** 60 cm   **c.** 50 cm   **d.** 40 cm   **e.** 30 cm

38. Which equation has solutions $\frac{2}{3}$ and -2?

   a. $2x^2 - x - 6 = 0$ **b.** $2x^2 + x - 6 = 0$ **c.** $3x^2 + 4x - 4 = 0$

   d. $3x^2 - 4x - 4 = 0$ **e.** $3x^2 + 8x + 4 = 0$

39. What is the axis of symmetry of the graph of $f(x) = x^2 + 8x - 10$?

   a. $x = 4$ **b.** $x = -4$ **c.** $x = 5$ **d.** $x = -5$ **e.** $x = 10$

40. For the function $f(x) = ax^2 + bx + c$, $-\frac{b}{2a}$ is positive, a is negative, and c is positive. In what quadrant is the vertex of the graph?

   a. 1   **b.** 2   **c.** 3   **d.** 4   **e.** cannot tell

41. The square of a number decreased by 3 times the number is 10. What is the number?

   a. -2 only   **b.** 5 only   **c.** 2 only   **d.** -2 or 5   **e.** 2 or 5

42. The length of the base of a triangle is twice the height of the triangle. What is the base length if the area of the triangle is 100 cm²?

   a. 5 cm   **b.** $5\sqrt{2}$ cm   **c.** 10 cm   **d.** 20 cm   **e.** $10\sqrt{2}$ cm

43. A driver went 10 km/h faster on a 360-km trip than on the return trip. The return trip took 0.5 hour longer. How long did the return trip take?

   a. 3.5 h   **b.** 4 h   **c.** 4.5 h   **d.** 5 h   **e.** 5.5 h

CUMULATIVE REVIEW

Give the word or symbol to complete each sentence.

1. $(5, 0)$ and $(0, 4)$ are the ___?___ of the graph of $4x + 5y = 20$.

2. The relation $\{(2, 1), (7, -3), (8, 2), (1, 4), (4, 1)\}$ is a ___?___ .

3. The system $\begin{array}{|c|} \hline 3x - 2y = 6 \\ 3x - 2y = 5 \\ \hline \end{array}$ is ___?___ .   **4.** In $6 + \sqrt{2}i$, $\sqrt{2}$ is the ___?___ part.

5. $3\sqrt{2} + 4\sqrt{3}$ is the ___?___ of $3\sqrt{2} - 4\sqrt{3}$.

6. For the graph of $y = ax^2 + bx + c$, $a \neq 0$, the line $x = -\frac{b}{2a}$ is the ___?___ .

Briefly answer each question. Refer to the concept suggested.

7. The inverse of the function $y = x^3$ is a function. Why?   **8.** $(x^{-1})^{-2} = x^2$. Why?

9. The solutions of $3x^2 + 5x + 1 = 0$ are irrational. Why?

10. The function $f(x) = -\frac{3}{2}x^2 + \frac{5}{3}x - 12$ has a maximum value. Why?

11. The range of $f(x) = x^5 - 4x^3 + x - 6$ is the set of real numbers. Why?

Graph.

12. $4x - 3y = -12$

13. $-\frac{1}{3}x + \frac{1}{4}y = 1$

14. $-3x + 6y < 20$

15. $y = x^2 + 5x$ and $y = 2x^2 + 5x$

16. $y = 3x^2 + 5x + 2$ and $y = 3x^2 + 5x - 1$

Factor.

17. $a^4 - 4$

18. $x^2 - 6x + 9 - y^2$

19. Simplify the expression $\dfrac{x + \frac{2x}{x-3}}{x - \frac{2x}{x-3}}$.

Solve.

20. $\dfrac{x+1}{x-1} - \dfrac{x-1}{x+1} = \dfrac{3}{x-1}$

Simplify.

21. $\dfrac{x^4 y}{y^2} \cdot \dfrac{x^2 y^3}{x}$

22. $\left(\dfrac{x^4 y^3}{xy^{12}}\right)^3$

23. $\sqrt[5]{-32a^5 b^5}$

24. $\left(\dfrac{a^{\frac{1}{4}}}{a^{\frac{1}{8}}}\right)^n$

25. $\sqrt[3]{\dfrac{8}{9x^2}}$

26. $\dfrac{\sqrt{7} + \sqrt{3}}{\sqrt{7} - \sqrt{3}}$

Solve.

27. $y = 7x - \dfrac{1}{3}$
$6x + 5y = 12$

28. $-2x + y = 8$
$4x - y = 4$

29. $\dfrac{5}{x} + \dfrac{4}{y} = 12$
$\dfrac{3}{x} - \dfrac{2}{y} = 5$

30. $\sqrt{2x + 6} - \sqrt{x + 4} = 1$

31. $4x^2 + 5x = -2$

32. $3 + \dfrac{1}{x} = \dfrac{1}{x^2}$

33. Mrs. Jones has a total of $5000 invested. Part of it is invested at an annual rate of 4%, part at 5% per year and the rest at 6% per year. The annual income is $260. The amount invested at the 5% rate is $500 less than the amount invested at 4%. Find the amount invested at each rate.

34. The product of two positive numbers is 104. One number is 5 more than the other. Find the numbers.

35. To travel 500 kilometers between two cities a car requires $3\frac{1}{3}$ hours more time than a train. If the average speed of the train is 40 kilometers per hour faster than the car, find the average speed of the car.

Write the letter of the best response.

36. If g is the relation determined by the equation $g(x) = x^2 - x + 3$,

   a. both g and g^{-1} are functions   **b.** g is a function, g^{-1} is not

   c. g^{-1} is a function, g is not   **d.** neither g nor g^{-1} is a function

37. Use the discriminant of $5x^2 - 2x + 1 = 0$ to determine that its solutions are

   a. rational   **b.** irrational   **c.** complex   **d.** none of these

38. The function $f(x) = 2x^2 + 12x + 19$ has

   a. maximum value at $(-3, 1)$ **b.** minimum value at $(3, 1)$

   c. maximum value at $(3, 1)$ **d.** minimum value at $(-3, 1)$

   e. minimum value at $(-3, 10)$

39. The solution(s) of $\ |-7x + 3| = 24\ $ is (are)

   a. $3, \dfrac{-27}{7}$ **b.** $-3, 3$ **c.** $-3, \dfrac{27}{7}$ **d.** -3 **e.** none of these

40. For the line determined by the equation $x = 3$,

   a. $m = 0$ **b.** $m = 1$ **c.** $m = 3$ **d.** there is no slope

41. The variables x and y are linearly related. As the value of x changes from 7 to 9, the value of y changes from 11 to 7. The linear equation that describes this relationship is

   a. $2x + y = 25$ **b.** $x + 2y = 23$ **c.** $x = -\frac{1}{2}y$ **d.** $y = -\frac{1}{2}x$ **e.** $2x + y = 23$

42. The possible rational solutions of $6x^5 - 7x^3 + 4x - 5 = 0$ are

   a. $\pm 2, \pm 6, \pm 1, \pm \dfrac{1}{5}, \pm \dfrac{2}{5}, \pm \dfrac{3}{5}, \pm \dfrac{6}{5}, \pm 3$

   b. $\pm 5, \pm \dfrac{5}{2}, \pm \dfrac{5}{3}, \pm \dfrac{15}{2}, \pm \dfrac{3}{2}, \pm \dfrac{1}{2}, \pm \dfrac{1}{6}$

   c. $\pm \dfrac{1}{2}, \pm \dfrac{1}{6}, \pm \dfrac{5}{3}, \pm 5, \pm \dfrac{5}{2}, \pm \dfrac{5}{6}, \pm \dfrac{2}{3}, \pm 1$

   d. $\pm \dfrac{1}{2}, \pm \dfrac{1}{6}, \pm \dfrac{1}{3}, \pm 1, \pm 5, \pm \dfrac{5}{2}, \pm \dfrac{5}{3}, \pm \dfrac{5}{6}$

43. The quadratic equation whose solutions are -4 and $\dfrac{7}{4}$ is

   a. $4x^2 - 9x + 28 = 0$ **b.** $2x^2 + 9x - 14 = 0$ **c.** $2x^2 - 9x + 14 = 0$

   d. $4x^2 + 9x - 28 = 0$ **e.** $4x^2 - 9x - 28 = 0$

44. The solution to $-3(x - 1) < 6$ is

   a. $x < -1$ **b.** $x > -3$ **c.** $x < -3$ **d.** $x > 0$ **e.** $x > -1$

CHAPTER 9
CONICS AND
SYSTEMS OF EQUATIONS
INVOLVING QUADRATICS

A judge serves us by interpreting and clarifying the laws that regulate our lives. A background in mathematics, for which laws can be clearly stated and universally understood, serves us by enabling us to understand better the function of laws and rules in general. The thought processes of mathematics in particular, serve us by making us better able to understand legal interpretations, notably the ones that affect us directly.

OBJECTIVES: Identify and graph quadratic equations for circles, ellipses, parabolas, and hyperbolas.

9-1   THE DISTANCE AND MIDPOINT FORMULAS

In this chapter we investigate quadratic equations in two variables that are associated with geometric figures called *conic sections*.   The link between the algebra and the geometry is provided by the Distance Formula for the coordinate plane.   It, in turn, is based on the idea of distance related to the number line.

DISTANCE RELATED TO THE NUMBER LINE

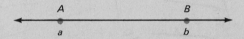

When the coordinate of point A is a and the coordinate of point B is b, the distance AB between A and B is defined as follows.

$$AB = |a - b|$$

EXAMPLE 1   Find the distance between A and B.

SOLUTION 1	**SOLUTION 2**
$AB = \|b - a\|$	$AB = \|a - b\|$
$\quad = \|7\frac{1}{4} - 1\frac{1}{2}\|$	$\quad = \|1\frac{1}{2} - 7\frac{1}{4}\|$
$\quad = \|5\frac{3}{4}\|$	$\quad = \|-5\frac{3}{4}\|$
$\quad = 5\frac{3}{4}$	$\quad = 5\frac{3}{4}$

CONCLUSION   The distance between A and B is $5\frac{3}{4}$.

Not all lines in a plane, however, are parallel to an axis. To find a formula for the distance between any two points in the coordinate plane, we use the formula given on the preceding page and the Pythagorean Theorem.

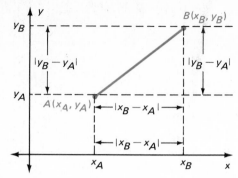

This diagram shows that B is $|x_B - x_A|$ units horizontally and $|y_B - y_A|$ units vertically from A. The Pythagorean Theorem can be used to find the length of $\overline{AB}$, or the distance AB between A and B.

DISTANCE RELATED TO THE COORDINATE PLANE

(The Distance Formula)

When the coordinates of A are (x_A, y_A) and the coordinates of B are (x_B, y_B), the distance AB is defined as follows.

$$AB = \sqrt{(x_B - x_A)^2 + (y_B - y_A)^2}$$

EXAMPLE 2 Find the distance between $A(5, 7)$ and $B(10, -5)$.

SOLUTION

$$AB = \sqrt{(x_B - x_A)^2 + (y_B - y_A)^2}$$
$$AB = \sqrt{(10 - 5)^2 + (-5 - 7)^2}$$
$$= \sqrt{5^2 + (-12)^2}$$
$$= \sqrt{25 + 144}$$
$$= \sqrt{169}$$
$$= 13$$

CHECK
$$(AC)^2 + (BC)^2 \overset{?}{=} (AB)^2$$
$$12^2 + 5^2 \overset{?}{=} 13^2$$
$$144 + 25 = 169$$
$$169 = 169 \quad ✔$$

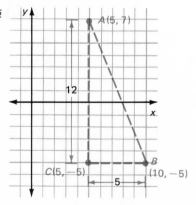

An *average* of two numbers is a number that is "halfway between" the two numbers. This idea can help you understand the midpoint formula.

MIDPOINT FORMULA RELATED TO THE NUMBER LINE

The midpoint M of a line segment AB has coordinate $\dfrac{x_A + x_B}{2}$ when x_A is the coordinate of A and x_B is the coordinate of B.

EXAMPLE 3   Find a number "halfway between" 4 and 9.

SOLUTION   Use n for the number.

$$n = \frac{4 + 9}{2}, \text{ or } 6\tfrac{1}{2}$$

CONCLUSION $6\tfrac{1}{2}$ is "halfway between" 4 and 9.

CHECK $|6\tfrac{1}{2} - 4| \overset{?}{=} 2\tfrac{1}{2}$ and $|9 - 6\tfrac{1}{2}| \overset{?}{=} 2\tfrac{1}{2}$

$\qquad\qquad 2\tfrac{1}{2} = 2\tfrac{1}{2}$ ✔ $\qquad\quad 2\tfrac{1}{2} = 2\tfrac{1}{2}$ ✔

In a similar way, you can find the two coordinates of the midpoint of any segment in the coordinate plane.

MIDPOINT FORMULA RELATED TO THE COORDINATE PLANE

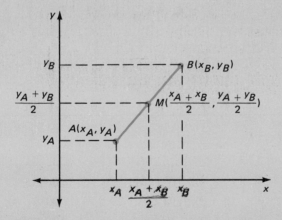

The midpoint M of line segment AB has coordinates $\left(\dfrac{x_A + x_B}{2}, \dfrac{y_A + y_B}{2}\right)$ when (x_A, y_A) are the coordinates of A and (x_B, y_B) are the coordinates of B.

EXAMPLE 4   Find the midpoint of the line segment having endpoints $A(-2, 2)$ and $B(6, 5)$.   Draw a graph to show your result.

SOLUTION   Use M for the midpoint of line segment AB.   The coordinates of M are given by $\left(\dfrac{x_A + x_B}{2}, \dfrac{y_A + y_B}{2}\right)$.

Thus, the coordinates of M are $\left(\dfrac{-2 + 6}{2}, \dfrac{2 + 5}{2}\right)$, or $\left(2, 3\frac{1}{2}\right)$.

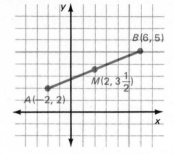

CHECK   The check that $AM = MB$ is left for the student.   Use the Distance Formula.

CLASSROOM EXERCISES

Find the distance between A and B.

1. $A(2, 8)$, $B(-1, 4)$

2. $A(-3, 6)$, $B(-1, -4)$

Find the midpoint of line segment AB.

3. $A(1, 1)$, $B(5, 9)$

4. $A(-2, 1)$, $B(3, -3)$

5. Show that $\triangle ABC$ with vertices $A(9, 9)$, $B(4, -3)$, and $C(16, -8)$ is a right isosceles triangle.   (Hint: Find the length of each side.)

EXERCISES

Ⓐ Find the distance between A and B.

1. $A(0, 0)$, $B(6, 8)$

2. $A(0, 0)$, $B(5, 12)$

3. $A(2, 0)$, $B(-3, 0)$

4. $A(5, 0)$, $B(-2, 0)$

5. $A(-2, 4)$, $B(7, -3)$

6. $A(-3, 5)$, $B(8, -2)$

7. $A(0, -6)$, $B(0, 4)$

8. $A(0, -3)$, $B(0, 5)$

9. $A(-6, -7)$, $B(0, 3)$

10. $A(-3, -5)$, $B(0, 4)$

11. $A(0.4, 1.3)$, $B(1.6, 0.4)$

12. $A(0.3, 0.9)$, $B(1.1, 0.3)$

Find the midpoint of $\overline{AB}$.

13. $A(3, 0)$, $B(8, 0)$

14. $A(2, 0)$, $B(7, 0)$

15. $A(3, -2)$, $B(4, 1)$

16. $A(5, -3)$, $B(6, 2)$

17. $A(0, -6)$, $B(0, -3)$

18. $A(0, -7)$, $B(0, -4)$

Show that $\triangle ABC$ is a right isosceles triangle.

19. $A(8, 23)$, $B(1, -1)$, $C(25, -8)$

20. $A(10, 13)$, $B(2, -2)$, $C(17, -10)$

21. $A(18, 10)$, $B(3, 2)$, $C(11, -13)$

22. $A(28, 12)$, $B(4, 5)$, $C(11, -19)$

B **23.** Find the length of the line segment with endpoints $A(\sqrt{6}, 7)$ and $B(3\sqrt{6}, 8\frac{1}{3})$. Find the midpoint of the line segment.

24. For $A(5, 10)$, $M(8, 7)$, and $B(x, y)$, find x and y such that M is the midpoint of $\overline{AB}$.

25. For $A(2, 8)$, $B(10, 14)$, $C(0, 18)$, M the midpoint of $\overline{AB}$, and N the midpoint of $\overline{AC}$, show that $MN = \frac{1}{2}BC$.

C **26.** Use the Distance Formula to verify the Midpoint Formula.

27. Find the area of one of the parallelograms determined by the points $(-2, 3)$, $(0, 1)$, and $(6, 11)$.

28. In $\triangle ABC$, points A, B, C have coordinates $(19, 1)$, $(2, 5)$, and $(3, 8)$, respectively. Find the coordinates of points P and Q in $\overline{BC}$ so that in $\triangle APQ$, $AP = AQ$ and the area of $\triangle APQ$ equals $\frac{1}{4}$ the area of $\triangle ABC$.

$\boxed{\text{1.618034}}$ **CHOOSE ANY NUMBER. . .**

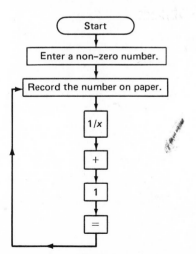

1. Use your calculator. Follow the steps of the flow chart.

2. Stop when the decimal digits stay the same.

3. Start with other numbers and follow the steps of the flow chart.

4. Compare your results with each other and with the number $\dfrac{1 + \sqrt{5}}{2}$.

5. Use your library. What can you find out about the number $\dfrac{1 + \sqrt{5}}{2}$?

9-2 CIRCLES

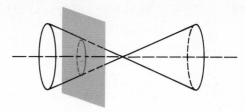

Geometrically, a **circle** is the set of points in a plane that are the same distance from a given point. The given point is the **center** of the circle. The distance is the **radius** of the circle.

Algebraically, a circle is described by the equation

$$(x - h)^2 + (y - k)^2 = r^2.$$

The graph of this equation is a circle with center (h, k) and radius r.

The Distance Formula for the coordinate plane shows how the algebraic equation given above is related to the geometric concept of the circle.

$$\text{Use} \begin{bmatrix} (x, y) & \text{for the coordinates of a point of the} \\ & \text{circle.} \\ (h, k) & \text{for the coordinates of the center.} \\ r & \text{for the distance between the points.} \end{bmatrix}$$

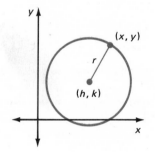

From the Distance Formula,

$$r = \sqrt{(x - h)^2 + (y - k)^2}.$$

Therefore, $r^2 = (x - h)^2 + (y - k)^2$

When the center of the circle is at the origin, $(0, 0)$, the following equation for the circle results.

$$r^2 = (x - 0)^2 + (y - 0)^2$$
$$r^2 = x^2 + y^2$$

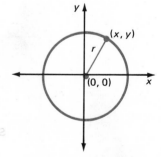

EXAMPLE 1   Write the equation for the circle with center at the origin $(0, 0)$ and radius 1.

SOLUTION $(x - h)^2 + (y - k)^2 = r^2$
$(x - 0)^2 + (y - 0)^2 = 1^2$
$x^2 + y^2 = 1$

EXAMPLE 2 Write the equation for the circle with center $(3, 2)$ and radius 5.

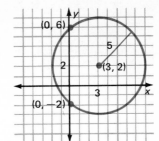

SOLUTION $(x - h)^2 + (y - k)^2 = r^2$
$(x - 3)^2 + (y - 2)^2 = 5^2$
$(x - 3)^2 + (y - 2)^2 = 25$

EXAMPLE 3 Find two points of the circle in Example 2.

SOLUTION 1 Graphically, $(0, 6)$ and $(0, -2)$ appear to be two such points.

CHECK Are $(0, 6)$ and $(0, -2)$ solutions of $(x - 3)^2 + (y - 2)^2 = 25$?

For $(0, 6)$:

$(x - 3)^2 + (y - 2)^2 = 25$
$(0 - 3)^2 + (6 - 2)^2 \overset{?}{=} 25$
$3^2 + 4^2 \overset{?}{=} 25$
$25 = 25$ ✔

For $(0, -2)$:

$(x - 3)^2 + (y - 2)^2 = 25$
$(0 - 3)^2 + (-2 - 2)^2 \overset{?}{=} 25$
$3^2 + (-4)^2 \overset{?}{=} 25$
$25 = 25$ ✔

CONCLUSION $(0, 6)$ and $(0, -2)$ are two points of the circle in Example 2.

SOLUTION 2 Algebraically, replace x by 0 in the equation.

$(x - 3)^2 + (y - 2)^2 = 25$
$(0 - 3)^2 + (y - 2)^2 = 25$
$9 + y^2 - 4y + 4 = 25$
$y^2 - 4y - 12 = 0$
$(y - 6)(y + 2) = 0$
$y = 6$ or $y = -2$

CONCLUSION $(0, 6)$ and $(0, -2)$ are two points of the circle.

CHECK The check is the same as for Solution 1.

EXAMPLE 4 Graph the equations
$x^2 + y^2 = 5$ and $(x - 2)^2 + (y + 7)^2 = 49$.
Use the same coordinate axes.

SOLUTION The graph of $x^2 + y^2 = 5$ is a circle with center $(0, 0)$. Its radius is $\sqrt{5}$.
The graph of $(x - 2)^2 + (y + 7)^2 = 49$ is a circle with center $(2, -7)$. Its radius is 7.

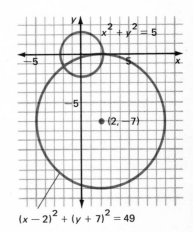

$(x - 2)^2 + (y + 7)^2 = 49$

CLASSROOM EXERCISES

Write an equation of the circle with center C and radius r.

1. $C(0, 0), r = 3$ **2.** $C(-1, 4), r = 7$ **3.** $C(1, -2), r = \sqrt{5}$ **4.** $C(-2, -3), r = 4$

Graph.

5. $x^2 + y^2 = 25$ **6.** $(x - 1)^2 + (y - 2)^2 = 4$ **7.** $(x + 2)^2 + (y - 3)^2 = 9$

8. Use the graph from Exercise 7. Find the coordinates of two points of the circle. Check your result.

9. Find the coordinates of each point of the circle in Exercise 6 whose first member is 1.

10. Find an equation of the circle whose diameter has endpoints $A(9, 2)$ and $B(17, 8)$.

EXERCISES

A

Write an equation of the circle with center C and radius r.

1. $C(0, 0), r = 4$ **2.** $C(0, 0), r = 2$ **3.** $C(0, 4), r = 3$ **4.** $C(6, 0), r = 5$
5. $C(-2, -4), r = 6$ **6.** $C(-3, -1), r = 4$ **7.** $C(4, -3), r = \sqrt{13}$ **8.** $C(5, -1), r = \sqrt{6}$

Graph.

9. $x^2 + (y + 1)^2 = 49$ **10.** $x^2 + (y + 3)^2 = 36$
11. $(x - 1)^2 + (y - 1)^2 = 9$ **12.** $(x - 2)^2 + (y - 2)^2 = 4$
13. $(x + 1)^2 + (y - 2)^2 = 64$ **14.** $(x + 2)^2 + (y + 3)^2 = 5$

Find an equation of the circle having diameter $\overline{AB}$.

15. $A(2, 4), B(14, 20)$ **16.** $A(3, 1), B(9, 9)$ **17.** $A(-2, 1), B(2, 7)$
18. $A(-3, 2), B(3, 4)$ **19.** $A(1, -4), B(2, -7)$ **20.** $A(2, -3), B(6, -4)$

B **21.** Find the coordinates of two points of the circle with center $(\sqrt{2}, -\sqrt{3})$ and radius $\sqrt{7}$.

22. The graph of $x^2 - 6x + y^2 = 7$ is a circle. Find the center and radius. (Hint: Complete the square in x.)

C **23.** $P(0, 3), Q(-3, 3 + \sqrt{3})$, and $R(-3, 3 - \sqrt{3})$ are vertices of a triangle that is inscribed in a circle. Find the equation of the circle.

24. A circle has $(2, 1)$ as its center. It is tangent to the line $3x + 4y = 35$. Find the equation of the circle.

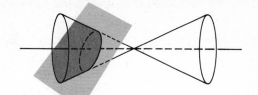

9-3 ELLIPSES

Geometrically, an **ellipse** is the set of points in a plane such that the *sum* of the distances from each point of the set to two given points is constant. With this definition, you should be able to give a reason why the curve drawn as shown, with a pencil and a piece of string fixed by two tacks, is a sketch of an ellipse.

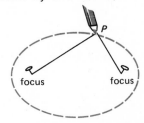

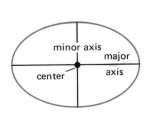

For an ellipse, each of the two given points is a **focus** of the ellipse. The line segment with points of the ellipse as endpoints and containing the foci is the **major axis** of the ellipse. Its perpendicular bisector with points of the ellipse as endpoints is the **minor axis.** The two axes meet at the **center** of the ellipse.

Algebraically, an ellipse centered at (0, 0) is described by the equation $\frac{x^2}{a^2} + \frac{y^2}{b^2} = 1$. We can sketch a graph for $\frac{x^2}{a^2} + \frac{y^2}{b^2} = 1$ by finding the inter-

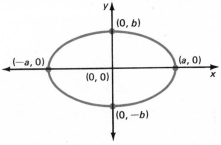

cepts. Replacing x by 0 in the equation, we find that $y = \pm b$. Hence the ellipse has y-intercepts b and $-b$. Replacing y by 0, we find that the ellipse has x-intercepts a and $-a$.

Since the intercepts for $\frac{x^2}{a^2} + \frac{y^2}{b^2} = 1$ are $\pm a$ and $\pm b$, the denominators in the equation indicate which axis is major and which is minor. When $a^2 > b^2$, the major axis is horizontal. When $a^2 < b^2$ the major axis is vertical. That this algebraic description of an ellipse agrees with the geometric description can be shown by using the Distance Formula for the coordinate plane. The procedure is suggested in the exercises at the end of this section.

EXAMPLE 1 Find the intercepts of the ellipse whose equation is $\frac{x^2}{16} + \frac{y^2}{9} = 1$. Sketch its graph.

SOLUTION Note that $a^2 = 16$ and $b^2 = 9$. The larger denominator is associated with x^2. Hence, the major axis of the ellipse is horizontal. The x-intercepts are 4 and -4. The y-intercepts are 3 and -3.

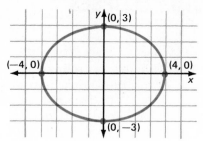

The intercepts give us four points of an ellipse. To draw an ellipse accurately, we should find more points that belong to the ellipse. To do this we observe that if (x, y) is a solution of $\frac{x^2}{a^2} + \frac{y^2}{b^2} = 1$, then so are $(-x, y)$, $(x, -y)$, and $(-x, -y)$. For example,

$$\frac{(-x)^2}{a^2} + \frac{(-y)^2}{b^2} = 1 \text{ simplifies to } \frac{x^2}{a^2} + \frac{y^2}{b^2} = 1$$

EXAMPLE 2 Plot 12 points of the graph of $\frac{x^2}{9} + \frac{y^2}{25} = 1$. Then draw the graph.

SOLUTION Note that $a^2 = 9$, $b^2 = 25$. Hence, the major axis is vertical. The intercepts give us the first four points in the table below. The others are found by replacing x or y by certain chosen numbers and then evaluating the other variable.

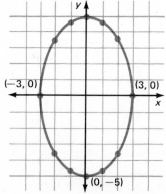

x	y
0	± 5
± 3	0
± 1	$\pm \frac{10}{3}\sqrt{2}$, or about ± 4.7
± 2	$\pm \frac{5}{3}\sqrt{5}$, or about ± 3.7

Suppose we replace the equation of a circle, $x^2 + y^2 = r^2$, by
$\dfrac{x^2}{r^2} + \dfrac{y^2}{r^2} = 1$. We see that a circle may be regarded as an ellipse having only one focus and two axes the same length. The equation of a
circle with center at (h, k), $(x - h)^2 + (y - k)^2 = r^2$, also may be written
$\dfrac{(x - h)^2}{r^2} + \dfrac{(y - k)^2}{r^2} = 1$. When the denominators are different, as in

$$\frac{(x - h)^2}{a^2} + \frac{(y - k)^2}{b^2} = 1,$$

the equation describes an ellipse centered at (h, k).

EXAMPLE 3 Graph $\dfrac{(x - 4)^2}{16} + \dfrac{(y + 1)^2}{4} = 1$.

SOLUTION The graph is an ellipse centered at $(4, -1)$. The horizontal major axis has length 8. The vertical minor axis has
length 4.

x	y
4	1 or -3
8	-1
0	-1
2	about 0.732 or about -2.732
6	about 0.732 or about -2.732

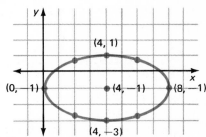

CLASSROOM EXERCISES

Find the intercepts. Sketch the graph.

1. $\dfrac{x^2}{36} + \dfrac{y^2}{9} = 1$

2. $\dfrac{x^2}{25} + \dfrac{y^2}{16} = 1$

3. $\dfrac{x^2}{4} + \dfrac{y^2}{49} = 1$

Graph.

4. $\dfrac{(x - 1)^2}{16} + \dfrac{(y - 1)^2}{25} = 1$

5. $\dfrac{(x - 3)^2}{9} + \dfrac{(y + 2)^2}{16} = 1$

EXERCISES

Ⓐ Find the intercepts. Sketch the graph.

1. $\dfrac{x^2}{9} + \dfrac{y^2}{4} = 1$

2. $\dfrac{x^2}{25} + \dfrac{y^2}{9} = 1$

3. $\dfrac{x^2}{4} + \dfrac{y^2}{36} = 1$

4. $\dfrac{x^2}{9} + \dfrac{y^2}{25} = 1$ **5.** $x^2 + \dfrac{y^2}{36} = 1$ **6.** $x^2 + \dfrac{y^2}{16} = 1$

7. $\dfrac{x^2}{144} + \dfrac{y^2}{121} = 1$ **8.** $\dfrac{x^2}{7} + \dfrac{y^2}{11} = 1$ **9.** $\dfrac{x^2}{5} + \dfrac{y^2}{13} = 1$

Graph.

10. $\dfrac{(x-3)^2}{4} + \dfrac{y^2}{9} = 1$ **11.** $\dfrac{(x-4)^2}{25} + \dfrac{y^2}{36} = 1$

12. $\dfrac{(x+1)^2}{25} + \dfrac{(y-2)^2}{16} = 1$ **13.** $\dfrac{(x+2)^2}{49} + \dfrac{(y-3)^2}{4} = 1$

14. $\dfrac{(x+3)^2}{4} + \dfrac{(y+2)^2}{9} = 1$ **15.** $\dfrac{(x+5)^2}{16} + \dfrac{(y+6)^2}{25} = 1$

B Find the intercepts. Sketch the graph.

16. $\dfrac{\sqrt{2}x^2}{2} + \dfrac{\sqrt{3}y^2}{3} = 1$ **17.** $3(x-1)^2 + 5(y+2)^2 = 15$

Graph.

18. $y = \sqrt{9 - \dfrac{9}{4}x^2}$ (Hint: Square both sides. Remember, y is non-negative.)

19. An ellipse has foci $(-4, 0)$ and $(4, 0)$. The sum of the distances from each point of the ellipse to the foci is 10. Use the geometric definition of an ellipse and the Distance Formula to find the equation of the ellipse.

C **20.** Suppose the foci for an ellipse are $F_1(c, 0)$ and $F_2(-c, 0)$. Let $P(x, y)$ be any point of the ellipse. Denote the sum of the distances from P to F_1 and P to F_2 by $2a$. Use the geometric definition of an ellipse and the Distance Formula to derive the formula $\dfrac{x^2}{a^2} + \dfrac{y^2}{b^2} = 1$ where $a > b$ and $b^2 = a^2 - c^2$.

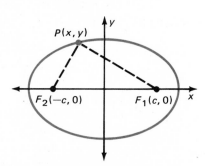

21. An ellipse has foci $(-3, 0)$ and $(3, 0)$. The sum of the distances from each point of the ellipse to the foci is 10. Find the equation of the ellipse. Use the result of Exercise 20.

22. Let a and b denote the positive intercepts of an ellipse $\dfrac{x^2}{a^2} + \dfrac{y^2}{b^2} = 1$.

Show that if $a + b = k$ where k is a positive constant, then the ellipse having maximum area is a circle. Find the radius of such a circle. (Hint: The area of an ellipse is πab.)

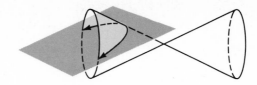

9-4 PARABOLAS

We already have studied the parabola as the graph of a quadratic equation in two variables. Geometrically, each point of a parabola is the same distance from a given point as it is from a given line. The given point is the **focus** and the given line is the **directrix** of the parabola.

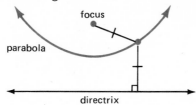

Suppose the focus is in the y-axis, a certain distance above the origin in the coordinate plane, and the directrix is the same distance below the origin. Then the geometric definition and the Distance Formula will give an algebraic equation of the form $y = ax^2$ for the parabola. As we saw in Sections 8-9 and 8-10, the constant, a, indicates whether the parabola opens upward ($a > 0$) or opens downward ($a < 0$). The constant a also indicates whether the parabola is wide ($|a|$ small), or narrow ($|a|$ large).

EXAMPLE 1 Sketch the graphs of
$$y = -\tfrac{1}{4}x^2, \ y = -\tfrac{1}{2}x^2, \ y = -x^2, \ y = -10x^2.$$
Use one set of coordinate axes.

SOLUTION

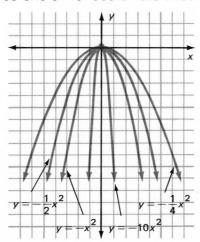

$y = -\tfrac{1}{2}x^2$ $y = -\tfrac{1}{4}x^2$

$y = -x^2$ $y = -10x^2$

Recall that for the equations

$$x^2 + y^2 = r^2 \qquad \text{and} \qquad (x - h)^2 + (y - k)^2 = r^2$$

the graphs are circles of radius r with centers at $(0, 0)$ and (h, k) respectively. Also, for the equations

$$\frac{x^2}{a^2} + \frac{y^2}{b^2} = 1 \qquad \text{and} \qquad \frac{(x - h)^2}{a^2} + \frac{(y - k)^2}{b^2} = 1,$$

the graphs are ellipses of the same size and shape, with centers at $(0, 0)$ and (h, k) respectively. Similarly, for

$$y = ax^2 \qquad \text{and} \qquad y - k = a(x - h)^2,$$

the graphs are parabolas of the same shape with vertices (plural of vertex) at $(0, 0)$ and (h, k) respectively.

EXAMPLE 2 Sketch the graphs of $y = \frac{1}{3}x^2$ and $y + 6 = \frac{1}{3}(x - 4)^2$. Use one set of coordinate axes.

SOLUTION The two graphs have the same shape. One has its vertex at $(0, 0)$, the other at $(4, -6)$

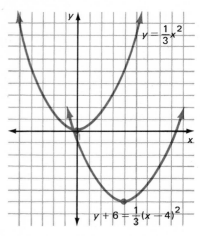

EXAMPLE 3 Graph $y = -2x^2 + 16x - 34$.

SOLUTION Complete the square and develop the form $y - k = a(x - h)^2$.

$$y = -2x^2 + 16x - 34$$
$$y = -2(x^2 - 8x \qquad) - 34$$
$$y - 32 = -2(x^2 - 8x + 16) - 34$$
$$y + 2 = -2(x - 4)^2$$

The vertex has coordinates $(4, -2)$. The graph has the same shape as the graph of $y = -2x^2$. Since the vertex is contained in the axis of symmetry, the equation of the axis of symmetry is $x = 4$.

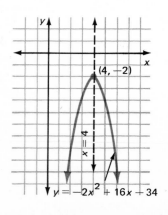

Until now, each parabola we have studied has been a graph of $y = ax^2 + bx + c$. The graph of $x = ay^2 + by + c$ also is a parabola. Since the variables have been interchanged from the first equation, the orientation of the graph is changed in the coordinate plane.

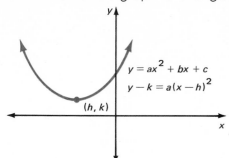
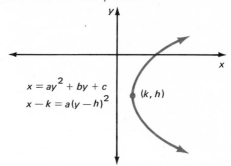

EXAMPLE 4   Graph $x = 3y^2$.

SOLUTION $x = 3y^2$.   Therefore, $x - 0 = 3(y - 0)^2$.
The graph is a parabola with vertex $(0, 0)$.
Since a is positive, the parabola will open to the right.
$y = 0$, a horizontal line, is the axis of symmetry.

GRAPH

x	y
0	0
3	±1
12	±2

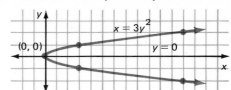

EXAMPLE 5   Graph $x = 3y^2 - 6y + 5$

SOLUTION   Complete the square and develop the form $x - h = a(y - k)^2$.

$$x = 3y^2 - 6y + 5$$
$$x = 3(y^2 - 2y \quad\ ) + 5$$
$$x + 3 = 3(y^2 - 2y + 1) + 5$$
$$x - 2 = 3(y - 1)^2$$

The vertex has coordinates $(2, 1)$
The axis of symmetry is $y = 1$, a horizontal line.
The graph has the same shape as the graph of $x = 3y^2$.

GRAPH

x	y
2	1
5	0
5	2 (by symmetry)

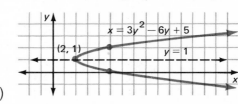

CLASSROOM EXERCISES

Graph. Use one set of coordinate axes.

1. $y = \frac{1}{3}x^2$, $y = x^2$, $y = 3x^2$ **2.** $y = -\frac{1}{2}x^2$, $y + 5 = -\frac{1}{2}(x - 1)^2$

Graph.

2. $y = \frac{1}{2}x^2 - 1$ **4.** $y = 2x^2 + 2$ **5.** $y = x^2 + 4x - 4$

6. $y = x^2 - 6x + 9$ **7.** $x = 3y^2 + 4$ **8.** $x = y^2 - 2y + 1$

EXERCISES

Ⓐ Graph. Use one set of coordinate axes.

1. $y = -\frac{1}{3}x^2$, $y = -x^2$, $y = -3x^2$ **2.** $y = \frac{1}{4}x^2$, $y = x^2$, $y = 4x^2$

3. $y = \frac{1}{3}x^2$, $y + 5 = \frac{1}{3}(x - 1)^2$ **4.** $y = -7x^2$, $y - 3 = -7(x + 2)^2$

Graph.

5. $y = 2x^2 - 6$ **6.** $y = 3x^2 - 4$ **7.** $y = -\frac{1}{2}x^2 + 2$

8. $y = -\frac{1}{4}x^2 + 8$ **9.** $y = -x^2 - 6x - 9$ **10.** $y = -x^2 - 10x - 25$

11. $x = y^2 + 2$ **12.** $x = y^2 + 3$ **13.** $x = y^2 + 6y + 9$

14. $x = y^2 + 8y + 16$ **15.** $x = -y^2 - 4y - 4$ **16.** $x = -y^2 - 10y - 25$

Ⓑ Use the geometric definition of the parabola and the Distance Formula. Find the equation of the parabola with focus F and the given directrix.

17. $F(0, 3)$, $y = -3$ **18.** $F(6, 0)$, $x = -6$ **19.** $F(-3, 4)$, $y = 6$

Ⓒ **20.** The line for $y = -p$ is the directrix of a parabola. The focus is $F(0, p)$. $P(x, y)$ represents any point of the parabola. Use the geometric definition of a parabola and the Distance Formula to derive the equation $y = \dfrac{1}{4p}x^2$.

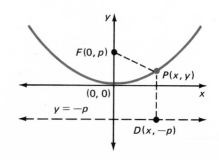

21. Use the result of Exercise 20 to find the focus and directrix for each parabola of Exercises 1 and 2.

9-5 HYPERBOLAS

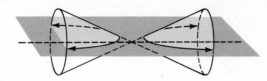

The graph of $\dfrac{x^2}{a^2} + \dfrac{y^2}{b^2} = 1$ is shown below in light red. Replacing the plus sign by a minus sign in the equation gives $\dfrac{x^2}{a^2} - \dfrac{y^2}{b^2} = 1$. This equation describes algebraically a *hyperbola* centered at $(0, 0)$.

Geometrically, a **hyperbola** is the set of points in a plane such that the *difference* of the distances from each point of the set to two given points is constant. Each of the two given points is a focus of the hyperbola. Each curve is a **branch** of the hyperbola. As we move farther from the center along each branch of the hyperbola, we see that the distance between the curve and each of two lines becomes smaller and smaller. However, the hyperbola never intersects the lines. Each of these lines is called an **asymptote** of the hyperbola.

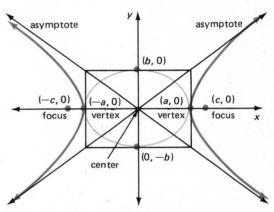

Note in the picture how we use the numbers for a, $-a$, b, and $-b$ to draw a rectangle. The asymptotes are the lines that contain the diagonals of this rectangle. In addition, if we replace y by 0, we find the x-intercepts to be a and $-a$. Note that there is no y-intercept.

EXAMPLE 1 Sketch the graph of the hyperbola $\dfrac{x^2}{9} - \dfrac{y^2}{16} = 1$.

SOLUTION Matching $\dfrac{x^2}{9} - \dfrac{y^2}{16} = 1$

with $\dfrac{x^2}{a^2} - \dfrac{y^2}{b^2} = 1$, gives $a^2 = 9$ and $b^2 = 16$. The x-intercepts are 3 and -3. The asymptotes are the lines containing the diagonals of the rectangle associated with $\dfrac{x^2}{9} + \dfrac{y^2}{16} = 1$.

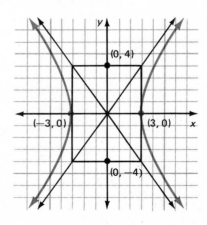

To test for a y-intercept in the preceding example, replace x by 0 in $\frac{x^2}{9} - \frac{y^2}{16} = 1$. This gives $-y^2 = 16$. Since y^2 is never negative, it is impossible for $-y^2$ to be positive. Hence, there is no y-intercept, as is shown by the graph.

EXAMPLE 2 Sketch the graph of the hyperbola for $\frac{y^2}{16} - \frac{x^2}{9} = 1$.

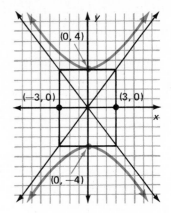

SOLUTION For the equation

$$\frac{y^2}{16} - \frac{x^2}{9} = 1,$$

there are no x-intercepts; the y-intercepts are 4 and -4. The graph is the hyperbola with the asymptotes shown.

As with an ellipse, we note that if (x, y) is a solution of $\frac{x^2}{a^2} - \frac{y^2}{b^2} = 1$ then so are $(-x, y)$, $(x, -y)$, and $(-x, -y)$. We also note that if there are x-intercepts at $(a, 0)$ and $(-a, 0)$, we should choose numbers for x such that $x \le -a$ or $x \ge a$ to get corresponding numbers for y.

EXAMPLE 3 Graph $\frac{x^2}{9} - \frac{y^2}{16} = 1$ by plotting points.

SOLUTION In Example 1 we found the x-intercepts to be at $(-3, 0)$ and $(3, 0)$. Hence, we choose numbers for x that are less than -3 or greater than 3. We replace x with these numbers and solve for y.

x	y
± 3	0
± 4	$\pm \frac{4}{3}\sqrt{7}$, or about ± 3.5
± 5	$\pm \frac{16}{3}$
± 6	$\pm 4\sqrt{3}$, or about ± 6.9

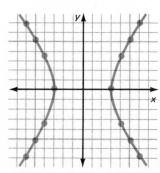

The graph of $\dfrac{(x-h)^2}{a^2} + \dfrac{(y-k)^2}{b^2} = 1$ is an ellipse with center (h,k). Its graph has the same shape as the graph of $\dfrac{x^2}{a^2} + \dfrac{y^2}{b^2} = 1$. The graph of $\dfrac{(x-h)^2}{a^2} - \dfrac{(y-k)^2}{b^2} = 1$ is a hyperbola that has the same shape as the graph of $\dfrac{x^2}{a^2} - \dfrac{y^2}{b^2} = 1$. As with the ellipse, however, it is centered at (h,k).

EXAMPLE 4 Sketch the graph for $\dfrac{(x+5)^2}{9} - \dfrac{(y-7)^2}{4} = 1$.

SOLUTION The graph is centered at $(-5, 7)$. $a = \pm 3$, $b = \pm 2$.
Draw the rectangle. Draw the asymptotes. Then sketch the curve.

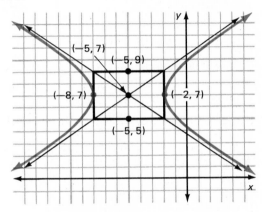

CLASSROOM EXERCISES

Graph.

1. $\dfrac{x^2}{9} - \dfrac{y^2}{4} = 1$

2. $\dfrac{y^2}{36} - \dfrac{x^2}{64} = 1$

3. $\dfrac{(x-1)^2}{25} - \dfrac{(y+2)^2}{4} = 1$

4. $\dfrac{(y+1)^2}{9} - \dfrac{(x+2)^2}{25} = 1$

EXERCISES

Ⓐ Graph.

1. $\dfrac{x^2}{16} - \dfrac{y^2}{9} = 1$

2. $\dfrac{x^2}{4} - \dfrac{y^2}{9} = 1$

3. $\dfrac{x^2}{4} - y^2 = 1$

4. $x^2 - \dfrac{y^2}{25} = 1$

5. $\dfrac{y^2}{4} - \dfrac{x^2}{16} = 1$

6. $\dfrac{y^2}{9} - \dfrac{x^2}{4} = 1$

7. $\dfrac{(x-1)^2}{49} - \dfrac{(y+1)^2}{100} = 1$

8. $\dfrac{(x+2)^2}{64} - \dfrac{(y-3)^2}{9} = 1$

9. $\dfrac{(y-3)^2}{4} - \dfrac{(x-2)^2}{9} = 1$

10. $\dfrac{(y-4)^2}{25} - \dfrac{(x-3)^2}{16} = 1$

B **11.** $5(x+1)^2 - 3(y+2)^2 = 15$

12. $(y-1)^2 - 2(x+3)^2 = 1$

13. Use the geometric definition of the hyperbola and the Distance Formula. Find the equation of the hyperbola with foci $(0, -5)$ and $(0, 5)$ and length difference 6.

14. The hyperbola $\dfrac{(x-h)^2}{144} - \dfrac{(y-k)^2}{25} = 1$ has foci $(14, -3)$ and $(-12, -3)$. Find the center.

C Find the equations of the asymptotes.

15. $\dfrac{x^2}{a^2} - \dfrac{y^2}{b^2} = 1$

16. $\dfrac{y^2}{a^2} - \dfrac{x^2}{b^2} = 1$

17. $\dfrac{(x-3)^2}{25} - \dfrac{(y+2)^2}{16} = 1$

18. Suppose that the foci of a hyperbola are $F_1(c, 0)$ and $F_2(-c, 0)$. Let $P(x, y)$ represent a point of the hyperbola. Then by definition, $|PF_1 - PF_2| = 2a$ where $2a$ is used to denote the constant difference. The absolute value symbol is used because P could be in either of the two branches of the hyperbola. Thus, either PF_1 or PF_2 could be the greater distance. Use the Distance Formula to show that

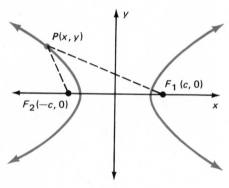

$\dfrac{x^2}{a^2} - \dfrac{y^2}{b^2} = 1$ when $b^2 = c^2 - a^2$.

19. A hyperbola has foci $(-3, 0)$ and $(3, 0)$. The difference of the distances from each point of the hyperbola to the foci is 4. Find the equation of the hyperbola. Use the result of Exercise 18.

20. Use the result of Exercise 18 to find the foci for the hyperbolas of Exercises 1 and 5.

A LOVELY GRAPH

Sketch the graph for $y = |x| \pm \sqrt{1 - x^2}$.

9-6   FORMS OF EQUATIONS FOR THE CONIC SECTIONS

One of the important objectives of second-year algebra is that you be familiar with equations involving two variables. To this end, we have studied several types of such equations and their graphs. We have found that the shape and position of each graph depends upon the degree and the coefficient of each variable.

	Standard or General Form	Standard Form for Graphing	Graph
Both variables degree 1	$Ax + By = C$ or $Ax + By + C = 0$	$y = mx + b$	▪ line with slope m, y-intercept b
One variable degree 1, one variable degree 2	$Ax^2 + By = C$ $Ax^2 + By + Cx = D$	$y = ax^2 + bx + c$ or $y - k = a(x - h)^2$	▪ parabola, vertex at $y = -\dfrac{b}{2a}$ or at (h, k), opens up or down
	$Ax + By^2 = C$ $Ax + By^2 + Cy = D$	$x = ay^2 + by + c$ or $x - h = a(y - k)^2$	▪ parabola, vertex at $y = -\dfrac{b}{2a}$ or at (h, k), opens to right or left
Both variables degree 2	$Ax^2 + Ay^2 = C$ $4x^2 + Ay^2 + Bx + Cy = D$	$x^2 + y^2 = r^2$ $(x - h)^2 + (y - k)^2 = r^2$	▪ circle, radius r center $(0, 0)$ ▪ circle, radius r center (h, k)
	$Ax^2 + By^2 = C$ $a > 0, B > 0$ $Ax^2 + By^2 + Cx + Dy = E$ $A > 0, B > 0$	$\dfrac{x^2}{a^2} + \dfrac{y^2}{b^2} = 1$ $\dfrac{(x - h)^2}{a^2} + \dfrac{(y - k)^2}{b^2} = 1$	▪ ellipse, center $(0, 0)$ ▪ ellipse, center (h, k)
	$Ax^2 - By^2 = C$ $A > 0, B > 0$ $Ax^2 - By^2 + Cx + Dy = E$ $A > 0, B > 0$	$\dfrac{x^2}{a^2} - \dfrac{y^2}{b^2} = 1$ $\dfrac{(x - h)^2}{a^2} - \dfrac{(y - k)^2}{b^2} = 1$	▪ hyperbola centered at $(0, 0)$ ▪ hyperbola centered at (h, k) Branches open to the right and left.

Equations in two variables often are given in a form different from the standard form. When this happens, examine the degrees of the variables and try to determine what kind of curve the graph will be. Then you will know which standard form to look for to help you draw the graph.

EXAMPLE 1 Graph $x^2 - 2x + y^2 + 4y = 4$.

SOLUTION x and y both appear as second-degree variables. The coefficients of x^2 and y^2 are equal. This is an equation for a circle.

Develop the standard form by completing the squares.

$$x^2 - 2x + y^2 + 4y = 4$$
$$(x^2 - 2x \quad\;) + (y^2 + 4y \quad\;) = 4$$
$$(x^2 - 2x + 1) + (y^2 + 4y + 4) = 4 + 1 + 4$$
$$(x - 1)^2 + (y + 2)^2 = 9$$
$$(x - 1)^2 + (y + 2)^2 = 3^2$$

The circle has center $(1, -2)$ and radius 3.

GRAPH

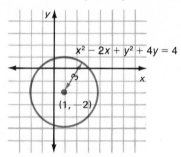

EXAMPLE 2 Graph $25x^2 + 9y^2 = 225$.

SOLUTION x and y are second-degree variables. The coefficients of x^2 and y^2 are positive and not equal. This is an equation for an ellipse.

Develop the standard form by dividing both members by 225.

$$25x^2 + 9y^2 = 225$$
$$\frac{25x^2}{225} + \frac{9y^2}{225} = 1$$
$$\frac{x^2}{9} + \frac{y^2}{25} = 1$$

The ellipse has center $(0, 0)$. The minor axis is in the x-axis from -3 to 3. The major axis is in the y-axis from -5 to 5.

GRAPH

x	y
±3	0
0	±5
±2	$±\dfrac{5}{3}\sqrt{5}$ or about ±3.7

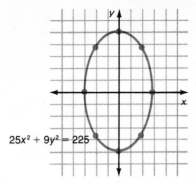

$25x^2 + 9y^2 = 225$

EXAMPLE 3 Graph $4y^2 - 9x^2 + 54x = 117$.

SOLUTION The equation shows the difference of two second-degree terms. This is an equation of a hyperbola.

Develop the standard form by completing the square.

$$4y^2 - 9(x^2 - 6x + 9) = 117 - 81$$
$$4y^2 - 9(x - 3)^2 = 36$$

Divide by 36.

$$\frac{y^2}{9} - \frac{(x - 3)^2}{4} = 1$$

The hyperbola is centered at $(3, 0)$.

The branches open upward and downward.

GRAPH

x	y
3	±3
5	$±3\sqrt{2}$ or about ±4.2
1	$±3\sqrt{2}$ or about ±4.2

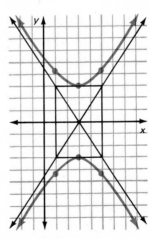

$4y^2 - 9x^2 + 54x = 117$

CLASSROOM EXERCISES

Graph.

1. $x^2 + 2x + y^2 - 4y = 4$

2. $9x^2 - 18x + 4y^2 - 8y = 23$

3. $9y^2 - 25x^2 = 225$

4. $x^2 - 4y^2 - 24y = 40$

5. $4x^2 + 9y^2 = 1$

6. $x = 3y^2 + 5y + 2$

EXERCISES

A Graph.

1. $x^2 + 6x + y^2 + 4y = 13$

2. $x^2 + 2x + y^2 + 10y = 10$

3. $4x^2 + 16y^2 = 64$

4. $9x^2 + 4y^2 = 36$

5. $x^2 - y^2 + 6y = 10$

6. $x^2 - y^2 + 8y = 17$

7. $25x^2 + 50x + y^2 = 0$

8. $4x^2 + 24x + y^2 = -32$

9. $x^2 - 25y^2 = 1$

10. $x^2 - 16y^2 = 1$

11. $4y^2 - 9x^2 = 1$

12. $25y^2 - 9x^2 = 1$

B **13.** $y - \dfrac{1}{3}x^2 + \dfrac{4}{3}x = \dfrac{7}{3}$

14. $y + \dfrac{1}{2}x^2 + 3x = -\dfrac{7}{2}$

15. $x^2 - 3x + y^2 + 4y = \sqrt{2} - \dfrac{25}{4}$

16. $3y^2 - 4x^2 - 15y - 16x = -\dfrac{7}{4}$

Graph the function. First, square both members. Graph the resulting .elation. Then find the graph of the given function by referring to its domain and range.

17. $y = \sqrt{x}$

18. $x = \sqrt{y - 1}$

19. $y = 3\sqrt{1 - \dfrac{x^2}{4}}$

Graph.

C **20.** $x^2 + 2xy + y^2 - 4 = 0$ (Hint: $x^2 + 2xy + y^2 - 4 = (x + y - 2)(x + y + 2)$)

21. $x^2 + xy - 2y^2 = 0$

22. $x^2 - 3xy = 0$

23. $y^2 + 3xy = 0$

QUADRATICS AND ABSOLUTE VALUE

Sketch the graph of $y = |x^2 - 4| + 2$ for $-3 \le x \le 3$.

Is it a "smooth" curve?

CHECKING YOUR UNDERSTANDING

WORDS AND SYMBOLS

asymptote

center of a circle

center of an ellipse

conic section

directrix of a parabola

ellipse

foci of an ellipse

foci of a hyperbola

focus of a parabola

hyperbola

major axis of an ellipse

minor axis of an ellipse

The Distance Formula   The Midpoint Formula

CONCEPTS

■ Conic sections may be defined either geometrically or algebraically. The fact that the definitions are equivalent may be proved using the Distance Formula for the coordinate plane. [9-1 to 9-5]

■ The four conic sections are the circle, the ellipse, the parabola, and the hyperbola. For a circle, any two points are the same distance from its center. For an ellipse, the sum of the distances to the two foci is the same for all its points. For a parabola, the distances from each point to the focus and to the directrix are the same. For a hyperbola, the difference of the distances to the two foci is the same for all its points. [9-2 to 9-5]

■ When an equation is in the standard form for graphing a conic section, the constants provide much information about the graph. [9-2 to 9-5]

PROCESSES

■ Use the Distance and Midpoint Formulas. [9-1]

1. Find the length and the midpoint of the line segment having endpoints

  a. $(-7, 3)$ and $(2, 9)$ **b.** $(2, -4)$ and $(4, 3)$ **c.** $(6, -2)$ and $(3, -6)$

2. Are $(-3, -3)$, $(1, -2)$, and $(-4, 5)$ vertices of a right triangle? Explain.

■ Write the equation of a circle. [9-2]

3. center $(2, -3)$, radius $\sqrt{17}$ **4.** center $(1, 2)$, containing $(6, 14)$

■ Graph conic sections. [9-2 to 9-6]

5. $x^2 + y^2 = 49$ **6.** $\dfrac{x^2}{25} + \dfrac{y^2}{81} = 1$ **7.** $4y + x^2 = 0$ **8.** $\dfrac{x^2}{36} - \dfrac{y^2}{9} = 1$

9. $(x + 3)^2 + (y - 2)^2 = 25$ **10.** $\dfrac{(x + 3)^2}{4} + \dfrac{(y - 2)^2}{9} = 1$

11. $\dfrac{(y + 3)^2}{25} - \dfrac{(x - 2)^2}{16} = 1$ **12.** $x^2 + y^2 + 2x - 6y = 15$

13. $16x^2 + 36y^2 + 128x - 144y = 176$ **14.** $x^2 - 9y^2 - 90y = 234$

OBJECTIVES: Graph quadratic inequalities. Solve quadratic inequalities in one variable.

9-7 QUADRATIC INEQUALITIES AND THEIR GRAPHS

To graph a quadratic inequality in two variables, it is helpful to recall how we graph a linear inequality in two variables. To graph $y > mx + b$, for example, we first draw the graph of $y = mx + b$. Then we determine on which side of the line the points for $y > mx + b$ are found.

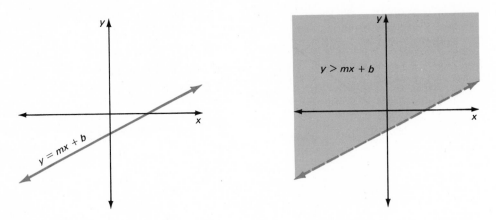

We graph quadratic inequalities in a similar way. We first draw the graph of the corresponding equation. Then we shade one of the regions formed by that graph to obtain the graph of the inequality.

GRAPHS OF QUADRATIC INEQUALITIES

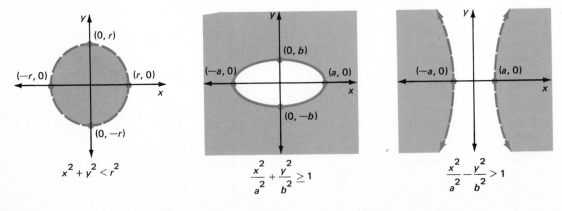

$$x^2 + y^2 < r^2$$

$$\frac{x^2}{a^2} + \frac{y^2}{b^2} \geq 1$$

$$\frac{x^2}{a^2} - \frac{y^2}{b^2} > 1$$

EXAMPLE 1   Graph $y < x^2 - 2x - 8$.

SOLUTION   Since y *is less than* $x^2 - 2x - 8$, the graph of the inequality is the region below the parabola for $y = x^2 - 2x - 8$. We use dashes to indicate that the parabola is not part of the graph.

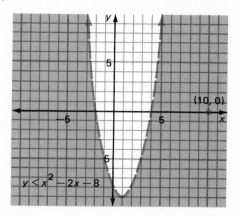

CHECK $(10, 0)$ are the coordinates of a point in the shaded region. Replace x by 10 and y by 0 in $y < x^2 - 2x - 8$.

$$y < x^2 - 2x - 8$$
$$0 \overset{?}{<} 10^2 - 2(10) - 8$$
$$0 < 72 \quad ✔$$

EXAMPLE 2   Graph $\dfrac{x^2}{16} + \dfrac{y^2}{9} \leq 1$.

SOLUTION   The graph of $\dfrac{x^2}{16} + \dfrac{y^2}{9} = 1$ is an ellipse.

The graph of $\dfrac{x^2}{16} + \dfrac{y^2}{9} < 1$ is the interior of the ellipse.

The graph of $\dfrac{x^2}{16} + \dfrac{y^2}{9} \leq 1$ is the ellipse together with the interior of the ellipse.

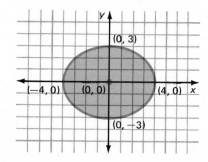

CHECK

$(0, 0)$ matches a point in the shaded region.

$$\frac{x^2}{16} + \frac{y^2}{9} \leq 1$$

$$\frac{0^2}{16} + \frac{0^2}{9} \overset{?}{\leq} 1$$

$$0 \leq 1 \quad ✔$$

EXAMPLE 3   Graph $25x^2 - 4y^2 - 200x - 24y > -264$.

SOLUTION $25x^2 - 4y^2 - 200x - 24y = -264$ is the equation for a hyperbola.

Develop the standard form by completing the squares.

$$25(x^2 - 8x \qquad) - 4(y^2 + 6y \qquad) = -264$$
$$25(x^2 - 8x + 16) - 4(y^2 + 6y + 9) = -264 + 25(16) - 4(9)$$
$$25(x - 4)^2 - 4(y + 3)^2 = 100$$

$$\frac{(x - 4)^2}{4} - \frac{(y + 3)^2}{25} = 1$$

The hyperbola is centered at $(4, -3)$. Replacing x by 4 and y by -3 in

$$\frac{(x - 4)^2}{4} - \frac{(y + 3)^2}{25} > 1,$$

we find that $(4, -3)$ is *not* a solution. Therefore the graph of the inequality is the region "within" each branch of the hyperbola, as shown.

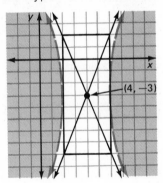

CHECK

The student should check that the coordinates of some points in the shaded regions are solutions of the inequality.

CLASSROOM EXERCISES

Graph.

1. $y < x^2 - 5x - 6$

2. $\dfrac{x^2}{4} + \dfrac{y^2}{9} \le 1$

3. $4x^2 - 9y^2 > 36$

EXERCISES

A   Graph.

1. $y < -x^2$

2. $y \ge x^2 + 12x + 34$

3. $x^2 + y^2 > 16$

4. $(x - 3)^2 + (y + 4)^2 \le 9$

5. $y - 128 > 5(x^2 + 10x)$

6. $3x^2 \le 4(6x - 13 - y)$

7. $\dfrac{x^2}{16} + \dfrac{y^2}{4} > 1$ **8.** $\dfrac{(x+2)^2}{9} + \dfrac{(y-5)^2}{1} \le 1$ **9.** $\dfrac{x^2}{36} - \dfrac{y^2}{9} < 1$

10. $\dfrac{(x-2)^2}{16} - \dfrac{(y+5)^2}{25} \ge 1$ **11.** $25x^2 + 4y^2 - 200x + 16y + 316 < 0$

12. $y^2 + 3x^2 - 12y + 30 \ge 0$ **13.** $4x^2 - y^2 + 48x - 6y + 131 > 15$

B **14.** $(x-5)(x+5) \ge 2(y-8x) - (80+y)^2$ **15.** $x^2 + y^2 + 13 < 2(5x+7y)$

16. $-24 \le 9x^2 + 18x + 4y^2 + 16y \le 11$ **17.** $\dfrac{x^2}{4} - \dfrac{y^2}{16} > 1 \text{ and } \dfrac{y^2}{4} - \dfrac{x^2}{16} > 1$

18. $64x^2 - y^2 \le 64 \text{ and } x^2 + 10y < 100$

19. $(x+4)^2 - (y+3)^2 \le 4 \le (x+4)^2 + (y+3)^2$

20. $y + 14x < x^2 + 52 \text{ and } 9x^2 + 49y^2 > 126x$

C **21.** $xy < 0$ **22.** $3xy + y^2 \ge 0$ **23.** $xy - y^2 \le 4(x-y)$

Find the area of the graph.

24. $x^2 + y^2 + 2y - 35 \le 0 \text{ and } x^2 + y^2 - 10y - 11 \le 0$

25. $3x^2 + 3y^2 - 20\sqrt{3}y \le 200, \ 3x^2 + 3y^2 + 30x + 10\sqrt{3}y \le 200$
  $\text{and } 3x^2 + 3y^2 - 30x + 10\sqrt{3}y \le 200$

$\boxed{2.1867241}$ # APPROXIMATING ROOTS

Roots may be approximated by finding smaller and smaller intervals containing them. We use the fact that $a < \sqrt[n]{b} < c$ when $a^n < b < c^n$ and $a, b, c > 0$.

For example, since $2^3 < 12 < 3^3$, $2 < \sqrt[3]{12} < 3$.

The chart at the right shows that
  $2.2^3 < 12 < 2.3^3$.

Therefore, we may conclude that
  $2.2 < \sqrt[3]{12} < 2.3$.

n	n^3
2.0	8
2.1	9.261
2.2	10.648
2.3	12.167

Since 2.3^3 is closer to 12 than 2.2^3, we write $\sqrt[3]{12} \doteq 2.3$.

Find a one-decimal-place approximation for each.

1. $\sqrt[3]{55}$ **2.** $\sqrt[3]{111}$ **3.** $\sqrt[3]{151}$ **4.** $\sqrt[3]{301}$ **5.** $\sqrt[4]{51}$ **6.** $\sqrt[4]{173}$

7. Find an approximation for $\sqrt[3]{50}$ to three decimal places.

9-8 SOLVING QUADRATIC INEQUALITIES HAVING ONE VARIABLE

In Section 9-7 we found that drawing the graph of $y = ax^2 + bx + c$ was essential for drawing the graphs of $y > ax^2 + bx + c$ and $y < ax^2 + bx + c$. The graph of $y = ax^2 + bx + c$ also may be helpful for understanding the solutions of the quadratic inequalities in one variable, $ax^2 + bx + c > 0$ and $ax^2 + bx + c < 0$.

EXAMPLE 1 Solve $x^2 - x > 6$.

SOLUTION
$$x^2 - x > 6$$
$$x^2 - x - 6 > 0$$

To solve this inequality, we have to find the numbers for x for which $x^2 - x - 6 > 0$.

Graphically, this means we want to find numbers for x for which the graph of $y = x^2 - x - 6$ is above the x-axis.

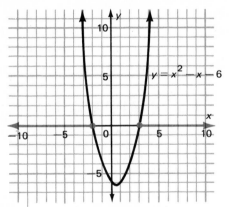

$x > 3$ *or* $x < -2$ is the solution of the inequality.

CHECK Use 5 for x.
$$x^2 - x > 6$$
$$5^2 - 5 \overset{?}{>} 6$$
$$20 > 6 \quad \text{✔}$$

Use -3 for x.
$$x^2 - x > 6$$
$$(-3)^2 - (-3) \overset{?}{>} 6$$
$$12 > 6 \quad \text{✔}$$

As shown in Example 1, the solutions of $x^2 - x > 6$ correspond to the points "outside" the points for -2 and 3 in the number line. The solutions of $x^2 - x < 6$ correspond to the points between -2 and 3 ($-2 < x < 6$). In general, the solutions of a quadratic inequality in one variable correspond to the points that are either "outside" or between two points of the number line.

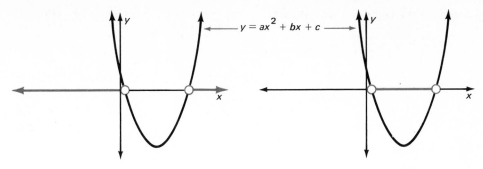

$ax^2 + bx + c > 0$ if

$$x < \frac{-b - \sqrt{b^2 - 4ac}}{2a} \text{ or } x > \frac{-b + \sqrt{b^2 - 4ac}}{2a}$$

$ax^2 + bx + c < 0$ if

$$\frac{-b - \sqrt{b^2 - 4ac}}{2a} < x < \frac{-b + \sqrt{b^2 - 4ac}}{2a}$$

It also is possible to solve a quadratic inequality algebraically. When you do so, pay attention to the source of the "or" or the "and" that is needed to describe the solution set.

EXAMPLE 2 Solve $x^2 - x > 6$.

SOLUTION

$$x^2 - x > 6$$
$$x^2 - x - 6 > 0$$
$$(x - 3)(x + 2) > 0 \quad \longleftarrow$$

For a product to be positive, (>0), *both* factors must be positive or *both* must be negative.

Therefore,

$x - 3 > 0$ and $x + 2 > 0$	or	$x - 3 < 0$ and $x + 2 < 0$
$x > 3$ and $x > -2$		$x < 3$ and $x < -2$

$$\underbrace{\phantom{x > 3 \text{ and } x > -2}}_{x > 3} \quad or \quad \underbrace{\phantom{x < 3 \text{ and } x < -2}}_{x < -2}$$

CHECK Compare with Example 1 on the preceding page.

EXAMPLE 3 Solve $x^2 - x < 6$.

SOLUTION

$$x^2 - x < 6$$
$$x^2 - x - 6 < 0$$
$$(x - 3)(x + 2) < 0 \quad \longleftarrow$$

For a product to be negative, (<0), one factor must be negative *and* the other positive.

Therefore,

$x - 3 < 0$ and $x + 2 > 0$	or	$x - 3 > 0$ and $x + 2 < 0$
$x < 3$ and $x > -2$		$x > 3$ and $x < -2$

$$\underbrace{\phantom{x < 3 \text{ and } x > -2}}_{-2 < x < 3} \quad or \quad \underbrace{\phantom{x > 3 \text{ and } x < -2}}_{\text{no numbers}}$$

CHECK The check is left for the student.
Use numbers between -2 and 3.

EXAMPLE 4   Solve $x^2 + 2x + 3 < 0$.

SOLUTION   Compare $x^2 + 2x + 3$ to $ax^2 + bx + c$.
$a = 1, b = 2, c = 3$.

Since $a > 0$, a *minimum* value for $x^2 + 2x + 3$ occurs at $x = -\dfrac{b}{2a}$, or -1.

Replace x by -1 in $x^2 + 2x + 3$.
$(-1)^2 + 2(-1) + 3 = 2$

2 is the *minimum* value for $x^2 + 2x + 3$. Therefore, there is no number for x that will cause $x^2 + 2x + 3$ to be less than 0.

CONCLUSION   There are no solutions of $x^2 + 2x + 3 < 0$.

CLASSROOM EXERCISES

Solve.

1. $x^2 + 2x > 3$ **2.** $x^2 + 2x < 3$ **3.** $x^2 > 4$ **4.** $-4 + x > x^2$

EXERCISES

A   Solve.

1. $x^2 - x - 12 > 0$ **2.** $x^2 + 3x - 10 > 0$ **3.** $x^2 - x - 12 < 0$

4. $x^2 + 3x - 10 < 0$ **5.** $x^2 - 3x + 2 < 0$ **6.** $x^2 - 11x + 30 < 0$

7. $-x^2 - 8x + 9 > 0$ **8.** $-x^2 - 9x + 36 > 0$ **9.** $x^2 - 2x + 4 < 0$

10. $x^2 - 4x + 8 < 0$ **11.** $4x^2 + 9 > -12x$ **12.** $16x^2 + 25 \geq -40x$

13. $-x^2 + 4x - 7 > 0$ **14.** $-x^2 + 2x - 9 > 0$ **15.** $x^2 + 5x + \dfrac{25}{4} < 0$

B   **16.** $x(x - 6) > 6$ **17.** $-x(x + 4) < 5$ **18.** $x^2 - \sqrt{5}x + \sqrt{30} < \sqrt{6}x$

19. $4x^2 + 5 > 4\sqrt{5}x$ **20.** $1 + \dfrac{3}{x} + \dfrac{2}{x^2} < 0$ **21.** $|x^2 - 7x + 12| > -1$

C   **22.** $\dfrac{7 - x}{x - 5} \geq 0$ (Hint: The solution is the same as the solution for $(7 - x)(x - 5) \geq 0$, except that the denominator cannot be zero.)

23. $\dfrac{2}{x - 5} > 1$ (Hint: Subtract 1 from each member. Combine terms in the left member and proceed as in Exercise 22.)

24. $\dfrac{2x - 3}{x - 4} < -2$ **25.** $\dfrac{3x + 1}{2x - 5} \leq 2$

OBJECTIVES: Solve problems involving inverse, joint, and combined variation.

9-9 PROBLEM SOLVING: VARIATION

When variables x and y are related in such a way that their *quotient* remains constant, they are said to **vary directly**. When they are related in such a way that their *product* remains constant, they are said to **vary inversely**.

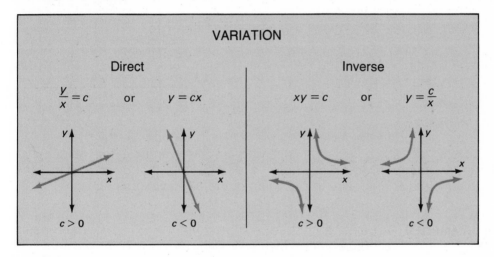

Each graph showing inverse variation, such as that for $y = \frac{1}{x}$ below, is a hyperbola with the coordinate axes as asymptotes.

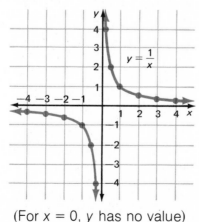

x	y
-4	$-\frac{1}{4}$
-3	$-\frac{1}{3}$
-2	$-\frac{1}{2}$
-1	-1
$-\frac{1}{2}$	-2
$-\frac{1}{4}$	-4

x	y
$\frac{1}{4}$	4
$\frac{1}{2}$	2
1	1
2	$\frac{1}{2}$
3	$\frac{1}{3}$
4	$\frac{1}{4}$

(For $x = 0$, y has no value)

EXAMPLE 1   For all rectangles with area 12, the lengths and widths vary inversely.   Write the equation.   Draw the graph.

SOLUTION   length · width = area

Use $\left[\begin{array}{l} l \text{ for length.} \\ w \text{ for width.} \end{array}\right.$

$$l \cdot w = 12$$

$$w = \frac{12}{l}, l \neq 0$$

GRAPH

l	w
1	12
12	1
2	6
6	2
3	4
4	3

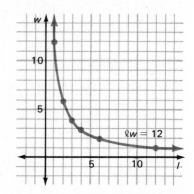

Note that for a situation involving inverse variation for which only positive numbers are meaningful, a decrease in the value of one variable means an increase in the value of the other variable.

EXAMPLE 2   A painting contractor knows that the time it takes to paint a house varies inversely with the number of painters.   If a house requires 300 work hours, how long will it take 10 painters to do this job?   18 painters?   25 painters?

SOLUTION   (number of painters) · (time per painter) = time needed

Use $\left[\begin{array}{l} p \text{ for the number of painters.} \\ n \text{ for the number of hours each works.} \end{array}\right.$

$$pn = 300$$

$$n = \frac{300}{p}$$

For $p = 10$,

$$n = \frac{300}{10}$$

$$n = 30$$

For $p = 18$,

$$n = \frac{300}{18}$$

$$n = 16\tfrac{2}{3}$$

For $p = 25$,

$$n = \frac{300}{25}$$

$$n = 12$$

CONCLUSION   To paint the house, it would take 10 painters 30 hours, 18 painters $16\tfrac{2}{3}$ hours, and 25 painters 12 hours.

When y varies directly or inversely as the nth power of x, the variables are related by $y = cx^n$ or $y = \dfrac{c}{x^n}$, respectively, with c representing a constant. When the variable z **varies jointly** with x and y, the three variables are related by the equation $z = cxy$. **Combined variation** occurs when z varies directly as x and inversely as y such as is indicated by the equation $z = c\dfrac{x}{y}$.

EXAMPLE 3 y varies inversely as the square of x. When $x = 4$, $y = 25$. Find y when $x = 10$.

SOLUTION   The variation is given by $y = \dfrac{c}{x^2}$.

When $x = 4$, $y = 25$, Find c.

$$y = \frac{c}{x^2}$$

$$25 = \frac{c}{16}$$

$$c = 400$$

For $c = 400$ and $x = 10$, Find y.

$$y = \frac{c}{x^2}$$

$$y = \frac{400}{10^2}$$

$$y = 4$$

EXAMPLE 4   The mass of a wooden rod varies jointly with its length and the square of its width. A 400-gram rod has width 2 centimeters and length 40 centimeters. Find the mass of a rod made from the same wood and having width 4 centimeters and length 30 centimeters.

SOLUTION   Use $\begin{bmatrix} r \text{ for the mass of a rod (grams).} \\ l \text{ for the length (centimeters).} \\ w \text{ for the width (centimeters).} \end{bmatrix}$

The variation is given by $r = clw^2$.

When $l = 40$ and $w = 2$, $r = 400$. Find c.

$$r = clw^2$$
$$400 = c \cdot 40 \cdot 2^2$$
$$400 = c \cdot 160$$
$$2.5 = c$$

For $c = 2.5$, $l = 30$, and $w = 4$, find r.

$$r = 2.5 \cdot 30 \cdot 4^2$$
$$r = 1200$$

CONCLUSION   The mass of the 30-centimeter rod is 1200 grams.

EXAMPLE 5 The electrical resistance of a wire is directly proportional to its length and inversely proportional to the square of its diameter. A wire 400 meters long, with diameter 0.6 millimeter, has a resistance of 2.5 ohms. Find the resistance of a wire, made from the same metal, that is 80 meters long with diameter 0.3 millimeter.

SOLUTION Use $\begin{bmatrix} R \text{ for resistance in ohms} \\ l \text{ for length in meters} \\ d \text{ for diameter in millimeters} \end{bmatrix}$

The variation is given by $R = c\,\dfrac{l}{d^2}$.

For $l = 400$ and $d = 0.6$, $R = 2.5$. Find c.

$$2.5 = c\,\frac{400}{(0.6)^2}$$

$$2.5 = c\,\frac{400}{0.36}$$

$$\frac{9}{4000} = c$$

For $c = \dfrac{9}{4000}$, $l = 80$, and $d = 0.3$, find R.

$$R = \frac{9}{4000} \cdot \frac{80}{(0.3)^2}$$

$$= 2$$

CONCLUSION The resistance of the 80-meter piece of wire is 2 ohms.

CLASSROOM EXERCISES

Solve.

1. A farmer has enough feed to last 42 days for 50 cattle. How long would the same amount of feed last for 35 cattle?

2. The illuminance, I, from a point source of light varies inversely as the square of the distance, d, from the source. Write an equation that expresses I in terms of d.

3. y varies inversely as the square of x. $y = 6$ when $x = 2$. Find y when $x = 8$.

4. x varies jointly as y and the square of z. $x = 48$ when $y = 8$ and $z = 3$. Find x when $y = 12$ and $z = 2$.

5. y varies directly as x and inversely as t. $y = 12$ when $x = 3$ and $t = 2$. Find y when $x = 2$ and $t = 400$.

6. w varies directly as t and inversely as the square of z. $w = 280$ when $t = 360$ and $z = 3$. Find w when $t = 200$ and $z = 2$.

EXERCISES

Ⓐ Solve.

1. S varies inversely as T. $S = 20$ when $T = 6$. Find S when $T = 20$.

2. z varies inversely as w. $z = 15$ when $w = 14$. Find z when $w = 21$.

3. The volume, V, of an enclosed gas at a constant temperature varies inversely as the pressure P. Write an equation for this and draw its graph. (Use 2 as the constant of proportionality.)

4. In Exercise 3, find V when $P = 4$.

5. y varies inversely as the square of x. $y = 90$ when $x = 2$. Find y when $x = 10$.

6. y varies inversely as the square of x. $y = \frac{1}{8}$ when $x = 2$. Find y when $x = \frac{1}{6}$.

7. x varies inversely as the square root of y. $x = \frac{1}{2}$ when $y = 4$. Find x when $y = 144$.

8. S varies inversely as the square root of T. $S = 5$ when $T = 100$. Find T when $S = 25$.

9. V varies directly as h and the square of r. $V = 105$ when $r = 5$ and $h = 4$. Find h when $V = 105$ and $r = 4$.

10. w varies directly as n and the square of s. $w = 12$ when $n = 9$ and $s = 2$. Find n when $w = 12$ and $s = 3$.

11. y varies directly as x and inversely as z. $y = 6$ when $x = 4$ and $z = 2$. Find y when $x = 5$ and $z = 3$.

12. An object is moving in a circular path. The centripetal force, F, acting on the body varies directly as the square of the velocity, v, of the body and inversely as the radius, r, of the circle. $F = 64$ when $v = 2$ and $r = 5$. Find F when $v = 3$ and $r = 4$.

13. F varies directly with h and inversely with the square of d. $F = 25$ when $h = 45$ and $d = 3$. Find F when $h = 20$ and $d = 2$.

Ⓑ **14.** G varies inversely as the sum of the squares of x and z. $G = \frac{6}{5}$ when $x = 1$ and $z = 3$. Find x when $G = \frac{3}{2}$ and $z = 2$.

15. Illuminance from a light source varies inversely as the square of the distance from the source. A person is standing 10 meters from a light source. If the light source is to appear 4 times as intense, how far should the person stand from the light?

16. H varies directly with the product of x and y and inversely with z. $H = 20$ when $x = 3$, $y = 4$ and $z = 6$. Find H when $x = 5$, $y = 6$, and $z = 30$.

17. The force between two electric charges varies directly as the product of their charges. It varies inversely with the square of the distance between the two charges. When two charges are 2×10^{-6} coulombs and 4×10^{-6} coulombs, a force of 20 newtons results when they are 0.06 meters apart. Find the force when these charges are 0.02 meters apart.

Ⓒ **18.** The revolution period of a planet is the amount of time it takes a planet to make a complete orbit. Kepler's third law states that the square of the period of any planet varies directly with the cube of the average distance from the planet to the sun. The proportionality constant is the same for all planets. The period of the earth is one year and its average distance is 150 million kilometers. The planet Jupiter's average distance is 770 million kilometers. Find the period of revolution for Jupiter.

OBJECTIVE: Solve systems of equations involving quadratics.

9-10 GRAPHICAL SOLUTION OF PAIRS OF EQUATIONS INVOLVING QUADRATICS

A system of two linear equations in two variables generally has one solution. Graphically, the solution corresponds to the point of intersection of the graphs of the linear equations.

When we have a system in which one equation is linear and one quadratic, their graphs may have two, one, or zero points in common. Hence, the system may have two, one, or zero real solutions. When both equations are quadratic, their graphs may have from zero to four points of intersection. Hence, the system may have from zero to four real solutions.

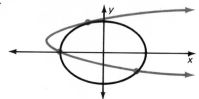

EXAMPLE 1 Solve the system $\boxed{2x - 3y = 3, \quad xy = 3}$ graphically.

SOLUTION

$2x - 3y = 3$

x	y
0	-1
$1\frac{1}{2}$	0
3	1

$xy = 3$

x	y
6	$\frac{1}{2}$
3	1
$\frac{1}{2}$	6
$-\frac{1}{2}$	-6
-3	-1
-6	$-\frac{1}{2}$

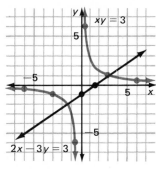

The two graphs appear to intersect at $(3, 1)$ and $\left(-\frac{3}{2}, -2\right)$. Hence, $(3, 1)$ and $\left(-\frac{3}{2}, -2\right)$ should be checked as possible solutions of the system.

CHECK That $(3, 1)$ is a solution is shown in the tables above.

For $\left(-\frac{3}{2}, -2\right)$,

$$xy = 3$$
$$\left(-\frac{3}{2}\right)(-2) \overset{?}{=} 3$$
$$3 = 3 \quad ✔$$

$$2x - 3y = 3$$
$$2\left(-\frac{3}{2}\right) - 3(-2) \overset{?}{=} 3$$
$$-3 + 6 \overset{?}{=} 3$$
$$3 = 3 \quad ✔$$

In general, it is difficult to determine solutions of a system graphically. However, by graphing carefully, it always is possible to find approximate solutions.

EXAMPLE 2 Solve the system $x^2 + y^2 = 25$, $x^2 - 3y = 21$ graphically.

SOLUTION The graph of $x^2 + y^2 = 25$ is a circle with center $(0, 0)$ and radius 5. The quadratic equation $x^2 - 3y = 21$ becomes $y = \frac{1}{3}x^2 - 7$ in standard form. Its graph is a parabola with vertex $(0, -7)$.

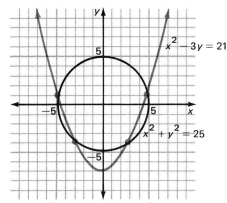

The parabola and circle appear to intersect in four points. Two of these points appear to be $(3, -4)$ and $(-3, -4)$. The other two appear to be approximately $(4.9, 1)$ and $(-4.9, 1)$.

CHECK For $(\pm 4.9, 1)$,

$x^2 + y^2 = 25$	$x^2 - 3y = 21$
$(\pm 4.9)^2 + 1^2 \overset{?}{=} 25$	$(\pm 4.9)^2 - 3(1) \overset{?}{=} 21$
$24.01 + 1 \overset{?}{=} 25$	$24.01 - 3 \overset{?}{=} 21$
$25.01 \doteq 25$ ✔	$21.01 \doteq 21$ ✔

The check for $(\pm 3, -4)$ is left for the student.

CLASSROOM EXERCISES

Solve graphically.

1. $xy = 3$
$x + y = 4$

2. $x^2 + y^2 = 2$
$y = x$

3. $y = x^2 + 4$
$x + y = 6$

4. $x^2 + y^2 = 16$
$4x^2 + y^2 = 144$

5. $x^2 + y^2 = 25$
$x^2 - y^2 = 7$

6. $xy = 4$
$x + y = 4$

EXERCISES

A Solve graphically.

1. $x^2 + y^2 = 25$
$x + y = 7$

2. $x^2 + y^2 = 169$
$x + y = 17$

3. $x^2 + y^2 = 25$
$2x - y = 2$

4. $x^2 + y^2 = 25$
$x + y = 3$

5. $x^2 - y^2 = 4$
$y = 2x$

6. $\dfrac{x^2}{9} + \dfrac{y^2}{4} = 1$
$y - x = 4$

7. $xy = 4$
$2x - y = 7$

8. $xy = 12$
$2x - 6y = 7$

9. $x^2 - y^2 = 16$
$x - 2y = -1$

10. $y^2 - x^2 = 1$
$y - 2x = 1$

11. $x^2 + y^2 = 82$
$xy = 9$

12. $xy = -5$
$x^2 + y^2 = 26$

13. $x^2 + y^2 = 169$
$5x + 12y = 169$

14. $x^2 + y^2 = 100$
$4x + 3y = 50$

15. $4x^2 + 9y^2 = 25$
$3x - 2y = 4$

16. $x^2 + 2y^2 = 8$
$x + 2y = 4$

B **17.** $x^2 + y^2 = 16$
$9x^2 + 16y^2 = 144$

18. $x^2 + y^2 = 25$
$xy = 12$

19. $x^2 + y^2 = 36$
$9x^2 - 16y^2 = 144$

20. $2x^2 - 5y^2 = 27$
$xy = 18$

21. $x^2 + 2x + y^2 - 8y = 8$
$x^2 - 14x + y^2 - 22y = -136$

22. $x^2 + 2x + y^2 - 16y = -49$
$x^2 + 2x - 16y = -65$

C **23.** $x^2 + y^2 = 25$
$3x^2 - y^2 = 11$
$2x^2 + y = 22$

24. $x^2 + xy = 2y^2$
$3x - y = 0$

25. Refer to the graph of a hyperbola. Explain why a line cannot intersect the graph in more than two points.

TOO MANY VARIABLES, TOO FEW EQUATIONS

Some problems for which we try to apply algebra yield a system of equations in which there are more variables than equations. This generally means that instead of a single solution of the system, there are infinitely many. Despite this difficulty some problems can be solved by considering the domains of the variables.

Try these.

1. Many years ago, a riverboat's steward bought some eggs, chickens, and turkeys. In all, the steward purchased 100 items of poultry for $100. The eggs cost 5¢ each, the chickens $1 each, and the turkeys $5 each. How many of each did the steward buy?

2. A few years later, due to inflation, the costs of these poultry items had increased. Eggs were 10¢ each, chickens were $3 each, and turkeys were $8 each. Due to this increased cost, the steward spent $200 for 100 items of poultry. How many of each did the steward buy this time?

9-11 ALGEBRAIC SOLUTION OF PAIRS OF EQUATIONS INVOLVING QUADRATICS

Solving pairs of equations involving quadratics in two variables can be complicated. It often leads to the need for solving higher-degree equations. Since we are not ready to solve higher degree equations, we will study the following two simple cases. The techniques shown are sufficient to enable us to solve many systems of two equations involving quadratics.

In the first case, the pair consists of one linear and one quadratic equation.

EXAMPLE 1   Solve
$$\begin{array}{l} x^2 + 4y^2 = 32 \\ x + 2y = 8 \end{array}$$
algebraically.

SOLUTION   It is good practice to sketch the graphs of the equations first. This may give an idea of how many solutions there are, and suggest approximations for the solutions. From the graphs shown below, it would be reasonable to expect a solution or solutions of approximately $(4, 2)$ for the given system.

To solve the system algebraically, use substitution. First, solve $x + 2y = 8$ for x.

$$x + 2y = 8$$
$$x = 8 - 2y$$

Find y.   Replace x by $8 - 2y$ in $x^2 + 4y^2 = 32$.

$$x^2 + 4y^2 = 32$$
$$(8 - 2y)^2 + 4y^2 = 32$$
$$64 - 32y + 4y^2 + 4y^2 = 32$$
$$8y^2 - 32y + 32 = 0$$
$$y^2 - 4y + 4 = 0$$
$$(y - 2)^2 = 0$$
$$y - 2 = 0$$
$$y = 2$$

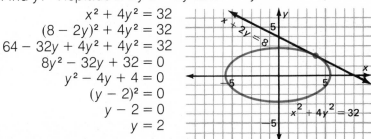

Find x.   Replace y by 2 in $x = 8 - 2y$.

$$x = 8 - 2y$$
$$x = 8 - 2(2)$$
$$x = 4$$

CONCLUSION   The solution of the system is $(4, 2)$.

CHECK   The check is left for the student.

In the second case, both equations are quadratic and have the form $Ax^2 + By^2 = C$.

EXAMPLE 2 Solve $\boxed{\begin{aligned} x^2 + y^2 &= 25 \\ x^2 + 4y^2 &= 36 \end{aligned}}$ algebraically.

GRAPH First, sketch the graphs of the equations.

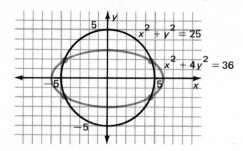

This suggests that there are four solutions of the system.

SOLUTION Find y by subtraction.

$$x^2 + y^2 = 25$$
$$x^2 + 4y^2 = 36$$

Subtract. $.-3y^2 = -11$

$$y^2 = \frac{11}{3}$$
$$y = \pm\frac{1}{3}\sqrt{33}$$

Find x by replacing y^2 by $\frac{11}{3}$ in $x^2 + y^2 = 25$.

$$x^2 + y^2 = 25$$
$$x^2 + \frac{11}{3} = 25$$
$$x^2 = \frac{64}{3}$$
$$x = \pm\frac{8}{3}\sqrt{3}$$

CONCLUSION The solutions are $\left(\frac{8}{3}\sqrt{3},\ \frac{1}{3}\sqrt{33}\right)$, $\left(\frac{8}{3}\sqrt{3},\ -\frac{1}{3}\sqrt{33}\right)$, $\left(-\frac{8}{3}\sqrt{3},\ \frac{1}{3}\sqrt{33}\right)$, and $\left(-\frac{8}{3}\sqrt{3},\ -\frac{1}{3}\sqrt{33}\right)$.

CHECK
$$x^2 + y^2 = 25$$
$$\left(\pm\frac{8}{3}\sqrt{3}\right)^2 + \left(\pm\frac{1}{3}\sqrt{33}\right)^2 \overset{?}{=} 25$$
$$\frac{64}{3} + \frac{11}{3} \overset{?}{=} 25$$
$$25 = 25 \quad ✔$$

The check for $x^2 + 4y^2 = 36$ is left for the student.

CLASSROOM EXERCISES

Solve algebraically.

1. $y = x + 1$
 $x^2 + y^2 = 13$

2. $x^2 + y^2 = 25$
 $x^2 - y^2 = 7$

3. $x^2 - y + 2 = 0$
 $x - y + 4 = 0$

4. $x^2 + y^2 = 36$
 $2x^2 - y^2 = 18$

EXERCISES

A Solve algebraically.

1. $x^2 - y = 3$
 $x - y = -3$

2. $x^2 - y = -4$
 $x - y = -4$

3. $y = x^2 - 4$
 $y = x - 5$

4. $y = 9 - x^2$
 $y = x + 10$

5. $x^2 + 2y^2 = 17$
 $2x^2 - 3y^2 = 6$

6. $3x^2 + 4y^2 = 31$
 $5x^2 - 6y^2 = 1$

7. $xy = 12$
 $x - y = 1$

8. $xy = 36$
 $y - x = 5$

9. $x^2 + 2y^2 = 51$
 $2x + y = 13$

10. $4x^2 + 25y^2 = 100$
 $2x - 35y = -50$

11. $5x^2 - 2y^2 = 13$
 $7x^2 - 3y^2 = 15$

12. $5x^2 - 3y^2 = 29$
 $2x^2 - 4y^2 = 6$

13. $x^2 + y^2 = 16$
 $9x^2 + 25y^2 = 225$

14. $3x + 5y^2 = 44$
 $5x - 2y^2 = 32$

15. $2x + 7y^2 = 277$
 $5x - 2y^2 = 10$

16. $x^2 - xy + y^2 = 7$
 $x + y = 4$

17. $x^2 - 2xy + y^2 = 4$
 $2x - y = 3$

18. $2xy + y^2 = 40$
 $3xy + 2y^2 = 68$

19. $4xy + y^2 = 28$
 $5xy + 3y^2 = 42$

20. $5xy + 2y + 60 = 0$
 $xy - 3y - 5 = 0$

B **21.** $x + y = 1$

 $\dfrac{1}{x} + \dfrac{1}{y} = 4$

22. $x^2 - 4x + y = 0$
 $xy - 2x - y = 0$

23. $x^2 + y^2 - 10x = 0$
 $x^2 + y^2 - 20y = 0$

24. $(x + 3)^2 + y^2 + 2y = 15$
 $-2x^2 - 12x + (y + 1)^2 = 7$

25. $2y^2 - 9x + 8y - 19 = 0$
 $4y^2 + 9x + 16y - 11 = 0$

C **26.** $x^2 + 2xy + y^2 = z^2$
 $2x + y + z = 3$
 $x - y + z = 4$

27. $x^2 + y^2 + z^2 = 56$
 $x + y + z = 8$
 $z(x + y) = 12$

28. Find all real solutions to
 $x^4 - 4x^2y^2 + 4y^4 = 1$
 $9y^4 - 6x^2y^2 + x^4 = 4$

INGENUITY REQUIRED

Solve each system.

1. $2x^2 - 3y^2 + 4x + 4y = 55$
 $3x^2 + 3y^2 + 6x - 4y = 120$

2. $x^2 + y^2 + 4x + 4y = 29$
 $xy = -12$

9-12 PROBLEM SOLVING: USING QUADRATIC SYSTEMS

Knowing how to solve systems of equations involving quadratics makes it easier for you to organize the solution of many problems. It gives you the option of beginning with two variables instead of one.

EXAMPLE 1   The sum of two numbers is 5. The sum of their squares is 13. Find the numbers.

SOLUTION   Use $\begin{bmatrix} x \text{ for one number.} \\ y \text{ for the other number.} \end{bmatrix}$

$$\boxed{\begin{array}{l} x + y = 5 \\ x^2 + y^2 = 13 \end{array}}$$

Find x by substitution.

Replace y by $5 - x$ in $x^2 + y^2 = 13$.

$$x^2 + y^2 = 13$$
$$x^2 + (5 - x)^2 = 13$$
$$x^2 + 25 - 10x + x^2 = 13$$
$$2x^2 - 10x + 12 = 0$$
$$x^2 - 5x + 6 = 0$$
$$(x - 3)(x - 2) = 0$$

Thus, $x - 3 = 0$ or $x - 2 = 0$
            $x = 3$ | $x = 2$

Find y by replacing x in $x + y = 5$.

For $x = 3$, | For $x = 2$,
  $3 + y = 5$ | $2 + y = 5$
     $y = 2$ | $y = 3$

CONCLUSION   The numbers are 2 and 3.

CHECK   The sum of 2 and 3 is 5.
The sum of their squares is 13. ✔

EXAMPLE 2   Find the length of line segment CD.

SOLUTION   Triangles ADC and BDC are right triangles. Therefore, the Pythagorean Theorem may be applied.

Use $\begin{bmatrix} x & \text{for length } CD. \\ y & \text{for length } AD. \\ 15 - y & \text{for length } DB. \end{bmatrix}$

Find y by subtraction.

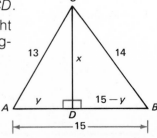

For △ ADC, $y^2 + x^2 = 13^2$
For △ CDB, $(15 - y)^2 + x^2 = 14^2$
Subtract. $y^2 - (15 - y)^2 = 13^2 - 14^2$
$y^2 - 225 + 30y - y^2 = 169 - 196$
$30y = 198$
$y = 6.6$

Find x. Replace y by 6.6 in $x^2 + y^2 = 169$.

$$x^2 + y^2 = 169$$
$$x^2 + (6.6)^2 = 169$$
$$x^2 = 125.44$$
$$x = 11.2 \text{ or } x = -11.2$$

Since x represents length, the negative number -11.2 is discarded as a solution.

CONCLUSION $CD = 11.2$

CHECK

$$x^2 + y^2 = 13^2$$
$$(11.2)^2 + (6.6)^2 \overset{?}{=} 13^2$$
$$125.44 + 43.56 \overset{?}{=} 169$$
$$169 = 169 \quad \checkmark$$

$$x^2 + (15 - y)^2 = 14^2$$
$$(11.2)^2 + (15 - 6.6)^2 \overset{?}{=} 14^2$$
$$(11.2)^2 + (8.4)^2 \overset{?}{=} 14^2$$
$$125.44 + 70.56 \overset{?}{=} 196$$
$$196 = 196 \quad \checkmark$$

CLASSROOM EXERCISES

Solve. Use two variables.

1. Find the length and width of a rectangle whose area is 35 square centimeters and whose length is 2 centimeters more than its width.

2. The difference of two numbers is 5 and the sum of their squares is 53. Find the numbers.

3. Find the length of line segment *CD*.

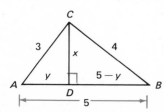

EXERCISES

Ⓐ Solve. Use two variables.

1. The sum of two numbers is 5 and the sum of their squares is 17. Find the numbers.

2. The difference of two numbers is 6 and the sum of their squares is 68. Find the numbers.

3. One train, running 10 kilometers an hour faster than a second train, required 2 hours less time to travel 400 kilometers. Find the rate of each train.

4. An airplane going a distance of 1050 kilometers can make the trip in 1 hour less time if it increases its speed 25 kilometers an hour. Find the rate of the airplane.

5. It takes one automobile 1 hour less time than another to travel a distance of 360 kilometers. The rate of the first automobile is 12 kilometers an hour faster than that of the second. Find the rate of each automobile.

6. The sum of the digits of a two-digit number is 9. The sum of the squares of the digits is 53. Find the number.

7. The sum of the squares of the digits of a two-digit number is 26. Find the number when the tens digit exceeds the units digit by four.

8. The sum of the squares of the digits of a two-digit number is 113. The square of the tens digit exceeds the square of the units digit by 15. Find the number.

9. In a two-digit number the square of the units digit is 72 less than the square of the tens digit. Find the number when the sum of the squares of the digits is 90.

10. Find CD.

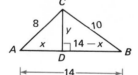

11. Find GH.

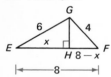

12. The perimeter of a floor is 44 m. Its area is 120 m². Find its dimensions.

13. It takes 56 m of fencing to enclose a rectangular lot with area 160 m². Find the dimensions of the lot.

14. The lengths of the sides of a triangle are 13, 14, and 15 cm. Find the length of the altitude to the longest side.

[B] 15. The lengths of the sides of an obtuse triangle are 5, 12, and 15 cm. Find the length of the altitude to the shortest side.

16. A rectangular field has area 6650 m². The ratio of the length to the width is 19 to 14. Find the dimensions.

17. The difference of the squares of two numbers is 1620. Find the numbers when they are in the ratio 7 to 2.

18. ABC is a semicircle. $\overline{BD} \perp \overline{AC}$. From geometry, $h^2 = xy$. Find h, x, and y for $AC = 20$ and $h = 2x$.

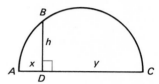

19. The base lengths of a trapezoid are 6 cm and 16 cm. The lengths of the nonparallel sides are 8 cm and 10 cm. Find the altitude of the trapezoid.

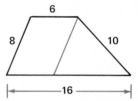

20. An airplane makes a trip of 600 kilometers and returns. Its rate going was 0.75 the rate returning. It took one hour longer to go than to return. What was the rate each way?

21. The length of the altitude of an isosceles triangle is 4 meters and the perimeter is 16 meters. Find the lengths of the sides of the triangle.

22. Find the equation of the circle containing the points $(0, 0)$, $(4, 0)$ and $(0, 2)$

[C] 23. A farmer contracted for the job of grading a township road. After working alone for two days, the farmer hired a neighbor and they completed the job in $5\frac{5}{7}$ days. If the farmer had worked alone, the job would have required 4 fewer days than it would have required for the neighbor working alone. Find the time each would have required to do the job alone.

24. The front wheel of a toy tractor makes 10 revolutions more than the rear wheel when going 360 cm. If the circumference of each wheel was increased by 6 cm, the front wheel would make only 5 revolutions more than the rear wheel when going this distance. Find the circumference of each wheel.

CHECKING YOUR UNDERSTANDING

WORDS AND SYMBOLS

combined variation
direct variation

inverse variation
joint variation

quadratic inequality

CONCEPTS

■ The graph of a quadratic inequality is the region in the coordinate plane on "one side" of the graph of the corresponding equation. [9-7]

■ The solutions of $ax^2 + bx + c > 0$ correspond to points of the x-axis which are "below" the graph for $y = ax^2 + bx + c$. The solutions of $ax^2 + bx + c < 0$ correspond to points of the x-axis which are "above" the graph for $y = ax^2 + bx + c$. [9-8]

■ Two related quantities that vary directly have a constant quotient. Two related quantities that vary inversely have a constant product. [9-9]

PROCESSES

■ Graph quadratic inequalities. [9-7]

1. $4(x - 2)^2 + 9(y + 3)^2 \leq 36$ 　　　 **2.** $x^2 - 4y^2 > 36$

■ Solve quadratic inequalities in one variable. [9-8]

3. $x^2 - 2x - 15 < 0$ 　　 **4.** $2x^2 - 3x + 1 \geq 0$ 　　 **5.** $4x^2 + 4x + 1 < 0$

■ Solve direct, inverse, joint, and combined variation problems. [9-9]

6. x and y vary inversely. $y = 3$ when $x = 18$. Find y when $x = 9$.

7. y varies directly as the square of x and inversely as z.
$y = \dfrac{5}{2}$ when $x = 2$ and $z = 4$. Find y when $x = 4$ and $z = 6$.

■ Solve systems of equations involving quadratics. [9-10 to 9-12]

8. $\dfrac{x^2}{16} + \dfrac{y^2}{9} = 1$
$3x + 4 = 12$

9. $\dfrac{x^2}{8} - \dfrac{y^2}{4} = 1$
$x + 6 = 6$

10. $9x^2 + 4y^2 = 36$
$x^2 + y^2 = 9$

CHAPTER REVIEW

Find the distance between points A and B in the coordinate plane. [9-1]

1. $A(8, -6)$, $B(3, 6)$ **2.** $A(-5, 3)$, $B(-1, -5)$

3. Find the distance between the midpoints of the segments from $(1, 3)$ to $(2, 8)$ and from $(-5, 4)$ to $(10, 1)$.

Write an equation for the circle having the given center and radius. [9-2]

4. center at origin, radius 6   **5.** center at $(4, -3)$. radius $2\sqrt{3}$

6. Write an equation for the circle which contains the point $(8, 5)$ and has its center at $(3, 2)$.

Find the four intercepts of each ellipse. [9-3]

7. $\dfrac{x^2}{121} + \dfrac{y^2}{4} = 1$ **8.** $\dfrac{(x - 2)^2}{4} + \dfrac{(y + 3)^2}{9} = 1$

9. Graph $\dfrac{(x + 1)^2}{25} + \dfrac{(y - 3)^2}{4} = 1$.

Find the coordinates of the vertex of each parabola. State whether the parabola opens up or down. [9-4, 9-5]

10. $y = 3x^2 + 4x + 4$ **11.** $y = -x^2 + 4x + 6$

12. Graph $x = -2y^2 - 4y + 1$.

13. Graph $\dfrac{x^2}{16} - y^2 = 1$.   **14.** Graph $\dfrac{(x + 3)^2}{9} - \dfrac{(y - 2)^2}{9} = 1$.

Write each equation in the standard form for graphing. Identify the conic section which is its graph. [9-6]

15. $3x^2 + 18x - 2y^2 + 16y = 11$ **16.** $x^2 + 6x + y^2 - 4y = 3$

17. $4x^2 + 16x + 9y^2 - 18y = 11$

Graph each inequality. [9-7]

18. $(x + 1)^2 + (y - 1)^2 < 9$ **19.** $4x^2 + 32x + 9y^2 - 54y > -109$

Solve each inequality. [9-8]

20. $x^2 + 5x < -4$ **21.** $x^2 - 2x > 1$

22. y varies directly as x. For $x = 7$, $y = \dfrac{1}{3}$. Find y for $x = 28$. [9-9]

23. x varies inversely as the cube of y and directly as z. For $z = 8$ and $y = 2$, $x = 3$. Find x for $z = 16$ and $y = 4$.

Solve each system of equations graphically. [9-10]

24.
$$x^2 + y^2 = 25$$
$$y = -3x - 15$$

25.
$$\frac{x^2}{4} + \frac{y^2}{9} = 1$$
$$3x - 2y = 6$$

Solve each system of equations algebraically. [9-11]

26.
$$x^2 + y^2 = 7$$
$$\frac{x^2}{9} + y^2 = 1$$

27.
$$x^2 + 4y^2 = 36$$
$$x - 2y = 6$$

28. The sum of two numbers is 11 and the difference of their squares is 187. Find the numbers. [9-12]

CAPSULE REVIEW

Write the letter of the best response.

1. Which two points are the endpoints of a segment whose midpoint is the origin?

a. $(6, 8)$ and $(0, 0)$

b. $(6, 8)$ and $(-3, -4)$

c. $(6, 8)$ and $(8, 6)$

d. $(6, 8)$ and $(-6, -8)$

2. Which of these is not an equation for the circle with center $C(4, -1)$ and radius 3?

a. $(x + 4)^2 + (y - 1)^2 = 9$

b. $x^2 - 8x + y^2 + 2y = -8$

c. $(x - 4)^2 + (y - (-1))^2 = 9$

d. $(y + 1)^2 + (x - 4)^2 - 9 = 0$

3. What is the length of the major axis of the ellipse $\frac{x^2}{9} + \frac{y^2}{16} = 1$?

a. 16

b. 9

c. 8

d. 4

4. Which equation determines a parabola which has its vertex at $(5, 1)$ and opens to the left?

a. $y = -4x^2 + 8x + 1$

b. $x = -4y^2 + 8y + 1$

c. $y = x^2 - 10x + 24$

d. $x = -y^2 + 10y - 24$

5. The graph of $9y^2 - 36y - 4x^2 - 8x = 4$ is a(n)

a. circle

b. parabola

c. ellipse

d. hyperbola

6. What is the radius of the circle whose equation is $x^2 + 4x + y^2 + 8y = -15$?

a. 5

b. $\sqrt{5}$

c. 15

d. $-\sqrt{15}$

7. Which quadratic inequality has no real solution?

a. $x^2 - 4x + 5 < 0$

b. $-x^2 - 4x + 2 < 0$

c. $x^2 - 4x + 3 < 0$

d. $-x^2 + 4x - 4 < 0$

8. If y varies inversely as the square of x and y is 36 when x is $\frac{1}{3}$, what is y when x is 2?

    a. 216   **b.** 6   **c.** 4   **d.** 1

9. What are the solutions of the system $\begin{array}{c} x + y = 1 \\ xy = -12 \end{array}$?

    a. $(6, -5)$ and $(5, -6)$ **b.** $(4, -3)$ and $(-3, 4)$
    c. $(12, -1)$ and $(-1, 12)$ **d.** $(8, -7)$ and $(8, 7)$

CHAPTER TEST

1. Find the distance between $A(2, 3)$ and $B(10, 18)$.

2. Find the midpoint of the line segment whose endpoints are $C(5, 8)$ and $D(8, 14)$.

3. Write an equation for the circle with center $(0, 0)$ and radius 3.

4. Sketch a graph of $(x - 4)^2 + (y - 4)^2 = 16$.

5. Write an equation for the ellipse with center $(0, 0)$, horizontal major axis length 6, and vertical minor axis length 3.

6. Sketch a graph of $\dfrac{(x + 5)^2}{25} + \dfrac{(y + 5)^2}{100} = 1$.

7. Write an equation for the parabola which has vertex $(2, 4)$, opens up, and has the same shape as $y = \frac{1}{2}x^2$.

8. Sketch a graph of $y + 3 = (x - 1)^2$.

9. Find where the graph of $\dfrac{x^2}{25} - \dfrac{y^2}{36} = 1$ intersects the x-axis.

10. Sketch a graph of $\dfrac{(y - 2)^2}{9} - \dfrac{(x - 3)^2}{16} = 1$.

11. If $ax^2 + 6y^2 = 10$ is an equation for a circle, what must be the number for a?

12. If $ax^2 + 6y^2 = 10$ is an equation for a hyperbola, what could be a number for a?

13. When $y = \dfrac{3}{x}$, do x and y vary directly or inversely?

14. p varies inversely with the square of q. $p = 4$ when $q = 3$. Find p when $q = 6$.

15. In how many points might an ellipse and a hyperbola intersect?

16. Find the intersection of the line $y = \dfrac{3}{4}x$ and the circle $x^2 + y^2 = 25$.

Solve algebraically.

17. $2x^2 + y^2 = 19$
$x^2 + y^2 = 10$

18. $y = x + 2$
$y = x^2$

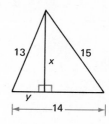

19. The sum of two numbers is 9. The difference of their squares is 45. Find the numbers.

20. Find x.

Write the letter of the best response.

21. What is the distance between $P(4, 7)$ and $Q(1, 11)$?

a. 3   **b.** 4   **c.** 5   **d.** 6   **e.** 7

22. What is an equation of the circle with center $(-5, 6)$ and radius 7?

a. $(x + 5)^2 + (y - 6)^2 = 49$ **b.** $(x + 5)^2 + (y - 6)^2 = 7$

c. $(x - 5)^2 + (y + 6)^2 = 49$ **d.** $(x - 5)^2 + (y + 6)^2 = 14$

e. $(x - 5)^2 + (y + 6)^2 = 7$

23. How long is the major axis of $\dfrac{(x - 10)^2}{4} + \dfrac{(y - 5)^2}{9} = 1$?

a. 4   **b.** 6   **c.** 9   **d.** 10   **e.** 18

24. What is the vertex of $y - 2 = 3(x + 6)^2$?

a. $(6, -2)$ **b.** $(18, -2)$ **c.** $(2, -2)$ **d.** $(-18, 2)$ **e.** $(-6, 2)$

25. Which of these lines is an asymptote of $\dfrac{x^2}{4} - \dfrac{y^2}{9} = 1$?

a. $y = \dfrac{4}{9}x$ **b.** $y = \dfrac{2}{3}x$ **c.** $y = 2.25x$ **d.** $y = 1.5x$ **e.** $y = 9x$

26. Which of these is an equation for a hyperbola?

a. $y = 3x^2$ **b.** $x = \dfrac{1}{2}y^2$ **c.** $x^2 + 3y^2 = 12$ **d.** $x^2 - 4y^2 = 64$ **e.** $x^2 + y^2 = 100$

27. Suppose x and y vary inversely and that $x = 3$ when $y = 6$. What does x equal when $y = 12$?

a. 1.5   **b.** 2   **c.** 4   **d.** 6   **e.** 36

28. Which of these is a possible number of intersection points for a line and a hyperbola?

a. 6   **b.** 5   **c.** 4   **d.** 3   **e.** 2

29. In how many points do the graphs of $9x^2 - 4y^2 = 36$ and $16x^2 + 25y^2 = 400$ intersect?

a. 0   **b.** 2   **c.** 4   **d.** 6   **e.** 8

30. The difference of two positive numbers is 4. The sum of their squares is 40. What is the larger of the two numbers?

a. 8   **b.** 6   **c.** 4   **d.** 3   **e.** 2

CHAPTER 10
EXPONENTIAL AND
LOGARITHMIC FUNCTIONS

A library saves a lot of work. Imagine learning about an automobile engine, proving the Pythagorean Theorem, understanding taxes, planning a future, and so on, without having any reference to the efforts of others. For the library, the payoff is that the more work it saves for us, the more work of ours there is for it to save. The growth of knowledge is exponential.

> **OBJECTIVES:** Identify and graph exponential functions. Solve exponential equations.

10-1 RATIONAL AND REAL NUMBERS AS EXPONENTS

In Chapter 7, meaning was given to rational-number exponents shown as fractions. $a^{\frac{m}{n}}$, for m and n positive integers and $a > 0$, was defined to be $(\sqrt[n]{a})^m$. Another form for $a^{\frac{m}{n}}$ is $\sqrt[n]{a^m}$. *Rational exponents* also may be shown as decimals.

RATIONAL EXPONENTS		
Fraction Form	Radical Form	Decimal Form
$3^{\frac{1}{2}}$	$\sqrt{3}$	$3^{0.5}$
$3^{\frac{7}{5}}$	$\sqrt[5]{3^7}$	$3^{1.4}$
$3^{\frac{141}{100}}$	$\sqrt[100]{3^{141}}$	$3^{1.41}$
$3^{\frac{707}{500}}$	$\sqrt[500]{3^{707}}$	$3^{1.414}$
$3^{\frac{7071}{5000}}$	$\sqrt[5000]{3^{7071}}$	$3^{1.4142}$

EXAMPLE 1 Write a radical form for $2^{1.8}$.

SOLUTION $2^{1.8} = 2^{\frac{9}{5}}$
$= \sqrt[5]{2^9}$, or $\sqrt[5]{512}$
$= 2\sqrt[5]{2^4}$, or $2\sqrt[5]{16}$

EXAMPLE 2 Simplify $\sqrt[5]{625}$ and write your result in decimal-exponent form.

SOLUTION $\sqrt[5]{625} = \sqrt[5]{5^4}$
$= 5^{\frac{4}{5}}$
$= 5^{0.8}$

Meaning also may be given to an exponent that is an irrational number, such as $\sqrt{2}$. We know, for example, that the numbers

$$1.4, \ 1.41, \ 1.414, \ 1.4142, \ \cdots$$

are successively closer to the real number $\sqrt{2}$. Using advanced mathematics it can be shown that the numbers

$$3^{1.4}, \ 3^{1.41}, \ 3^{1.414}, \ 3^{1.4142}, \ \cdots$$

also are successively closer to a real number. That number is defined to be $3^{\sqrt{2}}$.

When meaning is given to *irrational exponents* in this manner, the use of advanced mathematics also will verify that all rules for operating with exponents hold for all *real exponents*.

REAL EXPONENTS

a^x ($a > 0$, x a real number) is a real number.

$$2^{\frac{7}{5}} \qquad 2^{-1.4} \qquad 3^{\sqrt{2}} \qquad 5^{\pi} \qquad (\sqrt{2})^{2\pi-1} \qquad (4^{\sqrt{2}})^{\sqrt{3}} \qquad \left(\frac{1}{2}\right)^{\frac{3\pi}{4}}$$

EXAMPLE 3 Write an approximation for $9^{\sqrt{3}}$ in decimal-exponent form. Use a three-place decimal approximation for $\sqrt{3}$.

SOLUTION 1

$$9^{\sqrt{3}} \doteq 9^{1.732}$$

SOLUTION 2

$$9^{\sqrt{3}} = (3^2)^{\sqrt{3}}$$
$$\doteq 3^{2(1.732)}$$
$$\doteq 3^{3.464}$$

EXAMPLE 4 Simplify $(5^{\sqrt{2}})^{\sqrt{2}}$.

SOLUTION

$$(5^{\sqrt{2}})^{\sqrt{2}}$$
$$= 5^{\sqrt{2}\cdot\sqrt{2}}$$
$$= 5^2$$
$$= 25$$

EXAMPLE 5 Simplify $(x^{1-\sqrt{2}})(x^{1+\sqrt{2}})$.

SOLUTION

$$(x^{1-\sqrt{2}})(x^{1+\sqrt{2}})$$
$$= x^{(1-\sqrt{2})+(1+\sqrt{2})}$$
$$= x^2$$

EXAMPLE 6 Simplify $\dfrac{(3a)^{\sqrt{12}}}{a^{\sqrt{3}}}$.

SOLUTION

$$\frac{(3a)^{\sqrt{12}}}{a^{\sqrt{3}}} = \frac{(3a)^{2\sqrt{3}}}{a^{\sqrt{3}}}$$
$$= \left(\frac{9a^2}{a}\right)^{\sqrt{3}}$$
$$= (9a)^{\sqrt{3}}$$

CLASSROOM EXERCISES

Write the number in radical form.

1. $3^{0.25}$ **2.** $5^{1.6}$ **3.** $4^{1.2}$

Simplify and write in decimal-exponent form.

4. $\sqrt{8}$ **5.** $\sqrt[4]{27}$ **6.** $\sqrt[4]{49}$

Write an approximation in decimal-exponent form. Use 3 decimal places.

7. $3^{\sqrt{2}}$ **8.** 4^{π} **9.** $5^{4\sqrt{3}}$

Simplify.

10. $(2^{\sqrt{3}})(2^{3\sqrt{3}})$ **11.** $(x^{\sqrt{3}+1})(x^{\sqrt{3}-1})$

EXERCISES

A Write the number in radical form.

1. $5^{0.25}$ **2.** $6^{0.75}$ **3.** $5^{1.25}$ **4.** $7^{1.75}$ **5.** $100^{1.2}$ **6.** $100^{1.4}$

Simplify and write in decimal-exponent form.

7. $\sqrt[4]{8}$ **8.** $\sqrt[5]{16}$ **9.** $\sqrt[8]{8}$ **10.** $\sqrt{27}$ **11.** $\sqrt[5]{8}$ **12.** $\sqrt[10]{128}$

Write an approximation in decimal-exponent form. Use three decimal places.

13. $5^{\sqrt{2}}$ **14.** $3^{\pi-1}$ **15.** $10^{2\sqrt{3}}$ **16.** $10^{3\sqrt{2}}$ **17.** $9^{\sqrt{3}+1}$ **18.** $4^{1-\sqrt{2}}$

Simplify.

19. $(3^{2\sqrt{2}})^{\sqrt{2}}$ **20.** $(2^{2\sqrt{3}})^{\sqrt{3}}$ **21.** $(2^{\sqrt{3}-1})^{\sqrt{3}}$ **22.** $(5^{\sqrt{2}+1})^{\sqrt{2}}$

23. $\dfrac{x^{\sqrt{3}-2}}{x^{\sqrt{3}+2}}$ **24.** $\dfrac{x^{1-\sqrt{3}}}{x^{1+\sqrt{3}}}$ **25.** $(3^{\sqrt{2}-1})(3^{\sqrt{2}+1})$ **26.** $(2^{\sqrt{3}+1})(2^{\sqrt{3}-1})$

B **27.** $4 \cdot 2^{3\pi}$ **28.** $(x^{\sqrt{3}-1})^{(\sqrt{3}+1)}$ **29.** $\sqrt{(xy)^{\sqrt{12}}}$ **30.** $[(\sqrt{2})^3]^{\frac{1}{\sqrt{3}}}$

Write an approximation in decimal-exponent form. Use three decimal places.

31. $(3^{1-\sqrt{2}})^2$ **32.** $\left(\dfrac{1}{\sqrt{3}}\right)^{\sqrt{3}}$ **33.** $\sqrt{10^{2+\sqrt{2}}}$ **34.** $(4^{1+\sqrt{3}})^2$

Arrange the numbers in order from smallest to largest.

35. $\sqrt{2}$, $\sqrt{2^3}$, $\sqrt[3]{2}$, $\sqrt[3]{2^2}$, $2^{\sqrt{2}}$, $2^{\frac{\pi}{2}}$, $\left(\dfrac{1}{2}\right)^{\sqrt{2}}$, $\dfrac{1}{\sqrt{2}}$, $2^{0.21}$, $\sqrt[5]{2}$

C Simplify.

36. $3^{(\sqrt[3]{3})^3}$ **37.** $[(3^{\sqrt[3]{3}})^{\sqrt[3]{3}}]^{\sqrt[3]{3}}$ **38.** $\dfrac{y^{\sqrt{(a+b)^2 x}}}{y^{\sqrt{(a-b)^2 x}}}$ **39.** $\dfrac{[(x^{\sqrt{3}})^{\sqrt{2}}]^{\frac{1}{\sqrt{6}}}}{(x^{\sqrt{5}+2})(\sqrt{5}-2)}$

10-2 EXPONENTIAL FUNCTIONS

The meaning for a^x, $a > 0$, that was suggested in the previous section permits us to define a function using the equation $y = a^x$. Such a function is an **exponential function.** The domain of an exponential function is the set of real numbers. The graph has the shape, in general, of one of the following.

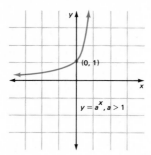

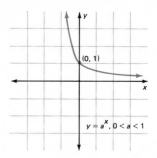

Since the graph for $y = a^x$ when $a = 1$ is the same as the graph for $y = 1$, $y = 1^x$ usually is not classified as an exponential function.

EXAMPLE 1   Graph $y = 2^x$.

SOLUTION

x	y
4	16
3	8
2	4
$\frac{3}{2}$	2.8 (approx.)
1	2
0	1
$-\frac{1}{2}$	0.7 (approx.)
-1	$\frac{1}{2}$
-2	$\frac{1}{4}$
-3	$\frac{1}{8}$

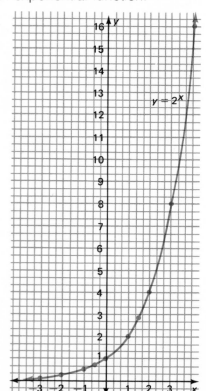

EXAMPLE 2   Graph $y = \left(\frac{1}{3}\right)^x$.   Graph $y = 3^{-x}$.

SOLUTION   Since $\left(\frac{1}{3}\right)^x = (3^{-1})^x$, or 3^{-x}, the two equations have the same graph.

x	y
$-\frac{3}{2}$	5.2 (approx.)
-1	3
0	1
$\frac{1}{2}$	0.6 (approx.)
1	$\frac{1}{3}$
2	$\frac{1}{9}$

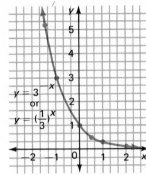

The graphs in Examples 1 and 2 suggest that *any* positive number for y, no matter how large or small, is possible for the function $y = a^x$. It can be proved, using advanced mathematics, that the range of the exponential function is indeed the set of positive real numbers.

The graphs of the exponential functions can help us find approximate values for exponential expressions containing irrational exponents.   They also can help us find approximate solutions for *exponential equations*.

EXAMPLE 3   Use the graph for $y = 2^x$ to approximate $2^{\sqrt{2}}$.

SOLUTION   Using the graph in Example 1 in the manner shown here, we see that

$$2^{\sqrt{2}} \doteq 2.6.$$

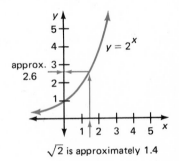

$\sqrt{2}$ is approximately 1.4

EXAMPLE 4   Use the graph of $y = 2^x$ to approximate the solution for $2^x = 5$.

SOLUTION   Using the graph in Example 1 as shown here, we see that for

$2^x = 5$,
   $x \doteq 2.3$.

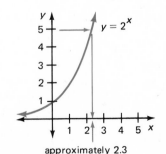

approximately 2.3

CLASSROOM EXERCISES

Graph.

Approximate to one decimal place.
Use your graph for $y = 3^x$.

1. $y = 3^x$ **2.** $y = \left(\frac{1}{2}\right)^x$ **3.** $3^{\sqrt{2}}$ **4.** $3^x = 7, x \doteq ?$

EXERCISES

A Graph.

1. $y = 4^x$ **2.** $y = 5^x$ **3.** $y = 10^x$ **4.** $y = 8^x$

5. $y = \left(\frac{1}{5}\right)^x$ **6.** $y = \left(\frac{1}{4}\right)^x$ **7.** $y = 2^{-x}$ **8.** $y = 3^{-x}$

Approximate to one decimal place. Use the graph for $y = 2^x$.

9. $2^{0.5}$ **10.** $2^{1.5}$ **11.** $2^{0.25}$ **12.** $2^{0.75}$ **13.** $2^{0.3}$ **14.** $2^{0.1}$

15. $2^{-0.5}$ **16.** $2^{-1.5}$ **17.** $2^{\sqrt{3}}$ **18.** $2^{\sqrt{2}}$ **19.** $2^{-\sqrt{2}}$ **20.** $2^{-\sqrt{3}}$

Approximate x to one decimal place. Use the graph for $y = 3^x$.

21. $3^x = 2$ **22.** $3^x = 4$ **23.** $3^x = 7.5$ **24.** $3^x = 8.8$

B Graph.

25. $y = (\sqrt{2})^x$ **26.** $y = (\sqrt{3})^{-x}$

27. Approximate $\sqrt{2}^{\sqrt{3}}$ to one decimal place. Use the graph for $y = (\sqrt{2})^x$.

28. For $(\sqrt{2})^x = 3$, approximate x to one decimal place. Use the graph for $y = (\sqrt{2})^x$.

Graph. Use the same set of axes.

29. $y = 2^x$ **30.** $y = 2^{x+1}$ **31.** $y = 2^x + 1$

32. What is the effect upon the graph of $y = a^x$ when a constant is added to the exponent?

33. What is the effect upon the graph of $y = a^x$ when a constant is added after the base is raised to a power?

Give the domain and range of the function defined by each equation.

34. $y = 5^x$ **35.** $y = 3^{-x}$ **36.** $y = 6^{x-3}$ **37.** $y = 10^x + 2$

C Sketch a graph. Give the domain and range of each function.

38. $y = 3^{x^2}$ **39.** $y = 3^{-x^2}$ **40.** $y = -(3^{x^2})$ **41.** $y = 3(3^{x^2})$ **42.** $y = 3^{x^2} + 3$

10-3 SOLVING EXPONENTIAL EQUATIONS

An **exponential equation** has a variable in an exponent. One method for solving an exponential equation is by showing each member using the same base. Then we may conclude that the exponents are equal.

The fact that $n = k$ when $a^n = a^k$ is shown graphically at the right.

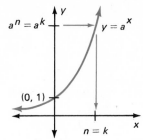

If $a^n = a^k$, $a > 0$, $a \neq 1$, then $n = k$.

EXAMPLE 1   Solve $5^{-x} = 125$.

SOLUTION
$$5^{-x} = 125$$
$$5^{-x} = 5^3$$
Thus, $-x = 3$
$$x = -3$$

CHECK
$$5^{-x} = 125$$
$$5^{-(-3)} \stackrel{?}{=} 125$$
$$5^3 \stackrel{?}{=} 125$$
$$125 = 125 \;\vee$$

EXAMPLE 2   Solve $2^{x+1} = 16$.

SOLUTION
$$2^{x+1} = 16$$
$$2^{x+1} = 2^4$$
Thus, $x + 1 = 4$
$$x = 3$$

CHECK $2^{x+1} = 16$
$$2^{3+1} \stackrel{?}{=} 16$$
$$2^4 \stackrel{?}{=} 16$$
$$16 = 16 \;\vee$$

EXAMPLE 3   Solve $\left(\frac{1}{3}\right)^{2x-1} = 27^{x-1}$.

SOLUTION
$$\left(\frac{1}{3}\right)^{2x-1} = 27^{x-1}$$
$$(3^{-1})^{2x-1} = (3^3)^{x-1}$$
$$3^{-2x+1} = 3^{3x-3}$$
Thus, $-2x + 1 = 3x - 3$
$$x = 0.8$$

CHECK
$$\left(\frac{1}{3}\right)^{2x-1} = 27^{x-1}$$
$$\left(\frac{1}{3}\right)^{2(0.8)-1} \stackrel{?}{=} 27^{0.8-1}$$
$$\left(\frac{1}{3}\right)^{0.6} \stackrel{?}{=} 27^{-0.2}$$
$$3^{-0.6} \stackrel{?}{=} (3^3)^{-0.2}$$
$$3^{-0.6} = 3^{-0.6} \;\vee$$

EXAMPLE 4   Solve $4^x = 32$

SOLUTION
$$4^x = 32$$
$$2^{2x} = 2^5$$
Thus, $2x = 5$
$$x = \frac{5}{2}$$

CHECK $4^x = 32$
$$4^{\frac{5}{2}} \stackrel{?}{=} 32$$
$$\sqrt{4}^{\,5} \stackrel{?}{=} 32$$
$$2^5 \stackrel{?}{=} 32$$
$$32 = 32 \;\vee$$

CLASSROOM EXERCISES

Solve.

1. $3^{-x} = 243$

2. $4^x = \dfrac{1}{16}$

3. $2^{2x-1} = 64$

4. $10^{x+1} = 1000$

5. $10^{-2x} = 0.001$

6. $\left(\dfrac{1}{3}\right)^{x+2} = 27^x$

EXERCISES

A Solve.

1. $4^x = 16$

2. $4^x = 64$

3. $7^x = 343$

4. $5^x = 625$

5. $2^{-x} = 4$

6. $3^{-x} = 27$

7. $5^{-x} = 125$

8. $6^{-x} = 36$

9. $3^{x-2} = 81$

10. $5^{x-2} = 125$

11. $2^{x-6} = 8$

12. $2^{x+6} = 8$

13. $2^{2x-1} = 128$

14. $2^{2x+1} = 256$

15. $3^{2x+3} = 81$

16. $3^{3x-2} = 243$

17. $5^{2x-3} = 125$

18. $6^{2x+5} = 216$

19. $5^{x+2} = \left(\dfrac{1}{25}\right)^{x-4}$

20. $3^{x+3} = \left(\dfrac{1}{27}\right)^{x-5}$

21. $4^x = 0.0625$

22. $5^x = 0.008$

23. $\left(\dfrac{1}{2}\right)^x = \left(\dfrac{1}{8}\right)^{x+1}$

24. $\left(\dfrac{1}{2}\right)^x = \left(\dfrac{1}{4}\right)^{x+1}$

B **25.** $0.1^{1-x} = 0.001^x$

26. $0.01^{2x} = 0.001^{2x+1}$

27. $5^{3x-1} = 1$

28. $16^{|2x-3|} = 8$

29. $3^{|7x-1|} = \dfrac{1}{81}$

30. $10^{|x|} = |10^x|$

31. $100^{3-x} = 0.01^{x-3}$

32. $5^{\frac{1}{x-3}} = \left(\dfrac{1}{25}\right)^{\frac{1}{4-x}}$

33. $2^{\frac{5}{x}} = \left(\dfrac{1}{4}\right)^{\left(\frac{1}{x^2} - \frac{3}{2}\right)}$

C **34.** $\dfrac{1}{729} = (3^{x+5})^x$

35. $3^a + 3^a + 3^a = 3^x$

36. $5^{x^2+9} - 25^{-3x} = 0$

37. $2^{2\sqrt{x+1}} + 2 \cdot 2^{\sqrt{x+1}} = 80$

38. Solve the system. $2^x = 8^{y+1}$ and $9^y = 3^{x-9}$

39. Let r represent the result of doubling both the base and the exponent of $a^b, b \neq 0, a > 0$. If r equals the product of a^b and x^b, find x.

A LINE BY ANY OTHER NAME . . .

Describe the graph for each equation.

1. $(3^y)(9^x) = 243$

2. $.04(5^x)^x = 125^y$

3. $(10^x)^x \cdot (10^y)^y = 10$

4. $(10^x)^y \cdot (10^y)^x = 10\,000$

OBJECTIVES: Interchange equations in corresponding exponential and logarithmic forms. Find selected logarithms. Solve logarithmic equations. Graph logarithmic functions.

10-4 LOGARITHMS AND EXPONENTS; LOGARITHMIC FUNCTIONS

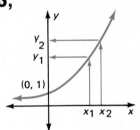

The graph of an exponential function suggests that two ordered pairs of the function cannot have the same second member. This may be shown to be true using advanced mathematics. Thus, the inverse of the exponential function is also a function, called the **logarithmic function.**

Since $y = a^x$ is the equation for the exponential function, $x = a^y$ is the equation for the logarithmic function. To show y "in terms of x" we write $y = \log_a x$ and read the right member as "the logarithm of x to the base a." The key to understanding logarithms and the logarithmic function lies in being able to use these two equivalent equations interchangeably.

THE LOGARITHMIC FUNCTION

$x = a^y$, $a > 0$, $a \neq 1$ (exponential form)

$y = \log_a x$, $a > 0$, $a \neq 1$ (logarithmic form)

These two equations have the same solution set. They show that y is an exponent. In particular, y is the exponent used with the base a that gives x. It is important that when you are given one form of these equations, you then can write the equivalent form.

EXAMPLE 1 Write the exponential form for $5 = \log_2 32$.

SOLUTION $5 = \log_2 32$ means that 5 is the exponent used with base 2 that gives 32.
$$2^5 = 32$$

EXAMPLE 2 Write the logarithmic form for $3^4 = 81$.

SOLUTION $3^4 = 81$ shows that 4 is the exponent used with base 3 that gives 81.
$$4 = \log_3 81$$

EXAMPLE 3 Write the exponential form for $\log_5 125 = 3$.

SOLUTION $\log_5 125 = 3$

3 is the exponent used with base 5 that gives 125.

$5^3 = 125$

EXAMPLE 4 Write the logarithmic form for $2^{-3} = \frac{1}{8}$.

SOLUTION $2^{-3} = \frac{1}{8}$

-3 is the exponent used with base 2 that gives $\frac{1}{8}$.

$\log_2 \frac{1}{8} = -3$

EXAMPLE 5 Write the exponential form for $\log_{10} 0.0001 = -4$.

SOLUTION $\log_{10} 0.0001 = -4$

-4 is the exponent used with base 10 that gives 0.0001.

$10^{-4} = 0.0001$.

EXAMPLE 6 Simplify $\log_2 8$.

SOLUTION 1 $\log_2 8$ is the exponent used with base 2 that gives 8. We know $2^3 = 8$.

Therefore, $\log_2 8 = 3$

SOLUTION 2 Let $n = \log_2 8$.

n is the exponent used with base 2 that gives 8.

$2^n = 8$
$2^n = 2^3$
$n = 3$

Therefore, $\log_2 8 = 3$.

EXAMPLE 7 Simplify $\log_{\frac{1}{9}} 3$.

SOLUTION Let $y = \log_{\frac{1}{9}} 3$.

$\left(\frac{1}{9}\right)^y = 3$

$\left(\frac{1}{9}\right)^y = \left(\frac{1}{9}\right)^{-\frac{1}{2}}$

$y = -\frac{1}{2}$

Therefore, $\log_{\frac{1}{9}} 3 = -\frac{1}{2}$.

CLASSROOM EXERCISES

Write in logarithmic form.

1. $3^2 = 9$

2. $4^0 = 1$

Write in exponential form.

3. $\log_4 16 = 2$

4. $\log_{10} 0.001 = -3$

Simplify.

5. $\log_{10} 0.01$

6. $\log_{10} 10^6$

7. $\log_{25} 625$

8. $\log_{\frac{1}{2}} 8$

EXERCISES

[A] Write in logarithmic form.

1. $2^4 = 16$

2. $2^1 = 2$

3. $2^3 = 8$

4. $2^5 = 32$

5. $2^{-1} = \frac{1}{2}$

6. $2^{-3} = \frac{1}{8}$

7. $5^0 = 1$

8. $10^0 = 1$

9. $5^{-1} = 0.2$

10. $5^{-2} = 0.04$

11. $10^{-1} = 0.1$

12. $10^{-2} = 0.01$

13. $\left(\frac{1}{2}\right)^{-2} = 4$

14. $\left(\frac{1}{3}\right)^{-1} = 3$

15. $7 = 7$

16. $11 = 11$

Write in exponential form.

17. $\log_{10} 1000 = 3$

18. $\log_{10} 10000 = 4$

19. $\log_4 64 = 3$

20. $\log_9 81 = 2$

21. $\log_2 1 = 0$

22. $\log_5 0.2 = -1$

23. $\log_5 0.04 = -2$

24. $\log_{10} 0.1 = -1$

25. $\log_{10} 0.01 = -2$

26. $\log_{\frac{1}{2}} \frac{1}{4} = 2$

27. $\log_{\frac{1}{3}} \frac{1}{27} = 3$

28. $\log_{\frac{1}{16}} \frac{1}{4} = \frac{1}{2}$

Simplify.

29. $\log_2 4$

30. $\log_{10} 100$

31. $\log_5 125$

32. $\log_4 256$

33. $\log_2 32$

34. $\log_8 512$

35. $\log_2 \frac{1}{2}$

36. $\log_2 \frac{1}{4}$

37. $\log_{10} 0.1$

38. $\log_{10} 0.001$

39. $\log_{\frac{1}{2}} \frac{1}{16}$

40. $\log_{\frac{1}{3}} \frac{1}{81}$

[B] Write in logarithmic form.

41. $(\sqrt{35})^{-2} = \frac{1}{35}$

42. $(\sqrt{2})^4 = 4$

Write in exponential form.

43. $\log_{0.2} 5 = -1$

44. $\log_{\sqrt{2}} \frac{1}{16} = -8$

Simplify.

45. $\log_b b^m, \, b > 0$

46. $\log_b 1, \, b > 0$

47. $\log_b b, \, b > 0$

48. $\log_{\sqrt{2}} 8$

49. $\log_{16} 2$

50. $\log_{0.1} 100$

[C] **51.** $\log_{\sqrt{3}} \frac{\sqrt[4]{27}}{9}$

52. $\log_{\sqrt{2}} \frac{\sqrt[5]{32}}{16}$

53. $\log_3 81 - \frac{4}{3} \log_2 8$

54. $\log_9 3 \sqrt[3]{9} + \log_4 2\sqrt{2}$

55. $(\log_3 81)(\log_{81} 3)$

56. $(\log_4 64)(\log_{64} 4)$

10-5 SOLVING EQUATIONS IN LOGARITHMIC FORM

To solve certain equations given in logarithmic form, we may use the equivalent exponential form.

EXAMPLE 1   Solve $2x = \log_2 64$.

SOLUTION $2x = \log_2 64$

$2x$ is the exponent used with the base 2 that gives 64.

$$2^{2x} = 64$$
$$2^{2x} = 2^6$$
$$2x = 6$$
$$x = 3$$

CHECK $2x = \log_2 64$
$2(3) \overset{?}{=} \log_2 64$
$2^6 \overset{?}{=} 64$
$64 = 64$ ✔

EXAMPLE 2   Solve $\log_2 x = 5$.

SOLUTION $\log_2 x = 5$

$$x = 2^5$$
$$x = 32$$

CHECK   The check is left for the student.

EXAMPLE 3   Solve $\log_x 64 = 2$.

SOLUTION $\log_x 64 = 2$

$$x^2 = 64$$
$$x = 8$$

(-8 is not a solution as the base used with a logarithm cannot be negative.)

CHECK $\log_x 64 = 2$
$\log_8 64 \overset{?}{=} 2$
$8^2 \overset{?}{=} 64$
$64 = 64$ ✔

EXAMPLE 4   Solve $2(\log_x 49) - 1 = 3$.

SOLUTION $2(\log_x 49) - 1 = 3$

A_1 $2(\log_x 49) = 4$
D_2 $\log_x 49 = 2$
$x^2 = 49$
$x = 7$

CHECK   The check is left for the student.

EXAMPLE 5   Solve $3 \log_2 (2x - 3) - 7 = 5$.

SOLUTION $3 \log_2 (2x - 3) - 7 = 5$

$$3 \log_2 (2x - 3) = 12$$
$$\log_2 (2x - 3) = 4$$
$$2x - 3 = 16$$
$$x = \frac{19}{2}$$

CHECK   The check is left for the student.

CLASSROOM EXERCISES

Solve.

1. $2x = \log_4 16$
2. $\log_2 x = 4$
3. $\log_x 25 = 2$
4. $2 \log_x 9 - 1 = 3$
5. $2 \log_3 (x + 4) - 3 = 5$
6. $2 \log_x 5 = 1$
7. $2 \log_3 (x - 1) = 6$
8. $3 \log_x 27 = 3$
9. $\log_x 16 = 2^2$

EXERCISES

A Solve.

1. $2n = \log_7 49$
2. $3n = \log_5 125$
3. $\log_2 x = 6$
4. $\log_3 x = 4$
5. $\log_6 x = -1$
6. $\log_{10} x = -2$
7. $\log_x 125 = 3$
8. $\log_x 128 = 7$
9. $\log_x 100 = 2$
10. $\log_x 36 = 2$
11. $2 \log_3 x = 8$
12. $5 \log_4 x = 20$
13. $6 \log_5 x - 18 = 0$
14. $4 \log_6 x + 4 = 0$
15. $3 \log_x 16 - 2 = 4$
16. $8 \log_x 81 + 1 = 17$
17. $2 \log_x \frac{1}{9} + 1 = 5$
18. $3 \log_x \frac{1}{25} + 2 = 8$

B **19.** $\log_{16} 8 = x$
20. $\log_{\frac{1}{2}} x = \frac{1}{2}$
21. $\log_{\sqrt{3}} x = 4$
22. $\log_{\sqrt{2}} x = 8$
23. $\log_x \sqrt{2} = \frac{1}{4}$
24. $\log_x 0.16 = -2$
25. $2 \log_3 (3x + 2) + 4 = 5$
26. $\log_3 |x| = 2$
27. $\log_{|x|} 64 = 2$
28. $3 \log_{10} x + 2 \log_{10} x = 10$
29. $\log_4 \left| \frac{1}{x} + 1 \right| = 2$
30. $\log_3 \sqrt{3x - 3} = 2$

C Solve the system.   Solve.

31. $\log_2 x = y - 3$
$\quad\ x^y = 2^{10}$
32. $x = \log_2 z$
$\quad\ z(4)^y = 64$
$\quad\ 8^x \cdot 2^{-y} = 16$
33. $\log_{10} |20x - x^2| = 0$

34. For $a = \log_8 81$ and $b = \log_2 9$, express a in terms of b.

A BASE RELATIONSHIP

Prove.   Solve for y.

1. $\log_c a \cdot \log_a b = \log_c b$
2. $\log_3 x \cdot \log_x 2x \cdot \log_{2x} y = \log_x x^2$

10-6 GRAPHING LOGARITHMIC FUNCTIONS

The exponential function and the logarithmic function are inverses of each other. Their graphs are shown here for base a greater than 1.

The Exponential Function

$y = a^x, a > 1$

The Logarithmic Function

$x = a^y$ or $y = \log_a x, a > 1$

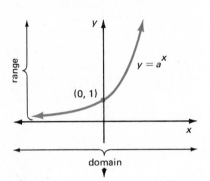
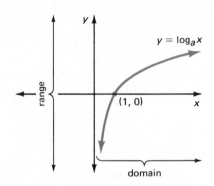

Note that the *range* of the exponential function is the set of positive real numbers. Therefore, the *domain* of the logarithmic function also is the set of positive real numbers. Expressions such as $\log_3 (-2)$, for example, are meaningless.

EXAMPLE 1 Graph $y = \log_2 x$.

SOLUTION y is the exponent used with base 2 that gives x. That is, $2^y = x$.

x	y
1	0
2	1
4	2
8	3
$\frac{1}{2}$	-1
$\frac{1}{4}$	-2
$\frac{1}{8}$	-3

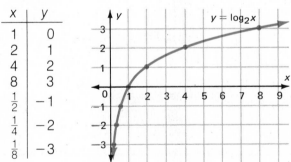

The positive real numbers form the domain of the logarithmic function since they form the range of the exponential function. At present, we are able to find y easily only for certain values of x. However, the graphs of these few number pairs suggest the way the complete graph of the function would look.

The graph of a logarithmic function can help us find approximations for logarithms.

EXAMPLE 2 Find an approximation for $\log_2 3$. Use the graph of $y = \log_2 x$.

SOLUTION Using the graph from Example 1 in the manner shown here, we see that

$\log_2 3 \doteq 1.6$.

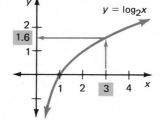

For a base between 0 and 1, the graphs of the exponential and logarithmic functions look like these.

The Exponential Function
$y = a^x, 0 < a < 1$

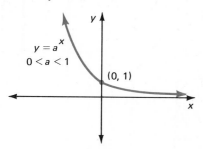

The Logarithmic Function
$y = \log_a x, 0 < a < 1$

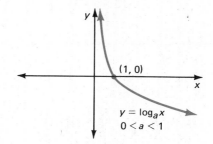

EXAMPLE 3 Graph $y = \log_{\frac{1}{3}} x$.

SOLUTION y is the exponent used with base $\frac{1}{3}$ that gives x. That is $\left(\frac{1}{3}\right)^y = x$.

x	y
1	0
$\frac{1}{3}$	1
$\frac{1}{9}$	2
$\frac{1}{27}$	3
3	-1
9	-2

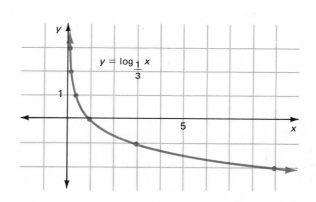

CLASSROOM EXERCISES

Graph.

Use your graph of $y = \log_3 x$.

1. $y = \log_3 x$

2. $y = \log_{\frac{1}{2}} x$

3. Approximate $\log_3 2$.

EXERCISES

A Graph.

1. $y = \log_4 x$

2. $y = \log_5 x$

3. $y = \log_{10} x$

4. $y = \log_6 x$

5. $y = \log_{\frac{1}{4}} x$

6. $y = \log_{\frac{1}{10}} x$

7. $y = \log_{\frac{3}{5}} x$

8. $y = \log_{\frac{2}{3}} x$

Approximate. Use the graph of $y = \log_2 x$.

9. $\log_2 6$

10. $\log_2 5$

11. $\log_2 10$

12. $\log_2 12$

13. $\log_2 1.5$

14. $\log_2 1.75$

B Graph.

15. $y = \log_{\sqrt{3}} x$

16. $y = \log_{\frac{\sqrt{2}}{2}} x$

17. $y = \log_2 |x|$

Graph the set of equations using the same set of axes.

18. $y = \log_2 x$, $y = \log_2 x + 1$, and $y = \log_2 x - 1$

19. $y = \log_2 x$, $y = \log_2 (x + 1)$, and $y = \log_2 (x - 1)$

20. $y = \log_2 x$ and $y = 2 \log_2 (x - 1) + 1$

Give the domain and range.

21. $y = \log_{10}(x - 1)$

22. $y = \log_{10} x + 2$

23. $y = \log_{10}(x + 2) + 1$

24. $y = \log_{10} |x|$

25. $y = 2 \log_3 x$

26. $y = -3 \log_4(2x + 1) + 8$

C Graph.

27. $y = \log_3 x^2$

28. $y = 2 \log_3 x$

29. $y = \log_2 x^3$

30. $y = \log_2 |x^3|$

31. $y = \log_3 (x^2 - 1)$

32. $y = \log_3 (1 - x^2)$

33. For $b > 0$, show that $\log_b x + \log_{\frac{1}{b}} x = 0$ for $x > 0$.

34. Find the minimum value of $\log_{10}(x^2 - 8x + 116)$.

How do different values of a, $a > 0$, affect the graph of the function given in x and y?

35. $y = \log_a x$

36. $y = \log ax$

37. $y = a \log x$

38. $y = \log (x + a)$

39. $y = \log x + a$

40. $y = \log a + x$

CHECKING YOUR UNDERSTANDING

WORDS

exponential equation

exponential function

logarithmic equation

logarithmic function

logarithm of a number

real exponent

CONCEPTS

- The rules for operating with exponents apply to all real-number exponents. [10-1]

- The domain of an exponential function defined by $y = a^x$ is the set of real numbers. The range is the set of positive real numbers. The graph contains $(0, 1)$. For $a > 1$, the graph curves upward to the right and becomes very steep for large positive values of x. For $0 < a < 1$, the graph curves downward to the right from a very steep position for large negative values of x; it is nearly horizontal just above the x-axis for large positive values of x. [10-2]

- If two powers having the same positive base (base $\neq 1$) are equal, the exponents used with the base are equal. [10-3]

- The inverse of the exponential function $y = a^x$ is the logarithmic function $x = a^y$ or $y = \log_a x$. The domain of the logarithmic function is the set of positive real numbers. The range is the set of real numbers. The logarithm of a number x to the base a is an exponent. [10-4, 10-6]

PROCESSES

- Use the rules for operating with exponents when the exponents are real numbers. [10-1]

   1. Simplify $32^{0.6}$.

   2. Simplify $\dfrac{5^{3\pi-1}}{5^{\pi}}$.

   3. Simplify $\dfrac{z^{\sqrt{2}}}{z^{\sqrt{8}}}$.

- Graph exponential functions. Solve exponential equations. [10-2, 10-3]

   4. Graph $y = \left(\dfrac{1}{2}\right)^x$.

   5. Use the graph of $y = \left(\dfrac{1}{2}\right)^x$ to approximate $\left(\dfrac{1}{2}\right)^{-\pi}$.

   6. Solve $3^{2x+1} - 1 = 80$.

   7. Solve $\left(\dfrac{1}{9}\right)^{x+1} = 81^{-x}$.

- Replace an equation in logarithmic form by the corresponding equation in exponential form, and vice-versa. [10-4]

   8. $2^4 = 16$ corresponds to $\log_? ? = ?$

   9. $\log_2 \dfrac{1}{8} = ?$

- Graph logarithmic functions. Solve logarithmic equations. [10-5, 10-6]

   10. Graph $y = \log_{\frac{3}{2}} x$.

   11. Solve $3 \log_8 x = 2$.

   12. Solve $\log_x 25 = -2$.

> **OBJECTIVES:** Use a table to find powers and logarithms with base 10. Compute using logarithms and their properties. Use logarithms to solve problems.

10-7 THE FUNCTIONS $y = 10^x$ AND $y = \log_{10} x$

The exponential and logarithmic functions with base 10 are particularly useful in computation. Base-10 logarithms have been so useful that they are called *common logarithms* and $\log_{10} x$ is written simply as $\log x$.

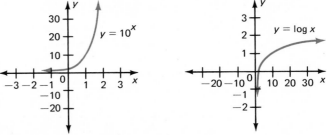

The graphs of these functions indicate that any positive real number may be represented as a power of 10. As shown by the red dots in the graphs, $10^0 = 1$ and $10^1 = 10$. Therefore, a number between 1 and 10 may be represented by 10 with an exponent that is between 0 and 1. Using advanced mathematics, some decimal approximations for these exponents have been computed and are the entries in Table I in the back of the book.

Thus, Table I may be viewed two ways. Either the entries, x, in the table or the numbers, N, along the outside may be considered a decimal approximation such that $N \doteq 10^x$.

EXAMPLE 1 Use Table I to approximate $10^{0.8176}$.

SOLUTION Find the entry 8176 in the table. Then combine the number 6.5 at the side of the table with the number 7 at the top as follows.

$$10^{0.8176} \doteq 6.57$$

Table I · Logarithms of Numbers

N	0	1	2	3	4	5	6	7	8	9
5.5	7404	7412	7419	7427	7435	7443	7451	7459	7466	7474
5.6	7⌐	⌐⌐00	7497	75⌐⌐		7520	7528	⌐		7551
6.4	8062	8069	8075	8082	8089	8096	8102	8109	8116	⌐22
6.5	8129	8136	8142	8149	8156	8162	8169	8176	8182	8189
6.6	8195	8202	8209	8215	8222	8228	8235	8241	8248	8254
6.7	8261	8267	8274	8280	8287	8293	8299	8306	8312	8319

Example 1 shows how we may use Table I to find an approximation for N between 1 and 10 when $N = 10^x$ for some number x between 0 and 1. Conversely, we also may use Table I to find an approximation for x between 0 and 1 when $N = 10^x$ for some number N between 1 and 10.

EXAMPLE 2 $3.56 = 10^x$. Use Table I to approximate x.

SOLUTION $3.56 = 10^x$

Forming 3.56 using the numbers 3.5 at the side and 6 at the top of the table, as shown, we find

$$3.56 \doteq 10^{0.5514}$$

Therefore, $x \doteq 0.5514$.

Table I · Logarithms of Numbers

N	0	1	2	3	4	5	6	7	8	9
1.0	0000	0043	0086	0128	0170	0212	0253	0294	0334	0374
1.1	␣␣	␣␣53	0492	05␣␣		␣607	0645	␣␣␣␣	07␣9	0755
	5185	5198	␣␣␣␣	␣224	5237	5␣␣␣		5276	␣␣	
3.4	5315	5328	5540	5353	5366	5378	5391	5403	5416	5426
3.5	5441	5453	5465	5478	5490	5502	5514	5527	5539	5551
3.6	5563	5575	5587	5599	5611	5623	5635	5647	5658	5670
3.7	5682	5694	5705	5717	5729	5740	5752	5763	5775	5786

The equation $3.56 = 10^x$ is equivalent to the equation $\log 3.56 = x$. In solving $3.56 = 10^x$, we solved $\log 3.56 = x$ also. That is, we used Table I to find an approximation for the common logarithm of 3.56.

EXAMPLE 3   Find log 2.79. Use Table I.

SOLUTION   Form 2.79 using the numbers 2.7 at the side and 9 at the top of the table. Following the procedure for using the table shown in Example 2, we find log $2.79 \doteq 0.4456$.

The exponents, or logarithms, that are the entries in Table I range from 0.0000 to 0.9996. Therefore, the powers that we can form using the numbers on the side and top of the table range from $10^{0.0000}$ to $10^{1.0000}$, or from 1 to 10. However, we can use this table for any exponent or any power of 10 because of the base-10 structure of our system of numeration.

Direct use of
Table I

Standard form	0.0001	0.001	0.01	0.1	1	10	100	1000	10 000
Exponential form	10^{-4}	10^{-3}	10^{-2}	10^{-1}	10^0	10^1	10^2	10^3	10^4
Logarithm of the number	-4	-3	-2	-1	0	1	2	3	4

EXAMPLE 4   Use Table I to approximate $10^{3.9106}$.

SOLUTION   The chart above suggests that $10^{3.9106}$ is between 1000 and 10 000.

$$10^{3.9106} = (10^{0.9106})(10^3)$$

From Table I, $10^{0.9106} \doteq 8.14$.

$$\text{Therefore, } 10^{3.9106} \doteq 8.14(10^3)$$
$$\doteq 8140$$

EXAMPLE 5   Approximate $10^{-0.3002}$.   Use Table I.

SOLUTION $10^{-0.3002}$ is between 0.1 and 1.

$$10^{-3.002} = 10^{0.6998 - 1}$$
$$= (10^{0.6998})(10^{-1})$$

From Table I, $10^{0.6998} \doteq 5.01$.

$$\text{Therefore, } 10^{-0.3002} \doteq 5.01(10^{-1})$$
$$\doteq 0.501$$

EXAMPLE 6 $10^x = 175$.   Approximate x.

SOLUTION   The chart above suggests that x is between 2 and 3.

$$10^x = 175$$
$$= 1.75(10^2)$$
$$\doteq (10^{0.2430})(10^2)$$
$$10^x \doteq 10^{2.2430}$$

Therefore, $x \doteq 2.2430$

Solving $10^x = 175$ in Example 6 is the same as solving $\log 175 = x$. In other words, we used Table I to find $\log 175$.

EXAMPLE 7   Approximate $\log 0.0086$.   Use Table I.

SOLUTION $\log 0.0086 = \log(8.6 \times 0.001)$
$$\doteq \log(10^{0.9345} \times 10^{-3})$$
$$\doteq \log 10^{0.9345 - 3}$$
$$\doteq 0.9345 - 3, \text{ or } -2.0655$$

CLASSROOM EXERCISES

Give an approximation. Use Table I.

1. $10^{0.8457}$ **2.** $10^{0.5159}$ **3.** $10^{2.9750}$ **4.** $10^{-0.3497}$

5. log 5.09   **6.** log 1.49   **7.** log 0.0432   **8.** log 0.843

Find x. Use Table I.

9. $10^x = 3.46$ **10.** log $x = 0.6990$

11. Graph $y = 10^x$ and $y = \log x$. Use Table I to help plot several points.

EXERCISES

Ⓐ Give an approximation. Use Table I.

1. $10^{0.8209}$ **2.** $10^{0.9694}$ **3.** $10^{-0.4437}$ **4.** $10^{-0.6635}$ **5.** $10^{2.8506}$

6. $10^{3.8136}$ **7.** $10^{3.9440}$ **8.** $10^{1.9996}$ **9.** $10^{-0.0991}$ **10.** $10^{-0.5186}$

11. $10^{-0.9355}$ **12.** $10^{-0.9793}$ **13.** $10^{0.9475}$ **14.** $10^{0.8888}$ **15.** $10^{0.8631}$

16. $10^{0.1129}$ **17.** $10^{2.3280}$ **18.** $10^{3.0253}$ **19.** $10^{-0.0456}$ **20.** $10^{-0.3040}$

21. log 8.32   **22.** log 5.17   **23.** log 2.64   **24.** log 7.18   **25.** log 31.0

26. log 82.0   **27.** log 499   **28.** log 9850   **29.** log 0.910   **30.** log 0.770

31. log 0.0290   **32.** log 0.014   **33.** log 0.00713   **34.** log 0.00411   **35.** log 0.003

Find x. Use Table I.

36. $10^x = 8.59$ **37.** $10^x = 7.88$ **38.** $10^x = 10.3$

39. $10^x = 12.6$ **40.** $10^x = 573$ **41.** $10^x = 1460$

42. log $x = 0.6571$ **43.** log $x = 0.9304$ **44.** log $x = 2.2945$

45. log $x = 3.4871$ **46.** log $x = 0.9042 - 1$ **47.** log $x = 0.4829 - 2$

Ⓑ **48.** $10^{3x} = 1890$ **49.** $10^{x+1} = 3$ **50.** $10^{-x} = 67.3$

51. $10^{2x-3} = 0.839$ **52.** log $2x = 1.7356$ **53.** log $(x + 3) = 2.8432$

Give an approximation. Use a three-place decimal approximation for $\sqrt{2}$, π, and $2.\overline{45}$.

54. log $\sqrt{2}$ **55.** log π **56.** log $2.\overline{45}$

Ⓒ Use Table I to approximate the left member. Use this information and Table I to give the number missing from the right member.

57. log 2 + log 4 = log ?   **58.** 2 log 3 = log ?   **59.** log 8 − log 4 = log ?

10-8 FINDING COMMON LOGARITHMS AND ANTILOGARITHMS

The equations $x = 10^y$ and $\log x = y$ are equivalent. y, the exponent, or common logarithm, is the sum of an integer and a number between 0 and 1. The integer is the *characteristic* of the exponent or logarithm. The number between 0 and 1 is the *mantissa*.

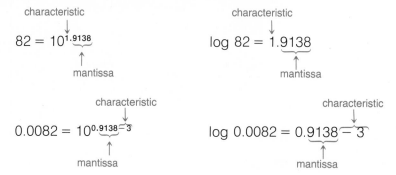

The logarithm of a number between 1 and 10 has characteristic 0. Its mantissa is found in Table I. To find the logarithm of any other positive number, we first write it as the product of a number between 1 and 10 and an integral power of 10. The integer exponent is the characteristic of the logarithm. The mantissa of the logarithm is found in Table I for the number between 1 and 10.

EXAMPLE 1 Find the characteristic and mantissa of log 847; of log 0.00847. Write the logarithm of each.

SOLUTION $847 = 8.47 \times 10^2$ | $0.00847 = 8.47 \times 10^{-3}$

The characteristic of log 847 is 2. | The characteristic of log 0.00847 is −3.

The mantissa is the same as the mantissa of log 8.47. From Table I, the mantissa is 0.9279.

$$847 = 10^{0.9279} \times 10^2$$ | $$0.00847 = 10^{0.9279} \times 10^{-3}$$
$$847 = 10^{2.9279}$$ | $$0.00847 = 10^{0.9279 - 3}$$
$$\log 847 = 2.9279$$ | $$\log 0.00847 = 0.9279 - 3$$

The logarithm of an integral power of 10 has mantissa 0.

EXAMPLE 2 Find log 1000; log 0.01.

SOLUTION $1000 = 10^3$ | $0.01 = 10^{-2}$

$\log 1000 = 3$, or 3.0000 | $\log 0.01 = -2$, or $0.0000 - 2$

The base-10 structure of our system of numeration and Table I permit us to find the common logarithm of a number quickly.

EXAMPLE 3   Find log 783.

SOLUTION   Place a caret to the right of the first non-zero digit.

$$7_\wedge 83$$

Count the places from the caret to the decimal point. There are 2 *counting to the right*. Find the mantissa for log 7.83 from Table I. It is 0.8938. Write

log 783 = 2.8938.

$783 = 7.83 \times 10^2$

$$\begin{bmatrix} \text{NOTE: } 7.83 \times 10^2 \\ \text{is called the} \\ \textit{scientific form} \\ \text{for 783.} \end{bmatrix}$$

$783 = 10^{0.8938} \times 10^2$
$783 = 10^{2.8938}$

EXAMPLE 4   Find log 0.58.

SOLUTION   Place a caret to the right of the first non-zero digit.

$$0.5_\wedge 8$$

Count the places from the caret to the decimal point. There is 1 *counting to the left*. Find the mantissa for 5.8 from Table I. It is 0.7634. Write

log 0.58 = 0.7634 − 1
or   log 0.58 = 9.7634 − 10.

$0.58 = 5.8 \times 10^{-1}$

$0.58 = 10^{0.7634} \times 10^{-1}$
$0.58 = 10^{0.7634-1}$

(You could write log 0.58 in different ways with the simplest being log 0.58 = −0.2366. However, if you use tables of logarithms to compute (Section 10-9), you will find that the most useful form for log 0.58 is 9.7634 − 10.)

The common logarithm of a number, x, is an exponent y with base 10 for which $10^y = x$. When, for example, log x = 2.8370 and we want to find x, we have to reverse our use of the table to find $10^{2.8370}$. This number x is called the *antilogarithm* or *antilog* of 2.8370.

EXAMPLE 5   log x = 2.8370. Find x.

SOLUTION   From Table I the mantissa 0.8370 is the logarithm of $6_\wedge 87$, when the caret represents a decimal point. Since the given characteristic is 2, we count two places to the right from the caret and place the decimal point.

$$x = 687.$$

EXAMPLE 6   Find the antilog of $7.7059 - 10$.

SOLUTION   The mantissa is the logarithm of $5_\wedge 08$ when the caret represents a decimal point.   The characteristic is -3. From the caret we count 3 places to the left and place the decimal point.

Therefore, antilog $7.7059 - 10 = 0.00508$.

We can find the approximate logarithm of a number such as 4.836 by using 4.84 for 4.836 and finding the logarithm of 4.84.   However, we can find a better approximation by **interpolation**.

EXAMPLE 7   Find log 48.36.

SOLUTION   The characteristic is 1.   To find the mantissa, use Table I.

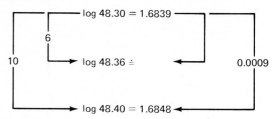

For log 48.36, find $\frac{6}{10}$ of 0.0009 and add it to 1.6839.

$$\log 48.36 \doteq 1.6839 + \frac{6}{10}(0.0009)$$
$$\doteq 1.6839 + 0.0005$$
$$\doteq 1.6844$$

We may use interpolation also, if necessary, to find better approximations of antilogarithms.

EXAMPLE 8   Find antilog 1.5445.

SOLUTION

For antilog 1.5445, find $\frac{4}{12}$ of 0.10 and add it to 35.00.

$$\text{Antilog } 1.5445 \doteq 35.00 + \frac{4}{12}(0.10)$$
$$\doteq 35.00 + 0.03$$
$$\doteq 35.03$$

CLASSROOM EXERCISES

Find the common logarithm. Identify the characteristic and mantissa of each.

1. 3.41 **2.** 341 **3.** 0.0341 **4.** 0.00341

Find the antilogarithm.

5. 1.9566 **6.** 7.9566 − 10 **7.** 0.3560 **8.** 9.3560 − 10

Find x. Use Table I.

9. $\log x = 1.9983$ **10.** $\log x = 9.5224 - 10$ **11.** $\log x = 0.6587$ **12.** $\log x = 1.9060$

EXERCISES

A Find the common logarithm. Identify the characteristic and mantissa of each.

1. 4.05 **2.** 405 **3.** 7.34 **4.** 734
5. 85.6 **6.** 0.856 **7.** 0.0158 **8.** 1580

Find the common logarithm.

9. 436 **10.** 7850 **11.** 0.563 **12.** 0.981
13. 0.068 **14.** 0.0143 **15.** 0.00728 **16.** 0.00443
17. 9.305 **18.** 6.326 **19.** 0.4723 **20.** 0.9714

Find the antilogarithm.

21. 2.8476 **22.** 1.8024 **23.** 3.6581 **24.** 4.5641
25. 9.6514 − 10 **26.** 8.7086 − 10 **27.** 7.7056 − 10 **28.** 9.8545 − 10

Find x. Use Table I.

29. $\log x = 2.7723$ **30.** $\log x = 2.5776$ **31.** $\log x = 8.8997 - 10$
32. $\log x = 0.8823 - 3$ **33.** $\log x = 0.9525 - 2$ **34.** $\log x = 8.4500 - 10$

B **35.** $\log |x| = 2.8910$ **36.** $\log \sqrt{x} = 0.7782$ **37.** $\log(\sqrt{x} + \sqrt{x - 5}) = 0.6990$

38. $\log 2x = 0.6415$ **39.** $10^{\log x} = 3$ **40.** $\log\left(\dfrac{1}{x} + \dfrac{1}{x + 1}\right) = 9.6532 - 10$

41. Approximate $\log \sqrt{3}$. **42.** Find $\log \sqrt{10}$.

C Find x.

43. $\log x - \log_{\frac{1}{10}} x = 4.98$ **44.** $3(10)^{-x^2} = 1.3095$ **45.** $6 \log x + \log(100^{\log x}) = 5$

10-9 PROPERTIES OF LOGARITHMS; COMPUTING WITH LOGARITHMS

In Chapter 7 we saw that radicals can be interpreted in terms of exponents in fraction form. As a result, we were able to derive properties of radicals from the rules for operating with exponents.

Similarly, since logarithms are exponents, we can derive properties of logarithms from the rules for exponents. The key to understanding the derivations is in the fact that $y = \log x$ and $10^y = x$ are equivalent. Replacing y by $\log x$ in $10^y = x$ gives us $10^{\log \boxed{x}} = \boxed{x}$. Replacing x by 10^y in $y = \log x$ gives us $\boxed{y} = \log 10^{\boxed{y}}$.

PROPERTY 1   The logarithm of a product equals the sum of the logarithms of its factors.

$$\log mn = \log m + \log n$$

PROOF
$$\log (mn) \overset{?}{=} \log m + \log n$$
$$\log (10^{\log m} \cdot 10^{\log n}) \overset{?}{=} \log m + \log n$$
$$\log 10^{\log m + \log n} \overset{?}{=} \log m + \log n$$
$$\log m + \log n = \log m + \log n \qquad \text{Q. E. D.}$$

PROPERTY 2   The logarithm of a quotient equals the logarithm of the dividend minus the logarithm of the divisor.

$$\log \frac{m}{n} = \log m - \log n$$

PROOF
$$\log \left(\frac{m}{n}\right) \overset{?}{=} \log m - \log n$$
$$\log \left(\frac{10^{\log m}}{10^{\log n}}\right) \overset{?}{=} \log m - \log n$$
$$\log 10^{\log m - \log n} \overset{?}{=} \log m - \log n$$
$$\log m - \log n = \log m - \log n \qquad \text{Q. E. D.}$$

PROPERTY 3   The logarithm of the nth power of a number equals n times the logarithm of the number.

$$\log m^n = n \log m$$

PROOF
$$\log [m^n] \overset{?}{=} n \log m$$
$$\log [(10^{\log m})^n] \overset{?}{=} n \log m$$
$$\log 10^{n \log m} \overset{?}{=} n \log m$$
$$n \log m = n \log m \qquad \text{Q. E. D.}$$

PROPERTY 4 The logarithm of the positive real nth root of a number equals $\frac{1}{n}$ times the logarithm of the number.

$$\log \sqrt[n]{m} = \frac{1}{n} \log m$$

PROOF The proof is left for the student. Note that a root may be represented by using an exponent in fraction form. Thus, Property 3 may be applied.

Before the use of electronic calculators and computers became commonplace, logarithms and their properties were among the most useful tools for simplifying difficult computations. Property 1 replaces a multiplication by an addition. Property 2 replaces a division by a subtraction. Property 3 replaces finding a power by a multiplication. Property 4 replaces finding a root by a division.

EXAMPLE 1 Multiply 47.2 and 3.61.

SOLUTION Let $p = (47.2)(3.61)$. Take the common logarithm of each member. Use Property 1 for the right member.

$$p = (47.2)(3.61)$$
$$\log p = \log [(47.2)(3.61)]$$
$$= \log 47.2 + \log 3.61$$
$$\doteq 1.6739 + 0.5575$$
$$\log p \doteq 2.2314$$
$$p \doteq \text{antilog } 2.2314$$
$$p \doteq 170.4$$

EXAMPLE 2 Multiply 79.43 and 0.057.

SOLUTION Let $p = (79.43)(0.057)$.

$$\text{Then, } \log p = \log 79.43 + \log 0.057 \qquad \text{(Property 1)}$$
$$\doteq 1.9000 + (8.7559 - 10)$$
$$\log p \doteq 0.6559$$
$$p \doteq \text{antilog } 0.6559$$
$$p \doteq 4.528$$

EXAMPLE 3 Divide 48 200 by 0.913.

SOLUTION Let $q = \dfrac{48\ 200}{0.913}$.

$$\text{Then, } \log q = \log 48\ 200 - \log 0.913 \qquad \text{(Property 2)}$$
$$\doteq 4.6830 - (9.9605 - 10)$$
$$\log q \doteq 4.7225$$
$$q \doteq \text{antilog } 4.7225$$
$$q \doteq 52\ 790$$

EXAMPLE 4 Divide -4.563 by 13.22.

SOLUTION Although the logarithm of a negative number is not defined, logs still may be used to approximate the quotient.

Let $\quad q = \dfrac{-4.563}{13.22}$. Then, $-q = \dfrac{4.563}{13.22}$.

$$\log(-q) = \log 4.563 - \log 13.22 \qquad \text{(Property 2)}$$
$$\doteq 0.6593 - 1.1213$$
$$\doteq (10.6593 - 10) - 1.1213$$
$$\log(-q) \doteq 9.5380 - 10$$
$$-q \doteq \text{antilog } (9.5380 - 10)$$
$$-q \doteq 0.3452$$

Thus, $q \doteq -0.3452$

EXAMPLE 5 Simplify 7.163^3.

SOLUTION Let $\quad p = 7.163^3$.

Then, $\log p = 3 \log 7.163 \qquad \text{(Property 3)}$
$$\log p \doteq 3(0.8551), \text{ or } 2.5653$$
$$p \doteq \text{antilog } 2.5653$$
$$p \doteq 367.5$$

EXAMPLE 6 Find the cube root of 0.0682.

SOLUTION Let $\quad r = \sqrt[3]{0.0682}$.

Then, $\log r = \frac{1}{3} \log 0.0682 \qquad \text{(Property 4)}$
$$\doteq \frac{1}{3}(8.8338 - 10)$$
$$\doteq \frac{1}{3}(28.8338 - 30)$$
$$\log r \doteq 9.6113 - 10$$
$$r \doteq \text{antilog } (9.6113 - 10)$$
$$r \doteq 0.4086$$

EXAMPLE 7 Simplify $\sqrt{\dfrac{(47.2)(9.6)}{0.032}}$.

SOLUTION Let $\quad n = \left[\dfrac{(47.2)(9.6)}{0.032} \right]^{\frac{1}{2}}$.

Then, $\log n = \frac{1}{2}(\log 47.2 + \log 9.6 - \log 0.032)$
$$\doteq \frac{1}{2}[1.6739 + 0.9823 - (8.5051 - 10)]$$
$$\log n \doteq \frac{1}{2}(4.1511), \text{ or } 2.0756$$
$$n \doteq \text{antilog } 2.0756$$
$$n \doteq 119$$

CLASSROOM EXERCISES

Approximate. Use logarithms.

1. $(8.4)(9.2)$

2. $\dfrac{27.5}{382}$

3. $(315.4)^2$

4. $\sqrt[3]{425.5}$

EXERCISES

A Approximate. Use logarithms.

1. $(3.44)(272)$ **2.** $(9.21)(326)$ **3.** $72.8 \div 3.62$ **4.** $603 \div 373$

5. $\sqrt{870}$ **6.** $\sqrt[3]{94}$ **7.** $2.34 \div 305$ **8.** $4.58 \div 76$

9. $(91)(172)$ **10.** $(200)(612)$ **11.** $(27)(0.0093)$ **12.** $(0.4)(0.316)$

13. $\sqrt[5]{343}$ **14.** $\sqrt[7]{728}$ **15.** $(90.8)^2$ **16.** $(1.732)^2$

17. $12.3 \div 0.0531$ **18.** $409 \div 0.00630$ **19.** $(-40.7)(5029)$ **20.** $(-365)(941)$

21. $-603.4 \div 3.75$ **22.** $1000 \div -3.14$ **23.** $(-7.063)^3$ **24.** $(-2.14)^5$

25. $\sqrt[6]{(785.2)^2}$ **26.** $\sqrt{(12.6)^3}$ **27.** $\sqrt[3]{84.9(1.04)^2}$ **28.** $\sqrt{1.04^3(75^2)}$

29. $\sqrt{\dfrac{27.35}{(0.064)(7.89)}}$ **30.** $\sqrt[5]{\dfrac{762.3}{(14.9)(0.47)}}$ **31.** $\left[\dfrac{(5.317)(4.787)}{18}\right]^2$

B Write the expression as a monomial. Use the properties of logarithms.

32. $\log x - \log y$ **33.** $\log 5x + \log x$ **34.** $\log x + \log 2x$

35. $\log (x^2) - \log y$ **36.** $2 \log x + \log x$ **37.** $\log x + 3 \log x$

Write the expression in an expanded form. Use the properties of logarithms.

38. $\log \left(\dfrac{x^5}{y^2}\right)$ **39.** $\log (\sqrt{x} \cdot y^2)$ **40.** $\log (\sqrt[3]{x} \cdot y^4)$

Approximate. Use logarithms.

41. $9.96(3.15)^2$ **42.** $\sqrt[4]{[(1.732)(1.414)]^3}$ **43.** $[(4832)(1.67)]^{\frac{2}{3}}$

C Solve. Use the properties of logarithms.

44. $\log 2 + \log 3 = \log x$ **45.** $\log_2 6 - \log_2 3 = \log_2 x$ **46.** $2 \log_2 x - \log_2 4 = 4$

The change-of-base formula, $\log_b N = \dfrac{\log_a N}{\log_a b}$, provides a way to find the logarithm of a number to a different base. Find each logarithm. Use $a = 10$.

47. $\log_2 10$ **48.** $\log_3 20$ **49.** $\log_4 75$

10-10   PROBLEM SOLVING: USING LOGARITHMS

We can use logarithms to help us solve problems that involve difficult computation.

EXAMPLE 1   The formula for the volume of a sphere is $V = \frac{4}{3}\pi r^3$.   How great should the radius be for a sphere to have a volume of 1 cubic meter?   (Use 3.142 for π.)

SOLUTION   Solve the formula for r.   Replace V by 1.000.   Use logarithms to approximate r.

$$V = \frac{4}{3}\pi r^3$$

$$r = \sqrt[3]{\frac{3V}{4\pi}}$$

$$r = \sqrt[3]{\frac{0.75(1.000)}{3.142}}$$

$$\log r = \frac{1}{3}(\log 0.75 - \log 3.142)$$
$$\doteq \frac{1}{3}(9.8751 - 10 - 0.4972)$$
$$\doteq \frac{1}{3}(9.3779 - 10)$$
$$\doteq \frac{1}{3}(29.3779 - 30)$$
$$\log r \doteq 9.7926 - 10$$
$$r \doteq \text{antilog }(9.7926 - 10)$$
$$r \doteq 0.6203$$

CONCLUSION   The radius should be about 0.6203 m or 62.03 cm.

CHECK   Use logarithms to check that $1 \doteq \frac{4}{3}(3.142)(0.6203)^3$

Logarithms also may be used to solve exponential equations in which both members cannot be written easily as powers of the same base.

EXAMPLE 2   Solve $4^x = 15$.

SOLUTION $$4^x = 15$$
$$\log 4^x = \log 15$$
$$x \log 4 = \log 15$$
$$x = \frac{\log 15}{\log 4}$$
$$x \doteq \frac{1.1761}{0.6021}$$
$$x \doteq 1.953$$

CHECK   Use logarithms to check that $4^{1.953} \doteq 15$.

EXAMPLE 3   Solve $x^{\sqrt{3}} = 10$

SOLUTION
$$x^{\sqrt{3}} = 10$$
$$\log x^{\sqrt{3}} = \log 10$$
$$\sqrt{3} \log x = 1$$
$$\log x = \frac{\sqrt{3}}{3}$$
$$\log x \doteq \frac{1.7321}{3}$$
$$\log x \doteq 0.5774$$
$$x \doteq \text{antilog } 0.5774$$
$$x \doteq 3.779$$

CHECK   Use logarithms to check that $(3.779)^{\sqrt{3}} \doteq 10$

Many growth and decay patterns in nature and technology can be described by exponential formulas. Logarithms are helpful in using these formulas.

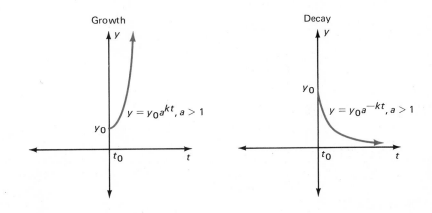

For these formulas, the variables have the following general meanings.

t is used for the elapsed time.

y_0 is used for the initial ($t = 0$) amount, number, temperature, population, and so on.

y is used for the amount, number, temperature, population, and so on, after time t.

a and k are positive constants with $a > 1$.

EXAMPLE 4 The number of bacteria in a colony is 100 at $t = 0$. Use the formula $N = N_0 \cdot 2^{4t}$ to find the number of bacteria after 5 hours have elapsed.

SOLUTION

$N = N_0 \cdot 2^{4t}$

$N = 100 \cdot 2^{4(5)}$

$N = 100 \cdot 2^{20}$

$\log N = \log 100 + 20 \log 2$

$\doteq 2 + 20(0.3010)$

$\log N \doteq 8.020$

$N \doteq$ antilog 8.020

$N \doteq 104\ 700\ 000$

CONCLUSION

After 5 hours, there are about 105 million bacteria in the colony.

Compound interest is another example of a growth situation. When money is invested in this way, the interest due is added to the principal to form a new principal. The value, A, of an investment of P dollars at an annual interest rate r is given by the Compound Interest Formula. In the formula, n represents the number of times interest is compounded each year and t represents the number of years.

> THE COMPOUND INTEREST FORMULA
>
> $$A = P\left(1 + \frac{r}{n}\right)^{nt}$$

EXAMPLE 5 Find the number of years required for an investment of $500 to grow in value to at least $800 at 8% annual interest compounded quarterly.

SOLUTION

$P\left(1 + \dfrac{r}{n}\right)^{nt} \geq A$ when $A = 800$

$\log P + nt \log\left(1 + \dfrac{r}{n}\right) \geq \log A$

$t \geq \dfrac{\log A - \log P}{n \log\left(1 + \dfrac{r}{n}\right)}$

$t \geq \dfrac{\log 800 - \log 500}{4 \log\left(1 + \dfrac{0.08}{4}\right)}$

$t \geq \dfrac{2.9030 - 2.6990}{4 \log 1.02}$

$t \geq \dfrac{0.2040}{4(0.0086)}$

$t \geq 5.9$

CONCLUSION

It would take 6 years for the investment to grow in value to at least $800.

CLASSROOM EXERCISES

Solve.

1. $2^x = 100$ **2.** $6^{-x} = 3$

3. $5^{-x} = 0.25$ **4.** $(0.5)^x = 2$

5. $S = \dfrac{\pi r^2 E}{180}$ is a formula for finding the area of a triangle contained in a sphere. Find S when $r = 3.44$ and $E = 75$. Use 3.14 for π.

6. The number of grams of a radioactive substance that are left after t years is given by $Q = Q_0 \, 10^{-0.006t}$. For an initial amount (Q_0) of 100 grams, find the number of grams left after 50 years.

7. Find the number of years required for an investment of $1000 to grow in value to at least $2000 at 8% annual interest compounded quarterly.

EXERCISES

A Solve.

1. $2^x = 1.5$ **2.** $3^x = 21$

3. $4.1^x = 36.9$ **4.** $5.8^x = 750$

5. $6^{-x} = 0.2$ **6.** $5^{-x} = 0.50$

7. $x^{1.4} = 36$ **8.** $x^{2.5} = 25$

9. $x^{-0.75} = 4$ **10.** $x^{-1.2} = 1.2$

11. $x^{\sqrt{2}} = 0.16$ **12.** $x^{\sqrt{3}} = 35$

13. The initial number (N_0) of bacteria in a colony is 1000. Use the formula $N = N_0 \cdot 2^{3t}$ to find the number of bacteria after 4 hours ($t = 4$) have elapsed.

14. The population of a city is 50 000. Use the formula $N = N_0 \cdot 2^{\frac{t}{60}}$ to predict the population fo the city in 20 years ($t = 20$).

15. The number of grams of a radioactive element that remains after t years is given by $Q = Q_0 \, 10^{-0.0045t}$. For an initial amount of 500 grams, find the number of grams of radioactive material remaining after 100 years.

16. Repeat Exercise 15 using the formula $Q = Q_0 \cdot 10^{-0.00045t}$.

17. Find the length of a side of an equilateral triangle whose area is 58.3 square centimeters.

18. Find the length of a side of an equilateral triangle whose area is 125 square centimeters.

19. Find the number of years required for an investment of $5000 to grow in value to at least $7000 at 8% annual interest compounded quarterly.

20. Find the number of years for an investment of $100 to grow in value to $1000 at 15% annual interest compounded semi-annually.

21. $650 is invested at 6% annual interest compounded quarterly. Find the value of the investment in 9 years.

22. The number of bacteria in a colony after t hours is given by $N = N_0 \cdot 3^{0.04t}$. If there are 1 000 000 000 bacteria in the colony in 5 hours, find the initial number present.

B Solve.

23. $3(5^x) - 1 = 8$ **24.** $2x^{1.7} + 3 = 4$

25. $3^{2x+1} = 245$ **26.** $8^{\sqrt{x}} = 3^x$

27. How long would it take a population to double if it followed the growth formula $N = N_0 \cdot 10^{\frac{t}{25}}$? t represents time in years.

28. Find the time required to double the principal at 10% annual interest compounded quarterly.

29. In the formula $Q = Q_0 \cdot 10^{-kt}$ where t represents days, the decay constant, k, for Polonium 210 is 0.00215. There are 2200 grams of Polonium 210 when $t = 0$. Find how many grams are left at $t = 7$ days.

30. Find the area of a triangle having sides with lengths 18, 26, and 31 centimeters. Use Hero's formula,
$$A = \sqrt{S(S - a)(S - b)(S - c)},$$
where the measures of the sides are a, b, and c and $S = \frac{1}{2}(a + b + c)$.

31. Research the meaning of the word "half-life". Find the half-life of a radioactive substance for which $Q = Q_0\, 10^{-0.24t}$.

C Solve.

32. $3^{x^2} \cdot 2^x = 5^{3x}$ **33.** $(\sqrt{2})^{x^2-1} = 3^{-x^2}$

34. What annual rate compounded quarterly is needed to double an investment in 8 years?

35. A population is given by $P = P_0 \cdot 4^{kt}$. $P_0 = 100$. $P = 115$ when $t = 5$. Find P when $t = 10$.

CHECKING YOUR UNDERSTANDING

WORDS

antilogarithm
characteristic

common logarithm
interpolation

mantissa

CONCEPTS

■ Since logarithms are exponents, the properties of logarithms follow directly from the rules for operating with exponents. [10-9]

■ $10^{\log x} = x$ and $\log 10^y = y$. [10-9]

PROCESSES

■ Find common logarithms and antilogarithms using a table. [10-7, 10-8]

1. $\log 4.83 \doteq ?$

2. antilog $0.9562 \doteq ?$

3. $10^{0.4829} \doteq ?$

4. $\log 7000 \doteq ?$

5. $\log 0.68 \doteq ?$

6. antilog $3.7412 \doteq ?$

7. antilog $8.0253 - 10 \doteq ?$

8. $\log 8714 \doteq ?$

9. antilog $1.5746 \doteq ?$

■ Compute using common logarithms. [10-9]

10. $\dfrac{(48.7)(0.028)}{17}$

11. $\sqrt[4]{\dfrac{89.6}{0.12}}$

12. $\sqrt[3]{-700}$

■ Solve exponential equations using logarithms. [10-10]

13. $3^x = 19$

14. $x^{\sqrt{5}} = 7$

15. $(0.5)^{x-1} = 1.5$

CHAPTER REVIEW

Simplify. [10-1]

1. $4^{0.75}$

2. $(3^{\sqrt{2}})^{\sqrt{8}}$

3. $\dfrac{6\pi}{6^{\pi-2}}$

4. $(a^{1+\sqrt{5}})(a^{1-\sqrt{5}})$

5. Graph $y = 3^x$. [10-2]

6. Graph $y = \left(\dfrac{2}{3}\right)^x$.

7. Use the graph from Exercise 5 to approximate $3^{\sqrt{2}}$.

Solve. [10-3]

8. $7^{3x+2} = 7^8$

9. $9^{x+4} = 3^{3x+1}$

10. $81^{2x} = \left(\dfrac{1}{27}\right)^{x+3}$

Change each equation in exponential form to one of logarithmic form, and vice versa. [10-4]

11. $5^{-2} = \dfrac{1}{25}$

12. $2^5 = 32$

13. $\log_4 16 = 2$

14. $\log_{27} 9 = \dfrac{2}{3}$

Simplify.

15. $\log_4 64$

16. $\log_5 \dfrac{1}{5}$

Solve each equation. [10-5]

17. $\log_x 2 = \dfrac{1}{3}$

18. $2\log_6 x - 6 = 0$

19. $\log_4 4x - 2 = 2$

20. Graph $y = \log_3 x$. [10-6]

21. Use the graph for Exercise 20 to approximate $\log_3 5$.

Approximate. Use Table I. [10-7]

22. $10^{0.7818}$

23. $10^{2.2095}$

Solve. Use Table I.

24. $7.76 = 10^x$

25. $83.2 = 10^x$

Simplify. Use Table I. [10-8]

26. $\log 47.3$

27. $\log 12.18$

28. antilog 2.8463

29. antilog 3.5484

Simplify by using logarithms. [10-9]

30. $\sqrt{\dfrac{(14.1)^4 (3.06)}{0.189}}$

31. $\sqrt[5]{-18}$

Solve. [10-10]

32. $5^x = 37$

33. $x^{\sqrt{2}} = 19$

CAPSULE REVIEW

Write the letter of the best response.

1. The value of $8^{0.\overline{6}}$ is

a. $5.\overline{3}$

b. 1

c. 6

d. 4

2. If 27^{x+1} equals $\left(\dfrac{1}{3}\right)^{-9-x}$, then x equals

    a. $\dfrac{1}{2}$ **b.** 3   **c.** $\dfrac{2}{3}$ **d.** 5

3. The logarithmic form for $5^{\pi} = x$ is

    a. $\log_5 \pi = x$ **b.** $\log_5 x = \pi$ **c.** $\log_{\pi} x = 5$ **d.** $\log_x 5 = \pi$

4. The solutions of the equation $(\log_2 x - 2)(\log_x 8 - 3) = 0$ are

    a. 2 and 4   **b.** 2 and 6   **c.** $\sqrt{2}$ and 5   **d.** 2 and 16

5. The number $10^{2.8446}$ is between

    a. 1 and 10   **b.** 10 and 100   **c.** 100 and 1000   **d.** 1000 and 10 000

6. Which of these numbers is greatest?

    a. antilog 4.0862   **b.** $10^{6.0829}$ **c.** antilog $(7.6104 - 10)$ **d.** log 8.9064

7. If $n = \sqrt[5]{\dfrac{187}{14^2}}$, then $\log n$ equals

    a. $\dfrac{1}{5} \log 187 - 2 \log 14$ **b.** $\log \dfrac{187}{5} - 2 \log \dfrac{14}{5}$

    c. $\dfrac{1}{5}(\log 187 + \log 28)$ **d.** $\dfrac{1}{5}(\log 187 - 2 \log 14)$

8. If $4^x = \sqrt{15}$ then

    a. $x = \dfrac{\log 15}{2 \log 4}$ **b.** $x = \dfrac{4 \log 15}{2}$ **c.** $x = \log \dfrac{15}{4}$ **d.** $x = \text{antilog} \dfrac{\sqrt{15}}{4}$

CHAPTER TEST

---

1. Simplify $(2^{\sqrt{3}})^{\sqrt{3}}$.   **2.** Simplify $2^{1+\sqrt{3}} \cdot 2^{1-\sqrt{3}}$.

3. Complete this member $(-3, \underline{\quad ? \quad})$ of the exponential function $y = 2^x$.

4. Complete this member $(2, \underline{\quad ? \quad})$ of the exponential function $y = \left(\dfrac{1}{3}\right)^x$.

5. Solve $2^{3x} = 2^4$.   **6.** Solve $5^{3x+1} = 125$.

7. Write an exponential equation equivalent to $a = \log_b c$.

8. Write an equation in logarithmic form for $2^5 = 32$.

9. Solve $\log_3 x = 2$.   **10.** Solve $\log_x 16 = 2$.

11. Sketch the graph of $y = \log_3 x$. Write the coordinates of three points.

12. Sketch the graph of $y = \log_{\frac{1}{3}} x$. Write the coordinates of three points.

13. Use Table I to solve $10^x = 3.51$.   **14.** Use Table I to solve $10^{1.8567} = x$.

15. What is the characteristic of the logarithm of 0.0317?

16. Find the logarithm of 1.913. Use Table I.

17. Find the logarithm of 2.47^{10}.   **18.** Find the logarithm of $\sqrt[6]{4.59}$.

19. Use Table I.   Find A when $P = 100$, $r = 0.07$, $t = 10$ and $A = P(1 + r)^t$.

20. Use Table I.   Approximate $3.^{1.414}$.

Write the letter of the best response.

21. How is $2^{1.4}$ written in radical form?

    a. $\sqrt[4]{2}$ **b.** $\sqrt[4]{2^{10}}$ **c.** $\sqrt[5]{2^7}$ **d.** $\sqrt[5]{5^{10}}$ **e.** $\sqrt[7]{2^5}$

22. Which function is shown by the graph?

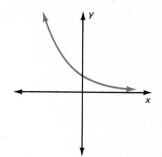

    a. $y = -2x$ **b.** $y = 2^x$ **c.** $y = -\left(\dfrac{1}{2}\right)^x$

    d. $y = \left(\dfrac{1}{2}\right)^x$ **e.** $y = (\sqrt{2})^x$

23. What is the solution of $4^{2x-1} = 16$?

    a. $\dfrac{1}{2}$ **b.** $\dfrac{2}{3}$ **c.** $1\dfrac{1}{2}$ **d.** 2 **e.** 3

24. What is $\log_2 64$ simplified?

    a. 6 **b.** 8 **c.** 32 **d.** 128 **e.** 4096

25. What is the solution of $\log_2 16 = x$?

    a. 4 **b.** 8 **c.** 32 **d.** 256 **e.** $65\,536$

26. Which function is shown by the graph?

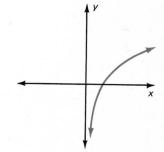

    a. $y = -\log_3 x$ **b.** $y = \log_{\frac{1}{3}} x$ **c.** $y = \log_{-3} x$

    d. $y = -\log_{\sqrt{3}} x$ **e.** $y = \log_{\sqrt{3}} x$

27. Use Table I.   What is the solution of $10^x = 53.2$?

    a. 0.7259 **b.** 1.7259 **c.** 2.7259 **d.** -0.2741 **e.** -1.2741

28. What is the common logarithm of 2.956?

    a. 0.4698 **b.** 0.4701 **c.** 0.4704 **d.** 0.4707 **e.** 0.4713

29. $\log \sqrt[3]{456} =$

    a. $\log 3.456$ **b.** $\sqrt[3]{\log 456}$ **c.** $3 \log 456$ **d.** $\log \dfrac{456}{3}$ **e.** $\dfrac{\log 456}{3}$

30. What does $2^{1.732}$ equal?

    a. 3.24 **b.** 3.32 **c.** 3.40 **d.** 3.48 **e.** 3.56

CHAPTER 11
SEQUENCES AND SERIES

Electronic information-processing equipment is having tremendous impact on business. For the more challenging jobs involving such equipment, employers often look for people who can think logically and are able to do exacting, analytical work. Such jobs also call for patience, persistence, and the ability to work with extreme accuracy. Ingenuity and imagination can be helpful.

OBJECTIVES: Identify arithmetic sequences and their characteristics.
Solve problems using arithmetic sequences.

11-1   ARITHMETIC SEQUENCES

A **sequence** is a set of numbers whose members are arranged in a definite order.   Each number in a sequence is a **term of the sequence**. A **finite sequence** has a first term and a last term.   An **infinite sequence** has a first term but no last term.   That is, it has infinitely many terms.

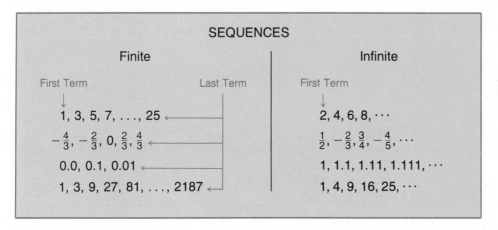

When each term of a sequence, except the first, can be obtained from the preceding term by *adding* a constant, the sequence is an **arithmetic sequence**.   The constant is called the **common difference** for the sequence since it may be found by subtracting *any* term from its succeeding term.

First Term	Common Difference	Arithmetic Sequence					
6	3	6,	9,	12,	15,	18,	21, $\cdots$
8	-2.5	8,	5.5,	3,	0.5,	-2,	-4.5, $\cdots$
$-\frac{2}{3}$	$\frac{2}{3}$	$-\frac{2}{3}$,	0,	$\frac{2}{3}$,	$1\frac{1}{3}$,	2,	$2\frac{2}{3}$, $\cdots$
a	d	$a, a+d,$	$a+2d,$	$a+3d,$	$a+4d,$	$a+5d, \cdots$	

first term   second term   third term   fourth term   fifth term   sixth term

When we use a for the first term and d for the common difference, note that the coefficient of d in each term is one less than the number of the term. When we use l to denote the nth term (that is, the last term) of a finite sequence, we have

$$l = a + (n - 1)d$$

EXAMPLE 1   Find the fourteenth term of the arithmetic sequence 5, 7, 9, 11, $\cdots$.

SOLUTION   Use the formula given above. Replace the variables as follows.

First term: $a = 5$
Common difference: $d = 2$
Number of terms: $n = 14$

Find l. $l = a + (n - 1)d$
$l = 5 + (14 - 1)2$
$= 5 + 26$
$l = 31$

EXAMPLE 2   The eighth term of an arithmetic sequence is 6. The common difference is $\frac{3}{4}$. Find the first term. Give the first six terms of the sequence.

SOLUTION   Use the formula. Replace l by 6, n by 8, and d by $\frac{3}{4}$. Find a.

$$l = a + (n - 1)d$$
$$6 = a + (8 - 1)\frac{3}{4}$$
$$6 = a + \frac{21}{4}$$
$$\frac{3}{4} = a$$

List the first six terms of the sequence.

$\frac{3}{4}, \frac{3}{4} + \frac{3}{4}, \frac{3}{4} + \frac{3}{4} + \frac{3}{4}$, and so on

$\frac{3}{4}, \quad \frac{6}{4}, \quad \frac{9}{4}, \quad \frac{12}{4}, \quad \frac{15}{4}, \quad \frac{18}{4}$

$\frac{3}{4}, \quad 1\frac{1}{2}, \quad 2\frac{1}{4}, \quad 3, \quad 3\frac{3}{4}, \quad 4\frac{1}{2}$

EXAMPLE 3   The seventh term of an arithmetic sequence is 22. The tenth term is 31. Find the first term and the common difference. Give the first six terms of the sequence.

SOLUTION   Since we wish to find two unknowns, we may write a system of two equations in two variables. Use the formula to help write each equation.

$$l = a + (n - 1)d$$

Replace l by 22 and n by 7.　　$22 = a + 6d$
Replace l by 31 and n by 10.　$\underline{31 = a + 9d}$
　　　　　　　　　Subtract.　　$-9 = \quad -3d$
　　　　　　　　　　　　　　$3 = d$

Find a.　Replace d by 3 in　　$22 = a + 6d.$
　　　　　　　　　　　　　　$22 = a + 6 \cdot 3$
　　　　　　　　　　　　　　$4 = a$

List the first six terms of the sequence.
　　　4, 7, 10, 13, 16, 19

　The terms between two nonconsecutive terms of an arithmetic sequence are **arithmetic means** between those terms.　If there is only one term between two other terms, it is **the arithmetic mean**, or **average**, of the two numbers.

EXAMPLE 4　Insert five arithmetic means between -3 and 21.

SOLUTION　Inserting 5 arithmetic means between two numbers gives a sequence of seven terms ($n = 7$).

Use the formula $l = a + (n - 1)d$.
Replace a by -3, l by 21, and n by 7.
Find d.　　　　　$l = a + (n - 1)d$
　　　　　$21 = -3 + (7 - 1)d$
　　　　　$21 = -3 + 6d$
　　　　　$24 = 6d$
　　　　　$4 = d$

List the seven terms of the sequence.
　　$-3, 1, 5, 9, 13, 17, 21$

Five arithmetic means between -3 and 21 are 1, 5, 9, 13, and 17.

EXAMPLE 5　Find *the* arithmetic mean between -3 and 21.

SOLUTION　Use m for the arithmetic mean between -3 and 21.

For the sequence　$-3, m, 21,$　the common difference may be found by subtracting *any* term from its succeeding term.

Therefore, $m - (-3) = 21 - m$.
　　　　　$2m = -3 + 21$
　　　　　$m = \dfrac{-3 + 21}{2}$
　　　　　$= 9$

The arithmetic mean between -3 and 21 is 9.

CLASSROOM EXERCISES

Find the indicated variables. Use $l = a + (n - 1)d$.

1. $a = ?$ $l = 73$
   $d = 4$ $n = 24$

2. $d = ?$ 1st term = 5
   7th term = 17

3. $a = ?$ 15th term = 91
   $d = ?$ 20th term = 121

4. Write the first five terms of the sequence for each exercise above.

Insert the indicated number of arithmetic means.

5. -5 and 7, one

6. -2 and 13, four

7. 12 and -12, six

EXERCISES

A Find the indicated term.

1. 20th term of $1, 3, 5, \cdots$

2. 18th term of $8, 3, -2, -7, \cdots$

3. 12th term of $a, a + 4, a + 8, a + 12, \cdots$

4. 8th term of $x + 5, x + 3, x + 1, \cdots$

Find the indicated variables. Use $l = a + (n - 1)d$.

5. $d = ?$ 1st term = 5
   17th term = 85

6. $a = ?$ 9th term = 21
   $d = ?$ 15th term = 33

7. $a = 9$ 6th term = $2\frac{1}{2}$
   $d = ?$

Write the first five terms of each arithmetic sequence.

8. $\underline{\ ?\ }, \underline{\ ?\ }, 1, \underline{\ ?\ }, \underline{\ ?\ }, \cdots$; 7th term = -11

9. $\underline{\ ?\ }, \underline{-1\ }, \underline{\ ?\ }, \underline{\ ?\ }, \underline{\ ?\ }, \cdots$; 18th term = 47

Insert the indicated number of arithmetic means.

10. 6 and 26, three

11. 1 and 29, one

12. 55 and -8, five

Find the arithmetic mean for each pair.

13. -7 and 41

14. 4 and $6\frac{1}{3}$

15. $2x^2$ and $7x^2$

16. $-4a$ and $5a$

B **17.** Find the 36th term of the sequence $x + 1, x + 1 - \dfrac{1}{x - 1}, x + 1 - \dfrac{2}{x - 1}, \cdots$.

18. $a = 2x + 1$. The 11th term is $3x^2 - 4x + 1$. Find the common difference.

19. $x - 9$ is the arithmetic mean between $x - 3$ and $2x + 4$. Find x.

C **20.** Prove that the term-by-term sum of two arithmetic sequences of the same length is another arithmetic sequence.

21. For the arithmetic sequence A: $a, a + d, a + 2d, \cdots$, prove that the sequence formed by the arithmetic means between successive odd-numbered terms of A is another arithmetic sequence.

11-2 FINDING THE SUM OF n TERMS OF AN ARITHMETIC SEQUENCE

One way to find the sum of a certain number of terms of an arithmetic sequence is to add the terms.   However, this method can take too long. Instead, we develop a formula for finding the sum of n terms.

Let $S =$ the sum of n terms of an arithmetic sequence.

$$S = \quad a \quad + (a + d) + (a + 2d) + \cdots + (l - 2d) \ + (l - d) \ + \quad l$$
$$S = \quad l \quad + (l - d) \ + (l - 2d) \ + \cdots + (a + 2d) + (a + d) + \quad a$$

Add. $2S = (a + l) + (a + l) \ + (a + l) \ \ + \cdots + (a + l) \ \ + (a + l) \ + (a + l)$

n terms

Then, $2S = n(a + l)$

$\qquad S = \dfrac{n}{2}(a + l)$

> The sum of n terms of an arithmetic sequence:
>
> $$S = \dfrac{n}{2}(a + l).$$

EXAMPLE 1 Find the sum of the terms of the sequence 5, 10, 15, $\cdots$, 100.

SOLUTION First, find the number of terms in the sequence.

Replace a by 5, l by 100, and d by 5 in

$l = a + (n - 1)d$.   Find n.

$$l = a + (n - 1)d$$
$$100 = 5 + (n - 1)5$$
$$100 = 5 + 5n - 5$$
$$100 = 5n$$
$$20 = n$$

Then, replace a by 5, l by 100, and n by 20

in $S = \dfrac{n}{2}(a + l)$.   Find S.

$$S = \dfrac{n}{2}(a + l)$$

$$S = \dfrac{20}{2}(5 + 100)$$

$$= 10(105)$$
$$S = 1050$$

EXAMPLE 2 A grocery clerk built a pyramid of cans. There were 15 cans in the bottom row, 14 in the next row, 13 in the next row, and so on. How many cans were in the pyramid?

SOLUTION The sequence 15, 14, 13, $\cdots$, 1 is an arithmetic sequence with 15 terms.

Use the formula $S = \frac{n}{2}(a + l)$.

Replace a by 15, l by 1 and n by 15.

$$S = \frac{15}{2}(15 + 1)$$

$$= 120$$

CONCLUSION There were 120 cans in the pyramid.

EXAMPLE 3 Mr. Hill borrowed $1000 from a loan company. He agreed to pay back $50 each month until the loan is repaid. He also agreed to pay interest at the rate of 2% each month on the unpaid amount. How much must Mr. Hill pay the loan company?

SOLUTION Determine the amounts in the sequence of payments made by Mr. Hill. Then find their sum. Make a chart to show all the sequences involved.

Month	Unpaid Amount ($)	Interest Payment ($)	Regular Payment ($)	Total Monthly Payment ($)
1	1000	20	50	70
2	950	19	50	69
3	900	18	50	68
.	.	.	.	.
.	.	.	.	.
.	.	.	.	.
19	100	2	50	52
20	50	1	50	51

Use the formula to find the sum of the monthly payments. Replace a by 70, l by 51, and n by 20.

$$S = \frac{n}{2}(a + l)$$

$$= \frac{20}{2}(70 + 51)$$

$$= 1210$$

CONCLUSION Mr. Hill must pay the loan company $1210.

CHECK Use the formula to find the sum of the interest payments and the regular payments. Compare their sum with 1210.

Since $S = \frac{n}{2}(a + l)$, it follows that $\frac{S}{n} = \frac{a + l}{2}$.   We know that a sum divided by the number of terms that are added is the average.   Likewise, $\frac{a + l}{2}$ is the average of the first and last terms.   Hence, we have the following facts.

1.   The average of n terms of an arithmetic sequence equals the average of the first and last terms.

$$\frac{S}{n} = \frac{a + l}{2}$$

(Either is the average.)

2.   The sum of n terms of an arithmetic sequence is n times the average of the terms.

$$S = n\left(\frac{a + l}{2}\right)$$

EXAMPLE 4   Find the average for these lengths:
5 cm, 10 cm, 15 cm, $\cdots$, 100 cm.

SOLUTION   Use A for the average.   Then $A = \frac{a + l}{2}$, or $A = \frac{S}{n}$.

Replace a by 5 and l by 100 in
$$A = \frac{a + l}{2}.$$
$$A = \frac{5 + 100}{2}$$
$$A = 52.5$$

Use the results of Example 1. Replace S by 1050 and n by 20 in
$$A = \frac{S}{n}.$$
$$A = \frac{1050}{20}$$
$$A = 52.5$$

CONCLUSION   The average length is 52.5 cm.

Sometimes the last term of a sequence is not known.   However, to represent the sum of n terms of an arithmetic sequence, there is another way that does not need the last term.   To find it, replace l by $a + (n - 1)d$ in $S = \frac{n}{2}(a + l)$.

$$S = \frac{n}{2}\left(a + \boxed{l}\right)$$
$$= \frac{n}{2}\left(a + \boxed{a + (n - 1)d}\right)$$

$$S = \frac{n}{2}[2a + (n - 1)d]$$

EXAMPLE 5 Find the sum of the first 40 terms of the sequence 6, 8, 10, $\cdots$.

SOLUTION Replace a by 6, n by 40, and d by 2 in

$$S = \frac{n}{2}[2a + (n - 1)d].$$

$$S = \frac{40}{2}[2(6) + (40 - 1)2]$$

$$= 20(12 + 78)$$
$$= 1800$$

Special notation may be used to indicate the sum of n terms of a sequence. It is called *summation notation*, or *sigma notation* because it uses the Greek letter capital sigma, Σ.

When $s_1, s_2, s_3, \cdots, s_k, \cdots, s_n$ are n terms of a sequence, their sum may be represented by $\sum_{k=1}^{n} s_k$. This may be read, "The sum of all s_k (s sub k) for k having the integral values from 1 to n." The sum may be written in the standard form, with each s_k as an addend, by replacing k by each of the integers from 1 to n.

EXAMPLE 6 Simplify $\sum_{k=1}^{4} k$.

SOLUTION $\sum_{k=1}^{4} k = 1 + 2 + 3 + 4$

$$= 10$$

For an arithmetic sequence, the kth term is $a + (k - 1)d$. Therefore, the sum of n terms may be represented

$$\sum_{k=1}^{n} [a + (k - 1)d].$$

EXAMPLE 7 Simplify $\sum_{k=1}^{5} [-6 + (k - 1)3]$.

SOLUTION $\sum_{k=1}^{5} [-6 + (k - 1)3]$

$$= \sum_{k=1}^{5} (-9 + 3k)$$

$$= [-9 + 3(1)] + [-9 + 3(2)] + [-9 + 3(3)] +$$
$$[-9 + 3(4)] + [-9 + 3(5)]$$
$$= (-6) + (-3) + 0 + 3 + 6$$
$$= 0$$

CLASSROOM EXERCISES

Find the sum of the terms.

1. 6, 12, 18, $\cdots$, 120

2. $-4, -8, -12, \cdots, -240$

Find the average for each sequence.

3. 6 m, 12 m, 18 m, $\cdots$, 120 m

4. $-10°C, -5°C, 0°C, \cdots, 55°C$

Find the sum of the first 26 terms.

5. 3, 6, 9, $\cdots$

Solve.

6. Susan's grandfather opened a bank account for her when she was one year old. He deposited $1 when Susan was one, $2 when she was two, $3 when she was three, and so on. How much will he have deposited when Susan is 21?

EXERCISES

A Find the sum and the average of the terms.

1. 2, 6, 10, $\cdots$, 38

2. 7, 10, 13, $\cdots$, 43

3. $-70, -72, -74, \cdots, -106$

4. 2, $2\frac{1}{3}$, $2\frac{2}{3}$, $\cdots$, 27

5. $-2.7, -1.5, -0.3, \cdots, 56.1$

Find the sum.

6. integers 1 through 50

7. integers 1 through 100

8. first 8 terms of 3, 6, 9, 12, $\cdots$

9. first 12 terms of 5, 7, 9, $\cdots$

10. odd integers 1 through 99

11. first 25 terms of 0, $-6, -12, \cdots$

Solve.

12. Suppose Julio receives 10 cents on the first day of the year, 12 cents on the second day, 14 cents on the third day, and so on. How much will he receive on the 365th day? What is the sum of the amounts he receives?

13. Janet deposited money in her toy bank as follows: 10 cents the first week, 13 cents the second week, 16 cents the third week, and so on until she made 52 deposits. What was the amount of her last deposit? What was the sum of her deposits?

14. The Grubers borrow $3000 from a loan company. They plan to pay back $125 per month until the loan is repaid plus interest at the rate of 2% each month on the unpaid amount. Find the total amount they must pay back.

15. The Grubers found they are able to pay back $250 plus 2% interest on the unpaid balance of their $3000 loan each month. What is the total amount they must pay back?

16. A city sets a fine of $10 for a driver's first parking offense. It adds $10 to the fine for each subsequent offense. How much must be paid by a person who is ticketed for 20 illegal parking offenses?

17. The average of three numbers is 56. The difference between the second and first equals the difference between the third and second. The sum of the first and second is 96. Find the three numbers.

B **18.** Find the sum of the first ten terms of the arithmetic sequence with first term $6 + \sqrt{3}$ and common difference $\dfrac{2 - \sqrt{3}}{2 + \sqrt{3}}$.

19. In an arithmetic sequence, the third term is 10 and the fifth term is 24. Find the sum of the first 10 terms.

20. The second term of an arithmetic sequence is 2.5. The 7th term is 8. Find the average of the first eight terms.

21. The arithmetic mean between the first and third terms of an arithmetic sequence equals the common difference. The fifth term is 16. Find the sum of the first eight terms.

22. Find a formula for the sum of the first n terms of the arithmetic sequence 2, -7, -16, $\cdots$. Is there a value for n for which the sum of the first n terms is -70?

23. A person borrows $1800 and agrees to pay back $50 a month plus a certain percentage of the unpaid balance each month until the loan is repaid. The total interest to be paid is $499.50. Find the monthly interest rate on the unpaid balance.

$\boxed{C}$ **24.** Assume that 5 units of oil are being used in the world this year, that 9 units will be used next year, that 13 units will be used the year after, and so on. The supply of oil is 17.5 units this year, 20.5 units next year, 23.5 units the year after, and so on. In how many years will the demand for oil be greater than the supply?

25. An arithmetic sequence with common difference 2 is formed by the solutions of $x^3 - bx^2 + 71x - 105 = 0$. Find b. (Hint: b equals the sum of the solutions and 105 equals their product.)

26. Prove that the average of the sums of the terms of two arithmetic sequences of the same length (same number of terms) equals the sum of the averages of the corresponding pairs of terms of the two sequences.

27. Find x such that the average of the terms of the arithmetic sequence $\sqrt{x}$, $\sqrt{x} + \sqrt{x-1}$, $\sqrt{x} + 2\sqrt{x-1}$ is 3.

⌐14641⌐ THE FIBONACCI SEQUENCE

The sequence

$$1, 1, 2, 3, 5, 8, 13, 21, 34, 55, \cdots$$

is known as the *Fibonacci sequence*. Note that each term after the second is the sum of the two that precede it. This is an example of a *recursive sequence*.

Here are examples of other recursive sequences. Find the first 15 terms of each sequence.

1. 2, 2, 4, 6, 10, 16, $\cdots$

2. 9, -7, 2, -5, -3, -8, $\cdots$

3. -5, 3, -2, 1, -1, 0, $\cdots$

4. 0.5, -2, 1.5, -0.5, 1.0, 0.5, $\cdots$

The Fibonacci sequence has some remarkable properties. Perhaps the most remarkable is the fact that the ratios comparing each term to its preceding term form a sequence that approaches a particular number.

5. Find that number.   **6.** Use your library. Research "The Golden Ratio."

OBJECTIVES: Identify geometric sequences and their characteristics. Solve problems using geometric sequences. Find the sum of an infinite geometric series.

11-3 GEOMETRIC SEQUENCES

When each term of a sequence, except the first, can be obtained from the preceding term by *multiplying* that term by a constant, the sequence is a **geometric sequence.** The constant is called the **common ratio** for the sequence since it may be found by comparing *any* term, except the first, to its preceding term by dividing by the preceding term.

First Term	Common Ratio	Geometric Sequence				
1	2	1,	2,	4,	8,	$16, \cdots$
6	$-\dfrac{1}{3}$	6,	$-2,$	$\dfrac{2}{3},$	$-\dfrac{2}{9},$	$\dfrac{2}{27}, \cdots$
9	0.1	9,	0.9,	0.09,	0.009,	$0.0009, \cdots$
a	r	$a,$	$ar,$	$ar^2,$	$ar^3,$	$ar^4, \cdots$
		↑	↑	↑	↑	↑
		first term	second term	third term	fourth term	fifth term

When we use a for the first term and r for the common ratio, note that the exponent of r in each term is one less than the number of the term. When we use l to denote the nth term, (that is, the last term) of a finite sequence, we have

$$l = ar^{n-1}.$$

EXAMPLE 1 Find the common ratio for the geometric sequence

$$25, -5, 1, -\frac{1}{5}, \cdots.$$

SOLUTION Choose any term of the sequence after the first and divide by its preceding term.

Divide -5 by 25. (or) Divide $-\dfrac{1}{5}$ by 1.

$$\text{common ratio} = \frac{-5}{25}, \text{ or } -\frac{1}{5} \qquad \text{common ratio} = \frac{-\dfrac{1}{5}}{1}, \text{ or } -\frac{1}{5}$$

EXAMPLE 2 Find the eighth term of the geometric sequence

$$6, 12, 24, \cdots.$$

SOLUTION Use the formula $l = ar^{n-1}$. Replace the variables as follows.

First term: $a = 6$
Common ratio: $r = 2$
Number of terms: $n = 8$

Find l.

$$l = ar^{n-1}$$
$$l = 6(2)^{8-1}$$
$$= 6(128)$$
$$= 768$$

EXAMPLE 3 The eighth term of a geometric sequence is 640. The sixth term is 160. Find the common ratio. Give the first eight terms.

SOLUTION Use the formula $l = ar^{n-1}$. Find r.

Replace l by 640 and n by 8. $\qquad 640 = ar^7$
Replace l by 160 and n by 6. $\qquad 160 = ar^5$

Divide. $\qquad \dfrac{640}{160} = \dfrac{ar^7}{ar^5}$

$$4 = r^2$$
$$\pm 2 = r$$

Find a.

Replace r by 2 in $ar^5 = 160$.	Replace r by -2 in $ar^5 = 160$.
$a(2)^5 = 160$	$a(-2)^5 = 160$
$32a = 160$	$-32a = 160$
$a = 5$	$a = -5$

Using $a = 5$ and $r = 2$, the first eight terms are

$$5, 10, 20, 40, 80, 160, 320, 640.$$

Using $a = -5$ and $r = -2$, the first eight terms are

$$-5, 10, -20, 40, -80, 160, -320, 640.$$

The terms between two nonconsecutive terms of a geometric sequence are **geometric means** between those terms.

EXAMPLE 4 Insert two geometric means between 3 and 24.

SOLUTION Inserting two geometric means between two numbers gives a sequence of four terms ($n = 4$).

Use the formula $l = ar^{n-1}$. Find r.
Replace a by 3, l by 24, and n by 4.

$$l = ar^{n-1}$$
$$24 = 3r^{4-1}$$
$$8 = r^3$$
$$2 = r$$

List the four terms of the sequence.
    3, 6, 12, 24

CONCLUSION The geometric means between 3 and 24 are 6 and 12.

When a, m, b are three consecutive terms of a geometric sequence, m is a geometric mean between a and b. It also is called a **mean proportional** of a and b. When each of a, m, and b is positive, m is **the geometric mean,** or **the mean proportional,** of a and b. The common ratio may be represented by either $\dfrac{m}{a}$ or $\dfrac{b}{m}$. Thus, we may

write $\dfrac{m}{a} = \dfrac{b}{m}$, or equivalently, $\boxed{\dfrac{a}{m} = \dfrac{m}{b}}$. It follows that $m^2 = ab$.

Therefore, when m is *the* mean proportional, we may write

$$\boxed{m = \sqrt{ab}}$$.

EXAMPLE 5 Find all mean proportionals of 2 and 8.
Find *the* mean proportional of 2 and 8.

SOLUTION Use m for a mean proportional of 2 and 8.

$$\frac{2}{m} = \frac{m}{8}$$
$$m^2 = 16$$
$$|m| = 4$$

Therefore, $m = 4$ or $m = -4$.
Complete each sequence.
    2, 4, 8 | 2, -4, 8

CONCLUSION Each of 4 and -4 is a mean proportional of 2 and 8.
Since 4 is positive, 4 is *the* mean proportional of 2 and 8.

CLASSROOM EXERCISES

Find the common ratio.

1. $1, 3, 9, 27$ **2.** $3125, 625, 125, 25$ **3.** $64, 4, \frac{1}{4}, \cdots$

Find the indicated terms.

4. $8, -4, 2, \underline{}, \underline{}, \cdots$ **5.** $\underline{}, 0.02, 0.0002, \underline{}.$

6. The seventh term of a geometric sequence is $1\,000\,000$. The first term is 1. Find the common ratio.

Insert the indicated number of geometric means.

7. 5 and 45, one   **8.** -2 and -32, three   **9.** -3 and 96, four

10. In which of Classroom Exercises 7-9 have you found the mean proportional?

EXERCISES

A Find the indicated term and the common ratio.

1. 10th term of $3, 3, 3, \cdots$ **2.** 6th term of $1, -2, 4, \cdots$

3. 7th term of $1, 3, 9, \cdots$ **4.** 6th term of $-8, -4, -2, \cdots$

Find the common ratio. Write the first three terms.

5. 5th term is 48   **6.** 8th term is 10 935   **7.** 6th term is -10
    7th term is 192   6th term is 1215   8th term is $-2\frac{1}{2}$

Find the mean proportional between the numbers.

8. 1 and 100   **9.** 3 and 12   **10.** $\frac{1}{2}$ and $\frac{1}{8}$ **11.** $\frac{1}{3}$ and $\frac{1}{27}$

Insert the indicated number of geometric means.

12. 16 and 4, one   **13.** 1 and -27, two   **14.** 0.1 and 0.00001, one

15. $\frac{1}{108}$ and $\frac{1}{4}$, two   **16.** $-\frac{1}{8}$ and -2, three   **17.** ar^3 and ar^5, one

B Write the first four terms of the geometric sequence.

18. 4th term = $2\sqrt{6}$ **19.** second term = $x^2 + 3x + 2$
    6th term = $4\sqrt{6}$ third term = $x^3 + 4x^2 + 5x + 2$

20. Solve $l = ar^{n-1}$ for a; for r; for n.

C **21.** Find all values of x for which $x + 2$ is the geometric mean of $3x - 4$ and $x - 1$.

FINE ARTS AND HUMANITIES

"Fine arts and humanities" suggests careers such as acting, dancing, painting, or photography. Drafting and architecture also are in this category. Tasks of a *draftsperson* include preparing clear, complete, accurate drawings from the following sources.

1. rough sketches
2. written specifications
3. calculations of an engineer, an architect, or a designer

A draftsperson must have a working knowledge of mathematics, physical sciences, engineering practices, and building materials.

An *architect* is involved with the design and planning of a facility and then the supervision of its construction.

Architects must be able to
1. solve technical problems,
2. create artistically,
3. work well with people.

High school courses useful for persons interested in architecture include physics, psychology, drafting, art, and four years of mathematics.

MATHEMATICAL SAMPLER

1. As an architectural draftsperson, you are making blueprints. A ceiling that is 8.6 m long is to be represented by a line that is 21.5 cm long. Of the two rafters that extend from the edge of the ceiling to a peak, the front one is to have an elevation of 60°, and the rear one an elevation of 45°. How many centimeters will represent each roof rafter?

2. As an architect, you are designing a school that will have a capacity of 1275 students. Enough classroom space must be provided so that all students can be in classrooms at any given time. Each student requires 8.5 m³ of classroom space. How many classrooms 8 m long by 5 m wide by 4 m high must be included in your design? If plans are changed so that each classroom is to be 7 m by 6 m by 3.5 m, how many more (or fewer) classrooms must be planned?

11-4   FINDING THE SUM OF n TERMS OF A GEOMETRIC SEQUENCE

The expression $\displaystyle\sum_{k=1}^{n} ar^{k-1}$ represents the sum of n terms of a geometric sequence with first term a and common ratio r. We let S name such a sum.

$$S = a + ar + ar^2 + ar^3 + \cdots + ar^{n-1}$$

M_r $\qquad\qquad rS = \qquad ar + ar^2 + ar^3 + \cdots + ar^{n-1} + ar^n$

Subtract. $\quad S - rS = a - ar^n$

$$(1 - r)S = a(1 - r^n)$$

$$S = \frac{a(1 - r^n)}{1 - r}, \text{ when } r \neq 1.$$

> The sum of n terms of a geometric sequence:
> $$S = \frac{a(1 - r^n)}{1 - r}, \text{ or } \frac{a(r^n - 1)}{r - 1}, \text{ or } \frac{ar^n - a}{r - 1}, r \neq 1.$$

EXAMPLE 1   Find the sum of the first five terms of the geometric sequence $10, 20, 40, \cdots$

SOLUTION 1

$a = 10, r = 2, n = 5$

$$S = \sum_{k=1}^{5} 10 \cdot 2^{k-1}$$

$$= 10 \cdot 2^{1-1} + 10 \cdot 2^{2-1} + 10 \cdot 2^{3-1}$$
$$+ 10 \cdot 2^{4-1} + 10 \cdot 2^{5-1}$$

$$= 10 + 20 + 40 + 80 + 160$$

$$S = 310$$

SOLUTION 2

$a = 10, r = 2, n = 5$

Use $S = \dfrac{a(r^n - 1)}{r - 1}$.

$$S = \frac{10(2^5 - 1)}{2 - 1}$$

$$S = 310$$

The formula for the last term of a geometric sequence is $l = ar^{n-1}$. Multiplying by r gives $lr = ar^n$. Replacing ar^n by lr in $S = \dfrac{ar^n - a}{r - 1}$ gives

$$S = \frac{lr - a}{r - 1}.$$

This formula is useful when the number of terms in a sequence is not known.

Formula	Variables Related to the Sum, S	Variables Not Present
$S = \dfrac{ar^n - a}{r - 1}, r \neq 1$	a, r, n	l
$S = \dfrac{lr - a}{r - 1}, r \neq 1$	a, r, l	n

EXAMPLE 2   The sum of n terms of the geometric sequence

$$2, -4, 8, \cdots$$

is 342.   Find the nth (last) term.   Find n, the number of terms.

SOLUTION 1

Use $S = \dfrac{lr - a}{r - 1}$.   Find l.

Replace a by 2, r by -2, and S by 342.

$$342 = \frac{l(-2) - 2}{-2 - 1}$$

$$342 = \frac{-2l - 2}{-3}$$

$$-1026 = -2l - 2$$
$$-1024 = -2l$$
$$512 = l$$

The nth (last) term is 512.

Find n.
Use $l = ar^{n-1}$.
$$512 = 2(-2)^{n-1}$$
$$256 = (-2)^{n-1}$$
$$(-2)^8 = (-2)^{n-1}$$
Therefore, $8 = n - 1$
$$9 = n$$
There are 9 terms.

SOLUTION 2

Use $S = \dfrac{ar^n - a}{r - 1}$.   Find n.

Replace a by 2, r by -2, and S by 342.

$$342 = \frac{2(-2)^n - 2}{-2 - 1}$$

$$-1026 = 2(-2)^n - 2$$
$$-1024 = 2(-2)^n$$
$$-512 = (-2)^n$$
$$(-2)^9 = (-2)^n$$
$$9 = n$$

There are 9 terms.

Find the 9th term.
Use $l = ar^{n-1}$.
$$l = 2(-2)^8$$
$$= 512$$
The nth (9th) term is 512.

EXAMPLE 3   40 000 people visited a park in its first year. Park planners expect the number of visitors to increase by $\frac{1}{5}$ each year through the fifth year. How many visitors do the park planners expect in the fifth year? How many visitors do they expect for all five years?

SOLUTION   Since the number of visitors grows by $\frac{1}{5}$ each year, the number of visitors each year is $1\frac{1}{5}$ times as great as the number of visitors the previous year.

$$a = 40\,000 \qquad r = 1\tfrac{1}{5}, \text{ or } \tfrac{6}{5} \qquad n = 5$$

To find the number of visitors expected in the fifth year, use

$$l = ar^{n-1}.$$
$$l = 40\,000 \left(\tfrac{6}{5}\right)^{5-1}$$
$$= 40\,000 \cdot \tfrac{1296}{625}$$
$$= 82\,944$$
$$l \doteq 83\,000$$

CONCLUSION 1   The park planners expect about 83 000 visitors in the fifth year.

To find the number of visitors expected for all five years, use

$$S = \frac{a(r^{n} - 1)}{r - 1}.$$
$$S = \frac{40\,000\left[\left(\tfrac{6}{5}\right)^{5} - 1\right]}{\tfrac{6}{5} - 1}$$
$$= \frac{40\,000\left(\tfrac{7776}{3125} - 1\right)}{\tfrac{1}{5}}$$
$$= 40\,000\left(\tfrac{4651}{3125}\right) \cdot \tfrac{5}{1}$$
$$= 297\,664$$
$$S \doteq 300\,000$$

CONCLUSION 2   The park planners expect about 300 000 visitors for all five years.

EXAMPLE 4 For the first year, the McClure's family income was $16 000. If the rate of inflation is 10% each year and the McClures keep pace with inflation, what should be the family income for the 11th year?

SOLUTION Since the inflation rate is 10%, or 0.10, the McClures must earn 1.10 times as much each year to keep pace with inflation.

$$a = 16\ 000 \qquad r = 1.10 \qquad n = 11$$

Use $l = ar^{n-1}$.

$$l = 16\ 000(1.1)^{11-1}$$
$$l = 16\ 000(1.1)^{10}$$
$$\log l = \log 16\ 000 + 10 \log 1.1$$
$$\doteq 4.2041 + 10(0.0414)$$
$$\log l \doteq 4.6181$$
$$l \doteq \text{antilog } 4.6181$$
$$l \doteq 41\ 500$$

CONCLUSION To keep pace with inflation, the McClure's family income for the 11th year should be about $41 500.

EXAMPLE 5 Suppose at age 21 you begin working for a salary of $12 000 per year. If your salary increases 7% each year, how much would you earn during 44 years before you retire?

SOLUTION $a = 12\ 000 \qquad r = 1.07 \qquad n = 44$

Use $S = \dfrac{a(r^n - 1)}{r - 1}$.

$$S = \frac{12\ 000(1.07^{44} - 1)}{1.07 - 1} \longrightarrow \begin{array}{l} \log 1.07^{44} = 44 \log 1.07 \\ \doteq 44(0.0294) \\ \log 1.07^{44} \doteq 1.2936 \\ 1.07^{44} \doteq \text{antilog } 1.2936 \end{array}$$

$$S \doteq \frac{12\ 000(19.66 - 1)}{1.07 - 1} \longleftarrow \quad 1.07^{44} \doteq 19.66$$

$$\doteq \frac{12\ 000(18.66)}{0.07}$$

$$\doteq 3\ 198\ 857$$
$$\doteq 3\ 200\ 000$$

CONCLUSION You would earn about $3 200 000 before you retire.

CLASSROOM EXERCISES

Write in expanded form and find the sum.

1. $\sum_{k=1}^{5} 2(3)^{k-1}$ **2.** $\sum_{k=1}^{5} 1\left(\frac{1}{2}\right)^{k-1}$

Use a formula for the sum of the terms of a geometric sequence.

3. For $a = 1$, $r = 3$, $n = 5$, find S.

4. For $a = 2$, $r = -\frac{1}{2}$, $n = 6$, find S.

5. Find n and the nth term of the sequence 256, 128, 64, $\cdots$, when the sum of n terms is 480.

6. For $a = 5$, $r = -\frac{1}{5}$, $l = \frac{1}{125}$, find n; find S.

Solve.

7. In the first year that a collector owns a painting, it is worth $10 000. It increases in value each year by 30%. How much will it be worth in the fourth year?

EXERCISES

A Write in expanded form and find the sum.

1. $\sum_{k=1}^{4} 3\left(\frac{1}{2}\right)^{k-1}$ **2.** $\sum_{k=1}^{5} 4\left(-\frac{1}{3}\right)^{k-1}$

3. $\sum_{k=1}^{5} 1(-2)^{k-1}$ **4.** $\sum_{k=1}^{5} 10(\sqrt{2})^{k-1}$

Use a formula for the sum of the terms of a geometric sequence.

5. For $a = 2$, $r = -2$, $n = 7$, find S.

6. For $a = 3$, $r = -\frac{1}{4}$, $n = 4$, find S.

7. For $a = 5$, $r = 3$, $n = 4$, find l; find S.

8. For $r = 2$, $n = 6$, $l = 64$, find a; find S.

9. For $r = 6$, $l = 1296$, $S = 1555$, find a; find n.

10. For $a = 4$, $r = -3$, $S = -728$, find l; find n.

Solve.

11. Ten years after being founded, the population of a city is 30 000. Assuming that its population will double every 10 years, what would be its population 80 years after the city was founded?

12. An appliance manufacturer doubles production every year. Suppose that 1040 items are produced in the first year. Find the number produced in the first five years. Find the number produced in the fifth year.

13. A medical lab finds that a certain strain of bacteria increases in number by 60% per hour. The initial count is 1200 bacteria per milliliter. What will be the count five hours later ($n = 6$)?

14. Each person has 2 biological parents. How many biological ancestors does a person have for the 10 preceding generations? Assume there are no duplications.

15. Suppose, after you graduate from school, you accept a job paying $15 000 a year with a guaranteed yearly increase of 10%. What could you expect your salary to be for your sixth year of work? How much could you expect to earn in six years?

B **16.** A golf ball is dropped to the pavement from a height of 30 meters. It rebounds to a height equal to one-fourth the distance it dropped. After each descent, it continues to rebound to a height equal to one-fourth the distance it dropped. How far has the ball traveled when it reaches the pavement on its fifth descent?

17. To shoe a horse, a blacksmith charges 1 cent for driving the first nail, 2 cents for the second nail, 4 cents for the third nail, and so on for the remaining nails. Find the cost of shoeing a horse, with each shoe requiring 6 nails.

18. Find the sum of the first eight terms of the sequence $1, (a + b)^{\frac{1}{2}}, (a + b), \cdots$.

19. Find the sum of the first four terms of a geometric sequence when the sum of the first two terms is 18 and the third term less the first term equals 72.

20. In 1980 a museum opened and attracted 10 000 visitors. Museum officials expected attendance to increase by 23% each year. During which year could they expect the ten-millionth visitor?

21. The sum of the first two terms of a geometric sequence is 8. The sum of the second and third terms is 24. Find the sum of the first six terms.

C **22.** *ABCD* is a square with $AB = 24$. A sequence of *inscribed* squares is formed using the midpoints of sides of squares as shown. Find the sum of the areas of the four squares pictured.

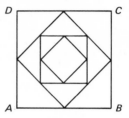

23. In a geometric sequence the first term is $12 - 4\sqrt{21}$ and the sum of the first three terms is $9 - 3\sqrt{21}$. Find all possible values of the common ratio r.

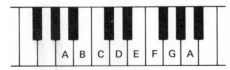

SOME MEAN MUSIC

The musical scale is made up of 12 different notes. On the piano, the 12 notes correspond to the 12 keys shown, both black and white.

The pitch of each note is related to the frequency at which the piano string vibrates. For A below middle C, the frequency is 220 cycles per second. For A above middle C, the frequency is 440 cycles per second. Each note in between has a frequency that is one of the geometric means between 220 and 440.

1. What is the common ratio for this geometric sequence?

2. Find the frequency of each note between 220 and 440 cycles per second.

11-5 INFINITE GEOMETRIC SERIES

A **geometric series** is the indicated sum of the terms of a geometric sequence. A **finite geometric series** has finitely many terms. An **infinite geometric series** has infinitely many terms.

Finite Geometric Sequence:	$8, \ 4, \ 2, \ 1, \ \frac{1}{2}, \ \frac{1}{4}$
Finite Geometric Series:	$8 + 4 + 2 + 1 + \frac{1}{2} + \frac{1}{4}$
Infinite Geometric Sequence:	$8, \ 4, \ 2, \ 1, \ \frac{1}{2}, \ \cdots$
Infinite Geometric Series:	$8 + 4 + 2 + 1 + \frac{1}{2} + \cdots$

To find the sum of a *finite* geometric series, $\sum_{k=1}^{n} ar^{k-1}$, we simply may add its terms. We cannot add infinitely many terms, however. Therefore, the sum of an infinite geometric series, $\sum_{k=1}^{\infty} ar^{k-1}$, must be given meaning in a different way.

From our work with sequences we know that the sum of the first n terms of a geometric sequence or a geometric series is given by the formula

$$S = \frac{ar^n - a}{r - 1}.$$

For some infinite geometric series, the numbers for S will never exceed certain numbers. When this occurs for an infinite geometric series having positive terms, the **sum of the series** is the *least* number that the numbers for S never exceed.

EXAMPLE 1 Find $\sum_{k=1}^{\infty} \frac{1}{2}\left(\frac{1}{2}\right)^{k-1}$. That is, find the sum of the infinite geometric series $\frac{1}{2} + \frac{1}{4} + \frac{1}{8} + \frac{1}{16} + \cdots$.

SOLUTION $\frac{1}{2} + \frac{1}{4} = \frac{3}{4}, \frac{1}{2} + \frac{1}{4} + \frac{1}{8} = \frac{7}{8}$, and so on.

By adding more terms of the series, the sum gets closer to 1. In fact, for each term we add, the remaining "distance" to 1 is reduced by one-half. Our intuition should tell us that by adding more and more terms we can get as close to 1 as we wish, yet never have a sum that exceeds 1. Therefore, we say that 1 is the *sum of the series* $\frac{1}{2} + \frac{1}{4} + \frac{1}{8} + \frac{1}{16} + \cdots$.

The formula $S = \dfrac{ar^n - a}{r - 1}$ will give us a formula for the sum of a geometric series for which $0 < r < 1$. When $0 < r < 1$ and the numbers for n become larger and larger, the numbers for r^n will approach zero. Therefore, $\dfrac{ar^n - a}{r - 1}$ will approach but never exceed $\dfrac{0 - a}{r - 1}$, or $\dfrac{a}{1 - r}$.

Thus, for an infinite geometric series with $0 < r < 1$, we say

$$S = \frac{a}{1 - r} \quad .$$

When $r > 1$, we may say that the series has no sum.

EXAMPLE 2 Find $\displaystyle\sum_{k=1}^{\infty} 1 \cdot \left(\tfrac{1}{3}\right)^{k-1}$. That is, find the sum of the infinite geometric series $1 + \tfrac{1}{3} + \tfrac{1}{9} + \cdots$.

SOLUTION $a = 1, r = \tfrac{1}{3}$

$$S = \frac{a}{1 - r}$$

$$S = \frac{1}{1 - \tfrac{1}{3}}$$

$$S = \tfrac{3}{2}$$

EXAMPLE 3 Express $0.\overline{45}$ in fraction form.

SOLUTION First, express $0.\overline{45}$ as a geometric series.

$0.\overline{45} = 0.454545 \cdots$

$\phantom{0.\overline{45}} = 0.45 + 0.0045 + 0.000045 + \cdots$

Then, find the sum of the series.

$a = 0.45, r = 0.01$

$$S = \frac{a}{1 - r}$$

$$S = \frac{0.45}{1 - 0.01}$$

$$= \frac{0.45}{0.99}$$

$$S = \frac{5}{11}$$

CONCLUSION $0.\overline{45} = \dfrac{5}{11}$

EXAMPLE 4 Write the first five terms of the infinite geometric series whose first term is 2 and whose sum is 3.

SOLUTION Find the common ratio.

$$S = \frac{a}{1-r}$$

$$S(1-r) = a$$
$$S - Sr = a$$
$$-Sr = a - S$$

$$r = \frac{a-S}{-S}$$

$$r = \frac{S-a}{S}$$

Replace a by 2 and S by 3 in $r = \frac{S-a}{S}$.

$$r = \frac{3-2}{3}$$

$$r = \frac{1}{3}$$

Develop the series. $2 + 2\left(\frac{1}{3}\right) + 2\left(\frac{1}{3}\right)^2 + 2\left(\frac{1}{3}\right)^3 + 2\left(\frac{1}{3}\right)^4 + \cdots$

CONCLUSION The series is $2 + \frac{2}{3} + \frac{2}{9} + \frac{2}{27} + \frac{2}{81} + \cdots$.

CLASSROOM EXERCISES

Decide whether the geometric series has a sum. If it does, find it.

1. $1 + \frac{2}{3} + \frac{4}{9} + \frac{8}{27} + \cdots$

2. $\frac{1}{12} + \frac{1}{9} + \frac{4}{27} + \cdots$

3. Find the common ratio and write the first three terms of the infinite geometric series whose first term is 100 and whose sum is 1000.

Write in fraction form.

4. $0.\overline{7}$

5. $0.\overline{9}$

6. $0.\overline{37}$

EXERCISES

[A] Decide whether the geometric series has a sum. If it does, find it.

1. $12 + 3 + \frac{3}{4} + \cdots$

2. $\frac{3}{2} + 1 + \frac{2}{3} + \cdots$

3. $\frac{1}{3} + \frac{2}{3} + \frac{4}{3} + \cdots$

4. $\frac{1}{8} + \frac{5}{8} + \frac{25}{8} + \cdots$

5. $4 + \frac{4}{3} + \frac{4}{9} + \frac{4}{27} + \cdots$

6. $\frac{2}{3} + \left(\frac{2}{3}\right)^2 + \left(\frac{2}{3}\right)^3 + \cdots$

7. $7 + \frac{7}{6} + \frac{7}{36} + \frac{7}{216} + \cdots$

8. $4 + 3 + \frac{9}{4} + \cdots$

9. $2 + \sqrt{2} + 1 + \cdots$

Write in fraction form.

10. $0.\overline{63}$

11. $0.\overline{36}$

12. $0.\overline{09}$

13. $0.\overline{123}$

14. $0.7\overline{2}$

15. $0.\overline{428571}$

Find the common ratio. Write the first 3 terms of the infinite geometric series.

16. $a = 72$, $S = 108$ **17.** $a = \frac{1}{16}$, $S = \frac{3}{64}$ **18.** $a = -\frac{2}{3}$, $S = -2$

B Find the sum of the infinite geometric series.

19. $1 + x + x^2 + \cdots$, for $0 < x < 1$ **20.** $1 + \frac{1}{x} + \left(\frac{1}{x}\right)^2 + \cdots$, for $x > 1$

21. The first term and common ratio of an infinite geometric series are both $2 - \sqrt{3}$. Find the sum.

Solve.

22. An infinite geometric series has the sum $\dfrac{5 + 3\sqrt{3}}{2}$. Its first term is $2 + \sqrt{3}$. Find the common ratio.

23. Use the conditions and diagram in Exercise 22 of Section 11-4. Find the sum of the areas of the squares if this process is continued indefinitely.

C **24.** Show that any number greater than a, $a > 0$, is the sum of a geometric series that has a as its first term.

25. The sum of an infinite geometric series is 32. The second term less the third term equals $\frac{3}{2}$. Find the first term and the common ratio of each series having these two properties.

TO BE CONTINUED

Previously we used a calculator to evaluate continued fractions and continued radicals. There is a pencil-and-paper method that also may be applied.

EXAMPLE Simplify $\sqrt{12 + \sqrt{12 + \sqrt{12 + \sqrt{12 + \cdots}}}}$.

SOLUTION Let $\qquad k = \sqrt{12 + \sqrt{12 + \sqrt{12 + \sqrt{12 + \cdots}}}}$.

Then, $\qquad k = \sqrt{12 + k}$

$\qquad\qquad k^2 = 12 + k$

$\qquad k^2 - k - 12 = 0$

$\qquad (k - 4)(k + 3) = 0$

Thus, $k = 4$. ($k \neq -3$ since $k > 0$.)

Simplify.

1. $\sqrt{5 + \sqrt{5 + \sqrt{5 + \sqrt{5 + \cdots}}}}$

2. $1 + \dfrac{2}{1 + \dfrac{2}{1 + \dfrac{2}{1 + \dfrac{2}{\cdots}}}}$

3. $\dfrac{6}{1 + \dfrac{6}{1 + \dfrac{6}{1 + \dfrac{6}{1 + \dfrac{6}{\cdots}}}}}$

4. $\sqrt{6 - \sqrt{6 - \sqrt{6 - \sqrt{6 - \cdots}}}}$

5. For what numbers c is $\sqrt{c + \sqrt{c + \sqrt{c + \sqrt{c + \cdots}}}}$ an integer?

CHECKING YOUR UNDERSTANDING

WORDS AND SYMBOLS

arithmetic means
arithmetic sequence
common difference
common ratio
finite sequence

geometric means
geometric sequence
geometric series
infinite sequence
mean proportional

sequence
sigma notation for a sum, Σ
sum of a geometric series
term of a sequence

CONCEPTS

- The average of the terms in an arithmetic sequence is the average of the first and last terms. The sum of the terms is the product of this average and the number of terms in the sequence. [11-2]

- Some infinite geometric series have a sum. Others do not. Those with positive common ratio less than 1 have a sum. [11-5]

PROCESSES

- For an arithmetic sequence, find unknown terms and arithmetic means. [11-1]

  1. Find the 26th term of the sequence $-\frac{2}{3}, -\frac{7}{3}, -4, \cdots$.

  2. Insert 5 arithmetic means between 4 and 8.

  3. Find the arithmetic mean of -7 and -13.

- Find the sum of the terms of a finite arithmetic sequence. [11-2]

  4. Find the sum of the positive even numbers up to and including 150.

  5. $\displaystyle\sum_{k=1}^{6} [13 + (k - 1)4]$ **6.** $\displaystyle\sum_{k=1}^{70} [-4 + (k - 1)(-3)]$

- For a geometric sequence, find unknown terms and geometric means. [11-3]

  7. Find the third term when the 7th term is $\frac{64}{125}$ and the common ratio is $\frac{2}{5}$.

  8. Find the mean proportional between 3 and 147.

- Find the sum of the terms of a finite geometric sequence. [11-4]

  9. Find the sum of the first 8 terms. $-\frac{1}{64}, -\frac{1}{32}, -\frac{1}{16}, \cdots$

  10. A geometric sequence with 6 terms and a common ratio 3 has 1820 as its sum. What is the first term of the sequence?

- Find the sum of an infinite geometric series having positive common ratio less than 1. [11-5]

  11. $6 + \frac{9}{2} + \frac{27}{8} + \cdots = ?$ **12.** $3 + 2 + \frac{4}{3} + \frac{8}{9} + \cdots = ?$

CHAPTER REVIEW

The sequences in Exercises 1-10 are arithmetic. [11-1]

1. Find the 20th term. $8, 5, 2, \cdots$

2. The ninth term is -31. The sixteenth term is -66. Find the first term.

3. The first term is 2. The fifth term is 64. Find the common difference.

Insert the given number of arithmetic means.

4. 3 between 4 and 20 **5.** 2 between 4 and -20 **6.** 1 between 9 and 14

Solve for the indicated variable. [11-2]

7. $n = 6$, $a = 8$, $l = 28$, find S. **8.** $S = 15$, $a = 4$, $l = 2$, find n.

9. $S = -41$, $n = 6$, $l = -\frac{43}{3}$, find a. **10.** $S = 245$, $n = 10$, $a = 2$, find l.

Simplify.

11. $\sum_{k=1}^{6} -10 + 4(k - 1)$ **12.** $\sum_{k=1}^{7} 10 - 5k$

13. Carmen's salary increases by $500 each year. Her starting salary was $12 000. She has earned a total of $142 500 at her job so far. How many years has she been working?

The sequences in Exercises 14-24 are geometric. [11-3]

14. Find the common ratio. $6, -\frac{2}{3}, \cdots$ **15.** Find the 7th term. $4, 12, 36, \cdots$

16. The first term is -3. The common ratio is -2. The nth term is -192. Find n.

Insert the given number of geometric means.

17. 4 between 4 and -4 **18.** 3 between 81 and 16 **19.** 1 between -3 and 27.

20. If $\sqrt{3}$ is the geometric mean of 5 and x, find x.

Find the sum of the given number of terms of the geometric sequence. [11-4]

21. first 7 terms of $-20, 60, -180, \cdots$ **22.** first 8 terms of $80, 40, 20, \cdots$

23. A geometric sequence has common ratio $-\frac{1}{2}$. Its first 5 terms have the sum $-13\frac{3}{4}$. Find the first term of the sequence.

24. The sum of the first n terms of the sequence $-1, -3, -9, \cdots$, is -3280. Find n.

25. A company has run at a deficit for 5 consecutive years. The first-year deficit was $400 000. Each year since then, the deficit has been 20% smaller than that of the preceding year. Find the deficit for the fifth year.

26. Given the information of Exercise 25, find the total deficit for the five years.

Evaluate. [11-5]

27. $\displaystyle\sum_{k=1}^{\infty} 7\left(\frac{3}{4}\right)^{k-1}$ **28.** $\displaystyle\sum_{k=1}^{\infty} 12\left(\frac{1}{3}\right)^{k-1}$ **29.** An infinite geometric series has first term 5 and sum $6\frac{1}{4}$. Find the common ratio.

30. Write $0.\overline{51}$ in fraction form.

CAPSULE REVIEW

Write the letter of the best response.

1. Which arithmetic sequence has an *n*th term of *n* for some *n* less than 7?

   a. 14, 11, $\cdots$ **b.** 11, 14, $\cdots$ **c.** 13, 11, $\cdots$ **d.** 13, 7, $\cdots$

2. Between which 2 numbers are there 3 arithmetic means that are integers?

   a. 8 and 20   **b.** 8 and 14   **c.** 6 and -1 **d.** $\frac{2}{3}$ and $11\frac{1}{3}$

3. Which expression equals 10?

   a. $\displaystyle\sum_{k=1}^{10} [-10 + (k-1)2]$ **b.** $\displaystyle\sum_{k=1}^{10} [-8 + (k-1)2]$

   c. $\displaystyle\sum_{k=1}^{5} [-3 + (k-1)8]$ **d.** $\displaystyle\sum_{k=1}^{7} [5 + (k-1)3]$

4. Which geometric sequence has a common ratio between -1 and 0?

   a. $-2, -\frac{2}{3}, \cdots$ **b.** $6, -9, \cdots$ **c.** $-6, 4\frac{1}{2}, \cdots$ **d.** $4, \frac{1}{4}, \cdots$

5. The geometric mean of 7 and 49 is

   a. 7   **b.** 343   **c.** $-\sqrt{343}$ **d.** $\sqrt{343}$

6. A geometric sequence has first term 3, common ratio 5, and sum 1018. Its last term is

   a. 75   **b.** 375   **c.** 815   **d.** 405

7. $\displaystyle\sum_{k=1}^{6} -5(-2)^{k-1} =$

   a. -5 **b.** 0   **c.** 105   **d.** -315

8. Which infinite geometric series has no sum?

   a. $5 + \frac{5}{2} + \frac{5}{4} + \cdots$ **b.** $3 + \frac{6}{7} + \frac{12}{49} + \cdots$ **c.** $\frac{1}{4} + \frac{3}{8} + \frac{9}{16} + \cdots$ **d.** $\frac{2}{3} + \frac{3}{5} + \frac{27}{50} + \cdots$

CHAPTER TEST

1. Give the common difference for the sequence $-6, -2, 2, 6, \cdots$.

2. The fifth term of an arithmetic sequence is 16. The common difference is 3. Write the first three terms of the sequence.

3. Insert three arithmetic means between 5 and 11.

4. Insert two arithmetic means between 5 and 11.

5. Find the average of the terms of the sequence $2, 4, 6, 8, \cdots, 20$.

6. Find the sum of the terms of the sequence, $2, 4, 6, 8, \cdots, 20$.

7. A pyramid of blocks has 20 blocks on the bottom row, 19 on the next row, and so on, with 1 block on the top row. Find the total number of blocks in the pyramid.

8. A worker saved $1 the first week, $2 the second week, $3 the third week and so on, saving one more dollar each week than the week before. Find the total amount the worker saved in 52 weeks.

9. Give the common ratio for the sequence $10, 20, 40, 80, \cdots$

10. The fifth term of a geometric sequence is 324. The common ratio is 3. Write the first three terms of the sequence.

11. Insert two geometric means between 2 and 54.

12. What is the mean proportional of 4 and 9?

13. Write a formula for finding the sum, S, of n terms of a geometric sequence with first term a and common ratio r.

14. Find the sum of the first 5 terms of the geometric sequence $64, 32, 16, \cdots$.

15. A "chain letter" is sent to 5 people. Each of the 5 sends it to 5 others, and so on, with each person sending it to 5 others. If 5 people receive the letter in the first round, how many receive it in the third round?

16. Each branch of a tree forms three new branches each year. In the first year there is one branch. How many branches are there after 4 years?

17. Find the sum of the series $1 + \frac{1}{4} + \frac{1}{16} + \cdots$.   **18.** Write $0.\overline{36}$ in fraction form.

Write the letter of the best response.

19. The first term of an arithmetic sequence is 100. The common difference is 0.5. What is the 21st term?

    a. 109.5   **b.** 110.0   **c.** 110.5   **d.** 120   **e.** 121

20. What is the arithmetic mean of 5 and 11?

    a. 6   **b.** 7   **c.** 8   **d.** 9   **e.** 10

21. What is the sum of the terms of the sequence $5, 10, 15, 20, \cdots, 500$?

    a. 505   **b.** 550   **c.** 12 625   **d.** 25 250   **e.** 50 500

22. The third term of a geometric sequence is 10. The sixth term is -80. What is the common ratio?

    a. -8 **b.** -2 **c.** $-\frac{1}{2}$ **d.** $\frac{1}{2}$ **e.** 2

23. What is the mean proportional of 2 and 50?

    a. 10   **b.** 24   **c.** 25   **d.** 26   **e.** 100

24. $2^{10} = 1024$. What is the sum of the first 10 terms of the sequence $1, 2, 4, 8, \cdots$?

    a. 511   **b.** 512   **c.** 1023   **d.** 2047   **e.** 2048

25. If you are paid 1¢ the first day, 2¢ the second day, 4¢ the third day, 8¢ the fourth, and so on, doubling the pay each day, how much would you receive for 30 days?

a. 465 cents   **b.** 930 cents   **c.** 1860 cents   **d.** $2^{29} - 1$ cents   **e.** $2^{30} - 1$ cents

26. Which infinite geometric series has no sum?

a. $16 + 4 + 1 + \cdots$ **b.** $1 + \frac{1}{4} + \frac{1}{16} + \cdots$ **c.** $1 + \frac{1}{2} + \frac{1}{4} + \cdots$ **d.** $\frac{1}{16} + \frac{1}{8} + \frac{1}{4} + \cdots$

CUMULATIVE REVIEW

Give the word or symbol to complete each sentence.

1. In log 783 = 2.8938, 2 is called the ___?___ .

2. The sequence $\frac{1}{2}, \frac{3}{4}, 1, \frac{5}{4}, \cdots$ is a(n) ___?___ sequence.

3. For the sequence $4, 3, \frac{9}{4}, \frac{27}{16}, \cdots$, $\frac{3}{4}$ is the ___?___ .

4. The graph of the conic section $16x^2 + 5x - 9y^2 + 6y = 160$ is a(n) ___?___ .

5. $f(x) = -2x + 3$ and $g(x) = \frac{3 - x}{2}$ are examples of ___?___ functions.

6. In a parabola, each point is the same distance from the focus as it is from the ___?___ .

Briefly answer each question.   Refer to the concept suggested.

7. $(x^{2\pi}y^3)^{\frac{3}{2}} = x^{3\pi}y^{\frac{9}{2}}$.   Why?   **8.** log 35 = log 5 + log 7.   Why?

9. The infinite geometric series $12 + 8 + \frac{16}{3} + \frac{32}{9} + \cdots$ has a sum.   Why?

10. The major axis of the ellipse $\frac{x^2}{9} + \frac{y^2}{25} = 1$ is in the y-axis rather than the x-axis.   Why?

11. Explain why the following statement is false.   There are three real-number solutions of the system $\begin{array}{l} 3x - 4y = 6 \\ 4x^2 + x - 1 = y \end{array}$.

12. Solve by completing the square. $2x^2 - 7x - 30 = 0$

13. Solve by using the quadratic formula. $3x^2 + 4x = 39$

Solve.

14. $x + 2 + \sqrt{x + 2} = 20$ **15.** $(y - 1)^{\frac{2}{3}} - (y - 1)^{\frac{1}{3}} - 2 = 0$

16. Write an equation for the circle with center $(0, 2)$ containing point $(3, 6)$.

Simplify.

17. $16^{0.75}$ **18.** $2 \log 8 + \log 25 - 4 \log 2$ **19.** $\dfrac{7^{3\sqrt{2} - 1}}{7^{\sqrt{2}}}$ **20.** $\displaystyle\sum_{k=1}^{10} [5 + (k - 1)3]$

Solve.

21. $\begin{array}{l} x^2 + 25y^2 = 25 \\ 4x + 15y = 25 \end{array}$ **22.** $\begin{array}{l} x^2 + y^2 = 4 \\ x + y = 3 \end{array}$ **23.** $\left(\frac{1}{4}\right)^{3x+1} = 16^{-2x}$ **24.** $x^{\sqrt{2}} = 3$

25. $4 \log_{16} x = 2$ **26.** $\log_x 49 = -2$ **27.** $x = \log_6 1296$

28. Find the common difference and the first four terms of the arithmetic sequence whose third term is -2 and whose 11th term is -26.

29. The sum of two numbers is 11. The sum of their squares is 65. Find the numbers.

30. A geometric sequence and an arithmetic sequence have the same first term, which is 6. Their second terms are equal. The third term of the geometric sequence exceeds the third term of the arithmetic sequence by 6. Find the geometric sequence.

Write the letter of the best response.

31. The triangle with vertices $(2, 1)$, $(8, 3)$, and $(12, -9)$ is

  a. equilateral **b.** isosceles **c.** right **d.** obtuse

32. If x varies jointly with y and z, by what factor is the value of x increased if the value of y is tripled and the value of z is quadrupled?

  a. 3 **b.** 6 **c.** 4 **d.** 7 **e.** 12

33. $2 \log 5 - 3 \log 2 =$

  a. $\dfrac{2 \log 5}{3 \log 2}$ **b.** $\dfrac{\log 10}{\log 6}$ **c.** $\log \dfrac{5}{3}$ **d.** $\log \dfrac{25}{8}$ **e.** $\dfrac{\log 25}{\log 8}$

34. An arithmetic sequence with 10 terms has second term 7 and last term 55. What is the common difference?

  a. 6 **b.** 1 **c.** -16 **d.** 10 **e.** 8

35. Four arithmetic means between 3 and 6 are

  a. $\dfrac{30}{9}, \dfrac{37}{9}, \dfrac{44}{9}, \dfrac{51}{9}$ **b.** $\dfrac{39}{12}, \dfrac{49}{12}, \dfrac{59}{12}, \dfrac{69}{12}$ **c.** $\dfrac{18}{5}, \dfrac{21}{5}, \dfrac{24}{5}, \dfrac{27}{5}$ **d.** $\dfrac{21}{6}, \dfrac{25}{6}, \dfrac{29}{6}, \dfrac{33}{6}$

36. Three geometric means between 81 and 16 are

  a. 64.75, 48.5, 32.25 **b.** 54, 36, 24 **c.** $75, 30\sqrt{2}, 24$ **d.** $\dfrac{405}{6}, \dfrac{2025}{36}, \dfrac{1012}{216}$

37. A geometric sequence with four terms has common ratio $-\dfrac{3}{2}$ and sum $-\dfrac{13}{18}$. What is the first term?

  a. $\dfrac{4}{9}$ **b.** $-\dfrac{16}{45}$ **c.** $-\dfrac{4}{9}$ **d.** $\dfrac{16}{45}$ **e.** $\dfrac{4}{45}$

38. The center of the circle $x^2 - 3x + y^2 + \dfrac{8}{3}y = \dfrac{-109}{36}$ is

  a. $\left(\dfrac{3}{4}, \dfrac{4}{3}\right)$ **b.** $\left(\dfrac{-3}{2}, \dfrac{4}{3}\right)$ **c.** $\left(\dfrac{3}{2}, \dfrac{2}{3}\right)$ **d.** $\left(\dfrac{3}{2}, \dfrac{-2}{3}\right)$ **e.** $\left(\dfrac{3}{2}, \dfrac{-4}{3}\right)$

39. $\log (0.000407) =$

  a. -4.6096 **b.** $0.5988 - 4$ **c.** $0.6107 - 4$ **d.** -4.6107 **e.** $0.6096 - 4$

40. Solve $3^{\frac{1}{x^2} + \frac{1}{x}} = 9$

  a. $x = -1, x = -\dfrac{1}{2}$ **b.** no solution **c.** $x = 1, x = -\dfrac{1}{2}$ **d.** $x = -1, x = \dfrac{1}{2}$

CHAPTER 12
PERMUTATIONS, COMBINATIONS, AND PROBABILITY

The effort to achieve energy self-sufficiency has renewed our interest in conventional energy sources other than oil, rekindled interest in former energy sources, and spurred development of new energy sources. These trends, along with further enforcement of health and safety regulations and increased emphasis on preserving the environment, have improved opportunities and created new and challenging directions in natural resources and environmental careers.

OBJECTIVE: Use multiplication and addition to "count" the number of ways an event can occur.

12-1   THE FUNDAMENTAL COUNTING PRINCIPLE

To work with probabilities, it is necessary to be able to count the number of ways a particular event can occur. Drawing a diagram or using multiplication often can simplify the counting.

EXAMPLE 1   A baseball coach has three players, Al, Bill, and Chuck, who can pitch and catch. In how many ways can the coach choose a pitcher and a catcher from the three?

SOLUTION 1   Draw a diagram:

PITCHER	CATCHER	COACH'S CHOICE
AL	BILL	AL – BILL
	CHUCK	AL – CHUCK
BILL	AL	BILL – AL
	CHUCK	BILL –CHUCK
CHUCK	AL	CHUCK – AL
	BILL	CHUCK –BILL

$$3 \qquad \times \qquad 2 \qquad = \qquad 6$$

The *tree diagram* above shows that multiplication also gives the total number of ways to make the choices.

SOLUTION 2   Use N for the number of ways to choose both a pitcher and a catcher.

$$N = \left(\begin{array}{c} \text{number of ways to} \\ \text{choose a pitcher} \end{array} \right) \cdot \left(\begin{array}{c} \text{number of ways to} \\ \text{choose a catcher} \\ \text{from the players} \\ \text{remaining} \end{array} \right)$$

$$N = \qquad\quad 3 \qquad\quad \cdot \qquad\quad 2$$

$$N = 6$$

CONCLUSION   The coach can choose a pitcher and a catcher in 6 ways.

EXAMPLE 2 Lisa has to take a mathematics course and a science course next year. She has three mathematics courses and four science courses from which to choose. In how many ways can she choose one of each?

SOLUTION 1

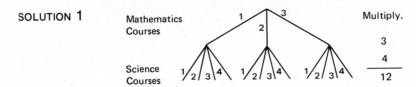

SOLUTION 2 Use N for the number of ways to choose both a mathematics course and a science course.

$$N = \begin{pmatrix} \text{number of ways to} \\ \text{choose a mathe-} \\ \text{matics course} \end{pmatrix} \cdot \begin{pmatrix} \text{number of ways to} \\ \text{choose a science} \\ \text{course} \end{pmatrix}$$

$$N = \qquad 3 \qquad \cdot \qquad 4$$

$$N = 12$$

CONCLUSION There are 12 ways Lisa can choose a mathematics course and a science course.

EXAMPLE 3 How many different automobile license plates can be made with two letters followed by four digits?

SOLUTION

$$26 \cdot 26 \quad \cdot \quad 10 \cdot 10 \cdot 10 \cdot 10$$

Use N for the number of different license plates.

$$N = \begin{pmatrix} \text{Number of ways} \\ \text{to choose} \\ \text{first letter} \end{pmatrix} \cdot \begin{pmatrix} \text{Number of ways} \\ \text{to choose} \\ \text{second letter} \end{pmatrix} \cdot \begin{pmatrix} \text{Number of ways} \\ \text{to choose} \\ \text{first digit} \end{pmatrix} \cdot \cdots \cdot \begin{pmatrix} \text{Number of ways} \\ \text{to choose} \\ \text{fourth digit} \end{pmatrix}$$

$$N = \qquad 26 \qquad \cdot \qquad 26 \qquad \cdot 10 \cdot \quad 10 \qquad \cdot \quad 10 \cdot \quad 10$$

$$N = 26^2 \cdot 10^4$$

$$N = 6\,760\,000$$

CONCLUSION 6 760 000 different license plates can be made.

The way we use multiplication to count the number of possible outcomes in the first four examples illustrates the *Fundamental Counting Principle*.

> ### THE FUNDAMENTAL COUNTING PRINCIPLE
>
> If one event can occur in *m* different ways and a second event in *n* different ways, then the number of ways the events can occur in succession is *m · n*.

For two events, Event *A* and Event *B*, multiplication helps us find the number of ways Event *A and* Event *B* can occur. If, instead, we are interested in the number of ways Event *A or* Event *B* can occur, we use addition. In this case, for the present, we shall assume that when one of *A* or *B* occurs, the other cannot occur. Such events are said to be *mutually exclusive*.

> ### THE ADDITION PRINCIPLE
>
> If one of two mutually exclusive events can occur in *m* different ways and the other in *n* different ways, then the number of ways either one or the other of the events can occur is *m + n*.

EXAMPLE 4 How many different license plates can be made if they must consist of two letters followed by four digits *or* three letters followed by three digits?

 or

$26 \cdot 26 \quad \cdot \quad 10 \cdot 10 \cdot 10 \cdot 10$ $26 \cdot 26 \cdot 26 \quad \cdot \quad 10 \cdot 10 \cdot 10$

The number of license plates that can be made is the sum of the number of each type that can be made.

Use *N* for the number of license plates that can be made.

$$N = \left(\begin{array}{c}\text{Number of first}\\\text{type plate}\end{array}\right) + \left(\begin{array}{c}\text{Number of second}\\\text{type plate}\end{array}\right)$$

$$N = \quad 26^2 \cdot 10^4 \quad + \quad 26^3 \cdot 10^3$$

$$N = \quad 6\,760\,000 \quad + \quad 17\,576\,000$$

$$N = 24\,336\,000$$

CONCLUSION 24 336 000 different license plates can be made.

CLASSROOM EXERCISES

Solve.

1. There are 5 roads from A to B and 6 roads from B to C. How many different routes are there from A to C?

2. How many different serial numbers are there when a serial number consists of either 2 letters followed by 3 digits or 1 letter followed by 4 digits?

EXERCISES

A   Solve.

1. Graham has 5 shirts, 3 ties, and 4 pairs of pants. If he always wears a shirt, a tie and a pair of pants, in how many different outfits can he appear?

2. Shirley has 3 pairs of slacks, 2 blouses, and 4 coats. In how many different outfits can she appear?

3. In how many different ways can Jane, Ellen, Sue, and Bob stand in a line?

4. In how many different ways can volumes I, II, and III of a set of encyclopedias be arranged on a shelf?

5. There are four high schools in a city. In how many different ways can three pupils attend these schools if no two of them attend the same school?

6. There are five sections of Algebra 2 in a school. In how many different ways can three students enroll in these sections if no two of them are in the same section?

7. How many different student numbers are possible when a student number consists of either a two-digit number followed by two letters, or a one-digit number followed by three letters? Assume that the first digit is not zero.

8. How many automobiles may be licensed when the license plates show six digits, or three letters followed by three digits? Not all digits may be zero.

9. Ten runners compete in a race. How many ways are possible for the runners to finish in first, second, and third places. Assume no ties occur.

B 10. How many even 3-digit numbers can be named using the digits 1, 3, 5, 6, 8, 9 when repetitions of the digits are allowed?

11. How many 3-digit numbers that are divisible by 5 can be named using the digits 0, 1, 2, 3, 4, 5, when repetitions of the digits are allowed?

12. A telephone number consists of a 3-digit area code followed by a 3-digit local exchange and a 4-digit number. The area code and local exchange cannot begin with a zero. Find the maximum number of telephone numbers possible.

13. Radio stations in the United States have call letters that begin with K or W followed by two or three letters. How many different sets of call letters are possible?

C 14. How many divisors of 12 are there?

15. How many divisors of 248 832 are there?

16. A local telephone number consists of 7 digits. Several years ago it consisted of 2 letters and 5 digits. If the letters Q and Z were not used at all and the letter O could not be used as the first letter, how many numbers of this type were possible? [Suggestion: Check a telephone dial.]

12-2 PERMUTATIONS

A **permutation** is an arrangement of things in some order. Rearranging into a different order gives a different permutation. The number of permutations of 3 things taken 2 at a time is represented by $_3P_2$. In general, the number of permutations of n things taken r at a time is represented by $_nP_r$.

EXAMPLE 1 In how many ways can the letters A, B, C, and D be arranged?

SOLUTION The number of permutations of A, B, C, and D is $_4P_4$.

This *box diagram* suggests how to use the Fundamental Counting Principle to find $_4P_4$.

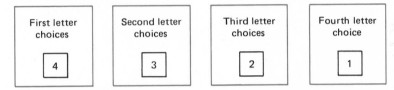

First letter choices	Second letter choices	Third letter choices	Fourth letter choice
4	3	2	1

Use N for the number of arrangements of A, B, C, and D.
$$N = {}_4P_4$$
$$= 4 \cdot 3 \cdot 2 \cdot 1$$
$$= 24$$

CONCLUSION There are 24 arrangements of the letters A, B, C, D.

EXAMPLE 2 How many 3-digit counting numbers can be shown using the digits 1, 2, 3, 4, 5 if no digit is used twice for any number?

SOLUTION The number of permutations of the digits 1, 2, 3, 4, 5, using 3 digits at a time, is $_5P_3$.

Use N for the number of three-digit numbers.
$$N = {}_5P_3$$
$$= 5 \cdot 4 \cdot 3$$
$$= 60$$

CONCLUSION 60 three-digit counting numbers with all digits different can be shown using the digits 1, 2, 3, 4, 5.

In counting the ways an event can occur, we shall refer frequently to the *product of the first* n *counting numbers*. The symbol $n!$ (read *n factorial*) represents this product. That is,
$$n! = n(n - 1)(n - 2) \cdot \cdots \cdot 3 \cdot 2 \cdot 1.$$
Because $0!$ can occur when using some formulas, $0!$ is defined to be 1.

EXAMPLE 3   Write the standard name for the number 7!.

SOLUTION $7! = 7 \cdot 6 \cdot 5 \cdot 4 \cdot 3 \cdot 2 \cdot 1$
$= 5040$

$_nP_n$ refers to the number of permutations of n things taken n at a time. Since the first can be chosen in n ways, the second in $n - 1$ ways, the third in $n - 2$ ways, and so on,

$$_nP_n = n(n - 1)(n - 2) \cdot \cdots \cdot 3 \cdot 2 \cdot 1.$$

$$\boxed{_nP_n = n!}$$

EXAMPLE 4   In how many ways can the letters of PLANE be arranged?

SOLUTION   The number of permutations of P, L, A, N, E is $_5P_5$.

Use N for the number of letter arrangements.
$$N = {_5P_5}$$
$$= 5!$$
$$= 120$$

CONCLUSION   The letters of PLANE can be arranged in 120 ways.

To understand $_nP_r$ in general, it is helpful to compare the indicated product for $_nP_r$ with that for a specific example, such as $_{14}P_{11}$.

$$_{14}P_{11} = 14 \cdot \; 13 \; \cdot \; 12 \quad \cdot \cdots \cdot \qquad 4$$
$$_{14}P_{11} = 14(14 - 1)(14 - 2) \cdot \; \cdots \; \cdot \; (14 - 10)$$
Thus, $\quad _nP_r = \quad n(n - 1)(n - 2) \cdot \; \cdots \; \cdot [n - (r - 1)].$

$_nP_r$ can be expressed in terms of factorials as follows.

$$_nP_r \qquad\qquad\qquad \cdot \qquad\qquad 1$$

$$_nP_r = \overbrace{n(n - 1)(n - 2) \cdot \cdots \cdot [n - (r - 1)]} \cdot \overbrace{\frac{(n - r)(n - r - 1) \cdot \cdots \cdot 3 \cdot 2 \cdot 1}{(n - r)(n - r - 1) \cdot \cdots \cdot 3 \cdot 2 \cdot 1}}$$

$$\boxed{_nP_r = \frac{n!}{(n - r)!}}$$

EXAMPLE 5   A football squad has 14 players who can play any position. There are 11 positions on the team. How many team arrangements are possible?

SOLUTION   The number of permutations of 14 players taken 11 at a time is $_{14}P_{11}$.

Use N for the number of possible team arrangements.

$$N = {}_{14}P_{11}$$
$$= \frac{14!}{(14-11)!}$$
$$= \frac{14!}{3!}$$
$$= 14 \cdot 13 \cdot 12 \cdot \cdots \cdot 5 \cdot 4$$
$$= 14\,529\,715\,200$$

CONCLUSION   There are 14 529 715 200 team arrangements possible.

Switching two *distinct* items in any permutation gives a new permutation.   Switching two items that are identical *does not* give a new permutation.

EXAMPLE 6   Find the number of distinct permutations that are possible using the eight letters of the word ILLINOIS.

SOLUTION   ILLINOIS contains three I s and two L's.   For any permutation of the letters, such as NLLOIIIS, neither permuting the L's nor permuting the I's forms a new permutation overall.   If, however, we identify the L's as L_1 and L_2, and the I's as I_1, I_2, and I_3, we can form 12 permutations.

$NL_1L_2OI_1I_2I_3S$ $NL_1L_2OI_1I_3I_2S$ $NL_1L_2OI_2I_1I_3S$ $NL_1L_2OI_2I_3I_1S$
$NL_1L_2OI_3I_1I_2S$ $NL_1L_2OI_3I_2I_1S$ $NL_2L_1OI_1I_2I_3S$ $NL_2L_1OI_1I_3I_2S$
$NL_2L_1OI_2I_1I_3S$ $NL_2L_1OI_2I_3I_1S$ $NL_2L_1OI_3I_1I_2S$ $NL_2L_1OI_3I_2I_1S$

Similarly, any other permutation of the eight letters can be changed into 12 permutations when the I's and L's are made to be distinct.

For eight distinct letters, the number of permutations is $_8P_8$.   When the I's are not distinct and the L's are not distinct, however, $_8P_8$ must be reduced by factors equal to the number of permutations of two L's ($_2P_2$) and the number of permutations of three I's ($_3P_3$).

Use N for the number of distinct permutations.

$$N = \frac{{}_8P_8}{{}_3P_3 \cdot {}_2P_2}$$
$$= \frac{8!}{3!\,2!}$$
$$= 3360$$

CONCLUSION   There are 3360 distinct permutations of I,L,L,I,N,O,I,S.

PERMUTATIONS

The number of permutations of n things taken r at a time:

$$_nP_r = n(n-1)(n-2)\cdot\cdots\cdot[n-(r-1)]$$

$$_nP_r = \frac{n!}{(n-r)!} \qquad\qquad _nP_n = n!$$

The number of permutations of n things of which q are alike, s are alike, t are alike, and so on:

$$\frac{_nP_n}{q!s!t!\cdots}.$$

EXAMPLE 7 How many standard six-digit numerals can be formed using the digits 1, 3, 1, 3, 1, and 3?

SOLUTION The number of standard six-digit numerals equals the number of distinct permutations of three 1's and three 3's. Use N for the number of standard six-digit numerals.

$$N = \frac{_6P_6}{3!3!}$$

$$= \frac{6!}{3!3!}$$

$$= 20$$

CONCLUSION 20 standard six-digit numerals can be formed from three 1's and three 3's. (Can you list them?)

CLASSROOM EXERCISES

Evaluate.

1. $5!$ **2.** $_8P_2$ **3.** $_4P_4$ **4.** $_5P_3$

Solve.

5. How many different ways can the letters of the word MISSISSIPPI be arranged?

6. How many different 4-digit numerals can be written using the digits 4, 5, 6, 7, 8 and 9 when no digit is used twice in any numeral?

EXERCISES

A Evaluate.

1. $_6P_4$ **2.** $_7P_7$ **3.** $_8P_3$ **4.** $_6P_0$

Solve.

5. How many permutations are there of 4 marbles when 10 marbles are used 4 at a time?

6. How many signals can be made with 5 different flags when 3 flags, one above the other, are used for each signal?

7. In how many ways can 10 flags, 5 white, 3 red, and 2 blue, be arranged one above the other?

8. In how many ways can 4 pennies, 5 nickels, and 3 dimes be given to 12 children if each child is to receive one coin?

9. How many 6-letter code words can be made from 2 A's, 2 B's, and 2 C's?

10. How many arrangements can be made with the letters of the word PANAMA if P is the first letter of each arrangement?

11. How many different bowling lineups can a 5-member team have when the last position is fixed?

12. How many permutations are there of 5 cards taken from a deck of 13?

13. In how many ways can 6 students be seated in a row having 9 chairs?

14. In how many ways can a student's daily schedule be arranged when there are 5 courses and there are 7 periods in the school day?

15. How many positive even integers can be formed with the digits 2, 5, 6, 7 and 8 when no digit is repeated?

16. How many positive odd integers can be formed with the digits 3, 4, 5, 6, 7, and 8 when no digit is repeated?

17. In the finals of the city track championship, there are 2 entries from Washing-ton High, 3 from Lincoln High, and 1 from King High in the 100-meter dash. By school, in how many ways can the race end if there are no ties and everyone finishes?

B **18.** How many serial numbers using 2 letters and 4 digits are possible when repetition of letters is not allowed but repetition of digits is allowed?

19. How many ways can 4 history books, 3 math books, and 2 science books be arranged by subject on a shelf?

20. Find the number of ways in which 3 boys and 3 girls can be seated in a row when the boys and girls are to have alternate seats.

21. In how many ways can the manager of a baseball team arrange the batting order of 9 players when the first four positions are fixed?

22. In how many ways can the manager of a baseball team arrange the batting order of 9 players when the first four positions must be filled from among four of the players?

23. A manager always uses the same nine people and fills the first four positions of the batting order by player and the last five positions by arranging batting averages in order. Of the five considered by average, 3 are hitting .250 and 2 are hitting .235. How many different batting orders are possible?

24. How many 3-digit integers with 3 different digits exceed 600?

C **25.** In how many different ways can *n* people be seated at a round table? In how many ways can 3 boys and 3 girls be seated alternately in a circle?

26. A coin is tossed 10 times for one trial. In how many ways could 5 heads and 5 tails appear? at least 9 heads?

12-3 COMBINATIONS; USING PERMUTATIONS AND COMBINATIONS

A combination is a group of objects in which the arrangement, or order, is not considered. The permutations AB and BA are the same combination of letters. A combination of nine baseball players is enough to form one team, even though there are 362 880 possible permutations of the players in the nine positions on the field.

EXAMPLE 1 In how many ways can a subcommittee of two be formed by Alex, Terese, and Rose?

SOLUTION The combinations possible for a two-person subcommittee are Alex-Terese, Alex-Rose, and Terese-Rose.

CONCLUSION There are 3 subcommittees possible.

The symbol $_nC_r$ represents the number of combinations of n things taken r at a time. From each combination of r things chosen, $r!$ permutations can be formed. Thus, we may write

$$r!_nC_r = {_nP_r}.$$

From Section 12-2, we know that $_nP_r = \dfrac{n!}{(n-r)!}$.

By replacement, $r!_nC_r = \dfrac{n!}{(n-r)!}$.

Therefore, $$_nC_r = \frac{n!}{r!(n-r)!}$$

EXAMPLE 2 Find the number of committees of three that can be formed from a group of 10 students.

SOLUTION The arrangement of students in committee is not considered.

The number of committees equals the number of combinations of 10 students taken 3 at a time.

Use N for the number of committees.

$$N = {_{10}C_3}$$
$$= \frac{10!}{3!(10-3)!}$$
$$= \frac{10!}{3!7!}$$
$$= 120$$

CONCLUSION There are 120 committees possible.

EXAMPLE 3   At a pizza shop, a Super Pizza consists of cheese and any five of the following: onions, peppers, mushrooms, pepperoni, hamburger, sausage, and anchovies. How many varieties of Super Pizza are possible?

SOLUTION   The number of varieties equals the number of combinations of 7 ingredients taken 5 at a time.

Use N for the number of varieties.

$$N = {}_7C_5$$
$$= \frac{7!}{5!(7-5)!}$$
$$= \frac{7!}{5!\,2!}$$
$$= 21$$

CONCLUSION   There are 21 varieties of Super Pizza possible.

To solve a grouping problem that involves permutations, combinations, or both, first determine whether things are to be arranged within each group. If they are to be arranged you have a permutation problem. If the arrangement is not to be considered, you have a combination problem.

EXAMPLE 4   Seven marbles are identical except for color. Three are red. Four are blue. In how many ways may they be arranged in line?

SOLUTION   The arrangement is to be considered, and some of the items are identical.

The number of arrangements equals the number of distinct permutations of 7 marbles, 3 of which are identical and 4 of which are identical.

Use N for the number of arrangements.

$$N = \frac{{}_7P_7}{3!\,4!}$$
$$= \frac{7!}{3!\,4!}$$
$$= \frac{7 \cdot 6 \cdot 5}{3 \cdot 2 \cdot 1}$$
$$N = 35$$

CONCLUSION   There are 35 arrangements possible for the 7 marbles.

EXAMPLE 5 How many different five-card hands may be formed from a deck of 52 playing cards?

SOLUTION In forming card hands, arrangements are not considered.

The number of different five-card hands equals the number of combinations of 52 cards taken 5 at a time.

Use N for the number of different five-card hands.

$$N = {}_{52}C_5$$
$$= \frac{52!}{5!(52-5)!}$$
$$= \frac{52!}{5!47!}$$
$$= \frac{52 \cdot 51 \cdot 50 \cdot 49 \cdot 48}{5 \cdot 4 \cdot 3 \cdot 2 \cdot 1}$$
$$= 2\ 598\ 960$$

CONCLUSION 2 598 960 different five-card hands may be formed from a deck of 52 playing cards.

For some problems you must find the number of one type of group and the number of a second type of group. Then you must use the Fundamental Counting Principle or the Addition Principle to find the total number of a combined group.

EXAMPLE 6 There are 12 girls and 8 boys in a mathematics club. In how many ways can a team of 2 girls and 3 boys be formed?

SOLUTION In forming a team, arrangements are not considered.

The number of ways to form a team equals the number of ways to select 2 girls from 12 *and* 3 boys from 8. Use the Fundamental Counting Principle.

Use N for the number of ways to form a team.

$$N = {}_{12}C_2 \cdot {}_8C_3$$
$$= \frac{12!}{2!10!} \cdot \frac{8!}{3!5!}$$
$$= \frac{12 \cdot 11}{2 \cdot 1} \cdot \frac{8 \cdot 7 \cdot 6}{3 \cdot 2 \cdot 1}$$
$$= 3696$$

CONCLUSION There are 3696 ways to form a team.

CLASSROOM EXERCISES

Evaluate.

1. $_3C_2$ **2.** $_5C_3$ **3.** $_{10}C_2$

Solve.

4. In how many ways can a committee of 4 be selected from 6 students?

5. How many committees of 6 consisting of 4 students and 2 teachers can be chosen from 7 students and 5 teachers?

EXERCISES

Solve.

Ⓐ **1.** In how many ways can a committee of 5 students be selected from a group of 30 students?

2. In Granville County 5 persons are to be elected School Commissioners. There are 8 candidates. In how many different ways may the Board of School Commissioners be filled?

3. Two points determine a line. How many lines are determined by 7 points, no 3 of which are in the same line?

4. There are 8 points in space, and no 4 of them are in the same plane. Any 3 of these points determine a plane. How many different planes are determined by the 8 points?

5. In how many ways can 8 teams in a basketball conference be paired for games?

6. How many different hands of 13 cards each can be dealt from a deck of 52 cards?

7. How many 5-letter words containing 2 different vowels and 3 different consonants can be formed from the letters a, e, i, o, b, c, s, t, w, and z?

8. In how many ways can 4 infielders and 3 outfielders be chosen for a baseball team from 7 infielders and 6 outfielders?

9. A basketball squad consists of 10 players. The coach can use 2 of the players as center, 4 of them as guards, and 4 of them as forwards. How many different teams can the coach form from the squad?

10. A high-school baseball coach has 3 pitchers, 2 catchers, and one player for each of the remaining positions on the team. In how many ways can the coach place a team on the diamond?

11. An algebra test consists of 2 parts, with each part having 5 problems. A student is to select 3 problems from each group. In how many ways can a student select 6 problems to solve?

Ⓑ **12.** How many arrangements of 3 vowels and 3 consonants each can be made from 5 vowels and 6 consonants?

13. How many combinations are there in the multiplication table from 1 times 1 to 9 times 9 inclusive?

14. There are 8 teams in the Alpha Field Hockey league. How many games will be played in the league if each team plays each of the others 5 times?

15. A die is a cube whose faces contain 1, 2, 3, 4, 5, and 6 dots respectively. The plural of die is dice. When 2 dice are thrown, in how many ways can a total of 2 dots turn up? In how many ways can the dice show a total of 7 dots?

16. Assume there are 8 points in a plane with no 3 of them in the same line. How many triangles are determined by these points? How many quadrilaterals are determined by the points? How many polygons are determined that have at least six sides?

17. How many diagonals does a convex polygon of n sides have?

18. Which convex polygons have the same number of diagonals as sides?

19. Which convex polygons have 8 times as many diagonals as sides?

20. A club has 5 members. In how many ways can a committee be formed in the organization? (Hint: What are the possible sizes of the committee?)

21. Prove that $_nC_r = {}_nC_{n-r}$.

C **22.** How many triangles are determined by the vertices of a convex polygon with n sides when the sides of the polygon are not to be sides of any triangle?

23. In how many ways can 4 people be selected from 8 people and seated at a round table?

24. In how many ways can 8 campers be assigned to two leaders when each leader is to have at least 3 campers?

2.7182818 — INTEREST CREATES INTEREST

When $1000 in the bank earns 7% simple annual interest, the amount in the bank at the end of one year will be $1070 ($1000 plus $70 interest). If the money then remains in the bank, interest is *compounded* (it too earns interest), and the following will happen. We use A_n to represent the amount of the investment at the end of n years.

$A_0 = 1000$

$A_1 = 1000(1.07)$, or 1070

$A_2 = 1000(1.07)^2$, or 1159.93

$A_3 = 1000(1.07)^3$, or 1225.04

$A_4 = 1000(1.07)^4$, or 1310.80

$A_n = 1000(1.07)^n$

In general, for principal p, annual interest rate r, and an annual compounding period, the amount of the investment after t years is

$$A = p(1 + r)^t$$

For principal p, annual interest rate r, and n compounding periods annually for t years, the amount of the investment after t years is

$$A = p\left(1 + \frac{r}{n}\right)^{nt}$$

This formula is known as the *Compound Interest Formula*.

1. Find the amount to which $1000 grows in 1 year at 7% annual interest compounded *monthly*.

2. Do Exercise 1 again. Use the interest rates and compounding periods offered by your bank. Compare your findings with the published values for the "effective annual yield".

OBJECTIVE: Determine the probability of an event.

12-4   THE PROBABILITY OF A SINGLE EVENT

The *probability of an event* is a number between 0 to 1, inclusive, that gives us some idea of how likely it is that the event will occur. The closer the probability is to zero, the less likely it is that the event will occur. The closer the probability is to one, the more likely it is that the event will occur.

We sometimes can compute the probability of an event. We need to know how many possible outcomes there are and how many of the possible outcomes correspond to the event occurring. We also need to know that all the possible outcomes are *equally likely* to occur. We will use P (event) to represent the *probability of an event*.

$$P(\text{event}) = \frac{\text{number of possible outcomes that correspond to the event}}{\text{total number of possible outcomes}}$$

EXAMPLE 1   A standard deck of 52 playing cards is to be shuffled well and one card drawn from the deck. What is the probability that this card will be red? will show clubs? will be an ace? will be a face card?

SOLUTION   For each case, use the formula for P(event).

a. 26 of 52 cards are red.

$$P(\text{red card}) = \frac{\text{number of red cards}}{\text{total number of cards}}$$

$$P(\text{red card}) = \frac{26}{52}, \text{ or } \frac{1}{2}$$

b. 13 of 52 cards show clubs.

$$P(\text{showing clubs}) = \frac{\text{number of cards showing clubs}}{\text{total number of cards}}$$

$$P(\text{showing clubs}) = \frac{13}{52}, \text{ or } \frac{1}{4}$$

c. 4 of 52 cards are aces.

$$P(\text{ace}) = \frac{\text{number of aces}}{\text{total number of cards}}$$

$$P(\text{ace}) = \frac{4}{52}, \text{ or } \frac{1}{13}$$

d. 12 of 52 cards are face cards.

$$P(\text{face card}) = \frac{\text{number of face cards}}{\text{total number of cards}}$$

$$P(\text{face card}) = \frac{12}{52}, \text{ or } \frac{3}{13}$$

EXAMPLE 2 Three coins are tossed. What is the probability that all three will turn up heads? that only one will turn up heads?

SOLUTION For each case, use the formula for $P(\text{event})$. For one toss of three coins there are eight possible outcomes. List them.

HHH	HHT	HTH	THH
HTT	THT	TTH	TTT

a. $P(3 \text{ heads}) = \dfrac{\text{number of outcomes showing 3 heads}}{8}$

$P(3 \text{ heads}) = \dfrac{1}{8}$

b. The outcomes HTT, THT, and TTH show only one head.

$P(1 \text{ head}) = \dfrac{\text{number of outcomes showing one head}}{8}$

$P(1 \text{ head}) = \dfrac{3}{8}$

Since determining probabilities can involve counting, the methods for counting given earlier in this chapter can be useful.

It is useful also to remember that an event either occurs or it does not occur. Therefore, the sum of the probability of an event occurring and the probability of it not occurring is 1.

EXAMPLE 3 Your name is on one of eight slips of paper placed in a hat. Three slips are to be drawn. Find the probability that your name will *not* be drawn. Find the probability that your name will be drawn.

SOLUTION Use the formula for $P(\text{event})$.

$$P\left(\begin{array}{c}\text{your name}\\\text{not drawn}\end{array}\right) = \frac{\begin{array}{c}\text{number of combinations of 3 slips from}\\\text{the 7 that do not have your name}\end{array}}{\begin{array}{c}\text{number of combinations of 3 slips}\\\text{from the 8 slips in the hat}\end{array}}$$

$$P\left(\begin{matrix} \text{your name} \\ \text{not drawn} \end{matrix}\right) = \frac{{}_7C_3}{{}_8C_3}$$

$$P\left(\begin{matrix} \text{your name} \\ \text{not drawn} \end{matrix}\right) = \frac{35}{56}, \text{ or } \frac{5}{8}$$

CONCLUSION 1 The probability that your name will not be drawn is $\frac{5}{8}$.

$$P(\text{your name drawn}) + P(\text{your name not drawn}) = 1$$

$$P(\text{your name drawn}) + \qquad \frac{5}{8} \qquad = 1$$

$$P(\text{your name drawn}) = \frac{3}{8}$$

CONCLUSION 2 The probability that your name will be drawn is $\frac{3}{8}$ or 0.375.

We use probability to help us make decisions. When the probability of an event is greater than $\frac{1}{2}$, we know that the event is more likely to occur than not occur. We say that "the *odds* are *in favor* of the event occurring."

In general, the odds in favor of an event occurring are given by

$$\frac{P(\text{event})}{P(\text{event does not occur})}.$$

When the probability of an event is $\frac{3}{4}$, the probability of it not occurring is $\frac{1}{4}$. We may say any of the following.

■ The odds that *the event will occur* are $\frac{3}{1}$, or 3 to 1.

■ The odds *in favor of the event* are $\frac{3}{1}$, or 3 to 1.

■ The odds *against the event not occurring* are $\frac{3}{1}$, or 3 to 1.

■ The odds that *the event will not occur* are $\frac{1}{3}$, or 1 to 3.

■ The odds *against the event* are $\frac{1}{3}$, or 1 to 3.

■ The odds *in favor of the event not occurring* are $\frac{1}{3}$, or 1 to 3.

EXAMPLE 4 A spinner has numerals 1 through 9 equally spaced around its face. Find the probability of spinning a number greater than 6. Find the odds in favor of spinning a number greater than 6.

SOLUTION 1 The probability of spinning a number greater than 6 is given by the formula for P(event).

$$P\binom{\text{number is}}{\text{greater than 6}} = \frac{\text{number of possible outcomes that give a number greater than 6}}{\text{total number of possible outcomes}}$$

$$= \tfrac{3}{9}, \text{ or } \tfrac{1}{3}$$

CONCLUSION 1 The probability of spinning a number greater than 6 is $\frac{1}{3}$.

SOLUTION 2 The odds in favor of spinning a number greater than 6 are given by the odds formula.

$$\text{Odds (in favor)} = \frac{P(\text{number is greater than 6})}{P(\text{number is not greater than 6})}$$

$$= \frac{\tfrac{1}{3}}{\tfrac{2}{3}}$$

$$= \tfrac{1}{2}$$

CONCLUSION 2 The odds in favor of spinning a number greater than 6 are $\frac{1}{2}$, or 1 to 2.

CLASSROOM EXERCISES

Solve.

1. A standard die is rolled. What is the probability of the top face showing 3 dots?

2. A box contains 3 red and 5 blue marbles. When a marble is drawn at random, what is the probability that it will be blue?

3. A card is drawn at random from a deck of playing cards. What is the probability that the card is a Jack?

4. Three coins are tossed in the air at the same time. What is the probability that exactly 2 of them will show tails?

5. Ten identical slips of paper are numbered from 1 to 10. The slips are put in a box and three are taken out in one random draw. Find the probability that one of these shows a number greater than 2.

6. The probability of an event occurring is $\frac{4}{7}$. What is the probability of the event not occurring?

7. When the probability of an event is $\frac{6}{11}$, what are the odds in favor of the event occurring?

EXERCISES

Solve.

[A]
1. If there are 4 white balls and 10 black balls in a bag, what is the chance of drawing a white ball in one draw? of drawing a black ball in one draw?

2. What is the probability of drawing a King when drawing one card from a deck of 52 cards?

3. What is the probability of drawing a heart when one card is drawn at random from a 52-card deck?

4. Bob is one of 20 students in a class. 15 students will be selected at random to participate in an assembly program, what is the probability that Bob will not be picked?

5. When Geri tosses two coins, what is the probability that just one will show a head? that two will show heads?

6. In Exercise 5, what is the probability of tossing at least 1 head?

7. The probability of an event is $\frac{17}{20}$. What is the probability of the event not happening?

8. The probability of an event not happening is $\frac{11}{13}$. What is the probability of the event happening?

9. When the probability of an event is $\frac{3}{5}$, what are the odds in favor of the event?

10. When the probability of an event is $\frac{2}{7}$, what are the odds against the event happening?

[B]
11. All possible words that use all four of the letters F, A, L, L, are written on separate slips of paper. The slips are put into a hat. One slip is drawn at random. What is the probability that the slip contains the word FALL? What is the probability that the slip contains a word with two consecutive L's?

12. All possible 3-digit numbers formed from the digits 1, 2, 3, 6, 8, and 9 are written on slips of paper. Repetition of digits within a number is allowed. If one of these slips is drawn at random, what is the probability that it contains the number 262? When the first-drawn slip is replaced and another random drawing of one slip is made, what is the probability that the first digit on this slip is 3?

13. You have 7 pennies and 5 dimes in a change purse. You select two coins at random. What are the odds in favor of drawing one of each kind of coin?

[C]
14. A student council committee of 5 must be selected from 7 seniors and 3 juniors at the Walker High School. If the committee is selected at random, find the probability that it contains 2 seniors and 2 juniors.

DO YOU RECOGNIZE THE NUMBER?

There is just one positive real number that is 1 greater than its reciprocal. Find that number.

A SURPRISING COMBINATION

Among the pleasing surprises to someone studying mathematics are the unexpected links that may occur between seemingly unrelated topics. An example is Pascal's Triangle (named to honor the French mathematician Blaise Pascal who lived from 1623 to 1662). It is the infinite array of numbers shown here in two ways.

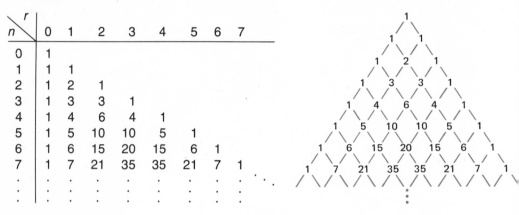

n \ r	0	1	2	3	4	5	6	7
0	1							
1	1	1						
2	1	2	1					
3	1	3	3	1				
4	1	4	6	4	1			
5	1	5	10	10	5	1		
6	1	6	15	20	15	6	1	
7	1	7	21	35	35	21	7	1

In addition to having many interesting properties in its own right, its members in the nth row are the numbers $_nC_r$, $0 \le r \le n$. They are also the coefficients of the terms obtained when $(a + b)^n$ is *expanded*.

BINOMIAL EXPANSIONS

$(a + b)^0$	1
$(a + b)^1$	$1a + 1b$
$(a + b)^2$	$1a^2 + 2ab + 1b^2$
$(a + b)^3$	$1a^3 + 3a^2b + 3ab^2 + 1b^3$
$(a + b)^4$	$1a^4 + 4a^3b + 6a^2b^2 + 4ab^3 + 1b^4$

Hence, we may use the numbers $_nC_r$ to state an expansion formula, the Binomial Formula, for $(a + b)^n$ as follows.

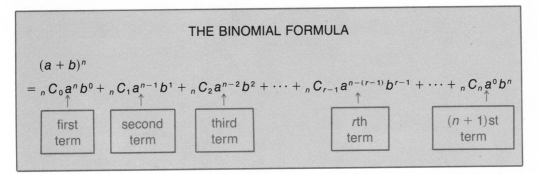

THE BINOMIAL FORMULA

$(a + b)^n$

$= {}_nC_0 a^n b^0 + {}_nC_1 a^{n-1} b^1 + {}_nC_2 a^{n-2} b^2 + \cdots + {}_nC_{r-1} a^{n-(r-1)} b^{r-1} + \cdots + {}_nC_n a^0 b^n$

| first term | second term | third term | rth term | $(n + 1)$st term |

To be able to use this formula it is important that you study and understand the number patterns that exist in the subscripts and exponents from term to term. You should note also how the subscripts and exponents relate to the number of the term.

EXERCISES

1. Expand $\sum_{r=0}^{n} {}_nC_r a^{n-r} b^r$ for $n = 6$.

2. Use the Binomial Formula to expand $(a + b)^2$; $(a + b)^8$; $(a + b)^{10}$.

3. Expand $(2x - 3y)^5$. [HINT: Use $(2x + (-3y))$.]

4. Find the fifth term in the expansion of $(x - y)^{12}$.

5. Find the term in the expansion of $(1 - x^2)^8$ that contains x^{10}.

6. Show that $\sum_{r=0}^{n} {}_nC_r = 2^n$. [HINT: $2 = 1 + 1$.]

An examination of the terms in any row of Pascal's Triangle reveals that each entry other than the 1 on each end is the sum of the two entries above it. This suggests a theorem about combinations, namely that

$${}_nC_r = {}_{n-1}C_{r-1} + {}_{n-1}C_r.$$

7. Prove ${}_nC_r = {}_{n-1}C_{r-1} + {}_{n-1}C_r$, for $n > 1$, $0 < r < n$.

12-5 THE PROBABILITY OF COMBINED EVENTS

Two single events often are combined to serve as one event for which we wish to find the probability. The *combined event* usually can be described using "and" or "or" between the words describing the single events. The Fundamental Counting Principle and the Addition Principle presented in Section 12-1 provide ways to count combined outcomes. The use of these principles is essential for finding and understanding probabilities of combined events.

EXAMPLE 1 Find the probability of rolling a total of 7 with two dice.

SOLUTION Use the formula for P(event).

$$P\left(\begin{array}{c}\text{total of 7}\\\text{with 2 dice}\end{array}\right) = \frac{\begin{array}{c}\text{number of ways to roll a}\\\text{total of 7 with 2 dice}\end{array}}{\begin{array}{c}\text{total number of possible outcomes}\\\text{for a roll of 2 dice}\end{array}}$$

A total of 7 may occur in any one of six ways: 1 and 6, 2 and 5, 3 and 4, 4 and 3, 5 and 2, or 6 and 1.

Since there are 6 outcomes for one die, there are $6 \cdot 6$, or 36 possible outcomes for two dice.

$$P\left(\begin{array}{c}\text{total of 7}\\\text{with 2 dice}\end{array}\right) = \frac{6}{36}$$
$$= \frac{1}{6}$$

CONCLUSION The probability of rolling a total of 7 with two dice is $\frac{1}{6}$.

EXAMPLE 2 A lottery sells 10 tickets and offers 3 prizes. Find the probability of winning one or more prizes with 4 tickets.

SOLUTION 1 $P\left(\begin{array}{c}\text{winning 1 or}\\\text{more prizes}\end{array}\right)$

$$= \frac{\text{number of ways to win 1 or more prizes}}{\text{number of ways to select 4 from 10}}$$

$$= \frac{\begin{array}{c}\text{number of ways}\\\text{to win 1 prize}\end{array} + \begin{array}{c}\text{number of ways}\\\text{to win 2 prizes}\end{array} + \begin{array}{c}\text{number of ways}\\\text{to win 3 prizes}\end{array}}{\begin{array}{c}\text{number of combinations of 4 tickets}\\\text{taken from 10 tickets}\end{array}}$$

$$P\left(\begin{array}{c}\text{winning 1 or}\\\text{more prizes}\end{array}\right) = \frac{{}_3C_1 \cdot {}_7C_3 + {}_3C_2 \cdot {}_7C_2 + {}_3C_3 \cdot {}_7C_1}{{}_{10}C_4}$$

$$= \frac{3 \cdot 35 + 3 \cdot 21 + 1 \cdot 7}{210}$$

$$= \frac{105 + 63 + 7}{210}$$

$$= \frac{175}{210}$$

$$= \frac{5}{6}$$

SOLUTION 2 The probability of an event occurring plus the probability of it *not* occurring is 1.

Therefore, $\quad P\left(\begin{array}{c}\text{winning 1 or}\\\text{more prizes}\end{array}\right)$

$$= 1 - P(\text{winning no prizes})$$

$$= 1 - \frac{\begin{array}{c}\text{number of combinations of 4 tickets}\\\text{taken from 7 tickets}\end{array}}{\begin{array}{c}\text{number of combinations of 4 tickets}\\\text{taken from 10 tickets}\end{array}}$$

$$= 1 - \frac{{}_7C_4}{{}_{10}C_4}$$

$$= 1 - \frac{35}{210}$$

$$= \frac{175}{210}$$

$$= \frac{5}{6}$$

CONCLUSION The probability of winning one or more prizes with 4 tickets is $\frac{5}{6}$.

Just as we multiply or add to find the *number* of combined *outcomes*, so we can multiply or add to find the *probability* of combined *events*. If we are interested in event A *and* event B occurring in order, then $P(A \text{ and } B) = P(A) \cdot P(B)$, where $P(B)$ is given as if event A has occurred. If we are interested in either A *or* B occurring, but know they cannot both occur, then $P(A \text{ or } B) = P(A) + P(B)$. When both A and B can occur together, $P(A \text{ or } B) = P(A) + P(B) - P(A \text{ and } B)$.

EXAMPLE 3 A bag contains 3 beans that are colored red and 4 that are colored blue. A bean is to be drawn and not replaced. Then a second bean is to be drawn. Find the probability that both beans will be red.

SOLUTION For the probability that both beans will be red, use the formula for P(event A *and* event B).

$$P\left(\begin{matrix}\text{first bean is red and}\\ \text{second bean is red}\end{matrix}\right) = P\left(\begin{matrix}\text{first bean}\\ \text{is red}\end{matrix}\right) \cdot P\left(\begin{matrix}\text{second bean}\\ \text{is red}\end{matrix}\right)$$

$$= \frac{3}{7} \cdot \frac{2}{6}$$

$$= \frac{1}{7}$$

CONCLUSION The probability of drawing two red beans is $\frac{1}{7}$.

EXAMPLE 4 You are to select one card from a standard deck of playing cards. Find the probability of drawing an 8 or a heart.

SOLUTION Use the formula for P(event A *or* event B). In this case events A and B can occur together if you were to draw the 8 of hearts.

$$P(8 \text{ or heart}) = P(8) + P(\text{heart}) - P(8 \text{ of hearts})$$

$$= \frac{\text{number of 8's}}{\begin{matrix}\text{number of}\\ \text{cards}\end{matrix}} + \frac{\begin{matrix}\text{number of}\\ \text{hearts}\end{matrix}}{\begin{matrix}\text{number of}\\ \text{cards}\end{matrix}} - \frac{\begin{matrix}\text{number of}\\ \text{8's of hearts}\end{matrix}}{\begin{matrix}\text{number of}\\ \text{cards}\end{matrix}}$$

$$= \frac{4}{52} + \frac{13}{52} - \frac{1}{52}$$

$$= \frac{16}{52}$$

$$= \frac{4}{13}$$

CONCLUSION The probability of drawing an 8 or a heart is $\frac{4}{13}$.

CLASSROOM EXERCISES

Solve.

1. What is the probability of throwing a total of 11 with 2 dice?

2. A box contains 4 blue marbles and 5 red marbles. A marble is drawn and not replaced. If a second marble is drawn, what is the probability that both marbles will be blue?

3. A lottery sells 10 tickets and offers 4 prizes. What is the probability of winning one or more prizes with 4 of the tickets?

4. Three coins are tossed. Find the probability that exactly one will show tails.

EXERCISES

Solve.

A

1. What is the probability of tossing a total of 9 in a single throw with 2 dice? a total of 4?

2. A bag contains 6 yellow marbles, 4 blue marbles, and 2 red marbles. When two marbles are drawn from the bag, what is the probability that both marbles will be blue?

3. When 3 cards are drawn from a standard deck, what is the probability of getting 3 hearts?

4. If a card is drawn from each suit, what is the probability that all 4 cards are aces?

5. A lottery sells 40 tickets and 2 prizes are to be given. What is the probability of winning at least one prize if a person holds 4 tickets?

6. Of 100 000 persons at the age of 10 years, 95 965 will live to be 16 years old and 69 517 will live to be 50 years old. If a person is 16 years old, what is the probability of that person living to be 50 years old?

You are to select one card from a standard deck of playing cards. Find the probability that the card is

7. an ace or a king;
an ace or a face card;
an ace or a red card.

8. a club or a queen;
a club or a red card;
a club or a face card.

B

Peter and Harry are competing in the high jump event at a track meet. The probability that Peter will clear 2 meters is $\frac{3}{5}$. The probability that Harry will clear the same height is $\frac{4}{5}$. Find the probability for each of the following situations.

9. both clear it

10. neither clears it

11. at least one clears it

12. only one clears it

13. at least one does not clear it

14. Assuming that $\frac{1}{2}$ is the probability that any child born is a boy, what is the probability that at least 3 children in a family of 6 offspring are girls?

The data in the following table gives the distribution of eye color among the students in grades 10 through 12 at a certain high school.

	blue eyes	brown eyes	totals
Sophomores	250	150	400
Juniors	225	200	425
Seniors	215	175	390
Totals	690	525	1215

For a student selected at random, find the probability that the student

15. has blue eyes

16. is a sophomore

17. has brown eyes, given that the student is a junior

18. is a senior, given that the student has brown eyes.

C

19. Arrange the letters of the alphabet in random order. Find the probability that X and Y are next to each other in the random order.

20. 20% of the seeds of a certain type never germinate. When you plant 10 of these seeds, what is the probability that 8 will germinate?

CHECKING YOUR UNDERSTANDING

WORDS AND SYMBOLS

combinations, $_nC_r$

combined event

equally likely

factorial, $n!$, $0!$

Fundamental Counting Principle

mutually exclusive

odds

permutations, $_nP_r$

probability of an event

CONCEPTS

■ The Fundamental Counting Principle and the Addition Principle enable us to count large numbers of possibilities by using multiplication and addition. [12-1]

■ Switching distinct objects in a permutation results in a different permutation. Switching objects that are not distinct does not result in a different permutation. [12-2]

■ Combinations differ from permutations in that order of arrangement is disregarded for the objects in a combination. [12-3]

■ The greater the probability of an event, the more likely it is to occur. When the probability is 1 the event *will* occur. When the probability is 0 the event *will not* occur. When the probability is greater than $\frac{1}{2}$, the odds are better than 1:1 in favor of the event occurring. [12-4]

PROCESSES

■ Find the number of possibilities. [12-1]

1. In how many ways can a five-question multiple choice test be completed if there are 4 choices for each question?

■ Find the number of permutations. [12-2]

2. $_7P_3 = ?$

3. In how many ways may 5 people be seated in a row with 7 chairs?

4. How many five-digit numbers may be formed using 1, 1, 8, 8, 8?

■ Find the number of combinations. [12-3]

5. $_7C_3 = ?$

6. How many different groups of 3 puppies may be chosen from a litter of 6?

■ Find the probability of an event. Determine the odds. [12-4, 12-5]

7. A letter is drawn at random from RECIPROCAL. What is the probability that it is a vowel? What are the odds against it being a vowel?

8. What is the probability of drawing 3 black marbles in a row from a bag containing 5 red and 5 black marbles?

`1.7112245 98` **CHANCES ARE . . .**

The Birthday Problem is a fascinating exercise in probability.

EXAMPLE What is the probability that two people share a birthday?

SOLUTION $P(\text{share}) + P(\text{do not share}) = 1$
Therefore, $P(\text{share}) = 1 - P(\text{do not share})$.

For the two persons to *not* share their birthday, the birthday of one is, of course, any of the 365 days of the year. The birthday of the other must be one of the remaining 364 days.

$$P(\text{share}) = 1 - \frac{365}{365} \cdot \frac{364}{365}$$

$$\doteq 0.0027$$

When there are three people, the probability that any two share a birthday is found again from the probability that all their birthdays are different. For the birthdays to be different, the birthday of the second person can be any of 364 days. The birthday of the third person can be any of 363 days.

$$P(\text{share}) = 1 - \frac{365}{365} \cdot \frac{364}{365} \cdot \frac{363}{365}$$

$$\doteq 0.0082$$

The Birthday Problem is fascinating because the number of persons needed in a group for the probability to be greater than 0.5 that two of the persons share a birthday is rather surprising.

Solve these problems.

1. How many people are required for the probability to be greater than 0.5 that any two of the people share a birthday.

2. Each of n persons chooses a letter of the alphabet. Find the probabilities for different n that two persons will choose the same letter. Find the smallest number n for which the odds favor two persons choosing the same letter.

3. From a list, each of n persons selects the name of a president of the United States. Determine n so that the probability of at least two persons selecting the same president is at least 0.9.

CHAPTER REVIEW

Solve. [12-1]

1. In how many ways can a secretary, treasurer, and vice-president be chosen from 6 candidates? Each candidate is eligible for all 3 positions.

2. A manufacturer's code contains 2 letters followed by 2 numbers. The 2 letters must be different and the 2 numbers must be different. How many distinct codes are available?

3. A certain kind of combination lock uses as combinations either one letter followed by 2 distinct numbers or one number followed by 2 distinct letters. How many different combinations are available?

Evaluate. [12-2]

4. 9!   **5.** $\dfrac{8!}{5!3!}$ **6.** $_{12}P_3$

Solve.

7. How many 3-digit numbers can be represented using the digits 1, 2, 3, 4, 5, 6, 7, 8 and 9 if no digit is to be used twice for any number?

8. A grand-prize winner, a first runnerup, and a second runnerup are to be selected from 10 contest finalists. In how many different ways can the 3 winners be selected?

9. List all possible different arrangements of the letters in the word TOY.

10. How many distinct arrangements of the letters of LLAMA are there?

11. Three quarters, two nickels, and two dimes are to be distributed (one coin each) to 7 people. How many different ways are there of making the distribution?

12. How many counting numbers can be named using the digits of 23 223?

Solve. [12-3]

13. In how many ways may two letters be chosen from the six letters A, B, C, D, E, F?

14. How many different 3-card hands can be drawn from a deck of 52 cards?

15. A 3-student delegation must be chosen to represent their school at a statewide mathematics conference. There are seven candidates for the 3 spots. How many ways are there of choosing the delegation?

16. Tanya has 10 red marbles and 15 blue marbles. In how many ways can she select a group of marbles that contains 6 red marbles and 2 blue marbles?

Compute the probability [12-4]

17. of drawing a red queen from a deck of 52 cards.

18. of drawing either a two or a face card from the deck.

19. of drawing either the ace of clubs or a diamond from the deck.

20. of rolling more than 4 with a standard die.

21. What are the odds against picking an even number from {1, 2, 3, 4, 5}?

Two numbers are drawn from {0, 1, 2, 3, 4}. What is the probability [12-5]

22. that their sum is even?   **23.** that their product is zero?

The probability that John will be absent is $\frac{2}{9}$. The probability that Suzanne will be absent is $\frac{3}{7}$. What is the probability that

24. both will be absent?   **25.** neither will be absent?   **26.** exactly one will be absent?

CAPSULE REVIEW

Write the letter of the best response.

1. How many ways are there of selecting 2 notebooks and one pen from a collection of 5 notebooks and 5 pens.

   a. 125   **b.** 25   **c.** 50   **d.** 100

2. Which of these is *not* equal to the number of possible arrangements of the letters of the alphabet?

   a. 26!   **b.** $\dfrac{26!}{26! - 26!}$ **c.** $\dfrac{26!}{(26 - 26)!}$ **d.** $_{26}P_{26}$

3. The number of distinct arrangements of the letters in the word LETTER is

   a. $\dfrac{_6P_6}{2!2!}$ **b.** $\dfrac{_6P_6}{4!}$ **c.** $\dfrac{_6P_6}{2!}$ **d.** $\dfrac{_6P_6}{6!}$

4. In how many ways can 8 sandwiches be selected from a menu of 12?

   a. 495   **b.** 11 880   **c.** 12   **d.** 196

5. Four marbles are drawn from a bag containing 3 red marbles and 5 blue marbles. What is the probability that they are all blue?

   a. $\frac{9}{10}$ **b.** $\frac{2}{7}$ **c.** $\frac{1}{14}$ **d.** $\frac{3}{5}$

6. The probability that Rachel will break the school long-jump record is $\frac{3}{8}$. The probability that Arlene will break the record is $\frac{2}{9}$. Which statement below is *false*?

   a. The odds are against Rachel's breaking the record.

   b. The odds are against Arlene's breaking the record.

   c. The odds are in favor of at least one of them breaking the record.

   d. The odds are in favor of exactly one of them breaking the record.

CHAPTER TEST

1. Three airlines fly between Anson and Barker. Four airlines fly between Barker and Clarkston. How many ways can a person fly from Anson to Clarkston by way of Barker?

2. How many different license plates can be made if each consists of one letter followed by five digits?

3. How many ways can 5 people line up at a drinking fountain?

4. In how many ways can two names be picked from 30 and written in order on a sheet of paper?

5. In how many ways can 2 identical nickels, 3 identical dimes, and 1 quarter be arranged?

6. How many 6-letter arrangements can be made with the letters in ALASKA?

7. How many different 2-person tennis matches can be played if there are 10 players?

8. How many different 3-topping pizzas can be made if there are 8 toppings from which to choose?

9. A 5-person committee is to be formed with 3 persons selected from 5 Nationalists and 2 persons selected from 6 Federalists. In how many ways can the committee be formed?

10. Two books are to be selected from four fiction books. Two books are to be selected from five non-fiction books. In how many ways can 4 such books be selected and arranged on a shelf?

11. Find the probability of getting a number larger than 2 when a standard die is rolled.

12. Find the probability of getting a "tail" when a penny is flipped.

13. Find the probability of getting at least one head when three coins are tossed.

14. Find the probability of getting no heads or all heads when three coins are tossed.

Write the letter of the best response.

15. There are 3 routes from Elm Creek to Oakdale, 4 routes from Oakdale to Aspenville, and 4 routes from Aspenville to Mapleton. How many ways can a person go from Elm Creek to Mapleton by way of Oakdale and Aspenville?

    a. 11   **b.** 28   **c.** 36   **d.** 48   **e.** 64

16. What does $6! - 4!$ equal?

    a. 2   **b.** 30   **c.** 120   **d.** 696   **e.** 716

17. How many 6-letter arrangements can be made with the letters in HAWAII?

    a. 24   **b.** 30   **c.** 180   **d.** 716   **e.** 720

18. How many 5-person committees can be formed if the members are to be selected from 8 eligible candidates?

    a. 56   **b.** 120   **c.** 336   **d.** 1680   **e.** 40 320

19. 3 players are to be picked from 25 seniors and 2 players are to be picked from 20 juniors. In how many ways can a 5-person team be chosen?

    a. 2490   **b.** 249 000   **c.** 437 000   **d.** 874 000   **e.** 1 121 759

20. Three red marbles and nine black marbles are in a bag. What is the probability of randomly selecting a red marble in one draw from the bag?

    a. $\frac{1}{4}$ **b.** $\frac{1}{3}$ **c.** $\frac{1}{2}$ **d.** $\frac{2}{3}$ **e.** $\frac{3}{4}$

21. The probability that a student in Room 152 is left-handed is $\frac{1}{6}$. The probability that a student is brown-haired is $\frac{6}{10}$. What is the probability that a randomly-selected student in Room 152 is both left-handed and brown-haired?

    a. $\frac{23}{30}$ **b.** $\frac{23}{60}$ **c.** $\frac{3}{10}$ **d.** $\frac{1}{12}$ **e.** $\frac{1}{10}$

CHAPTER 13

INTRODUCTION TO
MATRIX ALGEBRA

By producing too few of something that people will buy, a company may invite unwanted competition to take up the slack. By producing too much it suffers needless expense and waste. No industry operates in the dark. Market research can generate the numbers that an industry, large or small, needs to know to produce the right amount for the right place at the right time and the right pace.

OBJECTIVES: Define basic terminology for matrices. Define matrix addition, subtraction, and multiplication. Find the determinant of a 2-by-2 matrix. Determine whether a matrix has an inverse. Find the inverse of an invertible matrix.

13-1   MATRICES AND OPERATIONS WITH MATRICES

A **matrix** is a rectangular array of objects. The objects are arranged in rows and columns. In this book the objects are numerals or variables that represent real numbers. A matrix often is shown with brackets, [ ].

$$\begin{bmatrix} 1 & -2 & 0 \\ -3 & \frac{1}{2} & 4 \end{bmatrix} \quad \begin{bmatrix} 1 & x \\ 0 & 4 \\ -3 & y \end{bmatrix}$$

Each number or variable within a matrix is an **element** of the matrix. The **dimensions** of a matrix are given as the *number of rows* by the *number of columns* of the matrix. The number of rows always is given first. A matrix having one row is a **row matrix**. A matrix having one column is a **column matrix**. A matrix having the same number of rows and columns is a **square matrix**.

$$\begin{bmatrix} 1 & 0 & -1 \\ 2 & -3 & 5 \end{bmatrix} \qquad [a \quad -1] \qquad \begin{bmatrix} 6 \\ -\frac{1}{2} \\ n \end{bmatrix} \qquad \begin{bmatrix} 0 & 1 \\ -5 & \frac{1}{3} \end{bmatrix}$$

2-by-3 matrix   1-by-2-matrix 3-by-1 matrix 2-by-2 matrix
     a row matrix a column matrix a square matrix

Just as we learned to add, subtract, and multiply using real numbers, so we can learn to perform corresponding operations using matrices (plural of matrix). For each matrix operation, however, there are some restrictions.

Addition or subtraction is defined only for matrices that have the same dimensions. For two such matrices the sum or difference is another matrix. Each element of the sum is the sum of the elements having the same location in the two matrices. Each element of the difference is the difference of the elements having the same location in the two matrices.

EXAMPLE 1 Add $\begin{bmatrix} 7 & 0 & 1 \\ 3 & -4 & -1 \end{bmatrix}$ and $\begin{bmatrix} -2 & 4 & 6 \\ 0 & -3 & 5 \end{bmatrix}$.

SOLUTION $\begin{bmatrix} 7 & 0 & 1 \\ 3 & -4 & -1 \end{bmatrix} + \begin{bmatrix} -2 & 4 & 6 \\ 0 & -3 & 5 \end{bmatrix}$

$= \begin{bmatrix} 7 + (-2) & 0 + 4 & 1 + 6 \\ 3 + 0 & -4 + (-3) & -1 + 5 \end{bmatrix} = \begin{bmatrix} 5 & 4 & 7 \\ 3 & -7 & 4 \end{bmatrix}$

EXAMPLE 2 Simplify $\begin{bmatrix} 5 & 4 & 7 \\ 3 & -7 & 4 \end{bmatrix} - \begin{bmatrix} -2 & 4 & 6 \\ 0 & -3 & 5 \end{bmatrix}$.

SOLUTION $\begin{bmatrix} 5 & 4 & 7 \\ 3 & -7 & 4 \end{bmatrix} - \begin{bmatrix} -2 & 4 & 6 \\ 0 & -3 & 5 \end{bmatrix}$

$= \begin{bmatrix} 5 - (-2) & 4 - 4 & 7 - 6 \\ 3 - 0 & -7 - (-3) & 4 - 5 \end{bmatrix} = \begin{bmatrix} 7 & 0 & 1 \\ 3 & -4 & -1 \end{bmatrix}$

There are two kinds of products that involve matrices. One is the **scalar product** of a real number (called a *scalar*) and a matrix. It is the matrix in which the element in any particular location is the product of the scalar and the element in the same location in the given matrix.

EXAMPLE 3 Simplify $3\begin{bmatrix} 4 & 0 \\ 2 & -\frac{1}{3} \end{bmatrix}$.

SOLUTION $3\begin{bmatrix} 4 & 0 \\ 2 & -\frac{1}{3} \end{bmatrix} = \begin{bmatrix} 3(4) & 3(0) \\ 3(2) & 3\left(-\frac{1}{3}\right) \end{bmatrix}$

$= \begin{bmatrix} 12 & 0 \\ 6 & -1 \end{bmatrix}$

The other product, the product AB of two matrices A and B, is defined only when the number of elements in each row of A equals the number of elements in each column of B. Each element of the product is found by combining the elements in a row from the first matrix with the elements in a column from the second matrix following this pattern.

$$\begin{bmatrix} a & b & c \\ d & e & f \end{bmatrix} \cdot \begin{bmatrix} r & s \\ t & u \\ v & w \end{bmatrix} = \begin{bmatrix} ar + bt + cv & as + bu + cw \\ \text{(Row 1, Column 1)} & \text{(Row 1, Column 2)} \\ dr + et + fv & ds + eu + fw \\ \text{(Row 2, Column 1)} & \text{(Row 2, Column 2)} \end{bmatrix}$$

In general, when A has dimensions m by n and B has dimensions n by p, the product is a matrix having dimensions m by p. By examining the dimensions of two matrices you should be able to determine whether they have a product. If the product exists, you should be able to tell what its dimensions are.

the number of columns ┐ = ┌ the number of rows

$$A \cdot B = C$$
$$(m \text{ by } n) \quad (n \text{ by } p) \quad (m \text{ by } p) \longleftarrow \text{ dimensions of product}$$

dimensions of factors

EXAMPLE 4 Simplify $\begin{bmatrix} -3 & 1 \\ 0 & 5 \end{bmatrix} \cdot \begin{bmatrix} 2 & 4 \\ -6 & 8 \end{bmatrix}$.

SOLUTION
$$\begin{bmatrix} -3 & 1 \\ 0 & 5 \end{bmatrix} \cdot \begin{bmatrix} 2 & 4 \\ -6 & 8 \end{bmatrix} = \begin{bmatrix} -3(2) + 1(-6) & -3(4) + 1(8) \\ 0(2) + 5(-6) & 0(4) + 5(8) \end{bmatrix}$$
$$= \begin{bmatrix} -12 & -4 \\ -30 & 40 \end{bmatrix}.$$

It can be verified, using the properties of real numbers, that matrix addition is associative and commutative and that matrix multiplication is associative.

In general, matrix multiplication is not commutative. This is easily checked. For example, rearrange the factors of Example 4 and find the product. It is different from the product in Example 4. When the two factors of a product are not square matrices, the product may not even exist when the matrices are rearranged. If both products do exist, their dimensions are different. Make up some examples to check these facts.

There is an additive identity matrix for the set of matrices of any given dimension. It is called a **zero matrix**. Each of its elements is zero. There is a multiplicative identity for the set of square matrices of any dimension. It is called an **identity matrix**. Each element in its *main diagonal* is 1. Each of its other elements is 0.

main
diagonal ↘

$$\begin{bmatrix} 0 & 0 & 0 \\ 0 & 0 & 0 \end{bmatrix} \qquad \begin{bmatrix} 1 & 0 & 0 \\ 0 & 1 & 0 \\ 0 & 0 & 1 \end{bmatrix}$$

2-by-3
zero matrix

3-by-3
identity matrix

In the exercises you will be asked to verify that for a matrix A and an identity matrix I, $AI = A$ and $IA = A$.

CLASSROOM EXERCISES

Simplify.

1. $\begin{bmatrix} 8 & -3 & 2 \\ 6 & 0 & 0 \end{bmatrix} - \begin{bmatrix} -3 & 1 & 2 \\ -4 & 5 & 6 \end{bmatrix}$

2. $3\begin{bmatrix} 2 & 0 \\ -1 & 3 \\ 3 & 1 \end{bmatrix}$

3. $\begin{bmatrix} 2 & -1 \\ 0 & 3 \end{bmatrix} \cdot \begin{bmatrix} 1 & 5 \\ -2 & 4 \end{bmatrix}$

EXERCISES

A   Simplify. Use the given matrices.

$A = [1 \quad -3] \qquad B = [-1 \quad 0 \quad 3] \qquad C = \begin{bmatrix} -2 \\ 0 \end{bmatrix}$

1. $G + H$ **2.** $D - E$

3. $2H$ **4.** $-3E$

5. DG **6.** GD

7. EH **8.** HE

9. KJ **10.** BJ

11. HJ **12.** JB

13. FL **14.** LF

15. $-2K$ **16.** AE

$D = \begin{bmatrix} -1 & 1 & 2 \\ 0 & 4 & 3 \end{bmatrix} \qquad E = \begin{bmatrix} 2 & 1 & -1 \\ -5 & 3 & 2 \end{bmatrix} \qquad F = \begin{bmatrix} -1 & 2 \\ 3 & 4 \end{bmatrix}$

$G = \begin{bmatrix} 2 & 3 \\ -4 & 0 \\ 5 & 1 \end{bmatrix} \qquad H = \begin{bmatrix} 1 & -2 \\ -3 & 4 \\ 5 & -6 \end{bmatrix} \qquad I = \begin{bmatrix} 4 \\ 2 \\ 1 \end{bmatrix}$

$J = \begin{bmatrix} 2 & 0 & 4 \\ 1 & -1 & 1 \\ -3 & 2 & 1 \end{bmatrix} \qquad K = \begin{bmatrix} 1 & 0 & 0 \\ 0 & 1 & 0 \\ 0 & 0 & 1 \end{bmatrix} \qquad L = \begin{bmatrix} -\frac{2}{5} & \frac{1}{5} \\ \frac{3}{10} & \frac{1}{10} \end{bmatrix}$

B   **17.** Show that matrix addition is commutative and associative.

18. For $A = \begin{bmatrix} 1 & -1 \\ 0 & 2 \end{bmatrix}$, $B = \begin{bmatrix} 3 & 2 \\ 1 & 5 \end{bmatrix}$, and $C = \begin{bmatrix} 0 & 4 \\ -3 & 2 \end{bmatrix}$, show that $A(BC) = (AB)C$.

Let $A = \begin{bmatrix} a & b \\ c & d \end{bmatrix}$, $Z = \begin{bmatrix} 0 & 0 \\ 0 & 0 \end{bmatrix}$, and $I = \begin{bmatrix} 1 & 0 \\ 0 & 1 \end{bmatrix}$.

19. Show that $A + Z = A$ and $Z + A = A$.   **20.** Show that $AI = A$ and $IA = A$.

C   Verify. Use $A = \begin{bmatrix} a & b \\ c & d \end{bmatrix}$, $B = \begin{bmatrix} e & f \\ g & h \end{bmatrix}$, $C = \begin{bmatrix} i & j \\ k & m \end{bmatrix}$.

21. $A(B + C) = AB + AC$ **22.** $(B + C)A = BA + CA$ **23.** $A(B + C) \neq (B + C)A$

24. Describe all 2-by-2 matrices $A = \begin{bmatrix} a & b \\ c & d \end{bmatrix}$ such that $A^2 = \begin{bmatrix} a^2 & b^2 \\ c^2 & d^2 \end{bmatrix}$

13-2 THE INVERSE OF A MATRIX

Any non-zero real number has a multiplicative inverse. The product of a number and its inverse is the multiplicative identity 1. *Some* square matrices have multiplicative inverses. The product of such a matrix A, and its inverse, A^{-1}, is the identity matrix I. (Recall that an identity matrix is one in which each element of the main diagonal is 1. The other elements are 0.)

$$A\,A^{-1} = I \qquad A^{-1}\,A = I$$

A square matrix which has a multiplicative inverse is called an **invertible matrix.** To help identify invertible matrices it is helpful to refer to the *determinant* of a square matrix.

The **determinant** of the 2-by-2 matrix $\begin{bmatrix} a_1 & b_1 \\ a_2 & b_2 \end{bmatrix}$ is the number

$a_1 b_2 - a_2 b_1$. This number often is represented by the symbol $\begin{vmatrix} a_1 & b_1 \\ a_2 & b_2 \end{vmatrix}$. The definition of the determinant of larger square matrices

is suggested on page 504. When a matrix has a name, such as A, the determinant of A may be represented by the symbol det A.

EXAMPLE 1 For $A = \begin{bmatrix} 2 & -4 \\ 3 & 5 \end{bmatrix}$, find det A.

SOLUTION $\qquad A = \begin{bmatrix} 2 & -4 \\ 3 & 5 \end{bmatrix}$

$$\det A = \begin{vmatrix} 2 & -4 \\ 3 & 5 \end{vmatrix}$$

$$\det A = (2)(5) - (3)(-4)$$
$$\det A = 22$$

When the determinant of a square matrix is not zero, the matrix is invertible. For any matrix having non-zero determinant, there are methods for finding the inverse. For the present, however, we shall find inverses for invertible 2-by-2 matrices only.

THE INVERSE OF A 2-BY-2 MATRIX

For $A = \begin{bmatrix} a & b \\ c & d \end{bmatrix}$ with $\begin{vmatrix} a & b \\ c & d \end{vmatrix} \neq 0$, $\quad A^{-1} = \dfrac{1}{\det A} \begin{bmatrix} d & -b \\ -c & a \end{bmatrix}$.

EXAMPLE 2 For $A = \begin{bmatrix} 1 & 2 \\ 3 & 4 \end{bmatrix}$, find A^{-1}.

SOLUTION $A = \begin{bmatrix} 1 & 2 \\ 3 & 4 \end{bmatrix}$

$$A^{-1} = \frac{1}{\det A} \begin{bmatrix} 4 & -2 \\ -3 & 1 \end{bmatrix}$$

$$= \frac{1}{(1)(4) - (3)(2)} \begin{bmatrix} 4 & -2 \\ -3 & 1 \end{bmatrix}$$

$$= -\frac{1}{2} \begin{bmatrix} 4 & -2 \\ -3 & 1 \end{bmatrix}$$

$$A^{-1} = \begin{bmatrix} -2 & 1 \\ \frac{3}{2} & -\frac{1}{2} \end{bmatrix}$$

CHECK   The check that $AA^{-1} = I$ and $A^{-1}A = I$ is left for the student.

CLASSROOM EXERCISES

Find the determinant of each matrix.

1. $\begin{bmatrix} 3 & 2 \\ -1 & 2 \end{bmatrix}$ **2.** $\begin{bmatrix} 4 & 2 \\ 5 & 7 \end{bmatrix}$ **3.** $\begin{bmatrix} -3 & 0 \\ 2 & 1 \end{bmatrix}$

Find A^{-1}. When A^{-1} exists, show that $A^{-1}A = I$ and $AA^{-1} = I$.

4. $A = \begin{bmatrix} 0 & 1 \\ -6 & 3 \end{bmatrix}$ **5.** $A = \begin{bmatrix} 1 & -4 \\ \frac{1}{2} & -2 \end{bmatrix}$ **6.** $A = \begin{bmatrix} -2 & -1 \\ 9 & 4 \end{bmatrix}$

EXERCISES

A Find the determinant of each matrix.

1. $\begin{bmatrix} 3 & 4 \\ -5 & 6 \end{bmatrix}$ **2.** $\begin{bmatrix} 0 & 1 \\ 1 & 0 \end{bmatrix}$ **3.** $\begin{bmatrix} 3 & \frac{1}{3} \\ -1 & -\frac{1}{9} \end{bmatrix}$ **4.** $\begin{bmatrix} \frac{1}{5} & -2 \\ -\frac{3}{10} & 3 \end{bmatrix}$

Find A^{-1}. When A^{-1} exists, show that $A^{-1}A = I$ and $AA^{-1} = I$.

5. $A = \begin{bmatrix} 5 & 2 \\ -2 & 1 \end{bmatrix}$ **6.** $A = \begin{bmatrix} -2 & 1 \\ 0 & 6 \end{bmatrix}$ **7.** $A = \begin{bmatrix} 3 & 0 \\ 4 & -5 \end{bmatrix}$ **8.** $A = \begin{bmatrix} 4 & 1 \\ 8 & 2 \end{bmatrix}$

9. $A = \begin{bmatrix} 6 & -7 \\ 3 & -\frac{7}{2} \end{bmatrix}$ **10.** $A = \begin{bmatrix} 10 & 2 \\ -2 & -\frac{2}{5} \end{bmatrix}$ **11.** $A = \begin{bmatrix} \frac{1}{2} & -1 \\ \frac{2}{3} & \frac{3}{4} \end{bmatrix}$ **12.** $A = \begin{bmatrix} 1 & -\frac{1}{4} \\ \frac{2}{5} & \frac{3}{10} \end{bmatrix}$

B For $A = \begin{bmatrix} 2 & 1 \\ -1 & 3 \end{bmatrix}$ and $B = \begin{bmatrix} 4 & 8 \\ 3 & 1 \end{bmatrix}$, find

13. AB **14.** BA **15.** $\det A \cdot \det B$ **16.** $\det (AB)$ **17.** $\det (BA)$

18. For $M = \begin{bmatrix} 7 & 4 \\ 3 & 2 \end{bmatrix}$, find $(M^{-1})^{-1}$.

Find all matrices for A such that $A = A^{-1}$.

19. $A = \begin{bmatrix} 0 & b \\ c & 0 \end{bmatrix}$ **20.** $A = \begin{bmatrix} a & 0 \\ 0 & d \end{bmatrix}$

C Verify. Assume $\det A \neq 0$.   Verify.

21. $\det A^{-1} = \dfrac{1}{\det A}$ **22.** $(A^{-1})^{-1} = A$ **23.** $(I - A)^{-1} = -(A - I)^{-1}$

Let $I = \begin{bmatrix} 1 & 0 \\ 0 & 1 \end{bmatrix}$ and $A = \begin{bmatrix} \frac{1}{2} & 0 \\ 0 & \frac{1}{3} \end{bmatrix}$.

24. Simplify $(I - A)^{-1}$.   **25.** Find the matrix that would represent the sum of the series $I + A + A^2 + A^3 + A^4 + \cdots$.

WHAT WOULD YOU DO?

Just pretend that this chapter on matrices baffles you. Pretend also that your teacher wants you to have a chance for a passing grade and says, "Here are 50 green marbles and 50 red marbles. You may arrange them in these two bowls any way that you wish. I'll mix them thoroughly. Then blindfolded, you will choose one of the bowls at random. From the bowl you choose, you will remove a single marble. If it is green, you will get a C grade. If it is red, your grade will be lower."

Use your knowledge of probability. Tell how you would arrange the marbles.

OBJECTIVES: Solve the matrix equation $AX + B = C$.   Use determinants to solve a system of linear equations.

13-3   SOLVING MATRIX EQUATIONS

Suppose A, B, and C are 2-by-2 matrices whose elements are known. A *solution* of the matrix equation $AX + B = C$ is a 2-by-2 matrix which gives a true sentence when it replaces X.

When A is an invertible matrix (det $A \neq 0$), the equation $AX + B = C$ has a unique solution.   We use the fact that $A^{-1}A = I$.

$$AX + B = C$$
$$AX = C - B$$
$$A^{-1}AX = A^{-1}(C - B)$$
$$X = A^{-1}(C - B)$$

EXAMPLE 1   Solve $\begin{bmatrix} 2 & -3 \\ -1 & 1 \end{bmatrix} X + \begin{bmatrix} 0 & 4 \\ 3 & 3 \end{bmatrix} = \begin{bmatrix} -1 & 0 \\ 2 & 4 \end{bmatrix}$.

SOLUTION   First, find that $\begin{bmatrix} 2 & -3 \\ -1 & 1 \end{bmatrix}^{-1} = \dfrac{1}{\begin{vmatrix} 2 & -3 \\ -1 & 1 \end{vmatrix}} \begin{bmatrix} 1 & 3 \\ 1 & 2 \end{bmatrix}$

$$= \begin{bmatrix} -1 & -3 \\ -1 & -2 \end{bmatrix}$$

Then, solve the equation.

$$\begin{bmatrix} 2 & -3 \\ -1 & 1 \end{bmatrix} X + \begin{bmatrix} 0 & 4 \\ 3 & 3 \end{bmatrix} = \begin{bmatrix} -1 & 0 \\ 2 & 4 \end{bmatrix}$$

$$\begin{bmatrix} 2 & -3 \\ -1 & 1 \end{bmatrix} X = \begin{bmatrix} -1 & 0 \\ 2 & 4 \end{bmatrix} - \begin{bmatrix} 0 & 4 \\ 3 & 3 \end{bmatrix}$$

$$\begin{bmatrix} 2 & -3 \\ -1 & 1 \end{bmatrix} X = \begin{bmatrix} -1 & -4 \\ -1 & 1 \end{bmatrix}$$

$$\begin{bmatrix} -1 & -3 \\ -1 & -2 \end{bmatrix} \begin{bmatrix} 2 & -3 \\ -1 & 1 \end{bmatrix} X = \begin{bmatrix} -1 & -3 \\ -1 & -2 \end{bmatrix} \begin{bmatrix} -1 & -4 \\ -1 & 1 \end{bmatrix}$$

$$\begin{bmatrix} 1 & 0 \\ 0 & 1 \end{bmatrix} X = \begin{bmatrix} 4 & 1 \\ 3 & 2 \end{bmatrix}$$

$$X = \begin{bmatrix} 4 & 1 \\ 3 & 2 \end{bmatrix}$$

CHECK

$$\begin{bmatrix} 2 & -3 \\ -1 & 1 \end{bmatrix} X + \begin{bmatrix} 0 & 4 \\ 3 & 3 \end{bmatrix} = \begin{bmatrix} -1 & 0 \\ 2 & 4 \end{bmatrix}$$

$$\begin{bmatrix} 2 & -3 \\ -1 & 1 \end{bmatrix} \begin{bmatrix} 4 & 1 \\ 3 & 2 \end{bmatrix} + \begin{bmatrix} 0 & 4 \\ 3 & 3 \end{bmatrix} \stackrel{?}{=} \begin{bmatrix} -1 & 0 \\ 2 & 4 \end{bmatrix}$$

$$\begin{bmatrix} -1 & -4 \\ -1 & 1 \end{bmatrix} + \begin{bmatrix} 0 & 4 \\ 3 & 3 \end{bmatrix} \stackrel{?}{=} \begin{bmatrix} -1 & 0 \\ 2 & 4 \end{bmatrix}$$

$$\begin{bmatrix} -1 & 0 \\ 2 & 4 \end{bmatrix} = \begin{bmatrix} -1 & 0 \\ 2 & 4 \end{bmatrix} \ \checkmark$$

CLASSROOM EXERCISES

Solve for matrix X.

1. $X + \begin{bmatrix} 2 & 0 \\ -1 & 3 \end{bmatrix} = \begin{bmatrix} 10 & 4 \\ 0 & 3 \end{bmatrix}$

2. $\begin{bmatrix} 1 & 3 \\ 0 & -2 \end{bmatrix} X + \begin{bmatrix} 0 & -2 \\ 1 & 3 \end{bmatrix} = \begin{bmatrix} 1 & 2 \\ 1 & 1 \end{bmatrix}$

EXERCISES

A Solve for matrix X.

1. $X - \begin{bmatrix} 3 & 4 \\ -1 & 2 \end{bmatrix} = \begin{bmatrix} 6 & 1 \\ -4 & 3 \end{bmatrix}$

2. $\begin{bmatrix} 3 & -1 \\ 2 & 4 \end{bmatrix} + X = \begin{bmatrix} 2 & 3 \\ 0 & 6 \end{bmatrix}$

3. $\begin{bmatrix} 2 & 0 \\ 1 & 3 \end{bmatrix} X = \begin{bmatrix} -2 & 6 \\ -1 & 9 \end{bmatrix}$

4. $\begin{bmatrix} -1 & 4 \\ 0 & 2 \end{bmatrix} X = \begin{bmatrix} -5 & 4 \\ -2 & -2 \end{bmatrix}$

5. $\begin{bmatrix} 1 & 2 \\ 3 & 1 \end{bmatrix} X + \begin{bmatrix} 1 & 3 \\ 0 & 2 \end{bmatrix} = \begin{bmatrix} -1 & 4 \\ -1 & 5 \end{bmatrix}$

6. $\begin{bmatrix} -1 & 3 \\ 4 & 0 \end{bmatrix} X + \begin{bmatrix} 1 & 4 \\ 2 & 3 \end{bmatrix} = \begin{bmatrix} 2 & 7 \\ -2 & 3 \end{bmatrix}$

B **7.** $3X - 5 \begin{bmatrix} -1 & 2 \\ 3 & 4 \end{bmatrix} = \begin{bmatrix} 6 & 0 \\ -3 & 2 \end{bmatrix}$

8. $X \begin{bmatrix} 1 & -2 \\ 3 & 4 \end{bmatrix} + X \begin{bmatrix} 2 & 1 \\ 3 & 2 \end{bmatrix} = \begin{bmatrix} 15 & 11 \\ -6 & -6 \end{bmatrix}$

Let $A = \begin{bmatrix} 3 & -1 \\ 2 & 4 \end{bmatrix}$, $B = \begin{bmatrix} 4 & 6 \\ 8 & 0 \end{bmatrix}$, and $C = \begin{bmatrix} 8 & 5 \\ 8 & 20 \end{bmatrix}$. Solve for X.

9. $AX = B$

10. $XA = B$

11. $2AX + \frac{1}{2}B = C$

C **12.** Let $A = \begin{bmatrix} 2 & 1 \\ \frac{1}{2} & 0 \end{bmatrix}$ and $C = \begin{bmatrix} \log 4 & \log 2 \\ -2 + \log \sqrt{3} & -1 \end{bmatrix}$. Solve for X: $XA = C$.

Solve for X.

13. $\begin{bmatrix} 4 & 2 \\ -2 & -1 \end{bmatrix} X = \begin{bmatrix} 0 & 0 \\ 0 & 0 \end{bmatrix}$

14. $\begin{bmatrix} 1 & -3 \\ -2 & 6 \end{bmatrix} X = \begin{bmatrix} 0 & 0 \\ 0 & 0 \end{bmatrix}$

EXTENDING DETERMINANTS

Determinants are defined for square matrices of any size. The *order* of a determinant is the number of rows or columns in the matrix. A definition for a third-order determinant is suggested by the following example.

$$\begin{vmatrix} 1 & 3 & 2 \\ 0 & -1 & 4 \\ -2 & 1 & 0 \end{vmatrix} = \boxed{1} \begin{vmatrix} -1 & 4 \\ 1 & 0 \end{vmatrix} - \boxed{0} \begin{vmatrix} 3 & 2 \\ 1 & 0 \end{vmatrix} + \boxed{-2} \begin{vmatrix} 3 & 2 \\ -1 & 4 \end{vmatrix}$$

$$= 1((-1)(0) - 1(4)) - 0 - 2((3)(4) - (-1)(2))$$
$$= -32$$

Each element in a column (or row) is used with the determinant of a 2-by-2 matrix. The smaller matrix is the one that remains when the row and column of the single element (the scalar) are deleted from the larger matrix. The operations used to combine the second order determinants follow the pattern in this $\longrightarrow$ $\begin{vmatrix} + & - & + \\ - & + & - \\ + & - & + \end{vmatrix}$ diagram.

Try these.

1. Evaluate the above determinant using the second or third column. Be sure to follow the pattern of operation signs suggested by the diagram.

2. Evaluate the above determinant using one of its rows.

Evaluate.

3. $\begin{vmatrix} 4 & 2 & 4 \\ 4 & 2 & 6 \\ 3 & 1 & 5 \end{vmatrix}$

4. $\begin{vmatrix} 6 & 7 & -2 \\ -9 & 4 & 3 \\ 3 & 12 & -1 \end{vmatrix}$

5. $\begin{vmatrix} -2 & 3 & 0 & 4 \\ 7 & 3 & 4 & 0 \\ 5 & -6 & 2 & 1 \\ 4 & -6 & 0 & -8 \end{vmatrix}$

13-4   SOLVING LINEAR SYSTEMS

In Chapter 6 we solved the system $\boxed{\begin{array}{l} a_1x + b_1y = c_1 \\ a_2x + b_2y = c_2 \end{array}}$ of two linear

equations.   When $A = \begin{bmatrix} a_1 & b_1 \\ a_2 & b_2 \end{bmatrix}$, $X = \begin{bmatrix} x \\ y \end{bmatrix}$, and $C = \begin{bmatrix} c_1 \\ c_2 \end{bmatrix}$, the system
of two linear equations may be represented by the matrix equation
$$AX = C.$$
When A is invertible, this matrix equation has the unique solution
$$X = A^{-1}C.$$
Therefore, when A is invertible the linear system has a unique solution.
The solution may be found by solving the matrix equation.

EXAMPLE 1   Solve $\boxed{\begin{array}{l} 4x - y = 5 \\ 3x + 2y = 12 \end{array}}$.   Use a matrix equation.

SOLUTION   The system $\boxed{\begin{array}{l} 4x - y = 5 \\ 3x + 2y = 12 \end{array}}$ may be represented by the

matrix equation $\begin{bmatrix} 4 & -1 \\ 3 & 2 \end{bmatrix} \begin{bmatrix} x \\ y \end{bmatrix} = \begin{bmatrix} 5 \\ 12 \end{bmatrix}$.

Since $\begin{vmatrix} 4 & -1 \\ 3 & 2 \end{vmatrix} \neq 0$, $\begin{bmatrix} 4 & -1 \\ 3 & 2 \end{bmatrix}$ has an inverse.

Therefore, the equation has a unique solution.

$$\begin{bmatrix} 4 & -1 \\ 3 & 2 \end{bmatrix} \begin{bmatrix} x \\ y \end{bmatrix} = \begin{bmatrix} 5 \\ 12 \end{bmatrix}$$

$$\begin{bmatrix} x \\ y \end{bmatrix} = \begin{bmatrix} 4 & -1 \\ 3 & 2 \end{bmatrix}^{-1} \begin{bmatrix} 5 \\ 12 \end{bmatrix}$$

$$\begin{bmatrix} x \\ y \end{bmatrix} = \begin{bmatrix} \frac{2}{11} & \frac{1}{11} \\ -\frac{3}{11} & \frac{4}{11} \end{bmatrix} \begin{bmatrix} 5 \\ 12 \end{bmatrix}$$

$$\begin{bmatrix} x \\ y \end{bmatrix} = \begin{bmatrix} 2 \\ 3 \end{bmatrix}$$

Therefore, $x = 2$ and $y = 3$.

CHECK
The check is left
for the student.

CONCLUSION $(2, 3)$ is a solution of the system.

In general, when $\begin{vmatrix} a_1 & b_1 \\ a_2 & b_2 \end{vmatrix} \neq 0$, you can verify that solving

$$\begin{bmatrix} a_1 & b_1 \\ a_2 & b_2 \end{bmatrix} \begin{bmatrix} x \\ y \end{bmatrix} = \begin{bmatrix} c_1 \\ c_2 \end{bmatrix} \text{ gives } \begin{bmatrix} x \\ y \end{bmatrix} = \frac{1}{\begin{vmatrix} a_1 & b_1 \\ a_2 & b_2 \end{vmatrix}} \begin{bmatrix} c_1 b_2 - c_2 b_1 \\ a_1 c_2 - a_2 c_1 \end{bmatrix}.$$

Therefore, the solution of the system $\begin{array}{l} a_1 x + b_1 y = c_1 \\ b_2 x + b_2 y = c_2 \end{array}$ is

$$(x, y) = \left(\frac{c_1 b_2 - c_2 b_1}{\begin{vmatrix} a_1 & b_1 \\ a_2 & b_2 \end{vmatrix}}, \frac{a_1 c_2 - a_2 c_1}{\begin{vmatrix} a_1 & b_1 \\ a_2 & b_2 \end{vmatrix}} \right) \text{ or } \left(\frac{\begin{vmatrix} c_1 & b_1 \\ c_2 & b_2 \end{vmatrix}}{\begin{vmatrix} a_1 & b_1 \\ a_2 & b_2 \end{vmatrix}}, \frac{\begin{vmatrix} a_1 & c_1 \\ a_2 & c_2 \end{vmatrix}}{\begin{vmatrix} a_1 & b_1 \\ a_2 & b_2 \end{vmatrix}} \right).$$

Notice that the denominators for x and y are both $\begin{vmatrix} a_1 & b_1 \\ a_2 & b_2 \end{vmatrix}$.

The numerator for x is $\begin{vmatrix} c_1 & b_1 \\ c_2 & b_2 \end{vmatrix}$. The numerator for y is $\begin{vmatrix} a_1 & c_1 \\ a_2 & c_2 \end{vmatrix}$.

By using D for $\begin{vmatrix} a_1 & b_1 \\ a_2 & b_2 \end{vmatrix}$, D_x for $\begin{vmatrix} c_1 & b_1 \\ c_2 & b_2 \end{vmatrix}$, and D_y for $\begin{vmatrix} a_1 & c_1 \\ a_2 & c_2 \end{vmatrix}$,

the solution of the system may be given as $\left(\dfrac{D_x}{D}, \dfrac{D_y}{D} \right)$.

CRAMER'S RULE

When $D \neq 0$, the system $\begin{array}{l} a_1 x + b_1 y = c_1 \\ a_2 x + b_2 y = c_2 \end{array}$ has solution $\left(\dfrac{D_x}{D}, \dfrac{D_y}{D} \right)$.

To help you remember the determinants D, D_x, and D_y, note that D uses the coefficients of x and y in $\begin{array}{l} a_1 x + b_1 y = c_1 \\ a_2 x + b_2 y = c_2 \end{array}$.

To find D_x, replace a_1 and a_2 in D with c_1 and c_2 respectively. To find D_y, replace b_1 and b_2 in D with c_1 and c_2 respectively.

EXAMPLE 2 Solve $\boxed{\begin{array}{l} 2x - y = 10 \\ 5x + 2y = 7 \end{array}}$ by Cramer's Rule.

SOLUTION $D = \begin{vmatrix} 2 & -1 \\ 5 & 2 \end{vmatrix}$ $\qquad D_x = \begin{vmatrix} 10 & -1 \\ 7 & 2 \end{vmatrix}$ $\qquad D_y = \begin{vmatrix} 2 & 10 \\ 5 & 7 \end{vmatrix}$

$\qquad\qquad D = 9 \qquad\qquad\qquad D_x = 27 \qquad\qquad\qquad D_y = -36$

$$x = \frac{D_x}{D} \qquad\qquad y = \frac{D_y}{D}$$

$$= \frac{27}{9} \qquad\qquad\quad = \frac{-36}{9}$$

$$= 3 \qquad\qquad\qquad = -4$$

CONCLUSION $(3, -4)$ is a solution of the system.

CHECK The check is left for the student.

CLASSROOM EXERCISES

Solve. Use a matrix equation.

1. $2x - 7y = -1$
$\quad 5x - 4y = 11$

Solve. Use Cramer's Rule.

2. $2x + 5y = -2$
$\quad -4x + 9y = -15$

EXERCISES

A Solve. Use Cramer's Rule.

1. $4x - y = 5$
$\quad 3x + 2y = 12$

2. $3x + 2y = 1$
$\quad 2x - 3y = 18$

3. $5x - 2y = 19$
$\quad 7x + 3y = 15$

Solve. Use a matrix equation.

4. $5x - y = -29$
$\quad 2x + 3y = 2$

5. $3x + 7y = 17$
$\quad 2x - y = 0$

6. $ax + y = 5$
$\quad 3ax - 2y = 0$

B **7.** $\dfrac{7(x-5)}{3} + \dfrac{x}{3} = 1 - \dfrac{y}{6}$

$\quad \dfrac{x-y}{4} + \dfrac{y}{2} = \dfrac{5(x-1)}{3} - 1$

8. $\dfrac{1}{x} + \dfrac{3}{y} = 5$

$\quad \dfrac{3}{x} - \dfrac{4}{y} = 2$

9. $\dfrac{m}{x} + \dfrac{n}{y} = h$

$\quad \dfrac{r}{x} + \dfrac{s}{y} = k$

C **10.** Solve $\begin{bmatrix} a_1 & b_1 & c_1 \\ a_2 & b_2 & c_2 \\ a_3 & b_3 & c_3 \end{bmatrix} \begin{bmatrix} x \\ y \\ z \end{bmatrix} = \begin{bmatrix} d_1 \\ d_2 \\ d_3 \end{bmatrix}$ for $\begin{bmatrix} x \\ y \\ z \end{bmatrix}$. Suggest an extension of Cramer's Rule.

CHECKING YOUR UNDERSTANDING

WORDS AND SYMBOLS

column matrix

determinant of a matrix, det A

dimensions of a matrix

element of a matrix

identity matrix, I

inverse of a matrix, A^{-1}

invertible matrix

main diagonal of a matrix

matrix, [ ]

matrix equation

row matrix

scalar product

square matrix

zero matrix

CONCEPTS

■ Operations on matrices are defined in such a way that sums and products may be found only for certain pairs of matrices. For a sum, the matrices must have the same dimensions. For a product, the number of columns in the first factor must equal the number of rows in the second factor. In general, matrix multiplication is not commutative. [12-1]

■ A matrix has a multiplicative inverse if its determinant is not zero. [12-2]

■ A system of two linear equations in two unknowns has one solution if the determinant of its coefficient matrix is not zero. [12-4]

PROCESSES

■ Add, subtract, and multiply matrices.

1. $A + B = ?$ **2.** $A - B = ?$

3. $AB = ?$ **4.** $BA = ?$

$$A = \begin{bmatrix} 1 & 2 \\ -3 & 4 \end{bmatrix} \qquad B = \begin{bmatrix} -2 & 0 \\ \frac{1}{2} & 3 \end{bmatrix}$$

■ Find the determinant of a matrix.

5. det $A = ?$

6. det $B = ?$

7. det $C = ?$

$$C = \begin{bmatrix} 4 & 3 \\ 8 & 6 \end{bmatrix} \qquad D = \begin{bmatrix} -\frac{1}{2} & 0 \\ \frac{1}{12} & \frac{1}{3} \end{bmatrix}$$

■ Determine whether a matrix has an inverse. If it does, find it.

8. $D^{-1} = ?$ **9.** $C^{-1} = ?$ **10.** $B^{-1} = ?$

■ Solve a matrix equation.

11. $AX + B = C$, for A, B, C given above. Solve for X.

■ Solve a system of equations using matrices; using Cramer's Rule.

12. $\begin{array}{l} x + 2y = 5 \\ -3x + 4y = 15 \end{array}$

13. $\begin{array}{l} 4x + 3y = 5 \\ 8x - 6y = -26 \end{array}$

CHAPTER REVIEW

1. Give the dimensions of this matrix. $\begin{bmatrix} 1 & 0 \\ 3 & 1 \\ 2 & -4 \end{bmatrix}$ [13-1]

2. Give the element in the second row and first column of the matrix in Exercise 1.

Simplify.

3. $\begin{bmatrix} 1 & -2 & 4 \\ -3 & 0 & 1 \end{bmatrix} - \begin{bmatrix} 0 & -1 & 2 \\ 4 & 1 & 3 \end{bmatrix}$

4. $-2 \begin{bmatrix} 0 & 1 \\ \frac{1}{2} & -3 \end{bmatrix}$

5. $\begin{bmatrix} 0 & 3 \\ -1 & 2 \end{bmatrix} \begin{bmatrix} 4 & \frac{1}{2} \\ 1 & 0 \end{bmatrix}$

6. $\begin{bmatrix} -1 & 2 & 3 \\ 1 & 0 & 1 \\ 0 & 2 & 0 \end{bmatrix} \begin{bmatrix} 0 & 0 \\ 0 & 0 \\ 0 & 0 \end{bmatrix}$

7. $\begin{bmatrix} 0 & 3 & 4 \\ -1 & 2 & 1 \end{bmatrix} \begin{bmatrix} 1 & 0 \\ 3 & 1 \\ 2 & -4 \end{bmatrix}$

8. $\begin{bmatrix} 1 & 0 & 0 \\ 0 & 1 & 0 \\ 0 & 0 & 1 \end{bmatrix} \begin{bmatrix} 9 & 8 & 7 \\ 4 & 5 & 6 \\ 3 & 2 & 1 \end{bmatrix}$

Find det A. [13-2]

9. $A = \begin{bmatrix} 4 & -3 \\ 1 & 5 \end{bmatrix}$

10. $A = \begin{bmatrix} 2 & 0 \\ 3 & -10 \end{bmatrix}$

Find A^{-1}.

11. $A = \begin{bmatrix} 3 & -7 \\ -2 & 8 \end{bmatrix}$

12. $A = \begin{bmatrix} c & d \\ x & y \end{bmatrix}$

Solve for matrix X. [13-3]

13. $\begin{bmatrix} 1 & 2 \\ 1 & 3 \end{bmatrix} X = \begin{bmatrix} 0 & 1 \\ -1 & 2 \end{bmatrix}$

14. $\begin{bmatrix} 3 & 4 \\ 2 & 3 \end{bmatrix} X - \begin{bmatrix} 3 & -1 \\ 1 & 2 \end{bmatrix} = \begin{bmatrix} 0 & 2 \\ -1 & 1 \end{bmatrix}$

Solve. Use a matrix equation. [13-4]

15. $x + 3y = -4$
$2x - y = 13$

Solve. Use Cramer's Rule.

16. $2x - 7y = 15$
$3x + 5y = 7$

CAPSULE REVIEW

Write the letter of the best response.

1. Which statement is true?

a. $\begin{bmatrix} 3 & -4 \\ 0 & 2 \\ -1 & 1 \end{bmatrix} \begin{bmatrix} 1 & 0 \\ 6 & 1 \\ 4 & 2 \end{bmatrix} = \begin{bmatrix} -1 & 12 \\ -2 & 4 \end{bmatrix}$

b. $\begin{bmatrix} -1 & 0 \\ 3 & 8 \end{bmatrix} = -1 \begin{bmatrix} 1 & 0 \\ -3 & -8 \end{bmatrix}$

c. $\begin{bmatrix} -2 & 0 \\ 3 & 1 \end{bmatrix} \begin{bmatrix} 1 & 3 \\ 0 & 2 \end{bmatrix} = \begin{bmatrix} 1 & 3 \\ 0 & 2 \end{bmatrix} \begin{bmatrix} -2 & 0 \\ 3 & 1 \end{bmatrix}$

d. $\begin{bmatrix} 0 & 1 \\ 1 & 0 \end{bmatrix} \begin{bmatrix} 4 & 8 \\ 6 & 3 \end{bmatrix} = \begin{bmatrix} 4 & 8 \\ 6 & 3 \end{bmatrix}$

2. Which determinant does *not* equal zero?

a. $\begin{vmatrix} 0 & 0 \\ 0 & -1 \end{vmatrix}$

b. $\begin{vmatrix} 0 & 2 \\ 2 & 4 \end{vmatrix}$

c. $\begin{vmatrix} 0 & 2 \\ 0 & 6 \end{vmatrix}$

d. $\begin{vmatrix} 8 & -4 \\ 4 & -2 \end{vmatrix}$

3. The inverse of $\begin{bmatrix} 8 & 4 \\ 9 & 5 \end{bmatrix}$ is:

a. $\begin{bmatrix} 5 & -4 \\ -9 & 8 \end{bmatrix}$

b. $\begin{bmatrix} \frac{5}{4} & -1 \\ -\frac{9}{4} & 2 \end{bmatrix}$

c. $\begin{bmatrix} \frac{3}{2} & \frac{2}{5} \\ 1 & 4 \end{bmatrix}$

d. $\begin{bmatrix} 8 & 4 \\ 9 & 5 \end{bmatrix}$ has no inverse.

4. Solve for matrix X. $\begin{bmatrix} 2 & 0 \\ 1 & -2 \end{bmatrix} X = \begin{bmatrix} 6 & 2 \\ 1 & -1 \end{bmatrix}$

a. $X = \begin{bmatrix} 3 & 2 \\ -1 & 2 \end{bmatrix}$

b. $X = \begin{bmatrix} 1 & 0 \\ 0 & 1 \end{bmatrix}$

c. $X = \begin{bmatrix} 4 & 8 \\ 2 & 4 \end{bmatrix}$

d. $X = \begin{bmatrix} 3 & 1 \\ 1 & 1 \end{bmatrix}$

5. For the system $\boxed{\begin{array}{l} 3x - y = 3 \\ x + 2y = 8 \end{array}}$, 14 is the value of

a. y **b.** D_y **c.** D_x **d.** D

CHAPTER TEST

1. Give the dimensions of $\begin{bmatrix} 2 & 1 & 3 & 4 \\ 6 & 9 & 5 & 8 \end{bmatrix}$.

2. Add $\begin{bmatrix} 1 & 2 & 3 \\ 2 & 3 & 4 \end{bmatrix}$ and $\begin{bmatrix} 6 & 5 & 4 \\ 1 & 2 & 3 \end{bmatrix}$.

3. Find the product. $4 \begin{bmatrix} 3 & 2 \\ -1 & 0 \end{bmatrix}$

4. Find the product. $\begin{bmatrix} 7 & 0 \\ 1 & 2 \\ 0 & 6 \end{bmatrix} \begin{bmatrix} 1 \\ 4 \end{bmatrix}$

5. Find the determinant of $\begin{bmatrix} 1 & 3 \\ -1 & 5 \end{bmatrix}$.

6. Find det A for $A = \begin{bmatrix} 0 & 5 \\ 0 & 2 \end{bmatrix}$.

7. Find A^{-1} for $A = \begin{bmatrix} 4 & 3 \\ 6 & 5 \end{bmatrix}$.

8. Are $\begin{bmatrix} -1 & 2 \\ 2 & -3.5 \end{bmatrix}$ and $\begin{bmatrix} 4 & 7 \\ 2 & 4 \end{bmatrix}$ inverses? Explain why or why not.

9. Solve $\begin{bmatrix} 2 & -3 \\ 5 & 4 \end{bmatrix} + X = \begin{bmatrix} 10 & 10 \\ 10 & 10 \end{bmatrix}$.

10. Solve $\begin{bmatrix} 6 & 11 \\ 2 & 4 \end{bmatrix} X = \begin{bmatrix} 1 & 0 \\ 0 & 1 \end{bmatrix}$.

11. Solve $\boxed{\begin{array}{l} 2x + y = 1 \\ 4x + 3y = 11 \end{array}}$. Use a matrix equation.

12. Solve $\boxed{\begin{array}{l} x + 2y = 1 \\ x + 3y = 2 \end{array}}$. Use Cramer's Rule.

Write the letter of the best response.

13. What are the dimensions of the product of $\begin{bmatrix} 11 & 23 & 36 \\ 41 & 54 & 63 \end{bmatrix}$ and $\begin{bmatrix} 17 & 23 \\ 49 & 18 \\ -56 & 30 \end{bmatrix}$?

a. 2 by 3   **b.** 3 by 2   **c.** 2 by 2   **d.** 3 by 3   **e.** product not defined

14. $\begin{vmatrix} 0 & 3 \\ 2 & 0 \end{vmatrix} =$

a. 6   **b.** 0   **c.** 3   **d.** -5 **e.** -6

15. What is the inverse of $\begin{bmatrix} 8 & 3 \\ 5 & 2 \end{bmatrix}$?

a. $\begin{bmatrix} 2 & -3 \\ -5 & 8 \end{bmatrix}$ **b.** $\begin{bmatrix} -8 & 5 \\ 3 & -2 \end{bmatrix}$ **c.** $\begin{bmatrix} -8 & -3 \\ -5 & -2 \end{bmatrix}$ **d.** $\begin{bmatrix} \frac{1}{8} & \frac{1}{3} \\ \frac{1}{5} & \frac{1}{2} \end{bmatrix}$ **e.** $\begin{bmatrix} -2 & -5 \\ -3 & -8 \end{bmatrix}$

16. What is the solution of $\begin{bmatrix} 2 & 0 \\ 0 & 1 \end{bmatrix} X + \begin{bmatrix} 1 & 2 \\ 3 & 4 \end{bmatrix} = \begin{bmatrix} 9 & 8 \\ 7 & 6 \end{bmatrix}$?

a. $\begin{bmatrix} 8 & 6 \\ 4 & 2 \end{bmatrix}$ **b.** $\begin{bmatrix} 4 & 3 \\ 4 & 2 \end{bmatrix}$ **c.** $\begin{bmatrix} 4 & 6 \\ 4 & 2 \end{bmatrix}$ **d.** $\begin{bmatrix} 9 & 4 \\ 2\frac{1}{3} & 1\frac{1}{2} \end{bmatrix}$ **e.** $\begin{bmatrix} 8 & 3 \\ 2\frac{1}{3} & 1\frac{1}{2} \end{bmatrix}$

17. For the system of equations $\boxed{\begin{array}{l} 2x + 3y = 7 \\ 3x - y = 5 \end{array}}$, $D_x =$

a. 7   **b.** 8   **c.** 11   **d.** -22 **e.** -11

CHAPTER 14
CIRCULAR AND
TRIGONOMETRIC
FUNCTIONS

The dynamics of a discussion group requires patience, discipline, and responsive reasoning skills. The ability to identify connections and relationships is basic. Straightforward, valid reasoning using clear and simple statements can be effective. Mathematics provides good training in each of the above.

OBJECTIVES: Give the measure of an angle of rotation in degrees or in radians. Find values for the cosine and sine functions for any given angle measure. Graph the cosine and sine functions.

14-1 ANGLES AND THEIR MEASURES

In previous courses you may have learned that an angle is formed by two noncollinear rays with a common endpoint called the vertex. Each such angle has a number between 0 and 180 associated with it. This number is the *degree measure* of the angle. For the study of circular and trigonometric functions, the meaning of an angle, sometimes called an *angle of rotation*, and its measure are somewhat different. An angle of rotation does not necessarily have degree measure between 0 and 180. In fact, its measure can be any real number.

An angle of rotation usually is shown in *standard position* in the coordinate plane. Its vertex is the origin. One of its sides is the positive *x*-axis together with the origin. This side is the *initial side* of the angle. The other side is the *terminal side*.

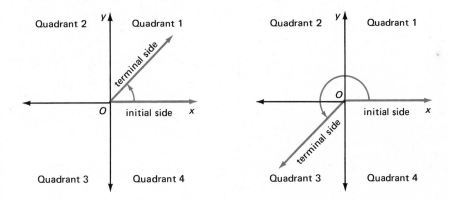

Pictures of angles of rotation include a curved arrow having one end in the initial side and the arrowhead pointing at the terminal side. This suggests that the terminal side has been rotated a certain amount. The measure of an angle of rotation indicates the amount of rotation and whether the rotation is counterclockwise (positive) or clockwise (negative).

Knowing how to find the degree measure of an angle with a protractor lets us measure any angle of rotation.

EXAMPLE 1 Find the measure of the angle of rotation. Use a protractor.

a.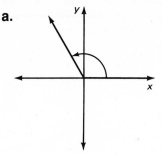

b.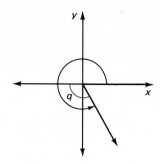

SOLUTION

The measure is 120°.

The measure of ∠q is 120°.

180° + 120° = 300°

The measure of the angle of rotation is 300°.

EXAMPLE 2 Draw an angle in standard position having measure 225°; having measure −270°.

SOLUTION Since 225° = 180° + 45°, we draw the terminal side in Quadrant 3 so that the measure of ∠t is 45°.

Since −270° = −180° − 90°, we draw the terminal side in the y-axis so that the measure of ∠w is 90°.

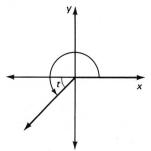

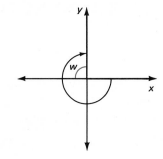

An angle whose terminal side is contained in a coordinate axis is a **quadrantal angle**. The second angle in Example 2 is a quadrantal angle having measure −270°. Quadrantal angles have measures 0°, 90°, −90°, 180°, −180°, 270°, −270°, and so on. The indicated rotation for an angle with measure 360° is one full turn about the origin. The indicated rotation is more than one full turn for measures greater than 360°, more than two full turns for measures greater than 720°, and so on.

There is another way to measure an angle of rotation. For it we refer to a circle in the coordinate plane having the origin as its center. The unit of measure used is the radian. We define **1 radian**, denoted 1^R, to be the counterclockwise measure of the angle of rotation when the angle intercepts an arc having length equal to the length of a radius of the circle.

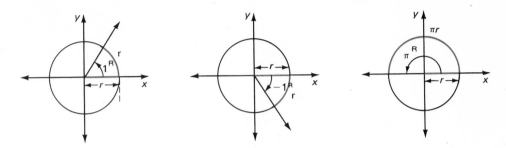

The formula for the circumference of a circle provides the key for understanding radian measure. Since the circumference is $2\pi r$, (the distance around the circle is equal to 2π radii) a 360° angle has radian measure 2π. A 180° angle has radian measure π. Thus, either of the following proportions can help us convert between the two types of angle measure. n and k are real numbers.

$$\frac{n°}{360°} = \frac{k^R}{2\pi^R} \qquad \frac{n°}{180°} = \frac{k^R}{\pi^R}$$

We may convert also by using either of the following equations. Each follows from the second proportion above.

$$n° = \frac{180°}{\pi^R} \, k^R \qquad k^R = \frac{\pi^R}{180°} \, n°$$

The number $\dfrac{180}{\pi}$ that we use with k radians to get degree measure and

the number $\dfrac{\pi}{180}$ that we use with n degrees to get radian measure are

known as *conversion factors*.

EXAMPLE 3 The measure of an angle is 60°.
Find its measure in radians.

SOLUTION 1	SOLUTION 2
$\dfrac{60°}{180°} = \dfrac{k}{\pi^R}$	$k = \dfrac{\pi^R}{180°} \cdot 60°$
$k = \dfrac{\pi}{3}^R$	$k = \dfrac{\pi}{3}^R$

EXAMPLE 4   An angle has measure -3^R. Find its degree measure.

SOLUTION 1	SOLUTION 2
$\dfrac{(-3)^R}{\pi^R} = \dfrac{n}{180°}$	$n = \dfrac{180°}{\pi^R} \cdot (-3)^R$
$n = -\dfrac{540°}{\pi}$	$n = -\dfrac{540°}{\pi}$
$\doteq -171.9°$	$\doteq -171.9°$

As suggested by the picture at the right, the radian measure of an angle does not depend on the size of a particular circle. This is because the unit used for arc length in each circle is the radius of the circle containing the arc.

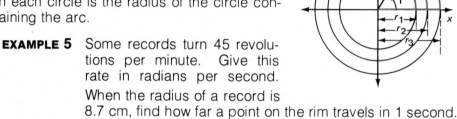

EXAMPLE 5   Some records turn 45 revolutions per minute. Give this rate in radians per second.

When the radius of a record is 8.7 cm, find how far a point on the rim travels in 1 second.

SOLUTION   Use $\begin{bmatrix} R_s & \text{for the rate in radians per second.} \\[4pt] 2\pi\left(\dfrac{\text{radians}}{\text{revolution}}\right) & \text{for a rate-conversion factor.} \\[4pt] \dfrac{1}{60}\left(\dfrac{\text{minute}}{\text{seconds}}\right) & \text{for a time-conversion factor.} \end{bmatrix}$

$$R_s = 45\left(\frac{\text{rev}}{\text{min}}\right) \cdot 2\pi\left(\frac{\text{rad}}{\text{rev}}\right) \cdot \frac{1}{60}\left(\frac{\text{min}}{\text{s}}\right)$$

$$R_s = \frac{3\pi}{2}\left(\frac{\text{rad}}{\text{s}}\right)$$

CONCLUSION 1   The records turn $\dfrac{3\pi}{2}$ radians per second.

Use $\begin{bmatrix} v & \text{for the rate of a point on the rim} \\ & \text{when the radius is 8.7 cm.} \\[4pt] \dfrac{8.7}{1}\left(\dfrac{\text{centimeters}}{\text{radian}}\right) & \text{for a distance-conversion factor.} \end{bmatrix}$

$$v = \frac{3\pi}{2}\left(\frac{\text{radians}}{\text{second}}\right) \cdot \frac{8.7}{1}\left(\frac{\text{centimeters}}{\text{radian}}\right)$$

$$v \doteq 41\left(\frac{\text{centimeters}}{\text{second}}\right), \text{ or } 41 \text{ cm/s.}$$

CONCLUSION 2   A point on the rim travels about 41 cm in one second.

CLASSROOM EXERCISES

Draw an angle in standard position having the given measure.

1. 120° **2.** 180° **3.** −110° **4.** −330°

Give the measure in radians. Use a multiple of π radians.

5. 60° **6.** −150° **7.** 120° **8.** 210°

Give the measure in degrees.

9. $\left(\frac{3}{4}\pi\right)^R$ **10.** $\left(-\frac{1}{12}\pi\right)^R$

11. $\left(-\frac{5}{4}\pi\right)^R$ **12.** $\left(\frac{3}{2}\pi\right)^R$

13. A wheel is rotating at 30 revolutions per minute. Give this rate in radians per second. If the wheel is 40 cm in diameter, how far will a point on the rim of the wheel travel in one second?

EXERCISES

A Give the measure of the angle of rotation.

1. 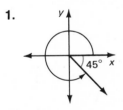 **2.**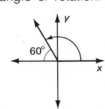

Draw an angle in standard position having the given measure.

3. 65° **4.** 35° **5.** 155° **6.** 115°
7. −275° **8.** −290° **9.** 315° **10.** −315°

Give the measure in radians. Use a multiple of π radians.

11. 30° **12.** −36° **13.** 150° **14.** −330°
15. 4.5° **16.** 240° **17.** 180° **18.** −18°

Give the measure in degrees.

19. $2\pi^R$ **20.** $\left(\frac{7}{4}\pi\right)^R$ **21.** $\left(\frac{4}{5}\pi\right)^R$

22. $\left(-\frac{7}{5}\pi\right)^R$ **23.** $\left(\frac{4}{3}\pi\right)^R$ **24.** $\left(-\frac{2}{3}\pi\right)^R$

25. $\left(\frac{1}{3}\pi\right)^R$ **26.** $\left(-\frac{7}{6}\pi\right)^R$ **27.** $\left(-\frac{1}{4}\pi\right)^R$

28. A wheel is rotating at 75 revolutions per minute. How many radians per second is this? If the wheel radius is 40 cm, how far does a point on the rim of the wheel travel in one second?

B The terminal side of an angle contains the given point. Find the measure of the angle.

29. (0, 1) **30.** (1, 1) **31.** (1, 0) **32.** (−1, 0)
33. (−1, −1) **34.** (−1, 1) **35.** (1, −1)

Give the measure in radians to the nearest one-thousandth of a radian.

36. 77.3° **37.** 1°

Give the measure in degrees to the nearest one-hundredth of a degree.

38. 2.5^R **39.** 1^R

C The area of a sector of a circle is directly proportional to the length of the arc that determines it.

40. Find the area of a sector determined by an arc of length π^R.

41. How much smaller than the area of a circle is the area of a sector determined by an arc of length 6^R?

42. Tell how to construct a circle such that the area determined by an arc of length 1^R is 1 square unit.

Graph each complex number. Find the measure (between 0° and 360°) of the angle of rotation determined by each.

43. $1 + i$ **44.** i **45.** $\frac{\sqrt{3}}{2} - \frac{1}{2}i$

14-2 THE COSINE AND SINE FUNCTIONS

The **unit circle** in the coordinate plane is the circle whose center is the origin and whose radius is 1. The terminal side of any angle of rotation, θ (THAY-tuh), intersects the unit circle in one point, $P(x,y)$, as shown in the diagram. In this way, each angle of rotation corresponds to two real numbers, namely the coordinates of that point of intersection.

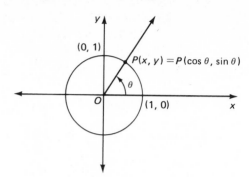

Two functions, the **cosine** and **sine** functions, are defined in the manner suggested by the diagram. An element of the domain of either function is thought of as either the angle itself or its measure in degrees or in radians. The corresponding range element for the cosine function is the x-coordinate of the point P. The corresponding range element for the sine function is the y-coordinate of P.

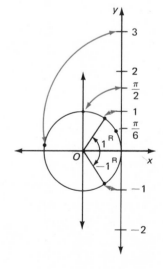

The diagram with the vertical number line suggests the relationship between the real numbers, arc length, and angle measure in radians. Any real number on the vertical number line corresponds to a unique arc length and to the radian measure of the associated angle of rotation. Thus, the domain of the sine and cosine functions may be thought of as being the set of real numbers.

For convenience, the abbreviation cos is used for the cosine function and the abbreviation sin is used for the sine function. Also, the [R] *superscript* that indicates measurement in radians generally is not used with the function notation.

EXAMPLE 1 θ is a right angle. Its measure is 90° or $\frac{\pi}{2}^R$. Find cos θ,

cos 90°, and cos $\frac{\pi}{2}$. Find sin θ, sin 90°, and sin $\frac{\pi}{2}$.

SOLUTION In the coordinate plane, the unit circle and the terminal side of angle θ intersect in the point $P(0, 1)$. Therefore, cos $\theta = 0$, cos 90° = 0,

and cos $\frac{\pi}{2} = 0$.

sin $\theta = 1$, sin 90° = 1,

and sin $\frac{\pi}{2} = 1$.

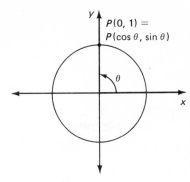

EXAMPLE 2 Find cos $\frac{3\pi}{2}$ and sin $\frac{3\pi}{2}$.

SOLUTION $\frac{3\pi}{2}^R$ is halfway between

π^R and $2\pi^R$.

As shown in the diagram,

$$\cos \frac{3\pi}{2} = 0$$

$$\sin \frac{3\pi}{2} = -1$$

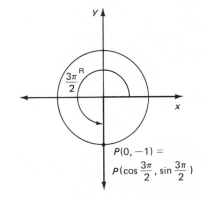

We can use facts about triangles to help us find cosine and sine values for certain angle measures.

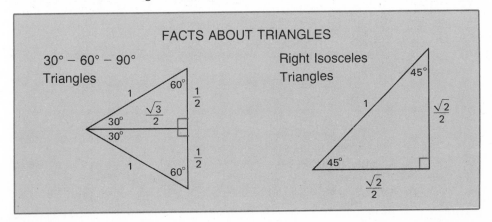

FACTS ABOUT TRIANGLES

30° − 60° − 90° Triangles

Right Isosceles Triangles

EXAMPLE 3 Find cos 30°.
Find sin 30°.

EXAMPLE 4 Find cos 60°.
Find sin 60°.

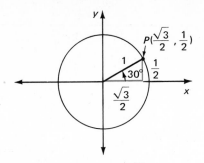

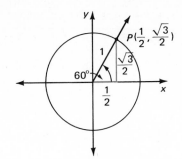

SOLUTION $\cos 30° = \dfrac{\sqrt{3}}{2}$

$\sin 30° = \dfrac{1}{2}$

SOLUTION $\cos 60° = \dfrac{1}{2}$

$\sin 60° = \dfrac{\sqrt{3}}{2}$

Examples 3 and 4 suggest that the sine of an angle equals the cosine of its complement and the cosine of an angle equals the sine of its complement. Later we shall show that this is true in general.

EXAMPLE 5 Find $\cos\left(-\dfrac{3\pi}{4}\right)$. Find $\sin\left(-\dfrac{3\pi}{4}\right)$.

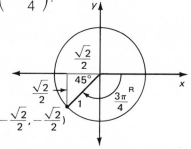

SOLUTION $-\dfrac{3\pi}{4}^{\text{R}}$ is $\dfrac{3}{4}$ of the way

between 0^{R} and $-\pi^{\text{R}}$.

$$\cos\left(-\frac{3\pi}{4}\right) = -\frac{\sqrt{2}}{2}$$

$$\sin\left(-\frac{3\pi}{4}\right) = -\frac{\sqrt{2}}{2}$$

EXAMPLE 6 Solve $2\sin\theta = \sqrt{2}$ for θ, $0 \le \theta < 2\pi$.

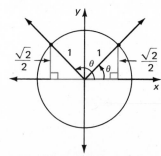

SOLUTION $2\sin\theta = \sqrt{2}$

$$\sin\theta = \frac{\sqrt{2}}{2}$$

Draw a diagram. By the Pythagorean Theorem, each right triangle is isosceles. Hence,

$$\theta = \frac{\pi}{4}^{\text{R}} \text{ or } \theta = \frac{3\pi}{4}^{\text{R}}.$$

CLASSROOM EXERCISES

Give the value for the function.

1. $\sin \pi$

2. $\cos \pi$

3. $\cos 45°$

4. $\sin 45°$

5. $\sin \left(-\dfrac{\pi}{4}\right)$

6. $\cos \left(-\dfrac{1}{4}\pi\right)$

7. $\sin \dfrac{\pi}{6}$

8. $\cos \dfrac{1}{6}\pi$

EXERCISES

A Give the value for the function.

1. $\sin 2\pi$

2. $\cos 2\pi$

3. $\cos \dfrac{3}{4}\pi$

4. $\sin \dfrac{3}{4}\pi$

5. $\sin 60°$

6. $\cos 60°$

7. $\cos 120°$

8. $\sin 120°$

9. $\sin \dfrac{7\pi}{4}$

10. $\cos \dfrac{7\pi}{4}$

11. $\sin \left(-\dfrac{5\pi}{6}\right)$

12. $\cos \left(-\dfrac{5\pi}{6}\right)$

13. $\cos 210°$

14. $\sin 210°$

15. $\cos (-90°)$

16. $\sin (-90°)$

Solve for θ, $0° \le \theta < 360°$.

17. $\sin \theta = \dfrac{1}{2}$

18. $\cos \theta = -\dfrac{\sqrt{3}}{2}$

19. $\sin \theta = -\dfrac{\sqrt{3}}{2}$

20. $\sin \theta = \dfrac{\sqrt{3}}{2}$

21. $\sin \theta = -\dfrac{1}{2}$

22. $\cos \theta = \dfrac{1}{2}$

23. $\cos \theta = -\dfrac{1}{2}$

24. $\sin \theta = 1$

B Copy and complete the table twice, first for $y = \sin \theta$ and then for $y = \cos \theta$. For each function, graph y plotted against θ for $-2\pi \le \theta \le 2\pi$.

25.

θ	0	$\pm \dfrac{\pi}{6}$	$\pm \dfrac{\pi}{4}$	$\pm \dfrac{\pi}{3}$	$\pm \dfrac{\pi}{2}$	$\pm \dfrac{2\pi}{3}$	$\pm \dfrac{3\pi}{4}$	$\pm \dfrac{5\pi}{6}$	$\pm \pi$	$\pm 2\pi$
y	?	?	?	?	?	?	?	?	?	?

26. For $\sin \theta = \dfrac{5}{13}$, find all possible values of $\cos \theta$ and give the quadrants in which the terminal side of θ is located.

27. In which quadrants is $\sin \theta > 0$? $\cos \theta > 0$?

C **28.** Find $\sin \dfrac{\pi}{3}$, $\sin \left(\dfrac{\pi}{3} + 2\pi\right)$, and $\sin \left(\dfrac{\pi}{3} + 2n\pi\right)$ where n is any integer.

29. Find $\cos \left(\dfrac{5}{6}\pi\right)$, $\cos \left(\dfrac{5}{6}\pi + 2\pi\right)$, and $\cos \left(\dfrac{5}{6}\pi + 2n\pi\right)$ where n is any integer.

30. For $\sin 2\theta = \dfrac{1}{2}$, find θ such that $0° \le \theta < 360°$.

31. For $\sin^2 \theta = \dfrac{1}{2}$, find all θ such that $0^R \le \theta < 2\pi^R$.

14-3 USING A TABLE

The values of the cosine and sine functions for angle measures between 0^R and $\frac{\pi}{2}^R$, or 0° and 90°, have been calculated by methods of more advanced mathematics. They are given to four decimal places in Table II at the end of the book.

To use Table II, find angle measures between 0° and 45°, or 0^R and $\frac{\pi}{4}^R$, in the columns at the left. Then refer to the column designated sin or cos at the top. Find angle measures between 45° and 90°, or $\frac{\pi}{4}^R$ and $\frac{\pi}{2}^R$ in the columns at the right. Then refer to the column designated sin or cos at the bottom.

EXAMPLE 1 Find cos 25°. Use Table II.

SOLUTION Find 25° in the Degrees column at the left. Then move to the right in that row to the column headed "cos".

$$\cos 25° \doteq 0.9063$$

Degrees	Radians	sin	tan		cos		
18°00'	0.3142	0.3090	0.3249	3.078	0.9511	1.2566	72°00'
10'	171	0.3118	0.3281	3.047	0.9502	537	50'
50'	334	0.4200	0.4628	2.161	0.9075	374	10'
25°00'	0.4363	0.4226	0.4663	2.145	0.9063	1.1345	65°00'
10'	392	0.4253	0.4699	2.128	0.9051	316	50'

EXAMPLE 2 Find sin $\frac{3\pi}{8}$. Use Table II.

SOLUTION $\sin \frac{3\pi}{8} \doteq \sin 1.1781$.

Find 1.1781 in the Radians column at the right. Then move to the left to the column with "sin" at its foot.

$$\sin \frac{3\pi}{8} \doteq 0.9239$$

22°00'	0.3840	0.3746	0.4040	2.475	0.9272	1.1868	68°00'
10'	869	0.3773	0.4074	2.455	0.9261	839	50'
20'	898	0.3800	0.4108	2.434	0.9250	810	40'
30'	0.3927	0.3827	0.4142	2.414	0.9239	1.1781	30'
40'	956	0.3854	0.4176	2.394	0.9228	752	20'
50'	683	0.4514	0.5059	1.977	0.8923	1.1025	10'
27°00'	0.4712	0.4540	0.5095	1.963	0.8910	1.0996	63°00'
		cos	tan		sin	Radians	Degrees

To find the approximate sine or cosine for an angle measure that is *between* two numbers in the "Degrees" or "Radians" column of Table II, we can *round* to the nearer of those two numbers. However, a better approximation may be found by *interpolation*.

EXAMPLE 3 Find $\sin 32°\,12'$. Use Table II.

SOLUTION

$$\begin{array}{ll}
\sin 32°\,10' \doteq 0.5324 \\
\sin 32°\,12' \doteq\ \ ? & \quad 0.0024 \\
\sin 32°\,20' \doteq 0.5348
\end{array}$$

(with $10'$ and $2'$ brackets on the left)

For $\sin 32°\,12'$, find $\frac{2}{10}$ of 0.0024 and *add* it to 0.5324.

$$\begin{aligned}
\sin 32°\,12' &\doteq 0.5324 + \tfrac{2}{10}(0.0024) \\
&\doteq 0.5324 + 0.0005 \\
&\doteq 0.5329
\end{aligned}$$

EXAMPLE 4 Find $\cos 0.5750$. Use Table II.

SOLUTION

$$\begin{array}{ll}
\cos 0.5730 \doteq 0.8403 \\
\cos 0.5750 \doteq\ \ ? & \quad 0.0016 \\
\cos 0.5760 \doteq 0.8387
\end{array}$$

(with 30 and 20 brackets on the left)

For $\cos 0.5750$, find $\frac{2}{3}$ of 0.0016 and *subtract* it from 0.8403.

$$\begin{aligned}
\cos 0.5750 &\doteq 0.8403 - \tfrac{2}{3}(0.0016) \\
&\doteq 0.8403 - 0.0011 \\
&\doteq 0.8392
\end{aligned}$$

We can use Table II to find the radian measure or degree measure when the cosine value or sine value is given. For a sine value equal to n, $0 \le n \le 1$, we use the symbol **Arcsin *n*** to represent the measure of the first-quadrant angle whose sine is n. Similarly, **Arccos *n*** represents the measure of the first-quadrant angle whose cosine is n.

EXAMPLE 5 $\sin \theta = 0.8290$. Find θ in degrees; in radians.

SOLUTION

$$\sin \theta = 0.8290$$

Therefore, $\theta = \text{Arcsin } 0.8290$.

In Table II, find 0.8290 in the sine column. Since "sin" is at the bottom of the column, find θ at the right.

$$\theta \doteq 56° \text{ or } 0.9774^{\text{R}}$$

EXAMPLE 6 $\cos \theta = 0.3140$. Find θ. Use Table II.

SOLUTION $\qquad$ $\cos \theta = 0.3140$

Therefore, $\theta = \text{Arccos } 0.3140$

$$\theta \doteq 71°42'$$

This result is found using the interpolation shown below.

$$
\begin{array}{c}
\left. \begin{array}{c}
\rightarrow \text{Arccos } 0.3118 \doteq 71°50' \leftarrow \\
27 \quad \left[\begin{array}{c} \rightarrow \text{Arccos } 0.3140 \doteq \theta \quad \leftarrow \\ 5 \end{array} \right. \quad 10' \\
\left[\quad \rightarrow \text{Arccos } 0.3145 \doteq 71°40' \end{array} \right.
\end{array}
$$

For θ, find $\frac{5}{27}$ of $10'$ and *add* it to $71°40'$.

$$\theta \doteq 71°40' + \frac{5}{27}(10')$$
$$\doteq 71°40' + 2'$$
$$\theta \doteq 71°42'$$

It is left for the student to find θ in radians.

CLASSROOM EXERCISES

Approximate. Use Table II.

1. $\sin 6°$ $\qquad$ **2.** $\cos 0.7010$ $\qquad$ **3.** $\cos \dfrac{3\pi}{8}$ $\qquad$ **4.** $\sin 19°24'$ $\qquad$ **5.** $\cos 50°18'$

Approximate A in degrees and in radians. Use Table II.

6. $\sin A = 0.2250$ $\qquad$ **7.** $\cos A = 0.4848$ $\qquad$ **8.** $\sin A = 0.4955$

EXERCISES

Ⓐ Approximate. Use Table II.

1. $\cos 5°$ $\qquad$ **2.** $\sin 6°10'$ $\qquad$ **3.** $\cos 21°50'$ $\qquad$ **4.** $\cos 49°20'$

5. $\cos 0.6894$ $\qquad$ **6.** $\cos 0.5701$ $\qquad$ **7.** $\sin 1.4457$ $\qquad$ **8.** $\sin 1.0908$

9. $\cos 54°10'$ $\qquad$ **10.** $\sin 54°50'$ $\qquad$ **11.** $\cos \dfrac{\pi}{10}$ $\qquad$ **12.** $\sin \dfrac{\pi}{5}$

13. $\sin 48.1°$ $\qquad$ **14.** $\cos 3.75°$ $\qquad$ **15.** $\cos \dfrac{\pi}{8}$ $\qquad$ **16.** $\sin \dfrac{\pi}{12}$

17. $\sin 36°15'$ $\qquad$ **18.** $\sin 3°9'$ $\qquad$ **19.** $\cos 8°16'$ $\qquad$ **20.** $\cos 36°23'$

21. $\sin 45°24'$ $\qquad$ **22.** $\sin 72°42'$ $\qquad$ **23.** $\cos 1.1729$ $\qquad$ **24.** $\cos 1.3102$

Approximate A in degrees and in radians. Use Table II.

25. $\sin A = 0.0843$ $\qquad$ **26.** $\sin A = 0.4067$ $\qquad$ **27.** $\cos A = 0.9932$

28. $\cos A = 0.6905$ $\qquad$ **29.** $\sin A = 0.7771$ $\qquad$ **30.** $\sin A = 0.8923$

B Approximate. Use Table II.

31. sin 1   **32.** sin (−1)   **33.** cos $\dfrac{7\pi}{24}$ **34.** cos 1   **35.** cos (−1)   **36.** sin $\dfrac{5\pi}{16}$

Approximate θ for 0° ≤ θ < 360°. Use Table II.

37. sin θ = −0.5878   **38.** cos θ = −0.6756   **39.** cos θ = −0.9883

40. Approximate the sum of the infinite series 4 + 4 sin 26° + 4(sin 26°)² + ⋯.

C **41.** If the infinite geometric series
$a + a \sin A + a \sin^2 A + \cdots$ and $a + a \cos B + a \cos^2 B + \cdots$ have
the same sum, what can be said about B? Assume 0 ≤ $m \angle A$ < 90°.

42. The common ratio of an infinite geometric series with first term 3912 and
sum 10 000 is approximately the sine of an acute angle having what positive measure in degrees?

FINITE DIFFERENCES

For data such as that shown in the chart, a branch of mathematics called *finite
differences* provides a way to find a formula for f in terms of n.

n	0	1	2	3	4	5	6	7
f	1	2	4	7	11	16	22	29

First differences   1   2   3   4   5   6   7

Second differences 1   1   1   1   1   1

The *second* differences are the same. This means that the relationship
between f and n may be given by an equation that is of *degree* 2 at most.
We may write $f = an^2 + bn + c$ where a, b, and c are to be determined.

1. Replace n and f by numbers from the table and find
    values for a, b, and c. Write the equation relating f and
    n. Find f when $n = 50$. Find f when $n = 100$.

2. Find a relationship for f and n using the information in
    this table.

n	0	1	2	3	4	5	6
f	1	2	4	8	15	26	42

14-4 THE REFERENCE ANGLE

The terminal side of a non-quadrantal angle θ and either the positive portion or the negative portion of the x-axis form an acute angle α. The angle α is called the *reference angle* of θ. The measure of a reference angle is considered to be positive.

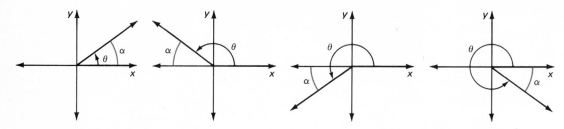

EXAMPLE 1 Find the measure of the reference angle when an angle in standard position has measure 45°; 240°; −210°.

SOLUTIONS   Make a diagram to show the angle and its reference angle.

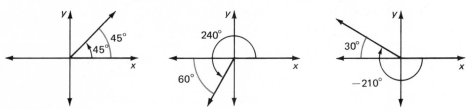

The measure of the reference angle is 45°.

The measure of the reference angle is 60°.

The measure of the reference angle is 30°.

Table II gives cosine and sine values only for angle measures between 0^R and $\frac{\pi}{2}^R$, or 0° and 90°. However, we may use Table II to find the cosine and sine of *any* angle measure by using the reference angle associated with the given angle.

By definition, (cos θ, sin θ) corresponds to a point of the unit circle. Two points of the unit circle that are contained in the same vertical line have the same first coordinate and opposite second coordinates. Two points that are contained in the same horizontal line have opposite first coordinates and the same second coordinate. When θ is a second-, third-, or fourth-quadrant angle, we remember that first coordinates are negative to the left of the origin and second coordinates are negative below the origin.

Using these ideas and the reference angle α as shown in the diagrams at the top of the next page, we can find cos θ and sin θ.

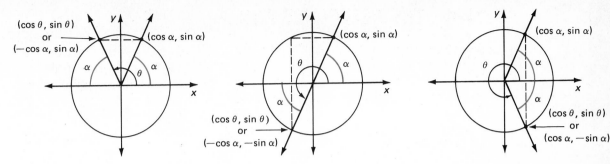

EXAMPLE 2   Find $\cos 130°$, $\sin 130°$, $\cos \dfrac{7\pi}{4}$, and $\sin \dfrac{7\pi}{4}$.

SOLUTION   Make a diagram.

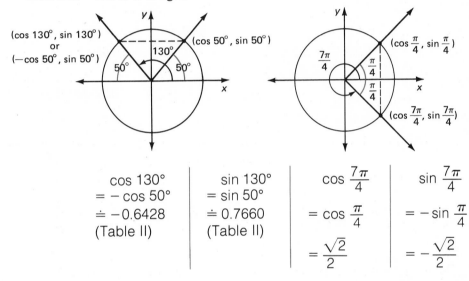

$\cos 130°$	$\sin 130°$	$\cos \dfrac{7\pi}{4}$	$\sin \dfrac{7\pi}{4}$
$= -\cos 50°$	$= \sin 50°$	$= \cos \dfrac{\pi}{4}$	$= -\sin \dfrac{\pi}{4}$
$\doteq -0.6428$	$\doteq 0.7660$		
(Table II)	(Table II)	$= \dfrac{\sqrt{2}}{2}$	$= -\dfrac{\sqrt{2}}{2}$

If you can picture this diagram in your mind, you should not have to make a new diagram each time to find $\cos \theta$ and $\sin \theta$.

$\cos < 0, \sin > 0$ $\cos > 0, \sin > 0$

$\cos < 0, \sin < 0$ $\cos > 0, \sin < 0$ x

EXAMPLE 3   Find $\cos(-115°)$ and $\sin(-115°)$.

SOLUTION   Imagine an angle in standard position and having measure $-115°$. Its terminal side is in the third quadrant where cosine values and sine values are both negative. The measure of the reference angle is $65°$.

$\cos(-115°) = -\cos 65°$ $\sin(-115°) = -\sin 65°$
$\doteq -0.4226$ $\doteq -0.9063$

CLASSROOM EXERCISES

Approximate. Use Table II.

1. cos 140°

2. sin 285°

3. cos 285°

4. sin $\frac{4\pi}{3}$

5. cos 320°

6. cos $\frac{4\pi}{3}$

EXERCISES

A Approximate. Use Table II.

1. sin 190°

2. cos 190°

3. cos 105°

4. sin 105°

5. sin 290°

6. cos 290°

7. cos (−105°)

8. sin (−105°)

9. sin (−200°)

10. cos (−200°)

11. cos (−46°)

12. sin (−46°)

13. sin $\frac{3\pi}{4}$

14. cos $\frac{3\pi}{4}$

15. cos $\frac{5\pi}{4}$

16. sin $\frac{5\pi}{4}$

17. sin 136°

18. cos 136°

19. cos 205°30′

20. sin 205°30′

21. sin 310°50′

22. cos 310°50′

23. cos (−235°30′)

24. sin (−235°30′)

25. cos $\frac{2\pi}{3}$

26. sin $\frac{2\pi}{3}$

27. sin $\left(-\frac{5}{3}\pi\right)$

B **28.** cos (−367°19′)

29. sin 277°6′

30. sin 322°15′

Approximate. Use Table II. Use $\pi = 3.1416$.

31. cos 2.7751

32. sin 4.2935

33. sin 5.6767

Find θ such that $0° \leq \theta < 360°$.

34. sin $\theta = 0.0287$

35. cos $\theta = 1.0364$

36. cos $\theta = 0.6420$

37. sin $\theta = -0.6053$

38. $|\sin \theta| = 0.4287$

39. cos² $\theta = \frac{3}{4}$

C **40.** For sin $\theta = 2$ sin 120° cos 120°, find θ such that $0° \leq \theta \leq 270°$.

41. For sin $\theta = $ sin 30° cos 120° + cos 30° sin 120°, find θ such that $90° \leq \theta \leq 180°$.

42. Verify the identity $-1 + \sqrt{3}i = 2$ cos 120° + 2i sin 120°. The right member of the identity is called the *trigonometric form of the complex number* $-1 + \sqrt{3}i$.

CONSUMER AND HOMEMAKING EDUCATION

Home economists, who comprise a large career group in consumer and home-making education, work to improve services and products. Their regular activities include conducting surveys and compiling and analyzing the resulting data.

A *government food inspector* is a type of home economist. The duties of a food inspector center around verifying manufacturers' claims about their products.

The career of an *environmental health officer* also can focus on consumer welfare in public health education and protection. Regular duties might include

1. collecting samples of shellfish, fish, water, or air for testing.
2. testing materials in a laboratory or "on site."
3. assisting a chemist in testing procedures.
4. preparing chemical solutions.
5. writing test procedures and results in report form.

For careers such as these an aptitude for mathematics and science is valuable. Other high school courses should include sociology, nutrition, foods, and journalism.

MATHEMATICAL SAMPLER

1. As a government food inspector, you are to verify product labeling. A label states that a product is 37% liquid. You centrifuge 84 mL of the product and find that you have 24 mL of liquid. Is the labeling correct? Another label states that 30 grams of a product contain 100% of the USDA vitamin A adult daily requirement. The USDA vitamin A daily requirement is 100 mg. A 4-gram sample is analyzed and the Vitamin A content is found to be 12 mg. Is this label correct?

2. You are an environmental health officer. You estimate that 12 000 people in the state capital (pop. 290 000) and a similar percentage throughout the state, will contract the xyz flu this winter. Give an estimate of the probability that a person who lives in the state will contract the flu.

14-5 GRAPHS OF THE COSINE AND SINE FUNCTIONS

For each value possible for θ, the pair $(\cos \theta, \sin \theta)$ is defined to be the co-ordinates of a point of the unit circle. Therefore, the range of both the cosine function and the sine function is the set of real numbers from -1 to 1. Much additional information about the cosine and sine functions is provided by the definition. Study the diagrams below.

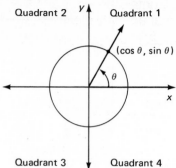

The Cosine Function, $y = \cos \theta$

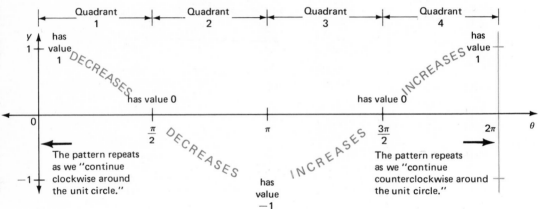

The Sine Function, $y = \sin \theta$

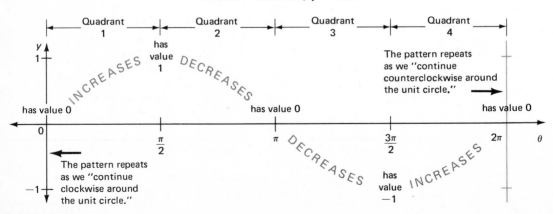

For the graphs of the cosine and sine functions we use radian measures for the domain values. We use the *same* unit length for the horizontal and vertical axes. However, the numbers shown for the horizontal axis often are multiples and submultiples of π. Note, for example, that $\frac{\pi}{2}$ is located near 1.5 since $\frac{\pi}{2} \doteq 1.57$.

The Graphs of $y = \cos \theta$ and $y = \sin \theta$

θ in degrees	0	30	45	60	90	120	135	150	180	210	225	240	270	300	315	330	360
θ in radians	0	$\frac{\pi}{6}$	$\frac{\pi}{4}$	$\frac{\pi}{3}$	$\frac{\pi}{2}$	$\frac{2\pi}{3}$	$\frac{3\pi}{4}$	$\frac{5\pi}{6}$	π	$\frac{7\pi}{6}$	$\frac{5\pi}{4}$	$\frac{4\pi}{3}$	$\frac{3\pi}{2}$	$\frac{5\pi}{3}$	$\frac{7\pi}{4}$	$\frac{11\pi}{6}$	2π
$\cos \theta$	1	0.9	0.7	0.5	0	−0.5	−0.7	−0.9	−1	−0.9	−0.7	−0.5	0	0.5	0.7	0.9	1
$\sin \theta$	0	0.5	0.7	0.9	1.0	0.9	0.7	0.5	0	−0.5	−0.7	−0.9	−1.0	−0.9	−0.7	−0.5	0

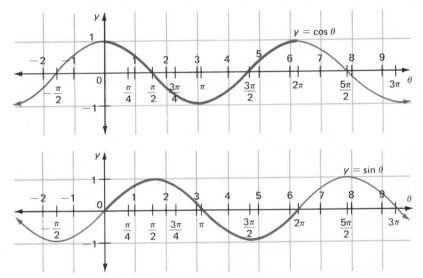

Since the patterns of values for both functions repeat over each interval of length 2π, each of the cosine and sine functions is a **periodic function** with **period** 2π. The **amplitude** of either function is $\left(\frac{M - m}{2}\right)$ where M and m are the maximum and minimum values of the function respectively. Thus, the amplitude of each function is 1.

A function of the form $y = \sin a\theta$ or $y = \cos a\theta$ has period $\left|\frac{2\pi}{a}\right|$.

The patterns for the functions repeat over each interval of length $\left|\frac{2\pi}{a}\right|$.

A function of the form $y = a \sin \theta$ or $y = a \cos \theta$ has maximum value $|a|$ and minimum value $-|a|$. Its amplitude, therefore, is $|a|$.

EXAMPLE 1 Graph $y = \cos 2\theta$.

SOLUTION As θ is replaced by values from 0 to π, 2θ assumes values from 0 to 2π, amounting to one period of the cosine function. Thus, the period of the function $y = \cos 2\theta$ is π.

GRAPH

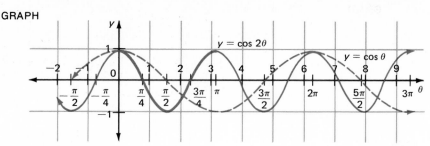

EXAMPLE 2 Graph $y = 3 \sin \theta$.

SOLUTION Since $\sin \theta$ ranges in value from -1 to 1, $3 \sin \theta$ ranges in value from -3 to 3. Therefore, the amplitude of the graph of $y = 3 \sin \theta$ is 3.

GRAPH

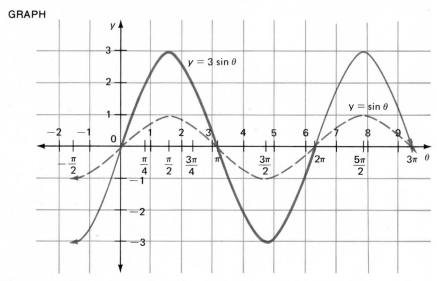

EXAMPLE 3 Find the period and amplitude of $y = \frac{1}{2} \sin(-2\theta)$.
Graph $y = \frac{1}{2} \sin(-2\theta)$.

SOLUTION As θ is replaced by values from 0 to π, -2θ assumes values from 0 to -2π which amounts to one period of the sine function. Therefore, the period of the function $y = \frac{1}{2} \sin(-2\theta)$ is π.

Since $\sin(-2\theta)$ ranges in value from -1 to 1, $\frac{1}{2}\sin(-2\theta)$ ranges in value from $-\frac{1}{2}$ to $\frac{1}{2}$. Therefore, the amplitude of $y = \frac{1}{2}\sin(-2\theta)$ is $\frac{1}{2}$.

GRAPH

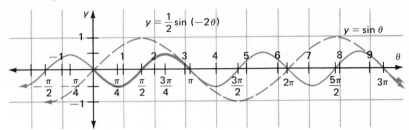

EXAMPLE 4 Graph $y = \cos\left(\theta - \dfrac{\pi}{2}\right)$.

SOLUTION Here, each replacement for θ is decreased by $\dfrac{\pi}{2}$ *before* the cosine of the number is found.

θ	$\theta - \dfrac{\pi}{2}$	$\cos\left(\theta - \dfrac{\pi}{2}\right)$
0	$-\dfrac{\pi}{2}$	0
$\dfrac{\pi}{2}$	0	1
π	$\dfrac{\pi}{2}$	0
$\dfrac{3\pi}{2}$	π	-1
2π	$\dfrac{3\pi}{2}$	0

GRAPH

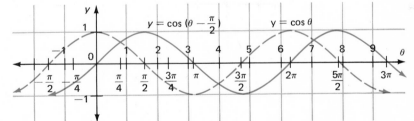

Graphically, the effect of subtracting $\dfrac{\pi}{2}$ from θ before evaluating the cosine is to "shift" the curve $\dfrac{\pi}{2}$ units to the right. We call this a *phase shift* of $\dfrac{\pi}{2}$. For such a phase shift, the graph of $\cos\left(\theta - \dfrac{\pi}{2}\right)$ is the same as the graph of $\sin\theta$. That is, $\cos\left(\theta - \dfrac{\pi}{2}\right) = \sin\theta$. Later, we shall show this equality in another manner.

In general, when a constant is *subtracted* from θ *before* evaluating the sine or cosine function, the graph is shifted to the *right*. When a constant is *added* to θ *before* evaluating either function, the graph is shifted to the *left*. When a constant is subtracted (or added) *after* the sine or cosine function is evaluated, the graph is shifted downward (upward).

The various coefficients that affect the shape of a basic sine curve can be summarized in the equation for the **general sinusoid**.

$$y = a \sin(b\theta + c) + d$$

CLASSROOM EXERCISES

Give the amplitude and period of the function. Graph the function.

1. $y = \sin 2\theta$

2. $y = \cos 4\theta$

3. $y = 3 \sin \theta$

4. $y = 2 \cos \theta$

5. $y = \sin\left(\theta + \frac{\pi}{2}\right)$

6. $y = -\sin \theta$

7. $y = \sin(-\theta)$

8. $y = \cos \frac{1}{2}\theta$

9. $y = \frac{1}{3} \sin 2\theta$

EXERCISES

A Give the amplitude and period of the function. Graph the function.

1. $y = 3 \cos \theta$

2. $y = 2 \sin \theta$

3. $y = -2 \sin \theta$

4. $y = -3 \cos \theta$

5. $y = \cos 4\theta$

6. $y = \sin 2\theta$

7. $y = \sin(-2\theta)$

8. $y = \cos(-4\theta)$

9. $y = -3 \sin(-4\theta)$

10. $y = -7 \sin(-\theta)$

11. $y = \cos\left(\theta + \frac{\pi}{2}\right)$

12. $y = \sin\left(\theta - \frac{\pi}{2}\right)$

B **13.** $y = -2 \sin \frac{\pi}{2}\theta$

14. $y = \frac{1}{3} \sin\left(-\frac{2}{3}\pi\theta\right)$

15. $y = -\frac{2}{3} \cos \frac{3}{2}\theta$

16. $y = 8 \cos(-\pi\theta)$

17. $y = -\cos 4\pi\theta$

18. $y = \frac{3}{4} \cos \frac{2}{5}\pi\theta$

Graph.

19. $y = 1 + 3 \cos \theta$

20. $y = |\sin \theta|$

21. $y = \sin\left(2\theta + \frac{1}{2}\pi\right)$

22. $y = \sin\left(2\theta - \frac{1}{2}\pi\right)$

C **23.** $y = -2 \sin\left(2\theta - \frac{\pi}{4}\right) + 1$

24. $y = -\cos(2\theta - 1) + 1$

25. $y = \sin \theta + \cos \theta$

26. $y = \sin \theta - \cos \theta$

27. $y = \dfrac{1}{\sin \theta}$

28. $y = \dfrac{1}{\cos \theta}$

29. $y = \dfrac{\sin \theta}{\cos \theta}$

30. $y = \dfrac{\cos \theta}{\sin \theta}$

OBJECTIVES: Find values for the tangent, cotangent, secant, and cosecant functions. Use trigonometric functions to solve right triangles.

14-6   THE TANGENT, COTANGENT, SECANT, AND COSECANT FUNCTIONS

We use the sine and cosine functions to help state the rules that define the **tangent, cotangent, secant,** and **cosecant** functions. The abbreviations tan, cot, sec, and csc are used for these functions.

$$\tan \theta = \frac{\sin \theta}{\cos \theta}, \cos \theta \neq 0 \qquad \cot \theta = \frac{\cos \theta}{\sin \theta}, \sin \theta \neq 0$$

$$\sec \theta = \frac{1}{\cos \theta}, \cos \theta \neq 0 \qquad \csc \theta = \frac{1}{\sin \theta}, \sin \theta \neq 0$$

EXAMPLE 1   Find tan 30°, cot 30°, sec 30°, and csc 30°.

SOLUTION $\cos 30° = \dfrac{\sqrt{3}}{2}$, and $\sin 30° = \frac{1}{2}$.

Therefore,

$$\tan 30° = \frac{\frac{1}{2}}{\frac{\sqrt{3}}{2}} \qquad \cot 30° = \frac{\frac{\sqrt{3}}{2}}{\frac{1}{2}}$$

$$= \frac{\sqrt{3}}{3} \qquad\qquad = \sqrt{3}$$

$$\sec 30° = \frac{1}{\frac{\sqrt{3}}{2}} \qquad \csc 30° = \frac{1}{\frac{1}{2}}$$

$$= \frac{2\sqrt{3}}{3} \qquad\qquad = 2$$

The tangent and secant functions are undefined for values of θ for which $\cos \theta = 0$. These values are $\pm \dfrac{\pi}{2}, \pm \dfrac{3\pi}{2}, \pm \dfrac{5\pi}{2}$, and so on. The cotangent and cosecant functions are undefined for values of θ for which $\sin \theta = 0$. These values are $0, \pm\pi, \pm2\pi$, and so on.

The patterns of values for the tangent and cotangent functions repeat over each interval of π units. For the secant and cosecant functions, the period is 2π. By graphing each function for one period, we know what each graph looks like over the entire domain of the function.

EXAMPLE 2 Sketch a graph of $y = \tan\theta$.

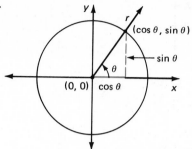

SOLUTION We know $(\cos\theta, \sin\theta)$ represents a point on the terminal side of angle θ. If we consider the terminal side as a portion of the line, r, containing points $(0, 0)$ and $(\cos\theta, \sin\theta)$, then $\dfrac{\sin\theta}{\cos\theta}$, or $\tan\theta$, is the slope of line r. To understand the graph of $\tan\theta$ it is helpful to imagine the picture above with θ increasing in value from 0 to 2π.

GRAPH Make a table of values for θ and $\tan\theta$.

θ	0	$\dfrac{\pi}{4}$	$\dfrac{\pi}{2}$	$\dfrac{3\pi}{4}$	π	$\dfrac{5\pi}{4}$	$\dfrac{3\pi}{2}$	$\dfrac{7\pi}{4}$	2π
$\tan\theta$	0	1	undef.	-1	0	1	undef.	-1	0

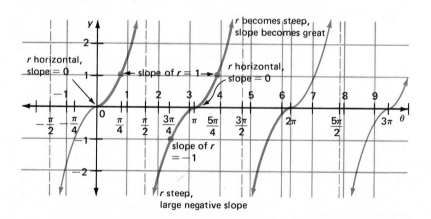

Values of the cotangent, secant, and cosecant functions are reciprocals of values of the tangent, cosine, and sine functions, respectively. Keeping in mind that the reciprocal of a small number is large and the reciprocal of a large number is small, we sketch the graphs of these functions.

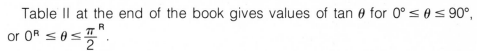

Table II at the end of the book gives values of tan θ for $0° \leq \theta \leq 90°$, or $0^R \leq \theta \leq \dfrac{\pi}{2}^R$.

We can use it to help us find tan θ for any value of θ. To do so, we use reference angles as we did for the sine and cosine functions. Also, we must keep in mind the ideas shown in this diagram so that we can give tan θ correctly as a positive or a negative number.

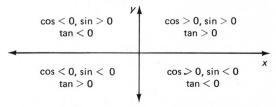

EXAMPLE 3 Find tan 125°. Use a reference angle and Table II.

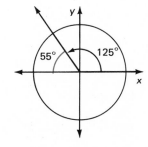

SOLUTION Since the terminal side is in the second quadrant, tan 125° is negative. The measure of the reference angle is 55°.

$$\tan 125° = -\tan 55°$$
$$\doteq -1.428$$

To find a value for the cosecant, secant, or cotangent function, we find a sine, cosine, or tangent value as an intermediate step. This may or may not require the use of Table II.

EXAMPLE 4 Find csc $\dfrac{4\pi}{3}$, sec $\dfrac{4\pi}{3}$, cot $\dfrac{4\pi}{3}$.

SOLUTION

$$\sin \frac{4\pi}{3} = -\frac{\sqrt{3}}{2} \quad \bigg| \quad \cos \frac{4\pi}{3} = -\frac{1}{2} \quad \bigg| \quad \tan \frac{4\pi}{3} = \sqrt{3}$$

$$\csc \frac{4\pi}{3} = -\frac{2\sqrt{3}}{3} \quad \bigg| \quad \sec \frac{4\pi}{3} = -2 \quad \bigg| \quad \cot \frac{4\pi}{3} = \frac{\sqrt{3}}{3}$$

CLASSROOM EXERCISES

Give the value for the function.

1. $\tan 250°$ **2.** $\sec 60°$ **3.** $\csc 60°$ **4.** $\cot 60°$

5. $\tan \dfrac{2\pi}{3}$ **6.** $\cot \dfrac{2\pi}{3}$ **7.** $\csc \dfrac{3\pi}{2}$ **8.** $\sec \dfrac{\pi}{2}$

Give the period of the function.   Graph the function.

9. $y = 2 \tan \theta$ **10.** $y = \tan 2\theta$ **11.** $y = 2 \sec \theta$ **12.** $y = \csc 2\theta$

EXERCISES

A   Give the value for the function.

1. $\tan 45°$ **2.** $\cot 45°$ **3.** $\csc 45°$ **4.** $\sec 45°$

5. $\csc \pi$ **6.** $\cot \pi$ **7.** $\tan 140°$ **8.** $\tan 160°$

9. $\tan(-50°)$ **10.** $\tan(-220°)$ **11.** $\sec \dfrac{5\pi}{3}$ **12.** $\sec \pi$

Give the period of the function.   Graph the function.

13. $y = 3 \tan \theta$ **14.** $y = 4 \tan \theta$ **15.** $y = -2 \tan \theta$

16. $y = -\tan \theta$ **17.** $y = \tan 4\theta$ **18.** $y = \tan 3\theta$

Graph each set of functions.   Use the same pair of axes.

19. $y = \sin 2\theta, y = \csc 2\theta$ **20.** $y = 3 \cos \theta, y = 3 \sec \theta$ **21.** $y = 2 \sin \theta, y = 2 \csc \theta$

Graph the function over two periods.

22. $y = \tan 2\theta$ **23.** $y = \cot \frac{1}{2}\theta$ **24.** $y = -\sec \theta$

B   Give the period of the function.   Graph the function.

25. $y = 2 \tan 2\theta$ **26.** $y = -\csc \frac{1}{4}\theta$ **27.** $y = \frac{1}{2}\sec \frac{1}{2}\theta$

28. $y = 3 \cot 2\theta$ **29.** $y = -\tan \frac{1}{3}\theta$ **30.** $y = -\tan(-\theta)$

31. $y = 1 + \csc \theta$ **32.** $y = -1 + \sec \theta$ **33.** $y = 2 + \tan \frac{1}{2}\theta$

C   Graph.   Solve the system graphically.

34. $y = 2 \tan(\theta - \frac{1}{2}\pi)$ **36.** $y = \sin(x + \frac{1}{2}\pi)$ **37.** $y = \sin 2x$

35. $y = -\tan(\theta + 1) - 1$ $y = \cos(x - \frac{1}{2}\pi)$ $y = \frac{1}{2}\csc 2x$

14-7 SOLVING RIGHT TRIANGLES

We can position a right triangle in the coordinate plane so that one acute angle is in standard position with the hypotenuse as its terminal side.

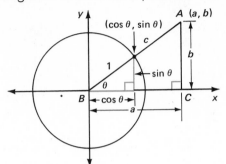

Using c for the length of the hypotenuse and using similar triangles, we see that

$$\sin \theta = \frac{b}{c},$$

$$\cos \theta = \frac{a}{c},$$

$$\tan \theta = \frac{b}{a}.$$

Sometimes these ratios are best remembered as follows.

sine: $\dfrac{\text{side opposite}}{\text{hypotenuse}}$; cosine: $\dfrac{\text{side adjacent}}{\text{hypotenuse}}$; tangent: $\dfrac{\text{side opposite}}{\text{side adjacent}}$

We can use these ratios along with the values of the sine, cosine, and tangent functions to help us *solve right triangles*. We shall find the measure of any of the angles and sides of a right triangle, given the measure of one side, and the measure of a second side or an acute angle.

EXAMPLE 1 For right triangle ABC, $c = 60$ and $b = 50$.
Find $m \angle A$, $m \angle B$, and a.

SOLUTION Find $m \angle A$.

$$\cos A = \frac{b}{c}$$

$$= \frac{50}{60}$$

$$\cos A \doteq 0.8333$$

Therefore, $A \doteq \text{Arccos } 0.8333$
$\doteq 33°34'$

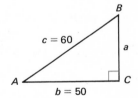

Find $m \angle B$.
$m \angle A + m \angle B = 90°$.

$$m \angle B = 90° - m \angle A$$
$$\doteq 90° - 33°34'$$
$$\doteq 56°26'$$

Find a.

$$\sin A = \frac{a}{c}$$

$$a = c \cdot \sin A$$
$$\doteq 60 \sin 33°34'$$
$$\doteq 60(0.5529)$$
$$\doteq 33.2$$

CONCLUSION $m \angle A \doteq 33°34'$, $m \angle B \doteq 56°26'$, and $a \doteq 33.2$.

EXAMPLE 2 A ladder leans against a building and makes an angle of 62°12′ with the ground. The ladder is 6.30 meters long. At what height on the building does it touch?

SOLUTION   Draw a diagram.

Use h for the height in meters reached by the ladder.

Find h.   Use the sine function.

$$\sin 62°12' = \frac{h}{6.30}$$

$$h = 6.30 \sin 62°12'$$
$$\doteq 6.30(0.8846)$$
$$\doteq 5.57$$

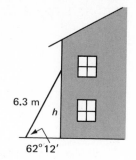

CONCLUSION   The ladder touches the building at a point that is about 5.57 meters above the ground.

In the picture, $\angle A$ is the *angle of eleva-tion* of B from A. $\angle DBA$ is the *angle of depression* of A from B.   Notice that the angle of elevation and the angle of depression are measured from the horizontal.

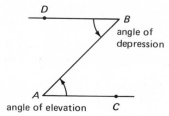

EXAMPLE 3 Find the angle of elevation of the sun when a utility pole that is 10 meters tall casts a shadow that is 14 meters long.

SOLUTION   Draw a diagram.

Use α for the measure of the angle of elevation.

Find α. Use the tangent function.

$$\tan \alpha = \frac{10}{14}$$

$$\tan \alpha \doteq 0.7143$$
$$\alpha = \text{Arctan } 0.7143$$
$$\alpha \doteq 35°32'$$

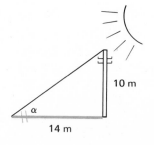

CONCLUSION   The angle of elevation of the sun is 35°32′.

CLASSROOM EXERCISES

Solve. Use the right triangle shown.

1. Find a, $m \angle A$, and $m \angle B$ when $c = 80$ and $b = 50$.

2. A pole casts a shadow 30 meters long on the ground. The angle of elevation of the sun is 48°10′. Find the height of the pole.

EXERCISES

A Solve. Use the right triangle shown in the Classroom Exercises above.

1. Find a, b, and $m \angle B$ when $m \angle A = 20°15′$ and $c = 80$.

2. Find c, $m \angle A$, and $m \angle B$ when $a = 4.84$ and $b = 3.63$.

3. Find a when $m \angle A = 12°30′$ and $b = 4.00$.

4. Find c when $m \angle A = 36°19′$ and $b = 38.04$.

Solve.

5. A carpenter standing 11.0 meters from the base of a chimney finds that the angle of elevation of the top of the chimney is 47°25′. Find the height of the chimney.

6. From a point 11.25 meters from the base of a tower, an observer notes the angle of elevation of the top of the tower is 69°24′. Find the height of the tower.

7. From the top of an observation tower 60 meters high, a forest ranger noted the angle of depression of a disabled camper was 4°18′. How far was the camper from the base of the tower?

8. The length of the shadow of a tree along a horizontal plane is 7.63 meters. The angle of elevation of the sun is 39°10′. Find the height of the tree.

9. A side of a rectangle is 18.5 meters long. A diagonal length is 21.2 meters. What are the measures of the angles that the diagonal forms with the sides of the rectangle?

B **10.** An airplane flying over an open field was 3 kilometers measured horizontally from an observer. The observer noted the angle of elevation of the airplane was 11°16′. What was the altitude of the airplane?

11. A pendulum 2.8 meters long swings from one end of a meter stick to the other end. Through what angle does the pendulum swing?

12. The base of an isosceles triangle has length 2.48 cm. The sides have length 16.4 cm. Find the measure of a base angle.

C **13.** A regular decagon with sides 12 centimeters long is inscribed in a circle. Find the apothem and the radius of the decagon.

14. A person standing on level ground is looking at a large billboard. From where the person is standing the angle of elevation of the top of the billboard is 50°. The angle of elevation of the bottom of the billboard is 20°. The billboard is 20 meters high. How far is the top of the billboard from the ground?

CHECKING YOUR UNDERSTANDING

WORDS AND SYMBOLS

amplitude	cotangent function	quadrantal angle	sine function
angle of rotation	initial side	radian, ᴿ	tangent function
cosecant function	period	reference angle	terminal side
cosine function	periodic function	secant function	unit circle

CONCEPTS

- The sine and cosine functions are periodic functions with period 2π. They may be defined by referring to the unit circle. They range in value from -1 to 1. [14-2, 14-5]

- Each sine and cosine function value corresponds to the ratio of the length of a leg of a right triangle to the length of the hypotenuse. The sine and cosine functions of an angle depend only on the size of the angle. [14-7]

PROCESSES

- Use degree measure. Use radian measure. [14-1]

    1. Draw an angle with measure 45°; with measure π radians.

    2. $60° = ?^R$ **3.** $\dfrac{3\pi^R}{4} = ?°$ **4.** $225° = ?^R$ **5.** $-\dfrac{\pi^R}{3} = ?°$

- Find values for the sine and cosine functions for any angle. [14-2 to 14-4]

    6. $\sin 315° = ?$ **7.** $\cos(-120°) = ?$ **8.** $\cos \pi = ?$ **9.** $\sin \frac{5}{6}\pi = ?$

    10. $\cos \frac{5}{12}\pi$ (Table II)   **11.** $\sin 93°$ (Table II)   **12.** $\cos 81°7'$ (Table II)

    13. For $\sin \theta = 0.4937$, $\theta = ?°$ **14.** Arccos $0.2749 = ?^R$

- Sketch a graph of $y = a \sin bx$ or $y = a \cos bx$ for various values of a and b. [14-5]

    15. $y = 2 \sin \theta$ **16.** $y = \cos \frac{1}{2}\theta$ **17.** $y = -2 \sin 4\theta$

- Use values for the sine and cosine functions to find values for the cosecant, secant, tangent, and cotangent functions. [14-6]

    18. $\tan \frac{4}{3}\pi = ?$ **19.** $\cot \frac{4}{3}\pi = ?$ **20.** $\sec \frac{4}{3}\pi = ?$ **21.** $\csc \frac{4}{3}\pi = ?$

- Solve right triangles. [14-7]

22.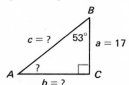

23.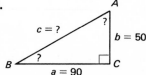

CHAPTER REVIEW

Give the measure of each angle of rotation. [14-1]

1.

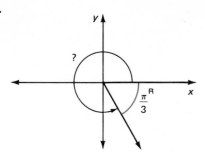

2.

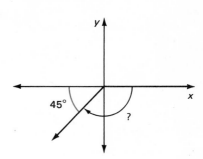

Draw an angle in standard position having the given measure.

3. $112\frac{1}{2}°$ **4.** $-120°$

Convert radian measure to degree measure and vice versa.

5. $80°$ **6.** $-320°$ **7.** $\frac{5\pi^R}{12}$ **8.** 5^R

9. A record turns 78 revolutions per minute. Give this rate in radians per second.

Simplify. [14-2]

10. $\sin(-90°)$ **11.** $\cos 5\pi$ **12.** $\cos 150°$ **13.** $\sin\frac{4\pi}{3}$

14. Given $\cos\theta = \frac{1}{5}$, find the possible values for $\sin\theta$.

Use Table II, and interpolation if necessary, to simplify. [14-3]

15. $\sin 86°40'$ **16.** $\cos 14°6'$ **17.** $\cos 43°37'$

Find the measure of θ for $0° \le \theta \le 90°$.   Find the measure of θ for $0 \le \theta \le \frac{\pi}{2}$.

18. $\sin\theta = 0.3290$ **19.** $\cos\theta = 0.8968$

Approximate. Use a reference angle and Table II. [14-4]

20. $\sin 158°$ **21.** $\cos(-93°)$ **22.** $\sin 204°12'$

Give the period and amplitude of each function. [14-5]   Graph.

23. $y = \frac{3}{2}\sin\frac{1}{2}\theta$ **24.** $y = 3\cos\pi\theta$ **25.** $y = 4\sin 2\theta$.

Simplify. [14-6]

26. $\cot\frac{\pi}{3}$ **27.** $\sec(-150°)$ **28.** $\tan 42°4'$

Solve. [14-7]

29. Wires from the top of a 25-meter vertical pole are to be attached to the ground in such a way as to make a 65° angle of elevation. How far from the foot of the pole should the wires be attached to the ground?

CAPSULE REVIEW

Write the letter of the best response.

1. An angle has measure in degrees n and measure in radians k. Which equation is incorrect?

   a. $\dfrac{n}{k} = \dfrac{180}{\pi}$ **b.** $\dfrac{n}{180} = \dfrac{k}{\pi}$ **c.** $n° = k^R$ **d.** $n = k$

2. For $\sin \theta = \dfrac{\sqrt{3}}{2}$, $\theta =$

   a. 30° or 60°   **b.** 60° or 120°   **c.** 30° or 150°   **d.** 60° or 150°

3. $[\sin 46°10' + \frac{1}{5}(\sin 46°10' - \sin 46°10')]$ gives an approximation for

   a. $\sin 46°25'$ **b.** $\sin 46°12'$ **c.** $\sin 46°8'$ **d.** $\sin 46.12°$

4. Which equation is correct?

   a. $\cos 130° = -\cos 50°$ **b.** $\cos 130° = -\cos 40°$

   c. $\cos 130° = \cos 50°$ **d.** $\cos 130° = \cos 40°$

5. Which function has the largest period?

   a. $y = 3 \sin \theta$ **b.** $y = 2 \sin 2\theta$ **c.** $y = \frac{5}{2} \sin \frac{1}{2}\theta$ **d.** $y = 2 \sin \pi\theta$

6. If $\tan \theta < 0$, the terminal side of θ must lie in

   a. quadrant 2   **b.** quadrant 1   **c.** quadrant 2 or 4   **d.** quadrant 1 or 3

7. For right triangle ABC, $m \angle C = 90°$, $a = 6$, and $b = 7$. Which statement is incorrect?

   a. $\sin A = \dfrac{6}{\sqrt{85}}$ **b.** $\tan B = \dfrac{7}{6}$ **c.** $\cot A = \dfrac{6}{7}$ **d.** $\sec B = \dfrac{\sqrt{85}}{6}$

CHAPTER TEST

---

1. Draw an angle in standard position having measure 330°.

2. Draw an angle in standard position having measure $-120°$.

3. An angle has radian measure $\dfrac{\pi}{4}$. Give its measure in degrees.

4. An angle has degree measure 120. Give its measure in radians.

5. Find the value of $\sin \dfrac{\pi}{6}$.   **6.** Find the value of $\cos \dfrac{3\pi}{4}$.

7. Approximate sin 76° to four decimal places.   Use Table II.

8. Approximate sin 20°15′ to four decimal places.   Use Table II.

9. sin 40° ≐ 0.6428.   For what angle measure between 90° and 180° is 0.6428 the value of the sine function?

10. sin 40° ≐ 0.6428.   Find sin 220°.   **11.** Give the period of $y = 4 \cos \theta$.

12. Give the amplitude of $y = 3 \sin \theta$.   **13.** Give the period of the tangent function.

14. For $\sin \theta = \frac{3}{5}$ and $\cos \theta = \frac{4}{5}$, what does $\tan \theta$ equal?

15. A 5-meter ladder leaning against a wall forms a 70° angle with the ground. Find how far the foot of the ladder is from the base of the wall.

16. When the angle of elevation of the sun is 50°, the shadow of a flagpole is 10 meters long. Find the height of the flagpole.

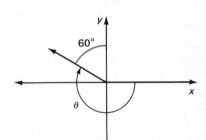

Write the letter of the best response.

17. What is the measure of θ?

   a. 210°   **b.** 150°   **c.** 60°

   d. −30°   **e.** −210°

18. The degree measure of an angle is $2k$.   What is its measure in radians?

   a. $\dfrac{\pi k}{90}$ **b.** $\dfrac{\pi k}{180}$ **c.** $\dfrac{\pi k}{360}$ **d.** $\dfrac{360k}{\pi}$ **e.** $\dfrac{90k}{\pi}$

19. $\sin \dfrac{\pi}{3} =$

   a. 0   **b.** $\dfrac{1}{2}$ **c.** $\dfrac{\sqrt{2}}{2}$ **d.** $\dfrac{\sqrt{3}}{2}$ **e.** 1

20. The measure of an angle is between 0° and 90° and its cosine is 0.6820. What is the measure of the angle?   Use Table II.

   a. 42°   **b.** 43°   **c.** 46°   **d.** 47°   **e.** 48°

21. Which of these radian measures has negative sine and positive cosine?

   a. 1   **b.** 2   **c.** 3   **d.** 4   **e.** 5

22. What is the period of $y = \sin 4\theta$?

   a. $\dfrac{\pi}{4}$ **b.** $\dfrac{\pi}{2}$ **c.** π **d.** 4π **e.** 8π

23. $\dfrac{1}{\sin \theta} =$

   a. $\cos \theta$ **b.** $\tan \theta$ **c.** $\cot \theta$ **d.** $\sec \theta$ **e.** $\csc \theta$

24. A rectangle is 10 cm long and 9 cm wide.   What is the approximate measure of the angle formed by a diagonal and the longer side?

   a. 42°   **b.** 44°   **c.** 46°   **d.** 48°   **e.** 50°

CHAPTER 15
TRIGONOMETRIC
IDENTITIES

After two years of algebra, you still may wonder how you will use the mathematics you learn in school. The question remains difficult to answer. You may use it for nothing more than occasional measurements and computations. On the other hand, it may help you build your home, improve your community, or strengthen your country. One thing is certain: Your knowledge of mathematics leaves far more doors open to you than there would be otherwise.

OBJECTIVES: Verify the fundamental trigonometric identities. Use the fundamental identities to verify other trigonometric identities. Solve trigonometric equations.

15-1 FUNDAMENTAL IDENTITIES

An identity is an equation whose two members are equal for every meaningful replacement for the variables. One fundamental trigonometric identity,

$$\sin^2 x + \cos^2 x = 1,$$

is based on the fact that for any value for x the pair $(\cos x, \sin x)$ represents a point of the unit circle.

Other trigonometric identities follow from the definitions of the functions given in Section 14-6.

$$\tan x = \frac{\sin x}{\cos x} \qquad \cot x = \frac{\cos x}{\sin x}$$

$$\sec x = \frac{1}{\cos x} \qquad \csc x = \frac{1}{\sin x}$$

Still others can be derived from the above.

EXAMPLE 1 Prove $\tan x \cdot \cot x = 1$.

  SOLUTION Use the definitions.

$$\tan x \cdot \cot x \overset{?}{=} 1$$

$$\frac{\sin x}{\cos x} \cdot \frac{\cos x}{\sin x} \overset{?}{=} 1$$

$$1 = 1 \quad \text{Q.E.D.}$$

The identity in Example 1 is a reciprocal identity. There are three reciprocal identities.

THE RECIPROCAL IDENTITIES

$$\cos x \sec x = 1 \qquad \sin x \csc x = 1 \qquad \tan x \cot x = 1$$

EXAMPLE 2 Prove $1 + \tan^2 x = \sec^2 x$.

SOLUTION 1

$$1 + \tan^2 x \overset{?}{=} \sec^2 x$$

$$1 + \frac{\sin^2 x}{\cos^2 x} \overset{?}{=} \sec^2 x$$

$$\frac{\cos^2 x + \sin^2 x}{\cos^2 x} \overset{?}{=} \sec^2 x$$

$$\frac{1}{\cos^2 x} \overset{?}{=} \sec^2 x$$

$$\sec^2 x = \sec^2 x$$

Q.E.D.

SOLUTION 2

$$\sin^2 x + \cos^2 x = 1$$

$$\frac{\sin^2 x}{\cos^2 x} + 1 = \frac{1}{\cos^2 x}$$

$$\left(\frac{\sin x}{\cos x}\right)^2 + 1 = \left(\frac{1}{\cos x}\right)^2$$

$$\tan^2 x + 1 = \sec^2 x$$

Q.E.D.

The identity in Example 2 is a Pythagorean Identity. There are three Pythagorean Identities.

THE PYTHAGOREAN IDENTITIES

$$\sin^2 x + \cos^2 x = 1 \qquad 1 + \tan^2 x = \sec^2 x \qquad 1 + \cot^2 x = \csc^2 x$$

The definitions, the Reciprocal Identities, and the Pythagorean Identities enable us to express any trigonometric function of an angle in terms of any other trigonometric function of that angle. They also permit us to simplify any expression involving various trigonometric functions to an expression involving only one trigonometric function.

EXAMPLE 3 Express $\dfrac{\sin x \sec x \tan x - \cos x \csc x \cot x}{\tan x - \cot x}$ in terms of $\tan x$ only.

SOLUTION

$$\frac{\sin x \sec x \tan x - \cos x \csc x \cot x}{\tan x - \cot x}$$

$$= \frac{\sin x \left(\dfrac{1}{\cos x}\right) \tan x - \cos x \left(\dfrac{1}{\sin x}\right) \cot x}{\tan x - \cot x}$$

$$= \frac{\tan x \tan x - \cot x \cot x}{\tan x - \cot x}$$

$$= \frac{(\tan x - \cot x)(\tan x + \cot x)}{\tan x - \cot x}$$

$$= \tan x + \cot x$$

$$= \tan x + \frac{1}{\tan x}, \text{ or } \frac{\tan^2 x + 1}{\tan x}$$

CLASSROOM EXERCISES

Use the definitions of the trigonometric functions to verify the identities.

1. $\cos x \sec x = 1$ **2.** $\cos x = \pm \sqrt{1 - \sin^2 x}$ **3.** $\tan^2 x = \sec^2 x - 1$

4. Express $\cot \theta$ in terms of $\sin \theta$.

5. Express $\dfrac{\cos x \csc x \cot x - \sin x \sec x \tan x}{\cot x - \tan x}$ in terms of $\cot x$.

6. Express $\sin \theta + \cot \theta \cos \theta$ in terms of $\csc \theta$.

EXERCISES

A Use the definitions of the trigonometric functions to verify the identities.

1. $\sin x \csc x = 1$ **2.** $\cos \theta = \dfrac{1}{\sec \theta}$ **3.** $\tan \theta = \dfrac{1}{\cot \theta}$

4. $\sin x = \dfrac{1}{\csc x}$ **5.** $\tan^2 \theta - \sec^2 \theta = -1$ **6.** $\cot^2 \theta - \csc^2 \cdot \theta = -1$

7. $\sec \theta = \pm \sqrt{1 + \tan^2 \theta}$ **8.** $\csc \theta = \pm \sqrt{1 + \cot^2 \theta}$ **9.** $\tan \theta = \pm \sqrt{\sec^2 \theta - 1}$

Write the given expression in terms of the indicated function.

10. $\dfrac{\tan x - \sin x \cos x + \tan x \sin x}{\tan x}$, $\sin x$ **11.** $\dfrac{2 \sin x - \tan x + \sin^3 x \sec x}{\tan x}$, $\cos x$

12. $\dfrac{\cot \theta \sin \theta \cos \theta - (1 + \tan^2 \theta)}{\cos \theta - \sec \theta}$, $\cos \theta$ **13.** $\dfrac{\tan \theta \cos \theta \sin \theta - 1 - \cot^2 \theta}{\sin \theta - \csc \theta}$, $\sin \theta$

14. $\dfrac{2 \sin x \cos x + \cot x \cos^2 x + 2 \cot x \sin x}{\cot x}$, $\sin x$

15. $\dfrac{\sec x \sin^2 x + 2 \cos x - 2}{\sec x}$, $\cos x$

B **16.** $\cot x$, $\csc x$ **17.** $\sec^2 x - 1$, $\csc x$

18. $\left(\dfrac{1}{\csc x} - \dfrac{1}{\sec x} \right)^2$, $\sec x$ **19.** $\dfrac{\cos 2\theta \sin 2\theta + \cot 2\theta}{\cos 2\theta}$, $\sin 2\theta$

Simplify.

20. $\dfrac{\tan^2 x}{\sec^2 x} + \dfrac{\cot^2 x}{\csc^2 x}$ **21.** $\dfrac{\sin \theta}{\tan \theta} - \dfrac{\tan \theta}{\sec \theta}$

22. $\dfrac{\sin \theta + \tan \theta}{1 + \sec \theta}$ **23.** $\dfrac{\csc x - \cot x}{\tan x + \cot x}$

Write the given expression in terms of the indicated function.

C **24.** $1 + \sin^2 \theta + \sin^4 \theta + \sin^6 \theta + \cdots$, $\sec \theta$ **25.** $2 \log (\sec x + \tan x)$, $\sin x$

15-2 PROVING IDENTITIES

To verify that two expressions are the members of an identity, transform one or both until you have an equation with two members that are identical. In a variation on this method, begin with one of the expressions and transform it into the other expression. These two methods are shown in Example 1.

EXAMPLE 1 Show that $\tan x \cos x = \sin x$ is an identity.

SOLUTION 1	SOLUTION 2
$\tan x \cos x \overset{?}{=} \sin x$	$\tan x \cos x = \dfrac{\sin x}{\cos x} \cos x$
$\dfrac{\sin x}{\cos x} \cos x \overset{?}{=} \sin x$	$= \sin x$
$\sin x = \sin x$	Q.E.D.
Q.E.D.	

EXAMPLE 2 Show that $\dfrac{\cos x + \sin x}{\cos x} + \dfrac{\cos x - \sin x}{\sin x} = \csc x \sec x$
is an identity.

SOLUTION

$$\frac{\cos x + \sin x}{\cos x} + \frac{\cos x - \sin x}{\sin x} \overset{?}{=} \csc x \sec x$$

$$\frac{\sin x \cos x + \sin^2 x + \cos^2 x - \sin x \cos x}{\sin x \cos x} \overset{?}{=} \csc x \sec x$$

$$\frac{\sin^2 x + \cos^2 x}{\sin x \cos x} \overset{?}{=} \csc x \sec x$$

$$\frac{1}{\sin x \cos x} \overset{?}{=} \csc x \sec x$$

$$\csc x \sec x = \csc x \sec x$$
$$\text{Q.E.D.}$$

An identity is true for all *meaningful* replacements for the variable. A trigonometric function may be undefined for certain numbers. Also, the function could produce the value 0 for a denominator. When we establish an identity, we should be aware of the restrictions that are necessary for the variable.

For example, verification of the identity of Example 1 involved $\cos x$ as a denominator. In Example 2, and in Example 3 that follows, $\cos x$ and $\sin x$ are denominators. The restriction on $\tan x \cos x = \sin x$ (Example 1) is that $x \neq \pm \dfrac{\pi}{2}, \pm \dfrac{3\pi}{2}, \pm \dfrac{5\pi}{2}$, and so on. The restriction

on the identities in Examples 2 and 3 is that $x \neq k\dfrac{\pi}{2}$ for any integer k.

EXAMPLE 3 Show that $\sec x \csc x = \cot x + \tan x$ is an identity.

SOLUTION $\sec x \csc x \overset{?}{=} \cot x + \tan x$

$$\frac{1}{\cos x} \cdot \frac{1}{\sin x} \overset{?}{=} \frac{\cos x}{\sin x} + \frac{\sin x}{\cos x}$$

$$\frac{1}{\sin x \cos x} \overset{?}{=} \frac{\cos^2 x + \sin^2 x}{\sin x \cos x}$$

$$\frac{1}{\sin x \cos x} = \frac{1}{\sin x \cos x} \qquad \text{Q.E.D.}$$

Finding a common denominator for the members of an equation can help in verifying that the equation is an identity.

EXAMPLE 4 Show that $\dfrac{\sec x - 1}{\tan x} = \dfrac{\tan x}{\sec x + 1}$ is an identity.

SOLUTION $\dfrac{\sec x - 1}{\tan x} \overset{?}{=} \dfrac{\tan x}{\sec x + 1}$

$$\frac{(\sec x - 1)(\sec x + 1)}{\tan x (\sec x + 1)} \overset{?}{=} \frac{\tan x \tan x}{\tan x (\sec x + 1)}$$

$$\frac{\sec^2 x - 1}{\tan x (\sec x + 1)} \overset{?}{=} \frac{\tan^2 x}{\tan x (\sec x + 1)}$$

$$\frac{\tan^2 x}{\tan x (\sec x + 1)} = \frac{\tan^2 x}{\tan x (\sec x + 1)} \qquad \text{Q.E.D.}$$

The two expressions that are members of an identity are equal for every meaningful replacement for the variables. This means that one expression may replace the other in a conditional equation. The solution set of the conditional equation will be unchanged by this replacement.

EXAMPLE 5 Solve $\sec x - \cos x = 0$ for $0 \le x < 2\pi$.

SOLUTION $\sec x - \cos x = 0$

$$\frac{1}{\cos x} - \cos x = 0$$

$$\frac{1 - \cos^2 x}{\cos x} = 0$$

$$1 - \cos^2 x = 0$$

$$\sin^2 x = 0$$

$$\sin x = 0$$

Thus, $x = 0$ or $x = \pi$.

CHECK
The check is left
for the student.

EXAMPLE 6   Solve $\sec^2 x - 2 \tan x = 0$ for $0 \le x < 2\pi$.

SOLUTION

$$\sec^2 x - 2 \tan x = 0$$
$$1 + \tan^2 x - 2 \tan x = 0$$
$$\tan^2 x - 2 \tan x + 1 = 0$$
$$(\tan x - 1)^2 = 0$$
$$\tan x = 1$$

Thus, $x = \dfrac{\pi}{4}$ or $x = \dfrac{5\pi}{4}$.

CHECK

$$\sec^2 x - 2 \tan x = 0 \qquad\qquad \sec^2 x - 2 \tan x = 0$$

$$\sec^2 \frac{\pi}{4} - 2 \tan \frac{\pi}{4} \overset{?}{=} 0 \qquad \sec^2 \frac{5\pi}{4} - 2 \tan \frac{5\pi}{4} \overset{?}{=} 0$$

$$(\sqrt{2})^2 - 2(1) \overset{?}{=} 0 \qquad\qquad (-\sqrt{2})^2 - 2(1) \overset{?}{=} 0$$

$$0 = 0 \quad \checkmark \qquad\qquad\qquad 0 = 0 \quad \checkmark$$

CLASSROOM EXERCISES

Verify each identity.

1. $\sin x \cot x = \cos x$

2. $\tan x \sin x + \cos x = \sec x$

3. $\sin x \tan x = \sec x - \cos x$

4. $\dfrac{\sin x - 1}{\cos x} = \dfrac{-\cos x}{\sin x + 1}$

5. $\dfrac{\cot x + \tan x}{\cot x} + \dfrac{\cot x - \tan x}{\tan x} = \tan^2 x + \cot^2 x$

6. Solve $\cos x + \sec x = 2$ for $0 \le x < 2\pi$.

EXERCISES

[A]   Verify each identity.

1. $\cos x \csc x \tan x = 1$

2. $\sin x \cot x \sec x = 1$

3. $\cos^2 x - \sin^2 x = 2 \cos^2 x - 1$

4. $\cos^2 x - \sin^2 x = 1 - 2 \sin^2 x$

5. $\cos x + \sin x \tan x = \sec x$

6. $\sin x + \cos x \cot x = \csc x$

7. $\sin x \,(1 + \cot^2 x) = \csc x$

8. $\cos x \,(1 + \tan^2 x) = \sec x$

9. $\tan x \,(\csc^2 x - 1) = \cot x$

10. $\cot x \,(\sec^2 x - 1) = \tan x$

11. $\dfrac{\sin x}{1 - \cos^2 x} = \csc x$

12. $\dfrac{\cos x}{1 - \sin^2 x} = \sec x$

13. $\dfrac{1}{\cos^2 x} - \dfrac{1}{\cot^2 x} = 1$

14. $\dfrac{1}{\sin^2 x} - \dfrac{1}{\tan^2 x} = 1$

15. $\left(\dfrac{1}{1 - \cos x}\right)\left(\dfrac{1}{1 + \cos x}\right) = \csc^2 x$

16. $\left(\dfrac{1}{\sec x - 1}\right)\left(\dfrac{1}{\sec x + 1}\right) = \cot^2 x$

17. $\tan x \cot x + \sin^2 x + \cos^2 x = 2$

18. $\cos^2 x \tan^2 x + \sin^2 x \cot^2 x = 1$

19. $(\cot x + 1)^2 - 2 \cot x = \csc^2 x$

20. $(\sin x + \cos x)^2 - 1 = 2 \sin x \cos x$

21. $\dfrac{1 - \sin x}{\cos x} = \dfrac{\cos x}{1 + \sin x}$

22. $\dfrac{\csc x - 1}{\cot x} = \dfrac{\cot x}{\csc x + 1}$

23. $\dfrac{\csc x}{\tan x + \cot x} = \cos x$

24. $\dfrac{\sec x}{\tan x + \cot x} = \sin x$

25. $\dfrac{\cos^2 x}{1 - \sin x} = \dfrac{\cos x}{\sec x - \tan x}$

26. $\dfrac{\sin x}{\csc x - \cot} = \dfrac{\sin^2 x}{1 - \cos x}$

Solve.   Use the domain $0 \le x < 2\pi$.   Check.

27. $\tan x + \cot x = 2$

28. $\sin^2 x - \cos^2 x = 0$

29. $\cos^2 x - 3 \sin^2 x = 0$

30. $\sin^2 x - 3 \cos^2 x = 0$

31. $\csc x - 3 \sin x + 2 = 0$

32. $2 - 3 \cos x + \sec x = 0$

B   Verify each identity.

33. $(\sin x + \cos x)^2 = 1 + 2 \cos x \sin x$

34. $\sec^4 x - \tan^4 x = 1 + 2 \tan^2 x$

35. $\dfrac{\sin x + \csc x}{\sin x} + \dfrac{\sin x - \csc x}{\csc x} = \dfrac{\sin^4 x + 1}{\sin^2 x}$

36. $\tan^3 x + 1 = (\tan x + 1)(\sec^2 x - \tan x)$

37. $\dfrac{\sec x + \csc x}{\sec x} + \dfrac{\sec x - \csc x}{\csc x} = \sec x \csc x$

38. $\dfrac{\sin x \cos x + \sin^2 x}{\tan x} + \dfrac{\cos x - \cot x \cos x}{\csc x} = 2 \sin x \cos x$

Solve.   Use the domain $0 \le x < 2\pi$.

39. $\cos^2 x - \sin^2 x - \frac{1}{2} = 0$

40. $\tan^2 x + \cot^2 x - 2 = 0$

41. $2 \cos x \cot x - 3 = 0$

42. $2 \cos^2 x + \sqrt{3} \sin x + 1 = 0$

Verify each identity.

C   **43.** $\dfrac{\sin x}{1 - \cos x} - \dfrac{\sec x + \csc x}{1 + \tan x} = \cot x$

44. $\tan^2 x \sec^2 y - \tan^2 y \sec^2 x - \tan^2 x + \tan^2 y = 0$

45. $\tan x \sqrt{\dfrac{\sec x - 1}{\sec x + 1}} = \sec x - 1,\ 0 \le x < \dfrac{\pi}{2}$

46. $\sqrt{\dfrac{1 - \cos \theta}{1 + \cos \theta}} = \dfrac{1}{\csc \theta + \cot \theta}$

Find *all* real number solutions for each system.   Use k for "any integer".

47. $y = 1 - \cos x$
$y = \cos x$

48. $y = 2 \sin x$
$y = \tan x$

49. $y = \sin x$
$y = \cos x$

OBJECTIVES: Verify The Law of Sines and The Law of Cosines. Use these laws to solve problems.

15-3   THE LAW OF COSINES

A point on the terminal side of an angle, θ, is a distance, r, from the origin. Using similar triangles, we can show that its coordinates may be written ($r \cos \theta$, $r \sin \theta$).

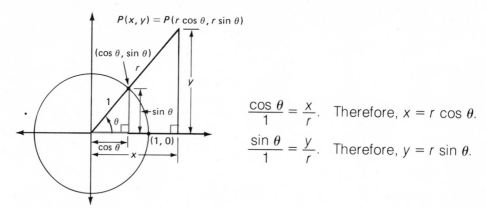

$\dfrac{\cos \theta}{1} = \dfrac{x}{r}$. Therefore, $x = r \cos \theta$.

$\dfrac{\sin \theta}{1} = \dfrac{y}{r}$. Therefore, $y = r \sin \theta$.

We can position any triangle in the coordinate plane so that any one of its angles is in standard position. The cosine and sine of that angle then may be used to help give the coordinates of the vertex not in the x-axis.

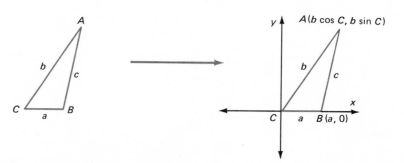

Using the Distance Formula, we can find the length, c, of $\overline{AB}$.

$$c = \sqrt{(b \cos C - a)^2 + (b \sin C - 0)^2}$$

Therefore, $c^2 = b^2 \cos^2 C - 2ab \cos C + a^2 + b^2 \sin^2 C$

$\qquad\quad c^2 = a^2 + b^2(\cos^2 C + \sin^2 C) - 2ab \cos C$

$\qquad\quad c^2 = a^2 + b^2 - 2ab \cos C$

This equation allows us to find the length of any side of a triangle when we know the lengths of two sides and the measure of their included angle. It is the Law of Cosines.

THE LAW OF COSINES

When a and b are the lengths of the sides that include $\angle C$ in triangle ABC and c is the length of the side that is opposite $\angle C$, then

$$c^2 = a^2 + b^2 - 2ab \cos C.$$

EXAMPLE 1   Triangle ABC has $a = 12$, $b = 10$, and $m \angle C = 120°$. Find c.

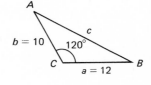

SOLUTION   Use the Law of Cosines.

$c^2 = 12^2 + 10^2 - 2(12)(10)(\cos 120°)$
$c^2 = 144 + 100 - 240(-\cos 60°)$
$c^2 = 144 + 100 + 240(0.5000)$
$c^2 = 364$
$c \doteq 19.1$

EXAMPLE 2   Find the measure of the largest angle of the triangle whose sides have lengths 10, 15, and 21.

SOLUTION   The largest angle, C, is opposite the longest side. Use the Law of Cosines.

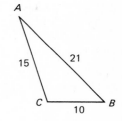

$$21^2 = 15^2 + 10^2 - 2(15)(10) \cos C$$
$$441 = 225 + 100 - 300 \cos C$$
$$300 \cos C = -116$$
$$\cos C \doteq -0.3867$$

Therefore, $m \angle C \doteq 112°45'$.

CLASSROOM EXERCISES

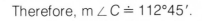

Find the length of side c for triangle ABC.

1. $a = 15$, $b = 8$, $m \angle C = 60°$ **2.** $a = 10$, $b = 22$, $m \angle C = 130°$

3. Points A and B are at opposite ends of a lake. At point C on land, the measure of angle ACB is 40°. The distance between A and C is 5 km. The distance between B and C is 7 km. Find the length of the lake.

EXERCISES

A Find the length of side c for triangle ABC.

1. $a = 3, b = 8, m \angle C = 60°$ **2.** $a = 5, b = 21, m \angle C = 60°$

3. $a = 1, b = 6, m \angle C = 120°$ **4.** $a = 2, b = 5, m \angle C = 120°$

5. $a = 4, b = 3, m \angle C = 50°$ **6.** $a = 8, b = 1, m \angle C = 35°$

7. $a = 2, b = 10, m \angle C = 170°$ **8.** $a = 1, b = 6, m \angle C = 160°$

Find the measure of the smallest angle of triangle ABC.

9. $a = 11, b = 8, c = 5$ **10.** $a = 19, b = 10, c = 17$

11. $a = 5, b = 5, c = 4$ **12.** $a = 7, b = 7, c = 5$

Find the measure of the largest angle of triangle ABC.

13. $a = 7, b = 5, c = 3$ **14.** $a = \sqrt{91}, b = 6, c = 5$

15. $a = 9, b = 7, c = 3$ **16.** $a = 9, b = 6, c = 6$

17. City A is 10 kilometers west of City B. City C is 12 kilometers from City A and 13 kilometers from City B. Find the measure of angle CAB.

B **18.** The high school in a town is 5 kilometers east of the pizza parlor. The bowling lanes are 6 kilometers northwest of the pizza parlor. How far is it from the high school to the bowling lanes?

19. A ship is 4 kilometers east of a lighthouse. Another ship is 3 kilometers southwest of the lighthouse. How far apart are the ships?

20. Find the measure of the smallest angle for a triangle with lengths of 19, 10, and 7. If this is not possible, give a reason.

21. Use the Law of Cosines to express side c, given legs a and b and right angle C for a triangle.

C **22.** Let k be any positive integer. In triangle ABC, $a = 2k + 1, c = 3k^2 + 4k + 1$, and $m \angle B = 60°$. Find b.

23. Let k be any positive integer. In triangle ABC, $a = 12k^2 + 4k - 1$, $b = 12k^2 + 1$, and $c = 8k$. Find the measure of angle B.

24. Establish the Law of Cosines for triangle ABC given a, b, and $m \angle C > 90°$.

25. Two forest rangers are 11 kilometers apart. One of them observes a hot air balloon between them at an angle of elevation of 65°. If the altitude of the balloon is 1 kilometer, at what angle of elevation would the second ranger see it? Find the distance from the second ranger to the point on the ground directly below the balloon.

26. Prove that the sum of the squares of the lengths of the diagonals of a parallelogram is equal to the sum of the squares of the lengths of the four sides of the parallelogram.

15-4   AREA FORMULAS AND THE LAW OF SINES

When we know the lengths of two sides of a triangle and the measure of their included angle, we can find the area of the triangle.

By positioning triangle *ABC* in the coordinate plane as shown, we know that the coordinates of *A* are ($b \cos C$, $b \sin C$). Therefore, triangle *ABC* has base length *a* and height $b \sin C$.

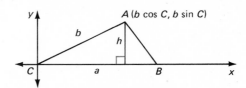

$$\text{Area} = \tfrac{1}{2}(\text{base})(\text{height})$$

$$\text{Area} = \tfrac{1}{2}ab \sin C$$

THE AREA OF A TRIANGLE

When *a* and *b* are the lengths of the sides that include $\angle C$ in triangle *ABC*, then

$$\text{Area} (\triangle ABC) = \tfrac{1}{2}ab \sin C.$$

EXAMPLE 1   Find the area of triangle *ABC* when $a = 20$, $b = 25$, and $m \angle C = 60°$.

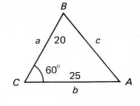

SOLUTION $\text{Area} = \tfrac{1}{2}ab \sin C$

$\qquad\quad = \tfrac{1}{2}(20)(25)(\sin 60°)$

$\qquad\quad \doteq 250(0.8660)$

$\qquad\quad \doteq 216.5$

EXAMPLE 2   Find the area of triangle *PQR* when $q = 30$, $r = 30$, and $m \angle Q = 30°$.

SOLUTION   To use the area formula, we need $m \angle P$.
Since the triangle is isosceles, $m \angle R = 30°$.

$\qquad m \angle P + m \angle Q + m \angle R = 180°$

$\qquad\quad m \angle P + 30° + 30° = 180°$

$\qquad\qquad\qquad\quad m \angle P = 120°$

By the area formula,

$\text{Area} = \tfrac{1}{2}qr \sin P$

$\text{Area} = \tfrac{1}{2}(30)(30)(\sin 120°)$

$\qquad\quad = 450(\sin 60°)$

$\qquad\quad \doteq 450(0.8660)$

$\qquad\quad \doteq 389.7$

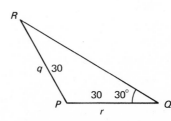

From the area formula, the area of triangle ABC may be given as

$$\tfrac{1}{2}bc \sin A, \quad \tfrac{1}{2}ac \sin B, \quad \text{or} \quad \tfrac{1}{2}ab \sin C,$$

depending upon the sides and included angle having the known measures.   Dividing each member of the compound sentence

$$\tfrac{1}{2}bc \sin A \;=\; \tfrac{1}{2}ac \sin B \;=\; \tfrac{1}{2}ab \sin C$$

by $\tfrac{1}{2}abc$ gives a relationship known as the Law of Sines.

THE LAW OF SINES

When a, b, and c are the lengths of the sides that are opposite angles A, B, and C, respectively, in triangle ABC, then

$$\frac{\sin A}{a} = \frac{\sin B}{b} = \frac{\sin C}{c}.$$

EXAMPLE 3   Triangle ABC has $a = 12$, $b = 6$, and $m \angle A = 45°$. Find $m \angle B$.

SOLUTION   From the Law of Sines,

$$\frac{\sin B}{b} = \frac{\sin A}{a}.$$

$$\frac{\sin B}{6} = \frac{\sin 45°}{12}$$

$$\sin B = \frac{6 \sin 45°}{12}$$

$$\doteq \frac{6(0.7071)}{12}$$

$$\sin B \doteq 0.3536$$

Therefore, $m \angle B \doteq 20° \; 42'$.

EXAMPLE 4   Triangle BCD has $d = 4$, $m \angle B = 45°$, and $m \angle D = 60°$. Find b.

SOLUTION   From the Law of Sines,

$$\frac{\sin D}{d} = \frac{\sin B}{b}.$$

$$\frac{\sin 60°}{4} = \frac{\sin 45°}{b}$$

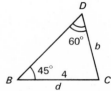

$$b = \frac{4 \sin 45°}{\sin 60°}$$

$$\doteq \frac{4(0.7071)}{0.8660}$$

$$b \doteq 3.266$$

CLASSROOM EXERCISES

Find the area of triangle ABC.

1. $a = 10$, $b = 16$, C is 30°

2. $b = 6$, $c = 7$, A is 45°

Solve the triangle for the indicated measure. Use the Law of Sines.

3. $a = 6$, C is 30°, A is 50°, $c = ?$

4. $c = 8$, C is 60°, $b = 6$, B is ?

EXERCISES

A Find the area of triangle ABC.

1. $a = 6$, $b = 4$, C is 30°   **2.** $a = 3$, $b = 6$, C is 30°   **3.** $a = 1$, $b = 2$, C is 50°

4. $a = 4$, $b = 1$, C is 70°   **5.** $b = 2$, $c = 3$, A is 40°   **6.** $b = 6$, $c = 5$, A is 40°

7. $a = 3$, $b = 3$, B is 50°   **8.** $b = 4$, $c = 4$, B is 70°   **9.** $a = 6$, $b = 2$, C is 90°

Solve the triangle for the indicated part. Use the Law of Sines.

10. $a = 2$, C is 40°, A is 60°, $c = ?$ **11.** $c = 10$, B is 60°, C is 40°, $b = ?$

12. $b = 13$, A is 20°, B is 110°, $a = ?$ **13.** A is 40°, $a = 20$, $b = 16$, B is ?

14. C is 32°, $c = 12$, $a = 10$, A is ?   **15.** A is 148°, $a = 4$, $c = 2$, C is ?

B Solve.

16. Find the area of the isosceles triangle with base 10 centimeters that can be formed from a piece of string 50 centimeters long.

17. A surveyor wants to find the distance from point A to point C on the opposite side of the river. *AB* is 100 meters. The angles *BAC* and *ABC* measure 50° and 70° respectively. Find the distance from A to C.

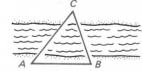

C **18.** θ is an acute angle formed by diagonals AC and BD of quadrilateral $ABCD$. Show that the area of $ABCD$ equals $\frac{1}{2}(AC)(BD) \sin \theta$.

19. The area of a triangle is 336 cm². The perimeter is 84 cm. The length of one side is 26 cm. Find the length of each of the other two sides.

15-5 PROBLEM SOLVING: USING IDEAS FROM TRIGONOMETRY

The Law of Cosines, the Law of Sines, and the area formula give us tools for solving many problems that involve geometric figures and their measurements. For most triangles we can find all six measurements associated with the sides and angles by knowing the length of one side and any two of the other five measurements. The only possible exception can occur when we know the lengths of two sides and the measure of a non-included angle. It is possible for two triangles to have such measurements.

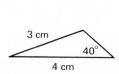

EXAMPLE 1 Find the lengths of the sides and the measures of the angles for triangle ABC.

$a = 12$, $m \angle A = 35°$, $m \angle C = 100°$

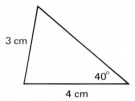

SOLUTION From $m \angle A + m \angle B + m \angle C = 180°$, we find that $m \angle B = 45°$.

Use the Law of Sines.

Find b.

$$\frac{\sin 45°}{b} = \frac{\sin 35°}{12}$$

$$b = \frac{12 \sin 45°}{\sin 35°}$$

$$b \doteq \frac{12(0.7071)}{0.5736}$$

$$b \doteq 14.8$$

Find c.

$$\frac{\sin 100°}{c} = \frac{\sin 35°}{12}$$

$$c = \frac{12 \sin 100°}{\sin 35°}$$

$$c \doteq \frac{12(0.9848)}{0.5736}$$

$$c \doteq 20.6$$

CONCLUSION The six measures of the triangle are shown in this diagram.

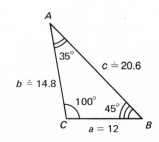

EXAMPLE 2   Find the area of parallelogram
ABCD.

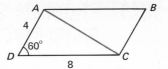

SOLUTION   The area of parallelogram
ABCD equals twice the area
of triangle ADC.

Use the trigonometric form of the formula for the area of
a triangle.

$$\text{Area}_{ABCD} = 2 \cdot \text{Area}_{ADC}$$
$$= 2 \cdot \tfrac{1}{2} \cdot 8 \cdot 4 \sin 60°$$
$$\doteq 32(0.8660)$$
$$\doteq 27.7$$

CONCLUSION   The area of the parallelogram is about 27.7 square units.

EXAMPLE 3   From home, Susan jogged 3 kilometers north, 5 kilometers northwest, and then
stopped. How far was she
from   home   when   she
stopped?

SOLUTION   Make a sketch.

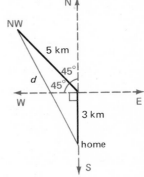

Use d for the distance from
home   to   where   Susan
stopped jogging.

Susan's path northwest bi-
sects the angle formed by
the north and west lines.
Thus, the angles have measures as indicated in the
diagram. In particular, the measure of the angle formed
by Susan's complete path, shown in black, is 135°.

The pattern of the data suggests the use of the Law of
Cosines to find d.

$$d^2 = 3^2 + 5^2 - 2(3)(5) \cos 135°$$
$$= 9 + 25 - 30(-\cos 45°)$$
$$\doteq 34 - 30(-0.7071)$$
$$\doteq 34 + 21.213$$
$$d^2 \doteq 55.213$$
$$d \doteq 7.4$$

CONCLUSION   Susan was about 7.4 km from home when she stopped
jogging.

EXAMPLE 4 How far is the tree from the base of the hill?

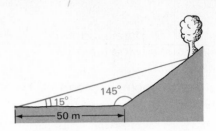

SOLUTION The pattern of the data suggests the use of the Law of Sines.

Use $\begin{bmatrix} d & \text{for the distance in meters of the} \\ & \text{tree from the base of the hill.} \\ T & \text{for the third angle of the triangle.} \end{bmatrix}$

Find $m \angle T$.

$$m \angle T + 15° + 145° = 180°$$
$$m \angle T = 20°$$

Find d. Use the Law of Sines.

$$\frac{\sin 20°}{50} = \frac{\sin 15°}{d}$$

$$d \sin 20° = 50 \sin 15°$$

$$d = \frac{50 \sin 15°}{\sin 20°}$$

$$\doteq \frac{50(0.2588)}{0.3420}$$

$$d \doteq 37.8$$

CONCLUSION The tree is about 37.8 meters from the base of the hill.

CLASSROOM EXERCISES

Solve.

1. Find the area of parallelogram $ABCD$.

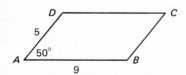

2. A surveyor determined the measurements shown for triangle ABC. Find BC.

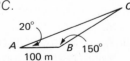

3. Find the missing measures for triangle PQR.

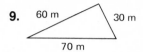

4. A ship travels 10 kilometers north and then travels 15 kilometers northeast. How far is the ship from where it started?

EXERCISES

Ａ Find the area of each parallelogram.

1.

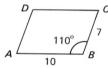

2.

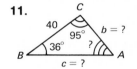

3. In Exercises 1 and 2, find DB.

4. A ship leaves port and travels 7 kilometers south. It then travels 17 kilometers southeast. How far is it from port?

5. Since leaving the campground, Jorge has hiked 2 kilometers east and 1 kilometer northeast. How far is he from the campground?

6. Sue drives her car to a point 10 kilometers north of her home. She then drives east 15 kilometers and stops. How many degrees east of north is she from her home?

7. A ship leaves its home port and travels south for 12 kilometers. It then travels west for 5 kilometers. How many degrees west of south is the boat from its home port?

8. On May 3, two observers along Interstate 91 observed a kite in the sky. One of them observed the kite at an angle of elevation of 30°. The other, 100 meters to the east, observed the

kite at an angle of elevation of 40°. If both were facing east, find the distance from each observer to the kite.

Find the area.

9.

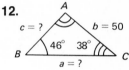

10.

30 cm ╱ 80 cm ╱ 100 cm

Find the missing measures.

11.

C 40 95° b = ? 36° ? B c = ? A

12.

A c = ? b = 50 46° 38° B a = ? C

Ｂ **13.** Repeat Exercise 8. Assume that the two observers were facing each other.

14. The area of triangle ABC is 50 square meters. For a = 0.02 kilometers and c = 0.01 kilometers, find all possible measures for angle B and side AC.

15. In quadrilateral ABCD, m ∠A = 120°, AB = BC, AD = 2(AB), CD = AB + 10, and BD = 7√7. Find the measure of angle C and the area of the quadrilateral.

Ｃ **16.** A triangle has sides whose lengths are 3 consecutive integers. Find the lengths of the sides when the area is 30√2 square units.

17. For any triangle ABC, show that a = b cos C + c cos B.

18. Points B and C are 29 800 meters apart on an east-west line. Point A is 100 meters from B along a line 30° northeast of B. Point D is 199 meters from C along a line 60° northwest of C. Find AD in meters.

CHECKING YOUR UNDERSTANDING

WORDS

Law of Cosines   Pythagorean identity   trigonometric identity
Law of Sines   reciprocal identity

CONCEPTS

■ Any trigonometric expression may be given in terms of any *one* trigonometric function. [15-1]

■ The measures of at least three parts of a triangle, including the length of one side, is enough information for solving any triangle, with certain exceptions. [15-5]

PROCESSES

■ Write an expression in terms of one trigonometric function. [15-1]

1. Express $\sin^2 x \cot^2 x$ in terms of $\cos x$.   **2.** Express $\dfrac{\cos x}{\sec x - \tan x}$ in terms of $\sin x$.

■ Prove identities. [15-2]

3. Prove $\sec \theta + \tan \theta = \dfrac{\cos \theta}{1 - \sin \theta}$.   **4.** Prove $\dfrac{\sin^2 \theta}{\tan \theta + \sin \theta} = \dfrac{1 - \cos \theta}{\tan \theta}$.

■ Use the Law of Cosines and the Law of Sines. [15-3 to 15-5]

5. Find c.   **6.** Find $m \angle A$.

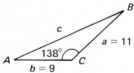

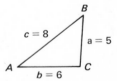

7. Find the area of triangle ABC.   **8.** Find $m \angle C$.

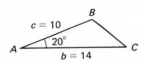

9. An isosceles triangle has a base length of 30 cm and a vertex angle of 30°. Find the perimeter of the triangle.

> **OBJECTIVES:** Verify trigonometric identities involving two angle measures, or a multiple or fraction of one angle measure. Find values for the inverse trigonometric functions.

15-6 FUNCTIONS OF SUMS AND DIFFERENCES

In the diagram, θ and ϕ (the Greek letter *phi*) are two angles in standard position. $P(\cos\theta, \sin\theta)$ and $Q(\cos\phi, \sin\phi)$ are the points of their terminal sides that are in the unit circle. $\angle POQ$ can be represented by $\theta - \phi$. We can find an expression for $\cos(\theta - \phi)$ by using the Law of Cosines and the Distance Formula.

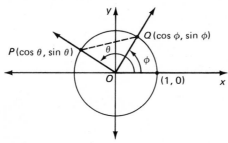

The Law of Cosines gives us $(PQ)^2 = 1^2 + 1^2 - 2(1)(1)\cos(\theta - \phi)$.

The Distance Formula gives us $(PQ)^2 = (\cos\theta - \cos\phi)^2 + (\sin\theta - \sin\phi)^2$.

To establish a meaning for $\cos(\theta - \phi)$, replace $(PQ)^2$ in the second equation by the expression for $(PQ)^2$ from the first equation. Then simplify the resulting identity.

$$1 + 1 - 2\cos(\theta - \phi) = (\cos\theta - \cos\phi)^2 + (\sin\theta - \sin\phi)^2$$
$$2 - 2\cos(\theta - \phi) = \cos^2\theta - 2\cos\theta\cos\phi + \cos^2\phi$$
$$+ \sin^2\theta - 2\sin\theta\sin\phi + \sin^2\phi$$
$$2 - 2\cos(\theta - \phi) = 2 - 2\cos\theta\cos\phi - 2\sin\theta\sin\phi$$
$$\cos(\theta - \phi) = \cos\theta\cos\phi + \sin\theta\sin\phi$$

This identity leads to some other useful identities. To prove these identities we show that one member may be transformed into the other member.

EXAMPLE 1 Prove $\cos(-\theta) = \cos\theta$.

SOLUTION Show that $\cos(-\theta)$ can be transformed into $\cos\theta$.

$$\cos(-\theta) = \cos(0 - \theta)$$
$$= \cos 0 \cos\theta + \sin 0 \sin\theta$$
$$= 1\cos\theta + 0\sin\theta$$
$$= \cos\theta$$

EXAMPLE 2 Prove $\cos \theta = \sin\left(\dfrac{\pi}{2} - \theta\right)$.

SOLUTION $\cos \theta = \cos\left[\dfrac{\pi}{2} - \left(\dfrac{\pi}{2} - \theta\right)\right]$

$$= \cos\dfrac{\pi}{2}\cos\left(\dfrac{\pi}{2} - \theta\right) + \sin\dfrac{\pi}{2}\sin\left(\dfrac{\pi}{2} - \theta\right)$$

$$= 0 \cos\left(\dfrac{\pi}{2} - \theta\right) + 1 \sin\left(\dfrac{\pi}{2} - \theta\right)$$

$$= \sin\left(\dfrac{\pi}{2} - \theta\right)$$

EXAMPLE 3 Prove $\sin \theta = \cos\left(\dfrac{\pi}{2} - \theta\right)$.

SOLUTION $\sin \theta = \sin\left[\dfrac{\pi}{2} - \left(\dfrac{\pi}{2} - \theta\right)\right]$

$$= \cos\left(\dfrac{\pi}{2} - \theta\right), \text{ by the identity of Example 2.}$$

EXAMPLE 4 Prove $\sin(-\theta) = -\sin\theta$.

SOLUTION $\sin(-\theta) = \cos\left(\dfrac{\pi}{2} - (-\theta)\right)$, by the identity of example 3.

$$= \cos\left(\dfrac{\pi}{2} + \theta\right)$$

$$= \cos\left(\theta - \left(-\dfrac{\pi}{2}\right)\right)$$

$$= \cos\theta\cos\left(-\dfrac{\pi}{2}\right) + \sin\theta\sin\left(-\dfrac{\pi}{2}\right)$$

$$= \cos\theta(0) + \sin\theta(-1)$$
$$= -\sin\theta$$

EXAMPLE 5 Prove $\cos(\theta + \phi) = \cos\theta\cos\phi - \sin\theta\sin\phi$.

SOLUTION $\cos(\theta + \phi) = \cos(\theta - (-\phi))$
$$= \cos\theta\cos(-\phi) + \sin\theta\sin(-\phi)$$
$$= \cos\theta\cos\phi - \sin\theta\sin\phi$$

EXAMPLE 6 Prove $\sin(\theta + \phi) = \sin\theta\cos\phi + \cos\theta\sin\phi$.

SOLUTION $\sin(\theta + \phi) = \cos\left[\dfrac{\pi}{2} - (\theta + \phi)\right]$

$$= \cos\left[\left(\dfrac{\pi}{2} - \theta\right) - \phi\right]$$

$$= \cos\left(\dfrac{\pi}{2} - \theta\right)\cos\phi + \sin\left(\dfrac{\pi}{2} - \theta\right)\sin\phi$$

$$= \sin\theta\cos\phi + \cos\theta\sin\phi.$$

EXAMPLE 7 Prove $\sin(\theta - \phi) = \sin \theta \cos \phi - \cos \theta \sin \phi$.

SOLUTION $\sin(\theta - \phi) = \sin(\theta + (-\phi))$
$= \sin \theta \cos(-\phi) + \cos \theta \sin(-\phi)$
$= \sin \theta \cos \phi - \cos \theta \sin \phi$

The eight identities verified above are summarized in this chart.

$$\cos(\theta - \phi) = \cos \theta \cos \phi + \sin \theta \sin \phi \quad \bigg| \quad \sin(\theta - \phi) = \sin \theta \cos \phi - \cos \theta \sin \phi$$
$$\cos(\theta + \phi) = \cos \theta \cos \phi - \sin \theta \sin \phi \quad \bigg| \quad \sin(\theta + \phi) = \sin \theta \cos \phi + \cos \theta \sin \phi$$
$$\cos(-\theta) = \cos \theta \;\bigg|\; \sin(-\theta) = -\sin \theta \;\bigg|\; \cos \theta = \sin\left(\frac{\pi}{2} - \theta\right) \;\bigg|\; \sin \theta = \cos\left(\frac{\pi}{2} - \theta\right)$$

There also are identities of the types shown above for the tangent function.   In particular,

$$\tan(\theta - \phi) = \frac{\tan \theta - \tan \phi}{1 + \tan \theta \tan \phi} \quad \text{and} \quad \tan(\theta + \phi) = \frac{\tan \theta + \tan \phi}{1 - \tan \theta \tan \phi}$$

You will be asked to prove some of these in the Exercises.

The above *angle sum* and *angle difference* identities may be used to verify facts about reference angles.

EXAMPLE 8 Prove $\sin(\pi + \alpha) = -\sin \alpha$.

SOLUTION $\sin(\pi + \alpha)$
$= \sin \pi \cos \alpha + \cos \pi \sin \alpha$
$= 0 \cos \alpha + (-1) \sin \alpha$
$= -\sin \alpha$

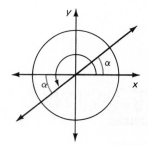

Also, we may use these identities to find values for the functions of certain angles without using tables.

EXAMPLE 9 Find $\cos 15°$.

SOLUTION $\cos 15° = \cos(45° - 30°)$
$= \cos 45° \cos 30° + \sin 45° \sin 30°$
$= \frac{\sqrt{2}}{2} \cdot \frac{\sqrt{3}}{2} + \frac{\sqrt{2}}{2} \cdot \frac{1}{2}$
$= \frac{1}{4}(\sqrt{6} + \sqrt{2})$

The last two identities in the chart on the preceding page suggest that a function of an angle is the *cofunction* of its complement. This is true in general.

EXAMPLE 10 Prove $\tan \theta = \cot\left(\dfrac{\pi}{2} - \theta\right)$.

SOLUTION $\quad \tan \theta = \dfrac{\sin \theta}{\cos \theta}$

$$= \dfrac{\cos\left(\dfrac{\pi}{2} - \theta\right)}{\sin\left(\dfrac{\pi}{2} - \theta\right)}$$

$$= \cot\left(\dfrac{\pi}{2} - \theta\right)$$

The identities in the chart also may be used for solving conditional equations involving trigonometric functions of angle sums and differences.

EXAMPLE 11 Solve $\quad 2 \sin\left(x - \dfrac{\pi}{6}\right) = \sqrt{3} \sin x \quad$ for $0 \le x < 2\pi$.

SOLUTION $\qquad\qquad\qquad 2 \sin\left(x - \dfrac{\pi}{6}\right) = \sqrt{3} \sin x$

$$2\left(\sin x \, \cos \dfrac{\pi}{6} - \cos x \, \sin \dfrac{\pi}{6}\right) = \sqrt{3} \sin x$$

$$2\left[(\sin x)\left(\dfrac{\sqrt{3}}{2}\right) - (\cos x)\left(\dfrac{1}{2}\right)\right] = \sqrt{3} \sin x$$

$$\sqrt{3} \sin x - \cos x = \sqrt{3} \sin x$$

$$\cos x = 0$$

Therefore, $x = \dfrac{\pi}{2}$ or $x = \dfrac{3\pi}{2}$.

CHECK $\quad 2 \sin\left(x - \dfrac{\pi}{6}\right) = \sqrt{3} \sin x$

$$2 \sin\left(\dfrac{\pi}{2} - \dfrac{\pi}{6}\right) \stackrel{?}{=} \sqrt{3} \sin \dfrac{\pi}{2}$$

$$2 \sin \dfrac{\pi}{3} \stackrel{?}{=} \sqrt{3}(1)$$

$$2\left(\dfrac{\sqrt{3}}{2}\right) \stackrel{?}{=} \sqrt{3}$$

$$\sqrt{3} = \sqrt{3} \quad ✔$$

The check for $x = \dfrac{3\pi}{2}$ is left for the student.

CLASSROOM EXERCISES

Verify each identity.

1. $\cos{(\pi + \alpha)} = -\cos{\alpha}$

2. $\sin{(x + 2\pi)} = \sin{x}$

Use the sum and difference identities. Find the value of the function.

3. $\sin{15°}$ **4.** $\cot{15°}$

Solve. Use the domain $0 \le x < 2\pi$. Check.

5. $\sin{\left(x - \frac{1}{2}\pi\right)} = \frac{1}{2}$

6. $\cos{\left(x + \frac{1}{2}\pi\right)} = 0$

EXERCISES

A Verify the identity.

1. $\sin{\left(x + \frac{1}{2}\pi\right)} = \cos{x}$ **2.** $\cos{\left(x + \frac{1}{2}\pi\right)} = -\sin{x}$ **3.** $\cot{\theta} = \tan{\left(\frac{1}{2}\pi - \theta\right)}$

4. $\tan{\theta} = \tan{(\theta + \pi)}$ **5.** $\cot{\theta} = \cot{(\theta + \pi)}$ **6.** $\cos{(\theta + 2\pi)} = \cos{\theta}$

7. $\tan{(-x)} = -\tan{x}$ **8.** $\cot{(-x)} = -\cot{x}$ **9.** $\csc{(-x)} = -\csc{x}$

10. $\sec{(-x)} = \sec{x}$ **11.** $\sin{2\theta} = 2\sin{\theta}\cos{\theta}$ **12.** $\cos{2\theta} = \cos^2{\theta} - \sin^2{\theta}$

13. $\cos{\left(\frac{1}{6}\pi + x\right)} = \frac{1}{2}\sqrt{3}\cos{x} - \frac{1}{2}\sin{x}$ **14.** $\sin{\left(x + \frac{1}{4}\pi\right)} = \frac{1}{2}\sqrt{2}(\sin{x} + \cos{x})$

Use the sum and difference identities. Find the value of the function.

15. $\sin{75°}$ **16.** $\cos{75°}$ **17.** $\cos{105°}$ **18.** $\sin{105°}$ **19.** $\sin{165°}$ **20.** $\cos{165°}$

Solve. Use the domain $0 \le x < 2\pi$. Check.

21. $\sin{\left(x - \frac{\pi}{2}\right)} = \frac{1}{2}$ **22.** $\sin{\left(x - \frac{3\pi}{2}\right)} = \frac{\sqrt{3}}{2}$ **23.** $\cos{\left(\frac{3\pi}{2} + x\right)} = \frac{\sqrt{3}}{2}$

B Verify the identity.

24. $\tan{(\theta + \phi)} = \dfrac{\tan{\theta} + \tan{\phi}}{1 - \tan{\theta}\tan{\phi}}$ **25.** $\tan{(\theta - \phi)} = \dfrac{\tan{\theta} - \tan{\phi}}{1 + \tan{\theta}\tan{\phi}}$

26. $\csc{(x + 2\pi)} = \csc{x}$ **27.** $\sin{x}\cos{y} = \dfrac{1}{2}[\sin{(x + y)} + \sin{(x - y)}]$

C Solve for all real numbers. Use k for "any integer".

28. $\sin{\left(\frac{\pi}{2} - x\right)} = \sqrt{3}\sin{x}$ **29.** $\sin{\left(\frac{\pi}{2} - x\right)} = \cos{\left(\frac{\pi}{2} + x\right)}$

30. $\cos{\left(x - \frac{\pi}{6}\right)}\cos{\left(x + \frac{\pi}{6}\right)} - \frac{1}{2} = 0$ **31.** $\cos{\left(\frac{\pi}{2} + x\right)} = \dfrac{\sin{x}}{2} + 1$

15-7 DOUBLE-ANGLE AND HALF-ANGLE IDENTITIES

The trigonometric identities

$$\cos(\theta + \phi) = \cos\theta\cos\phi - \sin\theta\sin\phi$$

$$\sin(\theta + \phi) = \sin\theta\cos\phi + \cos\theta\sin\phi$$

$$\tan(\theta + \phi) = \frac{\tan\theta + \tan\phi}{1 - \tan\theta\tan\phi}$$

lead to identities involving multiples and fractions of angle measures.

EXAMPLE 1   Prove $\cos 2\theta = \cos^2\theta - \sin^2\theta$, $\cos 2\theta = 2\cos^2\theta - 1$, and $\cos 2\theta = 1 - 2\sin^2\theta$.

SOLUTION $\cos 2\theta = \cos(\theta + \theta)$
$$= \cos\theta\cos\theta - \sin\theta\sin\theta$$
$$= \cos^2\theta - \sin^2\theta$$

Replace $\sin^2\theta$ by $1 - \cos^2\theta$.

$\cos 2\theta = \cos^2\theta - (1 - \cos^2\theta)$
$$= 2\cos^2\theta - 1$$

Replace $\cos^2\theta$ by $1 - \sin^2\theta$.

$\cos 2\theta = (1 - \sin^2\theta) - \sin^2\theta$
$$= 1 - 2\sin^2\theta$$

EXAMPLE 2   Find, in terms of θ, an expression equivalent to $\sin 2\theta$.

SOLUTION $\sin 2\theta = \sin(\theta + \theta)$
$$= \sin\theta\cos\theta + \cos\theta\sin\theta$$
$$= 2\sin\theta\cos\theta$$

EXAMPLE 3   Find an expression equivalent to each of the following.

$$\cos^2\frac{\theta}{2}, \quad \cos\frac{\theta}{2}, \quad \sin^2\frac{\theta}{2}, \quad \sin\frac{\theta}{2}$$

SOLUTION   Use the identities from Example 1.

$$\cos 2\theta = 2\cos^2\theta - 1$$

Thus, $\cos\theta = 2\cos^2\dfrac{\theta}{2} - 1$

$$\cos^2\frac{\theta}{2} = \frac{1 + \cos\theta}{2}$$

Also, $\cos\dfrac{\theta}{2} = \pm\sqrt{\dfrac{1 + \cos\theta}{2}}$.

$$\cos 2\theta = 1 - 2\sin^2\theta$$

Thus, $\sin^2\theta = \dfrac{1 - \cos 2\theta}{2}$

$$\sin^2\frac{\theta}{2} = \frac{1 - \cos\theta}{2}$$

Also, $\sin\dfrac{\theta}{2} = \pm\sqrt{\dfrac{1 - \cos\theta}{2}}$.

In the Exercises you will be asked to prove identities of the above types for the tangent function. These include

$$\tan 2\theta = \frac{2\tan\theta}{1 - \tan^2\theta} \quad \text{and} \quad \tan\frac{\theta}{2} = \pm\sqrt{\frac{1 - \cos\theta}{1 + \cos\theta}}.$$

For reference and comparison, the *double-angle* and *half-angle* *identities* on the preceding page are summarized in this chart.

$$\cos 2\theta = \begin{cases} \cos^2\theta - \sin^2\theta \\ 2\cos^2\theta - 1 \\ 1 - 2\sin^2\theta \end{cases} \qquad \sin 2\theta = 2\sin\theta\cos\theta \qquad \tan 2\theta = \frac{2\tan\theta}{1-\tan^2\theta}$$

$$\cos\frac{\theta}{2} = \pm\sqrt{\frac{1+\cos\theta}{2}} \qquad \sin\frac{\theta}{2} = \pm\sqrt{\frac{1-\cos\theta}{2}} \qquad \tan\frac{\theta}{2} = \pm\sqrt{\frac{1-\cos\theta}{1+\cos\theta}}$$

The angle sum, angle difference, double-angle, and half-angle identities may be used to simplify expressions.

EXAMPLE 4   Simplify $\dfrac{1-\cos 2\theta}{\sin 2\theta}$.

SOLUTION $\dfrac{1-\cos 2\theta}{\sin 2\theta} = \dfrac{1-(1-2\sin^2\theta)}{2\sin\theta\cos\theta}$

$$= \frac{2\sin^2\theta}{2\sin\theta\cos\theta}$$

$$= \frac{\sin\theta}{\cos\theta}$$

$$= \tan\theta$$

The double-angle and half-angle identities also are useful for solving trigonometric equations containing multiples of angle measures.

EXAMPLE 5   Solve $\sin 2x = 2\sin x$ for $0 \leq x < 2\pi$.

SOLUTION

$$\sin 2x = 2\sin x$$
$$2\sin x \cos x = 2\sin x$$
$$2\sin x \cos x - 2\sin x = 0$$
$$(2\sin x)(\cos x - 1) = 0$$

Therefore, $2\sin x = 0$ or $\cos x - 1 = 0$

$$\sin x = 0 \qquad\qquad \cos x = 1$$

Thus, $x = 0$ or $x = \pi$. $\qquad$ Thus, $x = 0$.

CHECK $\sin 2x \overset{?}{=} 2\sin x \qquad\qquad \sin 2x \overset{?}{=} 2\sin x$

$\sin 2(0) \overset{?}{=} 2\sin 0 \qquad\qquad \sin 2\pi \overset{?}{=} 2\sin \pi$

$0 = 0 \ \text{✔} \qquad\qquad\qquad 0 = 0 \ \text{✔}$

CLASSROOM EXERCISES

Approximate. Use a double-angle or half-angle identity.   Verify the identity.

1. $\sin 105°$ **2.** $\cos \dfrac{5\pi}{8}$ **3.** $\tan \theta + \cot \theta = \dfrac{2}{\sin 2\theta}$

Solve. Use the domain $0 \le x < 2\pi$. Check.

4. $\cos x = \sin \dfrac{1}{2}x$

EXERCISES

Ⓐ Approximate. Use a double-angle or half-angle identity.

1. $\sin 22\dfrac{1}{2}°$ **2.** $\cos 22\dfrac{1}{2}°$ **3.** $\cos 105°$ **4.** $\sin 67.5°$

5. $\sin \dfrac{7}{8}\pi$ **6.** $\cos \dfrac{3}{8}\pi$ **7.** $\tan \dfrac{1}{8}\pi$ **8.** $\cot \dfrac{7}{8}\pi$

Verify the identity.

9. $\cos 2\theta = \cos^4\theta - \sin^4\theta$ **10.** $\dfrac{1}{2}\cos \theta + \sin^2 \dfrac{\theta}{2} = \dfrac{1}{2}$ **11.** $\cos^2 \dfrac{\theta}{2} - \dfrac{1}{2}\cos \theta = \dfrac{1}{2}$

12. $\dfrac{\sin 2\theta}{1 - \cos 2\theta} = \cot \theta$ **13.** $\dfrac{1 - \tan^2\theta}{1 + \tan^2\theta} = \cos 2\theta$ **14.** $\tan 2\theta = \dfrac{2 \tan \theta}{1 - \tan^2\theta}$

15. $\tan \dfrac{\theta}{2} = \pm\sqrt{\dfrac{1 - \cos \theta}{1 + \cos \theta}}$ **16.** $\tan \dfrac{\theta}{2} = \dfrac{1 - \cos \theta}{\sin \theta}$ **17.** $\tan \dfrac{\theta}{2} = \dfrac{\sin \theta}{1 + \cos \theta}$

Solve. Use the domain $0 \le x < 2\pi$. Check.

18. $\cos 2x = \sin x$ **19.** $\sin x = 2 \sin \dfrac{1}{2}x$ **20.** $\tan 2x + \tan x = 0$

21. $\cot 2x - \cot x = 0$ **22.** $\tan 2x - \tan x = 0$ **23.** $\cot 2x + \cot x = 0$

Ⓑ **24.** $\tan 2x = \cot x$ **25.** $\cos 2x = 1 - \sin x$

26. $\tan 2x = 2 \sin x$ **27.** $2 \cot 2x = \csc x$

Verify each identity.

28. $\sin 3\theta = 3 \sin \theta - 4 \sin^3\theta$ **29.** $\cos 3\theta = 4 \cos^3\theta - 3 \cos \theta$

Ⓒ **30.** $\cos 4x = 8 \sin^4x - 8 \sin^2x + 1$ **31.** $\csc^2 2x - \sec^2 2x = 4 \cot 4x \cdot \csc 4x$

32. Show that $[r(\cos \theta + i \sin \theta)]^2 = r^2(\cos 2\theta + i \sin 2\theta)$.

33. Use the identity $[r(\cos \theta + i \sin \theta)]^n = r^n(\cos n\theta + i \sin n\theta)$ to evaluate $(\sqrt{3} + i)^{12}$. (Hint: Change to trigonometric form.)

15-8 INVERSE FUNCTIONS AND THEIR GRAPHS

The graph of the sine, cosine, or tangent function shows that many ordered pairs of each function have the same second coordinate.

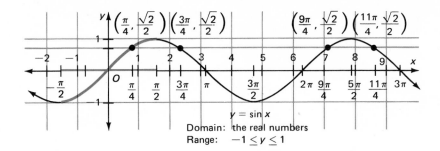

$y = \sin x$

Domain: the real numbers
Range: $-1 \le y \le 1$

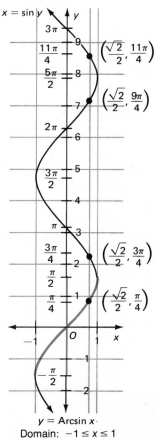

$x = \sin y$

$y = \text{Arcsin } x$
Domain: $-1 \le x \le 1$
Range: $-\dfrac{\pi}{2} \le y \le \dfrac{\pi}{2}$

Therefore, the inverse of each function, obtained by interchanging the members of the ordered pairs of the function, *is not* a function. Two ordered pairs of the inverse would have the same first member.

The inverse *is* a function only when the domain of the given function is restricted so that each value in the range occurs in only *one* ordered pair.

In the top diagram, red is used to show the part of the sine function where the domain is restricted to the numbers from $-\dfrac{\pi}{2}$ to $\dfrac{\pi}{2}$ $\left(-\dfrac{\pi}{2} \le x \le \dfrac{\pi}{2}\right)$. For this restricted domain, the inverse of the sine function also is a function. The *inverse sine function* may be defined by the sentence $x = \sin y,\ -\dfrac{\pi}{2} \le y \le \dfrac{\pi}{2}$. However, to have y "in terms of x" we write $y = \text{Arcsin } x$ (read Arc sine of x). The capital letter indicates that there is a restriction on the range of numbers possible for y. Arcsin x is the number from $-\dfrac{\pi}{2}$ to $\dfrac{\pi}{2}$ whose sine is x.

EXAMPLE 1 Find Arcsin $\frac{1}{2}$.

SOLUTION Write $\theta = $ Arcsin $\frac{1}{2}$.

θ is the number from $-\frac{\pi}{2}$

to $\frac{\pi}{2}$ whose sine is $\frac{1}{2}$.

Thus, $\theta = \frac{\pi}{6}$.

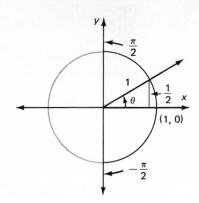

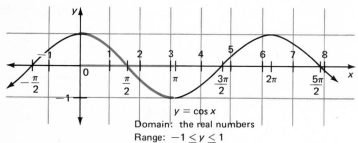

$y = \cos x$
Domain: the real numbers
Range: $-1 \leq y \leq 1$

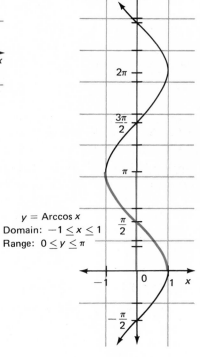

$y = $ Arccos x
Domain: $-1 \leq x \leq 1$
Range: $0 \leq y \leq \pi$

Restricting the domain of the cosine function to the numbers from 0 to π ($0 \leq x \leq \pi$) assures us that the inverse of the cosine function also is a function.

The sentence $x = \cos y$, $0 \leq y \leq \pi$, defines the *inverse cosine function*. However, to have y "in terms of x" we write

$y = $ Arccos x (read Arc cosine of x).

Arccos x is the number from 0 to π whose cosine is x.

EXAMPLE 2 Find Arccos $\left(-\frac{\sqrt{2}}{2}\right)$.

SOLUTION Write $\theta = $ Arccos $\left(-\frac{\sqrt{2}}{2}\right)$.

θ is the number from 0 to π whose

cosine is $-\frac{\sqrt{2}}{2}$. Thus, $\theta = \frac{3\pi}{4}$.

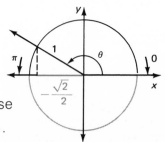

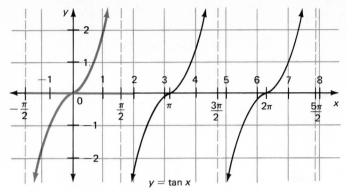

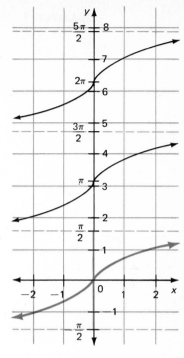

Domain: the real numbers except for odd integral multiples of $\frac{\pi}{2}$

Range: the real numbers

Restricting the domain of the tangent function to the numbers between $-\frac{\pi}{2}$ and $\frac{\pi}{2}$ $\left(-\frac{\pi}{2} < x < \frac{\pi}{2}\right)$ assures us that the inverse of the tangent function also is a function. For the *inverse tangent function*, we write $y = $ Arctan x (read Arc tangent of x). Arctan x is the number between $-\frac{\pi}{2}$ and $\frac{\pi}{2}$ whose tangent is x.

$y = $ Arctan x

Domain: the real numbers

Range: $-\frac{\pi}{2} < y < \frac{\pi}{2}$

EXAMPLE 3 Find Arctan (-1).

SOLUTION Write $\theta = $ Arctan (-1).

θ is the number from $-\frac{\pi}{2}$ to $\frac{\pi}{2}$ whose tangent is -1.

Thus, $\theta = -\frac{\pi}{4}$.

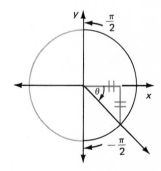

Sometimes a number x from the range of the Arc cosine function, for example, is in the domain of the sine function. Then the expression sin (Arccos x) represents a number in the range of the sine function.

EXAMPLE 4 Find $\sin\left(\text{Arccos}\left(-\frac{1}{2}\right)\right)$.

SOLUTION $\quad \sin\left(\text{Arccos}\left(-\frac{1}{2}\right)\right) = \sin\frac{2\pi}{3}$

$$= \frac{\sqrt{3}}{2}$$

EXAMPLE 5 Find $\text{Arccos}\left(\tan\frac{\pi}{6}\right)$. Find $\text{Arccos}\left(\tan\frac{\pi}{3}\right)$.

SOLUTION $\quad \text{Arccos}\left(\tan\frac{\pi}{6}\right) = \text{Arccos}\frac{\sqrt{3}}{3}$

$\qquad\qquad\qquad\quad \doteq \text{Arccos}\,(0.5773)$

$\qquad\qquad\qquad\quad \doteq 0.9553$

$\qquad\qquad\qquad\qquad\qquad\qquad \tan\frac{\pi}{3} = \sqrt{3}$

$\sqrt{3}$ is not in the domain of the Arc cosine function (the numbers from -1 to 1). Therefore, $\text{Arccos}\left(\tan\frac{\pi}{3}\right)$ is undefined.

EXAMPLE 6 Find $\cos\left(\text{Arcsin}\left(-\frac{3}{5}\right)\right)$.

SOLUTION 1 Use θ for $\text{Arcsin}\left(-\frac{3}{5}\right)$.

Then $\sin\theta = -\frac{3}{5}$.

Draw a diagram.
By the Pythagorean Theorem,
$\cos\theta = \frac{4}{5}$.

Therefore,
$\cos\left(\text{Arcsin}\left(-\frac{3}{5}\right)\right) = \frac{4}{5}$.

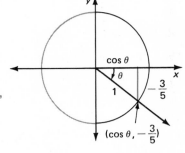

EXAMPLE 7 Solve $\text{Arcsin}\,x = \text{Arccos}\frac{\sqrt{3}}{2}$.

SOLUTION $\qquad \text{Arcsin}\,x = \text{Arccos}\frac{\sqrt{3}}{2}$

$$\text{Arcsin}\,x = \frac{\pi}{6}$$

Therefore, $x = \sin\frac{\pi}{6}$

$$x = \frac{1}{2}$$

CHECK The check is left for the student.

CLASSROOM EXERCISES

Simplify.

1. Arcsin 1

2. Arcsin 0

3. Arccos (-1)

4. Arccos $\frac{1}{2}\sqrt{3}$

5. Arctan (-1)

6. Arctan $\sqrt{3}$

7. sin $\left(\text{Arccos }\frac{1}{2}\right)$

8. sin (Arcsin 0.3)

Solve.

9. Arctan x = Arcsin $\frac{3}{5}$

10. Arccos x = Arcsin $\frac{1}{2}\sqrt{3}$

EXERCISES

A   Simplify.

1. Arcsin $\frac{\sqrt{3}}{2}$

2. Arcsin $\left(-\frac{\sqrt{2}}{2}\right)$

3. Arccos $\left(-\frac{\sqrt{3}}{2}\right)$

4. Arccos $\frac{\sqrt{3}}{2}$

5. Arccos $\frac{1}{2}$

6. Arccos $\left(-\frac{1}{2}\right)$

7. Arctan $-\frac{1}{3}\sqrt{3}$

8. Arctan $\sqrt{3}$

9. sin (Arctan 1)

10. cos (Arcsin 0)

11. tan $\left(\text{Arccos }\frac{1}{2}\sqrt{3}\right)$

12. sin (Arccos (-1))

13. sin (Arcsin 0.4)

14. cos (Arccos (-0.6))

15. tan (Arctan (-2))

16. sin (Arcsin 0.9)

17. cos $\left(\text{Arcsin }\frac{8}{17}\right)$

18. cos $\left(\text{Arcsin }\frac{15}{17}\right)$

19. cos $\left(\text{Arcsin }\left(-\frac{15}{17}\right)\right)$

20. sin $\left(\text{Arccos }\left(-\frac{5}{13}\right)\right)$

Solve.

21. Arcsin $2x$ = Arccos $\frac{1}{2}\sqrt{3}$

22. Arccos $2x$ = Arcsin $\frac{1}{2}$

23. Arccos $\frac{x}{2}$ = Arcsin $\frac{1}{2}$

B   Simplify.

24. sin 2 $\left(\text{Arctan }\frac{12}{5}\right)$

25. cos 2 $\left(\text{Arctan }\left(-\frac{12}{5}\right)\right)$

26. sin $\left(\frac{1}{2}\text{ Arcsin }\frac{3}{5}\right)$

C   **27.** sin $\left(\text{Arccos }\frac{\sqrt{3}}{2} + \text{Arctan }(-1)\right)$

28. cos $\left(\text{Arctan }\frac{3}{4} - \text{Arcsin }\frac{1}{2}\right)$

Verify.

29. Arctan 2 − Arctan 1 = Arctan $\frac{1}{3}$

30. Arctan x + Arctan y = Arctan $\frac{x+y}{1-xy}$

Solve.

31. Arctan $(x + \sqrt{3})$ − Arctan $(x - \sqrt{3})$ = Arctan $\sqrt{3}$

32. Arctan $3x$ + Arctan $2x$ = $\frac{1}{4}\pi$

CHAPTER REVIEW

1. Given $\sec \theta = \sqrt{3}$, find the possible values for $\tan \theta$.   [15-1]

2. Express $\cot \theta$ in terms of $\sin \theta$.   **3.** Simplify $\dfrac{\sin x \cdot \cot x + \cos x}{\sin x \cdot \cos x}$.

Verify each identity.   [15-2]

4. $\cos x \csc x = \cot x$ **5.** $\sin x + \cot x \cos x = \csc x$ **6.** $\dfrac{1 - \cos^2 x}{\tan x} = \sin x \cos x$

7. Triangle ABC has $b = 10$, $c = 12$ and $m \angle A = 35°$.   Find a.   [15-3]

8. Find the measure of the smallest angle of a triangle having sides that measure 160, 120 and 100.

Find the area of triangle ABC.   [15-4, 15-5]

9. $a = 28$, $b = 34$, $m \angle C = 50°$ **10.** $a = 10$, $m \angle B = 40°$, $m \angle A = 40°$

Find the indicated measure for triangle ABC.

11. $a = 4$, $b = 8$, $m \angle B = 35°$.   Find $m \angle A$.   **12.** $m \angle A = 80°$, $m \angle C = 30°$, $c = 6$.   Find a.

13. $a = 8$, $c = 7$, $m \angle B = 42°$.   Find b.   **14.** $m \angle B = 110°$, $m \angle C = 50°$, $c = 6$.   Find a.

15. Prove $\sin \left(\dfrac{3\pi}{2} - \theta \right) = -\cos \theta$.   [15-6]

Approximate.   Use an identity.   ($\sqrt{6} \doteq 2.449$, $\sqrt{2} \doteq 1.414$)

16. $\cos (-75°)$ **17.** $\sin 195°$ **18.** $\cos 30° \cos 15° - \sin 30° \sin 15°$

19. Prove $\dfrac{1 - \cos 2\theta}{2 \sin \theta \cos \theta} = \tan \theta$.   [15-7]

Simplify.

20. $\tan 22°30'$ **21.** $\sin \left(-\dfrac{\pi}{12} \right)$

Simplify.   [15-8]

22. $\text{Arctan} \left(-\dfrac{\sqrt{3}}{3} \right)$ **23.** $\cos \left(\text{Arcsin} \dfrac{\sqrt{3}}{2} \right)$ **24.** $\text{Arcsin} (\sin \pi)$

CAPSULE REVIEW

Write the letter of the best response.

1. Which equation is *not* an identity?

   a. $\sin \theta \csc \theta = 1$ **b.** $\cot^2 \theta = 1 - \csc^2 \theta$

   c. $\sin \theta = \cos \theta \tan \theta$ **d.** $\cos^2 \theta = 1 - \sin^2 \theta$

2. The measure of the largest angle in a triangle whose sides have lengths
$\sqrt{3}$, 3 and $2\sqrt{3}$ is

    a. 45°   **b.** 60°   **c.** 90°   **d.** 150°

3. To construct a triangle of greatest possible area having sides of 10 cm and
15 cm, the angle included by these sides must be

    a. an obtuse angle   **b.** an acute angle with measure less than 45°

    c. a right angle   **d.** an acute angle with measure greater than 45°

4. $\sin x \tan x + \cos x =$

    a. $\cos^2 x$ **b.** $\cot x$ **c.** $2 \sin x$ **d.** $\sec x$

5. $\sin 39° =$

    a. $\sin \theta \cos (\theta - 39°) - \sin (\theta - 39°) \cos \theta$

    b. $\sin (\theta + 39°) \cos (-39°) + \sin (-39°) \cos (\theta + 39°)$

    c. $\sin (\theta + 39°) \cos 39° - \sin 39° \cos (\theta + 39°)$

    d. $\sin (\theta - 39°) \cos 39° - \sin 39° \cos (\theta - 39°)$

6. $\cos 2\theta \neq$

    a. $\cos (\theta + \theta)$ **b.** $1 - 2 \sin^2 \theta$

    c. $\cos^2 \theta - 2 \sin^2 \theta$ **d.** $2 \cos^2 \theta - 1$

7. $\text{Arcsin} \left(\sin \dfrac{5\pi}{6} \right) =$

    a. $\dfrac{\pi}{6}$ **b.** $\dfrac{\pi}{3}$ **c.** $\dfrac{5\pi}{6}$ **d.** $\dfrac{1}{2}$

CHAPTER TEST

1. Write the three reciprocal identities.   **2.** Write the three Pythagorean identities.

3. Verify that $\sec x - \cos x$ and $\tan x \sin x$ are members of an identity.

4. Find x.

5. Find θ in degrees.

6. Find the area of the triangle.   **7.** Find x.   **8.** Find the area of parallelogram P.

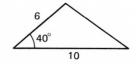

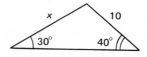

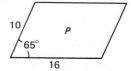

9. Find the length of the longer diagonal of rhombus R.

10. Use the identity
$\cos(\theta - \phi) = \cos\theta\cos\phi + \sin\theta\sin\phi$
to prove $\cos(\theta - \pi) = -\cos\theta$.

11. Use the identity
$\sin(\theta + \phi) = \sin\theta\cos\phi + \cos\theta\sin\phi$
to prove $\sin\left(\theta + \dfrac{\pi}{2}\right) = \cos\theta$.

12. Use an identity to approximate $\cos 15°$.

13. Use an identity to approximate $\sin 22.5°$.

14. Find Arccos 0.5.

15. Sketch a graph of $y = \text{Arcsin } x$.

Write the letter of the best response.

16. How is the expression $\cos x \tan x + \dfrac{1}{\csc x}$ written in terms of $\sin x$?

   a. $2\sin x$ **b.** $\sin^2 x$ **c.** $\pm\sin x\sqrt{1 - \sin^2 x}$ **d.** $\dfrac{1}{\sin x}$ **e.** $\sin x + \dfrac{1}{\sin x}$

17. What is the cosine of angle θ below?

   a. -0.4 **b.** -0.2 **c.** 0.2 **d.** 0.4 **e.** 0.5

  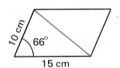

18. What is the sine of angle ϕ above?

   a. $\dfrac{15}{11\cos 70°}$ **b.** $\dfrac{15\cos 70°}{11}$ **c.** $\dfrac{11\cos 70°}{15}$ **d.** $\dfrac{15\sin 70°}{11}$ **e.** $\dfrac{11\sin 70°}{15}$

19. What is the length of the shorter diagonal in the parallelogram shown above?

   a. 15.2 cm   **b.** 14.2 cm   **c.** 13.2 cm   **d.** 12.2 cm   **e.** 11.2 cm

20. $\cos\left(\dfrac{\pi}{2} + \phi\right) =$

   a. $\cos\phi$ **b.** $-\cos\phi$ **c.** $\sin\phi$ **d.** $-\sin\phi$ **e.** $\cos\phi - \sin\phi$

21. $\tan\dfrac{\pi}{12} =$

   a. $\sqrt{3} - 2$ **b.** $-\sqrt{3} - 2$ **c.** $2 - \sqrt{3}$ **d.** $2 + \sqrt{3}$ **e.** $\dfrac{\sqrt{3}}{3}$

22. $\sin(\text{Arccos } 1) =$

   a. -1 **b.** 0 **c.** $\dfrac{\pi}{2}$ **d.** $\dfrac{\pi}{4}$ **e.** $-\pi$

CUMULATIVE REVIEW

Give the word or symbol to complete each sentence.

1. $\begin{bmatrix} 1 & 3 \\ 2 & 4 \end{bmatrix}$ is the __?__ of $\begin{bmatrix} -2 & \frac{3}{2} \\ 1 & -\frac{1}{2} \end{bmatrix}$

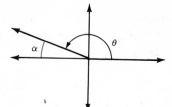

2. In the graph at right, angle α is called the __?__ of angle θ.

3. The name of the symbol $n!$ is __?__ .

4. For the function $y = a \sin bx$, $|a|$ is called the __?__ .

5. Approximations for log 5.783 and sin (78°46′) can be found by the method of __?__ .

6. The matrix $\begin{bmatrix} 1 & 0 \\ 0 & 1 \end{bmatrix}$ is the two-by-two __?__ matrix.

Briefly answer each question. Refer to the concept suggested.

7. The matrix $\begin{bmatrix} 2 & -1 \\ 1 & -\frac{1}{2} \end{bmatrix}$ does not have a multiplicative inverse. Why?

8. The number of committees of three people that can be chosen from ten people may be found by using $_{10}C_3$. Why?

9. For the polynomial function $y = (x + 3)^2(x - 1)^2$, y is never negative. Why?

10. $\sin (\text{Arcsin } x) = x$. Why?
11. $\tan 90°$ is undefined. Why?

Simplify.

12. $\dfrac{y(x - y)}{x^2 + y^2 + 2xy} \div \dfrac{x^2 + y^2 - 2xy}{x^2 + xy}$

13. $\dfrac{x^2 + 2xy + y^2}{x^2 + xy} \cdot \dfrac{x^2}{x^2 - y^2}$

Solve.

14. $\dfrac{3}{x - 1} - \dfrac{2}{x + 2} = \dfrac{x^2 - 4}{x^2 + x - 2}$

15. $\dfrac{3x - 1}{x + 2} = \dfrac{6x}{2x + 5}$

16. Write the equation of the line which has the slope $-\dfrac{2}{3}$ and contains the point $(-4, 3)$.

Solve for x and y.

17. $2x + 3y = 12$
    $x + 9y = 16$

18. $\dfrac{x}{3} + 3y = 15$
    $4x + \dfrac{y}{4} = 37$

19. $bx + cy = 2ab$
    $ax + cy = a^2 + b^2$

Simplify.

Multiply

20. $\sqrt{\dfrac{x^3}{y^3}}$ **21.** $\sqrt{\dfrac{2x}{9y}}$ **22.** $(3-i)(2+i)$

Solve.

23. $6x^2 - x = 1$ **24.** $\sqrt{2x+3} - \sqrt{x+1} = \sqrt{4-x}$

25. Graph the solutions of the inequality $3x^2 + 11x < 4$.

26. The square of a number exceeds the product of the number and 12 by 133.   Find the number.

27. Find the value of $\log_2 81$.   **28.** Solve $\log x - \log (x - 1) = 2$.

Solve the system.

29. $3x^2 - 2xy = 45$ **30.** $x^2 + y^2 = 5$
    $x + y = 0$ $x^2 + 3y^2 = 13$

31. Find the eighth term of the sequence $-4, 1, -\frac{1}{4}, \cdots$.

Solve.   Evaluate.

32. $x^4 - 34x^2 + 225 = 0$.   **33.** $_8P_3$ **34.** $_7C_2$ **35.** $4!$

36. In how many ways can a committee of three students be chosen from a class of 20 students?

37. If four cards are drawn from a deck of 52 cards, what is the probability that all four will be hearts?

Find the inverse of each matrix.

38. $\begin{bmatrix} 3 & 8 \\ 2 & 4 \end{bmatrix}$ **39.** $\begin{bmatrix} 2 & \frac{1}{2} \\ -4 & -1 \end{bmatrix}$

Solve. Use a matrix equation.   Solve. Use Cramer's Rule.

40. $2x - 7y = 1$ **41.** $4x + y = 2$
    $13x + 15y = 2$ $6x - \frac{1}{2}y = \frac{5}{2}$

42. Convert $\dfrac{11\pi^R}{12}$ to degree measure.

Find the value of each function.

43. $\text{Arccos}\left(-\dfrac{1}{2}\right)$ **44.** $\text{Arctan}\,(-1)$ **45.** $\text{Arcsin}\left(\sin \dfrac{\pi}{7}\right)$

46. Find the measures of b, c, and $\angle A$ in triangle ABC when $m\angle B = 40°$, $m\angle C = 80°$, and $a = 100$.

47. Give the period and amplitude of the function $y = 2 \sin \dfrac{\theta}{2}$.

Verify each identity.

48. $\cos x \cot x = \dfrac{\cos^2 x}{\sin x}$

49. $\dfrac{1 + \cot x}{\cos x} = \sec x + \csc x$

Write the letter of the best response.

50. Give the period and amplitude of $y = -6 \sin \left(\dfrac{2\pi}{3} \theta \right)$.

  a. period is 3π, amplitude is 6   **b.** period is 3, amplitude is -6

  c. period is 3, amplitude is 6   **d.** period is 6, amplitude is 6

51. $\dfrac{\sin x}{\csc x - \cot x} =$

  a. $1 + \cos x$ **b.** $1 - \cos x$ **c.** $\dfrac{1}{1 - \cos x}$ **d.** $\dfrac{1}{1 + \cos x}$ **e.** none of these

52. Simplify $\cos 82° \cos 22° + \sin 82° \sin 22°$

  a. $\cos 104°$ **b.** $\sin 104°$ **c.** $-\cos 104°$ **d.** $\dfrac{\sqrt{3}}{2}$ **e.** $\dfrac{1}{2}$

53. Simplify $\sqrt{\dfrac{1 + \cos \frac{\pi}{8}}{2}}$.

  a. $\cos \dfrac{\pi}{16}$ **b.** $\sin \dfrac{\pi}{16}$ **c.** $\cos \dfrac{\pi}{4}$ **d.** $\sin \dfrac{\pi}{4}$ **e.** none of these

54. The probability that student A will solve a problem is $\dfrac{2}{3}$. The probability that student B will solve the problem is $\dfrac{1}{2}$. Find the probability that neither will solve the problem.

  a. $\dfrac{1}{3}$ **b.** $\dfrac{3}{5}$ **c.** $\dfrac{1}{6}$ **d.** $\dfrac{2}{5}$ **e.** $\dfrac{1}{12}$

55. For the students in Exercise 54, find the probability that at least one will not solve the problem.

  a. $\dfrac{1}{2}$ **b.** $\dfrac{2}{3}$ **c.** $\dfrac{5}{6}$ **d.** $\dfrac{1}{3}$ **e.** $\dfrac{1}{6}$

56. Simplify $\left(\dfrac{x^4 \cdot y^0 \cdot z^{-\frac{3}{2}}}{xz^6} \right)^{-\frac{2}{3}}$

  a. $x^4 z$ **b.** $\dfrac{x^2}{z^5}$ **c.** $\dfrac{z^5}{x^2}$ **d.** $\dfrac{x^2}{z^5 y^{\frac{2}{3}}}$ **e.** $\dfrac{z^5 y^{\frac{2}{3}}}{x^2}$

57. If $A = \begin{bmatrix} 2 & 3 \\ -1 & 0 \end{bmatrix}$ and $B = \begin{bmatrix} 1 & -1 \\ 4 & 2 \end{bmatrix}$, then AB equals

  a. $\begin{bmatrix} 3 & 3 \\ 6 & 12 \end{bmatrix}$ **b.** $\begin{bmatrix} 9 & 4 \\ -1 & 1 \end{bmatrix}$ **c.** $\begin{bmatrix} 1 & 3 \\ 6 & 14 \end{bmatrix}$ **d.** $\begin{bmatrix} 2 & -3 \\ -4 & 0 \end{bmatrix}$ **e.** $\begin{bmatrix} 14 & 4 \\ -1 & 1 \end{bmatrix}$

Table I · Logarithms of Numbers

N	0	1	2	3	4	5	6	7	8	9
1.0	0000	0043	0086	0128	0170	0212	0253	0294	0334	0374
1.1	0414	0453	0492	0531	0569	0607	0645	0682	0719	0755
1.2	0792	0828	0864	0899	0934	0969	1004	1038	1072	1106
1.3	1139	1173	1206	1239	1271	1303	1335	1367	1399	1430
1.4	1461	1492	1523	1553	1584	1614	1644	1673	1703	1732
1.5	1761	1790	1818	1847	1875	1903	1931	1959	1987	2014
1.6	2041	2068	2095	2122	2148	2175	2201	2227	2253	2279
1.7	2304	2330	2355	2380	2405	2430	2455	2480	2504	2529
1.8	2553	2577	2601	2625	2648	2672	2695	2718	2742	2765
1.9	2788	2810	2833	2856	2878	2900	2923	2945	2967	2989
2.0	3010	3032	3054	3075	3096	3118	3139	3160	3181	3201
2.1	3222	3243	3263	3284	3304	3324	3345	3365	3385	3404
2.2	3424	3444	3464	3483	3502	3522	3541	3560	3579	3598
2.3	3617	3636	3655	3674	3692	3711	3729	3747	3766	3784
2.4	3802	3820	3838	3856	3874	3892	3909	3927	3945	3962
2.5	3979	3997	4014	4031	4048	4065	4082	4099	4116	4133
2.6	4150	4166	4183	4200	4216	4232	4249	4265	4281	4298
2.7	4314	4330	4346	4362	4378	4393	4409	4425	4440	4456
2.8	4472	4487	4502	4518	4533	4548	4564	4579	4594	4609
2.9	4624	4639	4654	4669	4683	4698	4713	4728	4742	4757
3.0	4771	4786	4800	4814	4829	4843	4857	4871	4886	4900
3.1	4914	4928	4942	4955	4969	4983	4997	5011	5024	5038
3.2	5051	5065	5079	5092	5105	5119	5132	5145	5159	5172
3.3	5185	5198	5211	5224	5237	5250	5263	5276	5289	5302
3.4	5315	5328	5340	5353	5366	5378	5391	5403	5416	5428
3.5	5441	5453	5465	5478	5490	5502	5514	5527	5539	5551
3.6	5563	5575	5587	5599	5611	5623	5635	5647	5658	5670
3.7	5682	5694	5705	5717	5729	5740	5752	5763	5775	5786
3.8	5798	5809	5821	5832	5843	5855	5866	5877	5888	5899
3.9	5911	5922	5933	5944	5955	5966	5977	5988	5999	6010
4.0	6021	6031	6042	6053	6064	6075	6085	6096	6107	6117
4.1	6128	6138	6149	6160	6170	6180	6191	6201	6212	6222
4.2	6232	6243	6253	6263	6274	6284	6294	6304	6314	6325
4.3	6335	6345	6355	6365	6375	6385	6395	6405	6415	6425
4.4	6435	6444	6454	6464	6474	6484	6493	6503	6513	6522
4.5	6532	6542	6551	6561	6571	6580	6590	6599	6609	6618
4.6	6628	6637	6646	6656	6665	6675	6684	6693	6702	6712
4.7	6721	6730	6739	6749	6758	6767	6776	6785	6794	6803
4.8	6812	6821	6830	6839	6848	6857	6866	6875	6884	6893
4.9	6902	6911	6920	6928	6937	6946	6955	6964	6972	6981
5.0	6990	6998	7007	7016	7024	7033	7042	7050	7059	7067
5.1	7076	7084	7093	7101	7110	7118	7126	7135	7143	7152
5.2	7160	7168	7177	7185	7193	7202	7210	7218	7226	7235
5.3	7243	7251	7259	7267	7275	7284	7292	7300	7308	7316
5.4	7324	7332	7340	7348	7356	7364	7372	7380	7388	7396

TABLE I · LOGARITHMS OF NUMBERS **585**

Logarithms of Numbers

N	0	1	2	3	4	5	6	7	8	9
5.5	7404	7412	7419	7427	7435	7443	7451	7459	7466	7474
5.6	7482	7490	7497	7505	7513	7520	7528	7536	7543	7551
5.7	7559	7566	7574	7582	7589	7597	7604	7612	7619	7627
5.8	7634	7642	7649	7657	7664	7672	7679	7686	7694	7701
5.9	7709	7716	7723	7731	7738	7745	7752	7760	7767	7774
6.0	7782	7789	7796	7803	7810	7818	7825	7832	7839	7846
6.1	7853	7860	7868	7875	7882	7889	7896	7903	7910	7917
6.2	7924	7931	7938	7945	7952	7959	7966	7973	7980	7987
6.3	7993	8000	8007	8014	8021	8028	8035	8041	8048	8055
6.4	8062	8069	8075	8082	8089	8096	8102	8109	8116	8122
6.5	8129	8136	8142	8149	8156	8162	8169	8176	8182	8189
6.6	8195	8202	8209	8215	8222	8228	8235	8241	8248	8254
6.7	8261	8267	8274	8280	8287	8293	8299	8306	8312	8319
6.8	8325	8331	8338	8344	8351	8357	8363	8370	8376	8382
6.9	8388	8395	8401	8407	8414	8420	8426	8432	8439	8445
7.0	8451	8457	8463	8470	8476	8482	8488	8494	8500	8506
7.1	8513	8519	8525	8531	8537	8543	8549	8555	8561	8567
7.2	8573	8579	8585	8591	8597	8603	8609	8615	8621	8627
7.3	8633	8639	8645	8651	8657	8663	8669	8675	8681	8686
7.4	8692	8698	8704	8710	8716	8722	8727	8733	8739	8745
7.5	8751	8756	8762	8768	8774	8779	8785	8791	8797	8802
7.6	8808	8814	8820	8825	8831	8837	8842	8848	8854	8859
7.7	8865	8871	8876	8882	8887	8893	8899	8904	8910	8915
7.8	8921	8927	8932	8938	8943	8949	8954	8960	8965	8971
7.9	8976	8982	8987	8993	8998	9004	9009	9015	9020	9025
8.0	9031	9036	9042	9047	9053	9058	9063	9069	9074	9079
8.1	9085	9090	9096	9101	9106	9112	9117	9122	9128	9133
8.2	9138	9143	9149	9154	9159	9165	9170	9175	9180	9186
8.3	9191	9196	9201	9206	9212	9217	9222	9227	9232	9238
8.4	9243	9248	9253	9258	9263	9269	9274	9279	9284	9289
8.5	9294	9299	9304	9309	9315	9320	9325	9330	9335	9340
8.6	9345	9350	9355	9360	9365	9370	9375	9380	9385	9390
8.7	9395	9400	9405	9410	9415	9420	9425	9430	9435	9440
8.8	9445	9450	9455	9460	9465	9469	9474	9479	9484	9489
8.9	9494	9499	9504	9509	9513	9518	9523	9528	9533	9538
9.0	9542	9547	9552	9557	9562	9566	9571	9576	9581	9586
9.1	9590	9595	9600	9605	9609	9614	9619	9624	9628	9633
9.2	9638	9643	9647	9652	9657	9661	9666	9671	9675	9680
9.3	9685	9689	9694	9699	9703	9708	9713	9717	9722	9727
9.4	9731	9736	9741	9745	9750	9754	9759	9763	9768	9773
9.5	9777	9782	9786	9791	9795	9800	9805	9809	9814	9818
9.6	9823	9827	9832	9836	9841	9845	9850	9854	9859	9863
9.7	9868	9872	9877	9881	9886	9890	9894	9899	9903	9908
9.8	9912	9917	9921	9926	9930	9934	9939	9943	9948	9952
9.9	9956	9961	9965	9969	9974	9978	9983	9987	9991	9996

Table II · Values of Trigonometric Functions

Degrees	Radians	sin	tan		cos		
0°00'	0.0000	0.0000	0.0000	-----	1.0000	1.5708	90°00'
10'	029	0.0029	0.0029	343.8	1.0000	679	50'
20'	058	0.0058	0.0058	171.9	1.0000	650	40'
30'	0.0087	0.0087	0.0087	114.6	1.0000	1.5621	30'
40'	116	0.0116	0.0116	85.94	0.9999	592	20'
50'	145	0.0145	0.0145	68.75	0.9999	563	10'
1°00'	0.0175	0.0175	0.0175	57.29	0.9998	1.5533	89°00'
10'	204	0.0204	0.0204	49.10	0.9998	504	50'
20'	233	0.0233	0.0233	42.96	0.9997	475	40'
30'	0.0262	0.0262	0.0262	38.19	0.9997	1.5446	30'
40'	291	0.0291	0.0291	34.37	0.9996	417	20'
50'	320	0.0320	0.0320	31.24	0.9995	388	10'
2°00'	0.0349	0.0349	0.0349	28.64	0.9994	1.5359	88°00'
10'	378	0.0378	0.0378	26.43	0.9993	330	50'
20'	407	0.0407	0.0407	24.54	0.9992	301	40'
30'	0.0436	0.0436	0.0437	22.90	0.9990	1.5272	30'
40'	465	0.0465	0.0466	21.47	0.9989	243	20'
50'	495	0.0494	0.0495	20.21	0.9988	213	10'
3°00'	0.0524	0.0523	0.0524	19.08	0.9986	1.5184	87°00'
10'	553	0.0552	0.0553	18.07	0.9985	155	50'
20'	582	0.0581	0.0582	17.17	0.9983	126	40'
30'	0.0611	0.0610	0.0612	16.35	0.9981	1.5097	30'
40'	640	0.0640	0.0641	15.60	0.9980	068	20'
50'	669	0.0669	0.0670	14.92	0.9978	039	10'
4°00'	0.0698	0.0698	0.0699	14.30	0.9976	1.5010	86°00'
10'	727	0.0727	0.0729	13.73	0.9974	1.4981	50'
20'	756	0.0756	0.0758	13.20	0.9971	952	40'
30'	0.0785	0.0785	0.0787	12.71	0.9969	1.4923	30'
40'	814	0.0814	0.0816	12.25	0.9967	893	20'
50'	844	0.0843	0.0846	11.83	0.9964	864	10'
5°00'	0.0873	0.0872	0.0875	11.43	0.9962	1.4835	85°00'
10'	902	0.0901	0.0904	11.06	0.9959	806	50'
20'	931	0.0929	0.0934	10.71	0.9957	777	40'
30'	0.0960	0.0958	0.0963	10.39	0.9954	1.4748	30'
40'	989	0.0987	0.0992	10.08	0.9951	719	20'
50'	0.1018	0.1016	0.1022	9.788	0.9948	690	10'
6°00'	0.1047	0.1045	0.1051	9.514	0.9945	1.4661	84°00'
10'	076	0.1074	0.1080	9.255	0.9942	632	50'
20'	105	0.1103	0.1110	9.010	0.9939	603	40'
30'	0.1134	0.1132	0.1139	8.777	0.9936	1.4573	30'
40'	164	0.1161	0.1169	8.556	0.9932	544	20'
50'	193	0.1190	0.1198	8.345	0.9929	515	10'
7°00'	0.1222	0.1219	0.1228	8.144	0.9925	1.4486	83°00'
10'	251	0.1248	0.1257	7.953	0.9922	457	50'
20'	280	0.1276	0.1287	7.770	0.9918	428	40'
30'	0.1309	0.1305	0.1317	7.596	0.9914	1.4399	30'
40'	338	0.1334	0.1346	7.429	0.9911	370	20'
50'	367	0.1363	0.1376	7.269	0.9907	341	10'
8°00'	0.1396	0.1392	0.1405	7.115	0.9903	1.4312	82°00'
10'	425	0.1421	0.1435	6.968	0.9899	283	50'
20'	454	0.1449	0.1465	6.827	0.9894	254	40'
30'	0.1484	0.1478	0.1495	6.691	0.9890	1.4224	30'
40'	513	0.1507	0.1524	6.561	0.9886	195	20'
50'	542	0.1536	0.1554	6.435	0.9881	166	10'
9°00'	0.1571	0.1564	0.1584	6.314	0.9877	1.4137	81°00'
		cos		tan	sin	Radians	Degrees

Degrees	Radians	sin	tan		cos		
9°00'	0.1571	0.1564	0.1584	6.314	0.9877	1.4137	81°00'
10'	600	0.1593	0.1614	6.197	0.9872	108	50'
20'	629	0.1622	0.1644	6.084	0.9868	079	40'
30'	0.1658	0.1650	0.1673	5.976	0.9863	1.4050	30'
40'	687	0.1679	0.1703	5.871	0.9858	1.4021	20'
50'	716	0.1708	0.1733	5.769	0.9853	1.3992	10'
10°00'	0.1745	0.1736	0.1763	5.671	0.9848	1.3963	80°00'
10'	774	0.1765	0.1793	5.576	0.9843	934	50'
20'	804	0.1794	0.1823	5.485	0.9838	904	40'
30'	0.1833	0.1822	0.1853	5.396	0.9833	1.3875	30'
40'	862	0.1851	0.1883	5.309	0.9827	846	20'
50'	891	0.1880	0.1914	5.226	0.9822	817	10'
11°00'	0.1920	0.1908	0.1944	5.145	0.9816	1.3788	79°00'
10'	949	0.1937	0.1974	5.066	0.9811	759	50'
20'	978	0.1965	0.2004	4.989	0.9805	730	40'
30'	0.2007	0.1994	0.2035	4.915	0.9799	1.3701	30'
40'	036	0.2022	0.2065	4.843	0.9793	672	20'
50'	065	0.2051	0.2095	4.773	0.9787	643	10'
12°00'	0.2094	0.2079	0.2126	4.705	0.9781	1.3614	78°00'
10'	123	0.2108	0.2156	4.638	0.9775	584	50'
20'	153	0.2136	0.2186	4.574	0.9769	555	40'
30'	0.2182	0.2164	0.2217	4.511	0.9763	1.3526	30'
40'	211	0.2193	0.2247	4.449	0.9757	497	20'
50'	240	0.2221	0.2278	4.390	0.9750	468	10'
13°00'	0.2269	0.2250	0.2309	4.331	0.9744	1.3439	77°00'
10'	298	0.2278	0.2339	4.275	0.9737	410	50'
20'	327	0.2306	0.2370	4.219	0.9730	381	40'
30'	0.2356	0.2334	0.2401	4.165	0.9724	1.3352	30'
40'	385	0.2363	0.2432	4.113	0.9717	323	20'
50'	414	0.2391	0.2462	4.061	0.9710	294	10'
14°00'	0.2443	0.2419	0.2493	4.011	0.9703	1.3265	76°00'
10'	473	0.2447	0.2524	3.962	0.9696	235	50'
20'	502	0.2476	0.2555	3.914	0.9689	206	40'
30'	0.2531	0.2504	0.2586	3.867	0.9681	1.3177	30'
40'	560	0.2532	0.2617	3.821	0.9674	148	20'
50'	589	0.2560	0.2648	3.776	0.9667	119	10'
15°00'	0.2618	0.2588	0.2679	3.732	0.9659	1.3090	75°00'
10'	647	0.2616	0.2711	3.689	0.9652	061	50'
20'	676	0.2644	0.2742	3.647	0.9644	032	40'
30'	0.2705	0.2672	0.2773	3.606	0.9636	1.3003	30'
40'	734	0.2700	0.2805	3.566	0.9628	1.2974	20'
50'	763	0.2728	0.2836	3.526	0.9621	945	10'
16°00'	0.2793	0.2756	0.2867	3.487	0.9613	1.2915	74°00'
10'	822	0.2784	0.2899	3.450	0.9605	886	50'
20'	851	0.2812	0.2931	3.412	0.9596	857	40'
30'	0.2880	0.2840	0.2962	3.376	0.9588	1.2828	30'
40'	909	0.2868	0.2994	3.340	0.9580	799	20'
50'	938	0.2896	0.3026	3.305	0.9572	770	10'
17°00'	0.2967	0.2924	0.3057	3.271	0.9563	1.2741	73°00'
10'	996	0.2952	0.3089	3.237	0.9555	712	50'
20'	0.3025	0.2979	0.3121	3.204	0.9546	683	40'
30'	0.3054	0.3007	0.3153	3.172	0.9537	1.2654	30'
40'	083	0.3035	0.3185	3.140	0.9528	625	20'
50'	113	0.3062	0.3217	3.108	0.9520	595	10'
18°00'	0.3142	0.3090	0.3249	3.078	0.9511	1.2566	72°00'
		cos		tan	sin	Radians	Degrees

TABLE II · VALUES OF TRIGONOMETRIC FUNCTIONS **587**

Values of Trigonometric Functions

Degrees	Radians	sin	tan		cos		
18°00'	0.3142	0.3090	0.3249	3.078	0.9511	1.2566	72°00'
10'	171	0.3118	0.3281	3.047	0.9502	537	50'
20'	200	0.3145	0.3314	3.018	0.9492	508	40'
30'	0.3229	0.3173	0.3346	2.989	0.9483	1.2479	30'
40'	258	0.3201	0.3378	2.960	0.9474	450	20'
50'	287	0.3228	0.3411	2.932	0.9465	421	10'
19°00'	0.3316	0.3256	0.3443	2.904	0.9455	1.2392	71°00'
10'	345	0.3283	0.3476	2.877	0.9446	363	50'
20'	374	0.3311	0.3508	2.850	0.9436	334	40'
30'	0.3403	0.3338	0.3541	2.824	0.9426	1.2305	30'
40'	432	0.3365	0.3574	2.798	0.9417	275	20'
50'	462	0.3393	0.3607	2.773	0.9407	246	10'
20°00'	0.3491	0.3420	0.3640	2.747	0.9397	1.2217	70°00'
10'	520	0.3448	0.3673	2.723	0.9387	188	50'
20'	549	0.3475	0.3706	2.699	0.9377	159	40'
30'	0.3578	0.3502	0.3739	2.675	0.9367	1.2130	30'
40'	607	0.3529	0.3772	2.651	0.9356	101	20'
50'	636	0.3557	0.3805	2.628	0.9346	072	10'
21°00'	0.3665	0.3584	0.3839	2.605	0.9336	1.2043	69°00'
10'	694	0.3611	0.3872	2.583	0.9325	1.2014	50'
20'	723	0.3638	0.3906	2.560	0.9315	1.1985	40'
30'	0.3752	0.3665	0.3939	2.539	0.9304	1.1956	30'
40'	782	0.3692	0.3973	2.517	0.9293	926	20'
50'	811	0.3719	0.4006	2.496	0.9283	897	10'
22°00'	0.3840	0.3746	0.4040	2.475	0.9272	1.1868	68°00'
10'	869	0.3773	0.4074	2.455	0.9261	839	50'
20'	898	0.3800	0.4108	2.434	0.9250	810	40'
30'	0.3927	0.3827	0.4142	2.414	0.9239	1.1781	30'
40'	956	0.3854	0.4176	2.394	0.9228	752	20'
50'	985	0.3881	0.4210	2.375	0.9216	723	10'
23°00'	0.4014	0.3907	0.4245	2.356	0.9205	1.1694	67°00'
10'	043	0.3934	0.4279	2.337	0.9194	665	50'
20'	072	0.3961	0.4314	2.318	0.9182	636	40'
30'	0.4102	0.3987	0.4348	2.300	0.9171	1.1606	30'
40'	131	0.4014	0.4383	2.282	0.9159	577	20'
50'	160	0.4041	0.4417	2.264	0.9147	548	10'
24°00'	0.4189	0.4067	0.4452	2.246	0.9135	1.1519	66°00'
10'	218	0.4094	0.4487	2.229	0.9124	490	50'
20'	247	0.4120	0.4522	2.211	0.9112	461	40'
30'	0.4276	0.4147	0.4557	2.194	0.9100	1.1432	30'
40'	305	0.4173	0.4592	2.177	0.9088	403	20'
50'	334	0.4200	0.4628	2.161	0.9075	374	10'
25°00'	0.4363	0.4226	0.4663	2.145	0.9063	1.1345	65°00'
10'	392	0.4253	0.4699	2.128	0.9051	316	50'
20'	422	0.4279	0.4734	2.112	0.9038	286	40'
30'	0.4451	0.4305	0.4770	2.097	0.9026	1.1257	30'
40'	480	0.4331	0.4806	2.081	0.9013	228	20'
50'	509	0.4358	0.4841	2.066	0.9001	199	10'
26°00'	0.4538	0.4384	0.4877	2.050	0.8988	1.1170	64°00'
10'	567	0.4410	0.4913	2.035	0.8975	141	50'
20'	596	0.4436	0.4950	2.020	0.8962	112	40'
30'	0.4625	0.4462	0.4986	2.006	0.8949	1.1083	30'
40'	654	0.4488	0.5022	1.991	0.8936	054	20'
50'	683	0.4514	0.5059	1.977	0.8923	1.1025	10'
27°00'	0.4712	0.4540	0.5095	1.963	0.8910	1.0996	63°00'
		cos	tan		sin	Radians	Degrees

Degrees	Radians	sin	tan		cos		
27°00'	0.4712	0.4540	0.5095	1.963	0.8910	1.0996	63°00'
10'	741	0.4566	0.5132	1.949	0.8897	966	50'
20'	771	0.4592	0.5169	1.935	0.8884	937	40'
30'	0.4800	0.4617	0.5206	1.921	0.8870	1.0908	30'
40'	829	0.4643	0.5243	1.907	0.8857	879	20'
50'	858	0.4669	0.5280	1.894	0.8843	850	10'
28°00'	0.4887	0.4695	0.5317	1.881	0.8829	1.0821	62°00'
10'	916	0.4720	0.5354	1.868	0.8816	792	50'
20'	945	0.4746	0.5392	1.855	0.8802	763	40'
30'	0.4974	0.4772	0.5430	1.842	0.8788	1.0734	30'
40'	0.5003	0.4797	0.5467	1.829	0.8774	705	20'
50'	032	0.4823	0.5505	1.816	0.8760	676	10'
29°00'	0.5061	0.4848	0.5543	1.804	0.8746	1.0647	61°00'
10'	091	0.4874	0.5581	1.792	0.8732	617	50'
20'	120	0.4899	0.5619	1.780	0.8718	588	40'
30'	0.5149	0.4924	0.5658	1.767	0.8704	1.0559	30'
40'	178	0.4950	0.5696	1.756	0.8689	530	20'
50'	207	0.4975	0.5735	1.744	0.8675	501	10'
30°00'	0.5236	0.5000	0.5774	1.732	0.8660	1.0472	60°00'
10'	265	0.5025	0.5812	1.720	0.8646	443	50'
20'	294	0.5050	0.5851	1.709	0.8631	414	40'
30'	0.5323	0.5075	0.5890	1.698	0.8616	1.0385	30'
40'	352	0.5100	0.5930	1.686	0.8601	356	20'
50'	381	0.5125	0.5969	1.675	0.8587	327	10'
31°00'	0.5411	0.5150	0.6009	1.664	0.8572	1.0297	59°00'
10'	440	0.5175	0.6048	1.653	0.8557	268	50'
20'	469	0.5200	0.6088	1.643	0.8542	239	40'
30'	0.5498	0.5225	0.6128	1.632	0.8526	1.0210	30'
40'	527	0.5250	0.6168	1.621	0.8511	181	20'
50'	556	0.5275	0.6208	1.611	0.8496	152	10'
32°00'	0.5585	0.5299	0.6249	1.600	0.8480	1.0123	58°00'
10'	614	0.5324	0.6289	1.590	0.8465	094	50'
20'	643	0.5348	0.6330	1.580	0.8450	065	40'
30'	0.5672	0.5373	0.6371	1.570	0.8434	1.0036	30'
40'	701	0.5398	0.6412	1.560	0.8418	1.0007	20'
50'	730	0.5422	0.6453	1.550	0.8403	0.9977	10'
33°00'	0.5760	0.5446	0.6494	1.540	0.8387	0.9948	57°00'
10'	789	0.5471	0.6536	1.530	0.8371	919	50'
20'	818	0.5495	0.6577	1.520	0.8355	890	40'
30'	0.5847	0.5519	0.6619	1.511	0.8339	0.9861	30'
40'	876	0.5544	0.6661	1.501	0.8323	832	20'
50'	905	0.5568	0.6703	1.492	0.8307	803	10'
34°00'	0.5934	0.5592	0.6745	1.483	0.8290	0.9774	56°00'
10'	963	0.5616	0.6787	1.473	0.8274	745	50'
20'	992	0.5640	0.6830	1.464	0.8258	716	40'
30'	0.6021	0.5664	0.6873	1.455	0.8241	0.9687	30'
40'	050	0.5688	0.6916	1.446	0.8225	657	20'
50'	080	0.5712	0.6959	1.437	0.8208	628	10'
35°00'	0.6109	0.5736	0.7002	1.428	0.8192	0.9599	55°00'
10'	138	0.5760	0.7046	1.419	0.8175	570	50'
20'	167	0.5783	0.7089	1.411	0.8158	541	40'
30'	0.6196	0.5807	0.7133	1.402	0.8141	0.9512	30'
40'	225	0.5831	0.7177	1.393	0.8124	483	20'
50'	254	0.5854	0.7221	1.385	0.8107	454	10'
36°00'	0.6283	0.5878	0.7265	1.376	0.8090	0.9425	54°00'
		cos		tan	sin	Radians	Degrees

Values of Trigonometric Functions

Degrees	Radians	sin	tan		cos		
36°00′	0.6283	0.5878	0.7265	1.376	0.8090	0.9425	54°00′
10′	312	0.5901	0.7310	1.368	0.8073	396	50′
20′	341	0.5925	0.7355	1.360	0.8056	367	40′
30′	0.6370	0.5948	0.7400	1.351	0.8039	0.9338	30′
40′	400	0.5972	0.7445	1.343	0.8021	308	20′
50′	429	0.5995	0.7490	1.335	0.8004	279	10′
37°00′	0.6458	0.6018	0.7536	1.327	0.7986	0.9250	53°00′
10′	487	0.6041	0.7581	1.319	0.7969	221	50′
20′	516	0.6065	0.7627	1.311	0.7951	192	40′
30′	0.6545	0.6088	0.7673	1.303	0.7934	0.9163	30′
40′	574	0.6111	0.7720	1.295	0.7916	134	20′
50′	603	0.6134	0.7766	1.288	0.7898	105	10′
38°00′	0.6632	0.6157	0.7813	1.280	0.7880	0.9076	52°00′
10′	661	0.6180	0.7860	1.272	0.7862	047	50′
20′	690	0.6202	0.7907	1.265	0.7844	0.9018	40′
30′	0.6720	0.6225	0.7954	1.257	0.7826	0.8988	30′
40′	749	0.6248	0.8002	1.250	0.7808	959	20′
50′	778	0.6271	0.8050	1.242	0.7790	930	10′
39°00′	0.6807	0.6293	0.8098	1.235	0.7771	0.8901	51°00′
10′	836	0.6316	0.8146	1.228	0.7753	872	50′
20′	865	0.6338	0.8195	1.220	0.7735	843	40′
30′	0.6894	0.6361	0.8243	1.213	0.7716	0.8814	30′
40′	923	0.6383	0.8292	1.206	0.7698	785	20′
50′	952	0.6406	0.8342	1.199	0.7679	756	10′
40°00′	0.6981	0.6428	0.8391	1.192	0.7660	0.8727	50°00′
10′	0.7010	0.6450	0.8441	1.185	0.7642	698	50′
20′	039	0.6472	0.8491	1.178	0.7623	668	40′
30′	0.7069	0.6494	0.8541	1.171	0.7604	0.8639	30′
40′	098	0.6517	0.8591	1.164	0.7585	610	20′
50′	127	0.6539	0.8642	1.157	0.7566	581	10′
41°00′	0.7156	0.6561	0.8693	1.150	0.7547	0.8552	49°00′
10′	185	0.6583	0.8744	1.144	0.7528	523	50′
20′	214	0.6604	0.8796	1.137	0.7509	494	40′
30′	0.7243	0.6626	0.8847	1.130	0.7490	0.8465	30′
40′	272	0.6648	0.8899	1.124	0.7470	436	20′
50′	301	0.6670	0.8952	1.117	0.7451	407	10′
42°00′	0.7330	0.6691	0.9004	1.111	0.7431	0.8378	48°00′
10′	359	0.6713	0.9057	1.104	0.7412	348	50′
20′	389	0.6734	0.9110	1.098	0.7392	319	40′
30′	0.7418	0.6756	0.9163	1.091	0.7373	0.8290	30′
40′	447	0.6777	0.9217	1.085	0.7353	261	20′
50′	476	0.6799	0.9271	1.079	0.7333	232	10′
43°00′	0.7505	0.6820	0.9325	1.072	0.7314	0.8203	47°00′
10′	534	0.6841	0.9380	1.066	0.7294	174	50′
20′	563	0.6862	0.9435	1.060	0.7274	145	40′
30′	0.7592	0.6884	0.9490	1.054	0.7254	0.8116	30′
40′	621	0.6905	0.9545	1.048	0.7234	087	20′
50′	650	0.6926	0.9601	1.042	0.7214	058	10′
44°00′	0.7679	0.6947	0.9657	1.036	0.7193	0.8029	46°00′
10′	709	0.6967	0.9713	1.030	0.7173	0.7999	50′
20′	738	0.6988	0.9770	1.024	0.7153	970	40′
30′	0.7767	0.7009	0.9827	1.018	0.7133	0.7941	30′
40′	796	0.7030	0.9884	1.012	0.7112	912	20′
50′	825	0.7050	0.9942	1.006	0.7092	883	10′
45°00′	0.7854	0.7071	1.000	1.000	0.7071	0.7854	45°00′
		cos	tan		sin	Radians	Degrees

TABLE III · SQUARE ROOTS AND CUBE ROOTS **589**

Table III · Square Roots and Cube Roots

N	$\sqrt{N}$	$\sqrt[3]{N}$	N	$\sqrt{N}$	$\sqrt[3]{N}$	N	$\sqrt{N}$	$\sqrt[3]{N}$	N	$\sqrt{N}$	$\sqrt[3]{N}$
1	1.000	1.000	51	7.141	3.708	101	10.050	4.657	151	12.288	5.325
2	1.414	1.260	52	7.211	3.733	102	10.100	4.672	152	12.329	5.337
3	1.732	1.442	53	7.280	3.756	103	10.149	4.688	153	12.369	5.348
4	2.000	1.587	54	7.348	3.780	104	10.198	4.703	154	12.410	5.360
5	2.236	1.710	55	7.416	3.803	105	10.247	4.718	155	12.450	5.372
6	2.449	1.817	56	7.483	3.826	106	10.296	4.733	156	12.490	5.383
7	2.646	1.913	57	7.550	3.849	107	10.344	4.747	157	12.530	5.395
8	2.828	2.000	58	7.616	3.871	108	10.392	4.762	158	12.570	5.406
9	3.000	2.080	59	7.681	3.893	109	10.440	4.777	159	12.610	5.418
10	3.162	2.154	60	7.746	3.915	110	10.488	4.791	160	12.649	5.429
11	3.317	2.224	61	7.810	3.936	111	10.536	4.806	161	12.689	5.440
12	3.464	2.289	62	7.874	3.958	112	10.583	4.820	162	12.728	5.451
13	3.606	2.351	63	7.937	3.979	113	10.630	4.835	163	12.767	5.463
14	3.742	2.410	64	8.000	4.000	114	10.677	4.849	164	12.806	5.474
15	3.873	2.466	65	8.062	4.021	115	10.724	4.863	165	12.845	5.485
16	4.000	2.520	66	8.124	4.041	116	10.770	4.877	166	12.884	5.496
17	4.123	2.571	67	8.185	4.062	117	10.817	4.891	167	12.923	5.507
18	4.243	2.621	68	8.246	4.082	118	10.863	4.905	168	12.961	5.518
19	4.359	2.668	69	8.307	4.102	119	10.909	4.919	169	13.000	5.529
20	4.472	2.714	70	8.367	4.121	120	10.954	4.932	170	13.038	5.540
21	4.583	2.759	71	8.426	4.141	121	11.000	4.946	171	13.077	5.550
22	4.690	2.802	72	8.485	4.160	122	11.045	4.960	172	13.115	5.561
23	4.796	2.844	73	8.544	4.179	123	11.091	4.973	173	13.153	5.572
24	4.899	2.884	74	8.602	4.198	124	11.136	4.987	174	13.191	5.583
25	5.000	2.924	75	8.660	4.217	125	11.180	5.000	175	13.229	5.593
26	5.099	2.962	76	8.718	4.236	126	11.225	5.013	176	13.266	5.604
27	5.196	3.000	77	8.775	4.254	127	11.269	5.027	177	13.304	5.615
28	5.292	3.037	78	8.832	4.273	128	11.314	5.040	178	13.342	5.625
29	5.385	3.072	79	8.888	4.291	129	11.358	5.053	179	13.379	5.636
30	5.477	3.107	80	8.944	4.309	130	11.402	5.066	180	13.416	5.646
31	5.568	3.141	81	9.000	4.327	131	11.446	5.079	181	13.454	5.657
32	5.657	3.175	82	9.055	4.344	132	11.489	5.092	182	13.491	5.667
33	5.745	3.208	83	9.110	4.362	133	11.533	5.104	183	13.528	5.677
34	5.831	3.240	84	9.165	4.380	134	11.576	5.117	184	13.565	5.688
35	5.916	3.271	85	9.220	4.397	135	11.619	5.130	185	13.601	5.698
36	6.000	3.302	86	9.274	4.414	136	11.662	5.143	186	13.638	5.708
37	6.083	3.332	87	9.327	4.431	137	11.705	5.155	187	13.675	5.718
38	6.164	3.362	88	9.381	4.448	138	11.747	5.168	188	13.711	5.729
39	6.245	3.391	89	9.434	4.465	139	11.790	5.180	189	13.748	5.739
40	6.325	3.420	90	9.487	4.481	140	11.832	5.192	190	13.784	5.749
41	6.403	3.448	91	9.539	4.498	141	11.874	5.205	191	13.820	5.759
42	6.481	3.476	92	9.592	4.514	142	11.916	5.217	192	13.856	5.769
43	6.557	3.503	93	9.644	4.531	143	11.958	5.229	193	13.892	5.779
44	6.633	3.530	94	9.695	4.547	144	12.000	5.241	194	13.928	5.789
45	6.708	3.557	95	9.747	4.563	145	12.042	5.254	195	13.964	5.799
46	6.782	3.583	96	9.798	4.579	146	12.083	5.266	196	14.000	5.809
47	6.856	3.609	97	9.849	4.595	147	12.124	5.278	197	14.036	5.819
48	6.928	3.634	98	9.899	4.610	148	12.166	5.290	198	14.071	5.828
49	7.000	3.659	99	9.950	4.626	149	12.207	5.301	199	14.107	5.838
50	7.071	3.684	100	10.000	4.642	150	12.247	5.313	200	14.142	5.848

GLOSSARY

abscissa The first number of the ordered pair of numbers for a point in the coordinate plane.

absolute value The absolute value of a positive number or zero is the number itself. The absolute value of a negative number is its opposite.

addition principle (for counting) When one of two mutually-exclusive events can occur in m different ways and the other in n different ways, then the number of ways either one or the other of the events can occur is $m + n$.

angle of depression The acute or right angle formed by the horizontal and a line from a point on the horizontal to a point below.

angle of elevation The acute or right angle formed by the horizontal and a line from a point on the horizontal to a point above.

antilogarithm (antilog) of a number The number whose logarithm is the given number.

Arccos n The measure (from $0°$ or 0^R to $180°$ or π^R) of the angle whose cosine is n, $-1 \le n \le 1$.

Arcsin n The measure (from $-90°$ or $-\frac{\pi}{2}^R$ to $90°$ or $\frac{\pi}{2}^R$) of the angle whose sine is n, $-1 \le n \le 1$.

Arctan n The measure (from $-90°$ or $-\frac{\pi}{2}^R$ to $90°$ or $\frac{\pi}{2}^R$) of the angle whose tangent is the real number n.

arithmetic means Terms that are between two nonconsecutive terms in an arithmetic sequence.

arithmetic sequence A sequence in which each term except the first may be found by adding a constant (the *common difference*) to the preceding term.

axis of symmetry (of a parabola) A line, containing the vertex of the parabola, about which the points of the parabola are symmetric.

base (of power) *See* exponent.

binomial A polynomial having two terms.

circle The graph of the quadratic relation $(x - h)^2 + (y - k)^2 = r^2$.

coefficient Any factor of a product is the coefficient of the other factor or factors. When a constant occurs with variables, *coefficient* often refers to the constant.

combination A selection of objects in which the arrangement of the objects is not important.

common logarithm A logarithm having base 10.

completing the square Forming a perfect-square trinomial when 2 terms are given.

complex conjugates The pair $a + bi$ and $a - bi$.

complex fraction A fraction containing a fraction in its numerator or denominator.

complex numbers The numbers that correspond to the points in a plane. A complex number may be shown in the form $a + bi$ or as an ordered pair (a, b).

conditional equation An equation which may give a true number sentence for some, but not all, of the numbers that may replace the variable(s).

conic section The graph (circle, parabola, ellipse, or hyperbola) of a second-degree equation in two variables; A curve that represents the intersection of a cone and a plane.

consistent equations A system of equations that have a common solution.

coordinate axis The horizontal or vertical number line used to establish the coordinate plane.

cosecant function The reciprocal of the sine function.

cosine function A function with the set of real numbers as its domain. For the real number x and for $\angle\theta$ having measure x, $\cos x$ is the first coordinate of the intersection of the terminal side of $\angle\theta$ with the unit circle.

cosine of an angle The ratio

$$\frac{\text{length of the leg adjacent the angle}}{\text{length of the hypotenuse}}$$

when the angle is an acute angle of a right triangle.

cotangent function The reciprocal of the tangent function.

degree of an equation The degree of polynomial $p(x)$ when the equation is given in the form $p(x) = 0$.

degree of a polynomial The degree of the highest-degree term in the polynomial.

degree of a term The sum of the exponents of the variables in the term.

dependent equations *See* equivalent equations.

determinant of a matrix A number associated with a square matrix.

$$\det \begin{bmatrix} a & b \\ c & d \end{bmatrix} = ad - cb$$

directrix of a parabola *See* parabola.

direct variation A relationship between two variables x and y described by an equation of the form $y = kx^n$, k a nonzero constant, n a counting number. When $n = 1$, the variation is *linear* and direct.

discriminant The number $b^2 - 4ac$ when $ax^2 + bx + c = 0$ and $a \neq 0$.

domain The set of first members of the ordered pairs of a function. The set of numbers that may replace a variable.

ellipse The graph of the quadratic relation $\frac{(x-h)^2}{a^2} + \frac{(y-k)^2}{b^2} = 1$. The set of points in a plane for which the sum of the distances of any such point from two given points is constant. Each of the given points is a *focus* of the ellipse.

equation A number sentence showing that two expressions represent the same number.

equivalent (or dependent) equations Equations that have the same solution(s).

exponent The number b in the term a^b. The number a^b is a power. The number a is the *base* of the power. Also, the exponent b is called the *logarithm* to the base a of the number a^b.

exponential equation An equation that includes a variable as an exponent.

exponential function A function defined by an equation of the form $y = a^x$, $a > 0$.

extraneous solutions Solutions of an equation that are not solutions of a given equation from which the first equation is derived.

factorial *See* n factorial.

finite sequence A sequence with a first term and a last term.

focus *See* parabola, ellipse, hyperbola.

formula An equation which expresses a relationship in concise form, usually with a single variable as the left member.

fractional equation An equation with a variable in a denominator.

function A set of ordered pairs, no two of which have the same first member.

Fundamental Counting Principle When one event can occur in m different ways and a second event in n different ways, then the number of ways the events can occur in succession is $m \cdot n$.

geometric means Terms that are between two nonconsecutive terms in a geometric sequence. When there is just one term between two nonconsecutive terms, that term is *the geometric mean* or the *mean proportional* between the two given terms.

geometric sequence A sequence in which each term except the first may be found by multiplying the preceding term by a constant (the *common ratio*).

geometric series The indicated sum of the terms of a geometric sequence.

graph The point in the coordinate plane associated with an ordered pair of real numbers. The set of points in the coordinate plane associated with a set of ordered pairs of real numbers. Also, the process or result of representing such a point.

greatest common factor (GCF) The product of the prime factors common to two or more expressions.

hyperbola The graph of the quadratic relation $\frac{(x-h)^2}{a^2} - \frac{(y-k)^2}{b^2} = 1$; The set of points in a plane for which the *difference* of the distances of any such point from two given points is constant. Each of the given points is a *focus* of the hyperbola.

identity equation An equation which gives a true number sentence for any of the numbers that may replace the variable.

identity matrix A square matrix with each main diagonal element equal to 1 and each element elsewhere equal to 0.

incomplete quadratic equation A quadratic equation with no first-degree term.

inconsistent equations A system of equations that have no common solution.

index A number n associated with a radical sign to indicate the nth root.

inequality A number sentence showing that two expressions represent different numbers.

infinite sequence A sequence with no last term.

integers The numbers 0, 1, -1, 2, -2, and so on.

interpolation The process of approximating a value for a function between two known values.

inverse of a relation A relation obtained by interchanging the two members of each ordered pair of the given relation.

inverse variation A relationship between two variables x and y described by an equation in the form of $x^n y = k$, k a non-zero constant, n a counting number.

invertible matrix A square matrix which has a multiplicative inverse.

irrational numbers Real numbers that cannot be expressed in the form $\frac{a}{b}$ when a and b are integers and $b \neq 0$.

joint variation A relationship between three variables x, y and z, described by an equation of the form $z = kxy$ or of the form $z = k\frac{x}{y}$, k a non-zero constant.

least common denominator (LCD) The least common multiple of two or more denominators.

least common multiple (LCM) The product of the prime factors of two or more expressions, each factor appearing the greatest number of times it occurs in either expression.

linear equation A first-degree equation in two variables. Common forms for a linear equation include the general form $Ax + By = C$; the slope-intercept form, $y = mx + b$; the point-slope form, $y - y_1 = m(x - x_1)$, and the two-point form, $y - y_1 = \frac{y_2 - y_1}{x_2 - x_1}(x - x_1)$.

linear function A function defined by a linear equation.

linear inequality A first-degree inequality in one or two variables.

linear variation A relationship between two variables x and y described by a linear equation.

logarithmic function The inverse of an exponential function. It is described by an equation of the form $y = \log_a x$ where $a > 0$, $a \neq 1$.

logarithm of a given number *See* exponent.

matrix A rectangular array of numbers or variables arranged in rows and columns.

mean proportional *See* geometric means

monomial A constant, a variable, or an indicated product involving constants and variables.

mutually-exclusive events Two events that cannot occur at the same time.

n factorial (n!) The product of all the counting numbers less than or equal to n.

ordinate The second number of the ordered pair of numbers for a point in the coordinate plane.

origin The point of intersection of the two coordinate axes in the coordinate plane.

parabola The graph of the quadratic function $y = ax^2 + bx + c$, $a \neq 0$; the set of points in a plane each of which is the same distance from a given point as from a given line. The given point is the *focus* and the given line the *directrix* of the parabola.

parameter A variable that is treated as if it were a constant when solving an equation for another variable.

perfect-square trinomial A trinomial that is the square of a binomial.

periodic function A function f for which there is a positive number p such that $f(x + p) = f(x)$ for all x in the domain of f. The smallest such positive number p is the *period* of the function.

permutation An arrangement of things in some definite order.

polynomial A monomial or an indicated sum or difference of monomials.

polynomial function of degree n A function defined by an equation of the form
$$y = a_0 x^n + a_1 x^{n-1} + a_2 x^{n-2} + \cdots + a_{n-1} x + a_n$$
when n is a positive integer, a_0, a_1, a_2, $\cdots$, a_n are constants, and $a_0 \neq 0$.

power *See* exponent.

prime polynomial A polynomial that cannot be factored.

principal nth root of a real number a The positive nth root of a when a is positive; the negative nth root of a when a is negative and n is an odd integer.

probability of an event A number between 0 and 1, inclusive, that is a measure of how likely it is that the event will occur.

proportion An equation in which each member is a ratio. For the proportion $\frac{a}{b} = \frac{c}{d}$, a and d are the *extremes* and b and c are the *means*.

quadrant Each of the four parts into which the coordinate axes separate the rest of the coordinate plane.

quadratic relation A relation defined by a second-degree equation in two variables.

quadratic equation A second-degree equation in one variable.

quadratic function A function defined by an equation of the form
$$y = ax^2 + bx + c, a \neq 0.$$

quadratic inequality A second-degree inequality in one or two variables.

radian A unit of angular measure. One radian, denoted 1^R, is the measure of an angle of rotation that intercepts an arc equal in length to the radius of the circle containing the arc.

radical equation An equation in which a variable appears below a radical sign.

radical sign $\sqrt{}$ The symbol used to indicate a root of a number.

radicand The number shown below the radical sign.

range, function The set of second members of the ordered pairs of a function.

rational expression An expression that may be written in the form $\frac{P}{Q}$ when P and Q are polynomials.

rationalizing the denominator The eliminating of radicals from a denominator.

rational numbers The numbers each of which can be expressed in the form $\frac{a}{b}$ when a and b are integers and $b \neq 0$.

real numbers Numbers that are either rational or irrational.

reciprocals The pair $\frac{a}{b}$ and $\frac{b}{a}$, $a \neq 0$, $b \neq 0$.

reference angle The acute or right angle in the coordinate plane formed by the terminal side of an angle of rotation and the horizontal axis.

relation Any set of ordered pairs.

root of a number a is an nth root of b when $a^n = b$.

scalar product (of a real number and a matrix) A matrix in which the element in any location is the product of the scalar (the given number) and the element in the same location in the given matrix.

secant function The reciprocal of the cosine function.

sequence A set of numbers whose members are arranged in a definite order. Each number is a *term* of the sequence.

sine function A function with the set of real numbers as its domain. For the real number x and for $\angle \theta$ having measure x, sin x is the second coordinate of the intersection of the terminal side of $\angle \theta$ with the unit circle.

sine of an angle The ratio
$$\frac{\text{length of the leg opposite the angle}}{\text{length of the hypotenuse}}$$
when the angle is an acute angle of a right triangle.

slope of a nonvertical line For two points in the line, the ratio of the difference of the two ordinates to the difference of the two abscissas.

solution of an equation The number(s) that gives a true sentence when used in place of the variable.

solution of a system of equations Any common solution of the equations in the system.

system of equations A set of two or more equations in two or more variables.

tangent function A function with the set of real numbers as its domain. tan $x = \frac{\sin x}{\cos x}$ for the real numbers x for which cos $x \neq 0$.

tangent of an angle The ratio
$$\frac{\text{length of the leg opposite the angle}}{\text{length of the leg adjacent the angle}}$$
when the angle is an acute angle of a right triangle.

trinomial A polynomial having 3 terms.

unit circle A circle in the coordinate plane with center (0, 0) and radius 1.

variable A symbol for a number, usually a letter from the English or Greek alphabet.

vertex of a parabola The point of the parabola corresponding to the maximum or minimum value of one of the variables in the equation of the parabola.

x-axis The horizontal number line in the coordinate plane.

x-intercept The x-coordinate of the point that a graph shares with the x-axis.

y-axis The vertical number line in the coordinate plane.

y-intercept The y-coordinate of the point that a graph shares with the y-axis.

zero matrix A matrix with all elements equal to zero.

ANSWERS FOR SELECTED EXERCISES

Chapter 1 The Real Numbers

Page 4, Exercises 1. all **3.** 4 **5.** -7 **7.** 10 **9.** 4 **11.** 8.2 **13.** $\frac{3}{4}$ **15.** -10

Page 8, Exercises 1. $19\frac{1}{4}$ **3.** $4\frac{1}{6}$ **5.** $3+4$ **7.** 0×13 **9.** $23(15+10)$
11. $7\cdot15+7\cdot20$ **13.** 11 **15.** 120 **17.** 20 **19.** 45 **21.** 0 **23.** 7 **25.** 25 **27.** 1
29. 0 **31.** no, $1\div7=\frac{1}{7}$ is not an integer **Page 10, Exercises 1.** 1 **3.** -23 **5.** 0
7. -1.4 **9.** $-\frac{1}{4}$ **11.** $-\frac{3}{4}$ **13.** 3.2 **15.** -10 **17.** $-3\frac{1}{4}$ **19.** $-6\frac{7}{12}$ **21.** -30 **23.** 4
25. $m+(m+1)+(m+2)=3m+3=3(m+1)$
27. Use $2m$ as an even integer, $2n+1$ as an odd integer, and the sum
$2(m+n)+1$ is an odd integer **29.** $2x$ for $x\geq0$; 0 for $x<0$ **Page 12, Exercises**
1. 11 **3.** 7 **5.** -12 **7.** 9 **9.** 8 **11.** -10 **13.** 101 **15.** -7 **17.** -8 **19.** -5
21. $-1\frac{1}{8}$ **23.** 7.74 **25.** 21 **27.** 3 **29.** -8 **31.** -4 **33.** $-9\frac{7}{39}$
35. $10t+u-(t+u)=9t$ **37.** $-4, x\geq0$ **Page 14, Exercises 1.** -12 **3.** -24
5. 15 **7.** -30 **9.** 9 **11.** 9 **13.** 6.72 **15.** -31.62 **17.** 22.68 **19.** $-\frac{6}{35}$ **21.** $1\frac{5}{27}$
23. 18 **25.** -48 **27.** -6 **29.** $\frac{2}{21}$ **31.** $-\frac{77}{18}$ **33.** $-\frac{6}{35}$ **35.** -6.6 **37.** 26 **39.** $-\frac{5}{24}$
41. Use $2m$ as an even integer, $2n+1$ as an odd integer,
$2m(2n+1)=2(2mn+2)$ which is an even integer.
43. $x>0$, $x|x|=x^2$, $x|-x|=x^2$, $-x|x|=-x^2$; $x=0$, all three are equal;
$x<0$, $x|x|=-x^2$, $x|-x|=-x^2$, $-x|x|=x^2$; therefore, for all values,
$x|x|=x|-x|$. **Page 16, Exercises 1.** 2 **3.** 4 **5.** -2 **7.** -4 **9.** 2 **11.** -2.8
13. $\frac{1}{14}$ **15.** $-\frac{1}{11}$ **17.** -16 **19.** $\frac{3}{10}$ **21.** $-1\frac{1}{5}$ **23.** $\frac{6}{11}$ **25.** 2 **27.** $15\frac{5}{6}$ years
Page 19, Exercises 1. 125 **3.** -8 **5.** 4 **7.** $-\frac{27}{8}$ **9.** 5 **11.** -8 **13.** 5 **15.** 4
17. -1 **19.** $\frac{2}{3}$ **21.** Irrational **23.** Irrational **25.** Irrational **27.** 1 **29.** 72 **31.** 2
33. 10 **35.** 2 **37.** $3x$ **39.** $-2a$ **41.** For n even, $a^n=|a|^n$, $\sqrt[n]{a^n}=\sqrt[n]{|a|^n}=|a|$
Page 20, Checking Your Understanding 3. 8, 8 **4.** $-\frac{3}{4}, \frac{3}{4}$ **5.** 6.7, 6.7 **6.** 0, 0
7. -5 **8.** $-1\frac{1}{12}$ **9.** -7 **10.** 4.5 **11.** -32 **12.** $\frac{7}{2}$ **13.** $-3\frac{1}{4}$ **14.** 3 **15.** 9 **16.** $-\frac{2}{3}$
17. 5 **18.** 0.2 **Page 22, Exercises 1.** $3x$ **3.** $-2r^2$ **5.** $-6c$ **7.** $-\frac{1}{6}ab$
9. $-5.9m^2n$ **11.** $2x+y$ **13.** c^2-6c+6 **15.** $7d^3+8d^2+7$ **17.** $-p^2$
19. $6x^2-2ax+1$ **21.** $6x^2+5xy-3y^2$ **23.** $-4c^2-3cd+2d^2$
25. $-6x+8y+6$ **27.** $-11x+4$ **29.** x **Pages 24-25, Exercises**
1. $7a+3b$ **3.** $-2y^2+4y+1$ **5.** $2z^2-2z+10$ **7.** $-4c^2+cd+12d^2-2$
9. $-2x^3-4x^2-9$ **11.** $2r^2+13rs+6s^2+2$ **13.** $-11a^2+5b^2$
15. $\frac{5}{18}x-\frac{1}{2}y+\frac{29}{30}z$ **17.** $5k^2-5k-9$ **19.** $-7r^3-2r^2$ **21.** $3a-22$
23. $-x^2-3x-5$ **25.** $16a^2-4$ **27.** $2a^2-6ab$ **29.** $2a+10b-5c+8d$
31. $-\frac{1}{12}x+\frac{3}{8}y+\frac{2}{9}z$ **33.** $-2a-2b+c$ **35.** $8a-11b$
37. $4x^3+4x^2-4x+14$ **39.** $1179k$ **Page 30, Exercises 1.** x^9 **3.** z^{14}
5. c^{x+y} **7.** $-12x^2$ **9.** $-3x^7$ **11.** $4.2t^8$ **13.** $6x^2y^5$ **15.** x^{n+3} **17.** x^6 **19.** $-c$ **21.** 1
23. $4a^5$ **25.** $-5c$ **27.** $12c$ **29.** $-3x$ **31.** $4rs^3$ **33.** $4a^{n-1}$ **35.** a^2 **37.** $-2cd^{2m}$
39. $20a^3b^4c^7$ **41.** $\frac{1}{4x^2y^2}$ **43.** $2x^{2n-2}y^{n+1}$ **45.** $t=1.6x^{3m-7}y^{3n+4}$ **Page 32,**
Exercises 1. $-12x^5-15x^4-30x^2$ **3.** $3c^2+7c+2$ **5.** $x^2-10x+25$
7. $4x^2+12x+9$ **9.** $x^4-7x^2y+10y^2$ **11.** $\frac{1}{6}x^4-\frac{4}{3}x^2y+2y^2$
13. $8c^3-6c^2-2c-36$ **15.** $2a^4-3a^3b+2a^2b^2-ab^3$ **17.** x^3-1
19. a^4-a^2+2a-1 **21.** y^3-9y^2+14y **23.** $a^{2x}+2a^xb^y+b^{2y}$
25. $27x^3-108x^2+144x-64$ **Page 35, Exercises 1.** a^2-4 **3.** $6a^2-12a+18$

5. $6a^2 + 3a + 4$ **7.** $-5a^2 - 2ab$ **9.** $3 + n$ **11.** $x + y + 3$ **13.** $x + 2$ **15.** $5x + 7$
17. $2a + 8 + \frac{49}{2a - 5}$ **19.** $3x - 3 + \frac{-10}{7x + 5}$ **21.** $x^3 - 6$ **23.** $x^2 - xy + y^2$
25. $c^2 + 3c + 9$ **27.** $-x^2 + 4x - 17 + \frac{84}{4 - x}$ **29.** $3a^2 + 8a + 6 + \frac{-5}{2a - 5}$
31. $x^2 + 2xy + 2y^2$ **33.** $x^2 + 3x - 4 + \frac{-24x + 32}{x^2 - 3x + 4}$ **35.** $x^n - 3$ **37.** $x^2 + 3x - 5$
39. $a^{2n} - a^n b^n + b^{2n}$ **41.** $a - 1$ **Pages 37-38, Exercises 1.** $3x + 2$
3. $5c + 1$ **5.** $10x^2 - x$ **7.** $4x^3 - 3x^2 - 2x$ **9.** $-b - 2$ **11.** $m + n + (p - q)$
13. $b - a + (-ax + bx)$ **15.** $x^2 + 1 - (ax^2 + a)$ **17.** $2a - 2b - 2c$ **19.** $2y$
21. $3x - 4$ **23.** $25x^2 - 13x - 3$ **25.** $x^{n+1} - 22x^n$ **27.** $-9c^2 + 21c - 6$
29. $a^3 - 2ab - b^3$ **31.** 1 **Page 38, Checking Your Understanding 1.** $x^7 y^7$
2. $-6a^3 b^5$ **3.** $-3xy$ **4.** $-\frac{4r}{t^3}$ **5.** $7x + 4y$ **6.** $4x^2 - 2x + 1$ **7.** $15x^2 + 17x - 4$
8. $a - 1$ **9.** $2x^2 - xy$ **10.** $5x + 18$ **11.** $-5y - 4xy$ **12.** $5x + 5$ **13.** $x - 10$
Page 41, Exercises 1. $3n + 7$ **3.** $\frac{2}{3}n + 7$ **5.** $3(2x + 4)$ **7.** $100x + 5y$
9. $x + 13$ **11.** $50 - 3\frac{x}{y}$ **13.** $6(a - b) + 4$ **15.** $y - x(x - 5)$ **17.** $\frac{2 - x}{x - 3}$ **19.** $4n + 2$
21. $8x + 30$ **23.** $60n + 180$ (cents), $0.60n + 1.80$ (dollars) **25.** $3n^3 + 60n^2 + 225n$
27. $4b - 6$

Chapter 2 First-Degree Equations and Inequalities Having One Variable
Page 49, Exercises 1. 5 **3.** 1 **5.** 100 **7.** $x > 5$ **9.** no solution
11. all real numbers **13.** 12 **15.** $x > 1$ **17.** $x > 3$ or $x < -3$
19. I, all real numbers **21.** I, all real numbers **23.** C, 1 **25.** C, 1
27. I, all real numbers **29.** C, O **31.** Identity **33.** Identity **35.** Identity
37. Conditional **39.** Identity **41.** Identity **Page 52, Exercises 1.** 7 **3.** 6 **5.** -5
7. 3 **9.** -2 **11.** 3 **13.** 0 **15.** -108 **17.** 10 **19.** $\frac{5}{3}$ **21.** $-\frac{11}{4}$ **23.** 5 **25.** $-\frac{3}{2}$
27. -7 **29.** 7 **31.** -2 **Page 54, Exercises 1.** $2c$ **3.** $\frac{b}{a}$ **5.** $b - a$ **7.** $\frac{3}{b}$ **9.** $2a$
11. $\frac{c}{rt}$ **13.** $c + 2$ **15.** $2p$ **17.** $\frac{b + c}{a}$ **19.** $\frac{5m}{2}$ **21.** $40h$ **23.** $\frac{m + 1}{m^2}$ **25.** $\frac{C}{2\pi}$ **27.** $\frac{3V}{b}$
29. $\frac{W}{I^2}$ **31.** $\frac{S}{2\pi r}$ **33.** $\frac{2S - In}{n}$ **35.** $\frac{2S}{t^2}$ **37.** c^n **39.** $-\frac{2}{3}$ **41.** $\frac{Rmg + 2f}{2}$ **43.** $\frac{RT(V^2 - K)}{V - b}$
Pages 56-57, Exercises 1. 33.5 m³ **3.** 785 m³ **5.** 589.8 cm³ **7.** 3.98 cm
9. 5 m, 10 m, 9 m **11.** 5 **13.** 84 **Page 57, Checking Your Understanding**
1. yes **2.** yes **3.** 1 **4.** 15 **5.** no solution **6.** all real numbers **7.** $d = \frac{a}{a - 2b}$
8. $z = \frac{x - yw}{2y}$ **9.** $a = 3$ **10.** $a = 6$ **Pages 59-60, Exercises 1.** $x > -5$ **3.** $x < 3$
5. $x \leq -9$ **7.** $x > 1$ **9.** $x > 4$ **11.** $x < 3$ **13.** $x \leq 3$ **15.** $x < \frac{8}{3}$ **17.** $x < -9$
19. $x \geq -\frac{10}{3}$ **21.** $x > 1$ **23.** $x > -\frac{3}{2}$ **25.** $x > 4$ **27.** $x \geq -\frac{7}{2}$ **29.** $x \geq 2$
31. $x \leq -5$ **33.** no solution **35.** $x < \frac{-b^2}{1 + b^2}$, $b \neq 0$ **Page 63, Exercises**
1. $2 < x < 5$ **3.** $x > 1$ or $x < 0$ **5.** $-4 < x < 2$ **7.** $x \geq 6$ **9.** $x \leq -3$ or $x \geq 3$
11. $1 \leq x \leq 3$ **13.** $-7 < x \leq -1$ **15.** all real numbers **17.** $-\frac{1}{3}$ **19.** $-\frac{5}{4} < x \leq \frac{13}{9}$
21. $x > 1$ **23.** $x > 1$ **Page 66, Exercises 1.** $8, -8$ **3.** $5, -3$ **5.** $-1, -5$
7. no solution **9.** $x > 8$ or $x < 4$ **11.** $x > -1$ or $x < -7$ **13.** $4 < x < 8$
15. $-5 < x < -1$ **17.** $x < -15$ or $x > 5$ **19.** $x \leq 6$ or $x \geq 8$ **21.** $6 < x < 8$
23. $-7 < x < 1$ **25.** $3, -9$ **27.** no solution **29.** $-15 \leq x \leq 3$ **31.** $\frac{14}{3}, -6$
33. no solution **35.** $\frac{1}{3} \leq x \leq \frac{4}{3}$ **37.** $\frac{2 - 4a}{3} < x < \frac{2 + 4a}{3}$ **39.** $\frac{3}{10}, \frac{5}{4}$ **41.** $x \geq 2$
Page 67, Checking Your Understanding 1. $x > 3$ **2.** $x < \frac{8}{5}$ **3.** $x > \frac{3}{2}$ **4.** $x \leq 3$
5. $-1 \leq x \leq 2$ **6:** $x < -3$ or $x > \frac{5}{3}$ **7.** no solution **8.** $3, -7$ **9.** $-2 < x < 8$
10. $1 \leq x \leq 3$ **11.** no solution **Pages 72-73, Exercises 1.** $28, 12$ **3.** $41°, 49°$
5. $50°, 58°, 72°$ **7.** $l = 50$ m, $w = 10$ m
9. First brother is 16 years old, second brother is 9 years old.

11. 125 km/h, 140 km/h **13.** $2\frac{1}{4}$ m from the 150 newton force. **15.** 320 L

17. 12.5 kg of \$2.40 tea and 37.5 kg of \$3.20 **19.** 26.7 km

21. between $8\frac{1}{3}$ L and 50 L

Chapter 3 Special Products, Factoring, Equations

Pages 80-81, Exercises 1. $ax + ay - bx - by$ **3.** $a^2 + 5a + 6$ **5.** $x^2 + x - 12$

7. $8a^2 - 2ab - 3b^2$ **9.** $6x^2 - 13x - 5$ **11.** $5x^2 - 32x + 12$ **13.** $14x^2 + 22x + \frac{3}{2}$

15. $1 + 2x - 63x^2$ **17.** $10x^2 - 17xy + 3y^2$ **19.** $49c^2 + 49cd + 12d^2$

21. $49c^2 - 9d^2$ **23.** $4x^2 - 9a^2$ **25.** $x^2 - \frac{1}{4}$ **27.** $9x^2 - 30x + 25$ **29.** $x^4 + x^2 + 0.25$

31. $r^2s^2 + 2rs - 3$ **33.** $15 - 17c^2d + 4c^4d^2$ **35.** $m^6n^2 + 2m^3n - 48$

37. $a^{2n} + 3a^n + 2$ **39.** $a^{4n} + 2a^{2n} - 3$ **41.** $x^{2n+2} + 3x^{n+1} - 10$

43. $x^{2n} + 2x^ny^n + y^{2n}$ **45.** $x^{2m} - y^{2n}$ **47.** $B^{2a} - 2A^bB^a + A^{2b}$ **49.** 6 **51.** 0

53. $\frac{13}{2}$ **55.** 32 **57.** $-x^2 + 2x + 3$ **Page 83, Exercises 1.** $x^2 + 6x + 9$

3. $x^2 - 8x + 16$ **5.** $h^2 + 14h + 49$ **7.** $1 - 2y + y^2$ **9.** $h^2 - 2hx + x^2$

11. $c^2 + 22cd + 121d^2$ **13.** $x^2 - 1$ **15.** $y^2 - 25$ **17.** $25a^2 - x^2$ **19.** $c^2 - 4d^2$

21. $9c^2 - \frac{4}{9}$ **23.** $x^2y^2 + 6xy + 9$ **25.** $m^2n^2 - 14mn + 49$ **27.** $c^2 + 2cxy + x^2y^2$

29. $0.25x^{12} - 0.1x^6y^2 + 0.01y^4$ **31.** $a^{2m}b^{2n} - 1$ **33.** $x \geq -\frac{3}{7}$ **35.** $x < -\frac{3}{2}$

37. 12 cm **39.** $(2n + 1)^2 - (2n - 1)^2 = 4n^2 + 4n + 1 - (4n^2 - 4n + 1) = 8n$, which

is divisible by 8. **Page 85, Exercises 1.** $ax + ay + bx + by + cx + cy$

3. $2mx + 2nx - 2px - m - n + p$ **5.** $c^2 + 2cd + d^2 - 25$

7. $4a^2 - 4ab + b^2 - m^2$ **9.** $c^2 - m^2 - 2mn - n^2$ **11.** $1 + r - s - 2r^2 + 4rs - 2s^2$

13. $x^2 + 2xy + y^2 + 6x + 6y + 9$ **15.** $9r^2 + 12rs + 4s^2 - 3r - 2s - 56$

17. $h^2 - k^2 + 8k - 16$ **19.** $9x^2 - 16y^2 - 40yz - 25z^2$ **21.** $x^4 - 2x^3 + x^2 - 36$

23. $x^4 + x^2y^2 + y^4$ **25.** $x^4 + 2x^3 + 3x^2 + 2x + 1$ **27.** $9x^2 - y^2 - 12y - 36$

29. $4x^{2n+2} - 12x^{n+1}y^n + 9y^{2n} + 20x^{n+1} - 30y^n + 25$ **31.** $4x + 4y + 4$

33. no real solution **Pages 87-88, Exercises 1.** $6(x - 2)$ **3.** $x(x - 1)$

5. $\pi(R - r)$ **7.** $4bx(a - 1)$ **9.** $ab(ac - b)$ **11.** $5m(m - 2)$ **13.** $7cd(1 - 2cd)$

15. $8a^2(a - 2)$ **17.** $xy(x - y)$ **19.** $5x(3x^2 - 2x + 1)$ **21.** $\pi r(r + h)$

23. $\frac{1}{3}\pi(r^2 + R^2 + rR)$ **25.** $2x^3(c^2 - c + d^2)$ **27.** $x^m(x - 1)$ **29.** $y^m(y^m - 1)$

31. $h^2(1 - 4h^n)$ **33.** $x^k(1 - 6x^3)$ **35.** $2a^2(1 - 3y)$ **37.** $7a(b^m - 3a^cb^c)$

39. $2(x^2y + 2a^2x + 3a^2y^2)$ **41.** $9(2m^x - 3x^{2m})$ **43.** $(x - c)(a - y)$

45. $(x - 4)(x - y)(x + y)$ **47.** $(x + 3)(x - 3)(m - 1)$ **49.** $(p + 2)(4 - y)$

51. $(t^2 + 2)(1 + r^2)$ **53.** $(m + n)(a - b - c)$ **55.** $3y^n(x^m - x^{m+1} + 1)$

57. $-x^3(x^n + y^n)$ **59.** $x(-10x + 17y)$ **61.** $(x^a - y^n)(a - c)(a + c)$

63. $(a + b)(x^n - y^n)$ **65.** $x^my^nz^k(y^2z + x^my^3 + z^{-1})$ or $x^my^nz^{k-1}(y^2z^2 + x^my^3 + 1)$

Pages 91-92, Exercises 1. $(m - 6)(m + 4)$ **3.** $(c - 6)(c + 2)$ **5.** $(b - 4)(b - 3)$

7. $(h - 5)(h - 4)$ **9.** $(k - 3)(k + 2)$ **11.** $(x + 6)(x - 5)$ **13.** $(x + 6)(x - 3)$

15. $(x - 7)(x - 6)$ **17.** $(2 - b)(10 + b)$ **19.** $(4 - y)(2 + y)$ **21.** $(z + 20)(z + 10)$

23. $(2x + 1)(x + 3)$ **25.** $(5x + 1)(2x + 3)$ **27.** $(3x - 4)(x - 2)$

29. $(2a - 3)(4a + 7)$ **31.** $(2p - 5)(p + 1)$ **33.** $(3c + 7)(c - 1)$

35. $(x + 5y)(x - 3y)$ **37.** $(x - 5y)(x + 3y)$ **39.** $(m - 8n)(m + 7n)$ **41.** prime

43. $(2c + d)(c - 2d)$ **45.** $(2a - b)(a - 2b)$ **47.** $(1 - 3x)^2$ **49.** $(x + 1)^2$

51. $(x - 1)^2$ **53.** $(c + d)^2$ **55.** $(c - d)^2$ **57.** $(\frac{1}{2}x + \frac{1}{8})(4x - 3)$ **59.** prime

61. $(xy - 5)(xy - 2)$ **63.** $(5xy + 4)(xy - 1)$ **65.** $(x^a - 5)(x^a + 4)$ **67.** $(a^{2x} - 3)^2$

69. $(3x^2y^2 + 5)(x^2y^2 - 6)$ **71.** $|h + 2|$ **73.** $|6 + 3x|$ **75.** $|c - \frac{5}{2}|$

77. $(14y^{2x} - 3z^w)(2y^{2x} + 5z^w)$ **79.** $3(3w + 5)(w + 1)(3w + 1)(3w + 7)$

Page 94, Exercises 1. $(y + 2)(y - 2)$ **3.** $(m - 1)(m + 1)$ **5.** $(1 - y)(1 + y)$

7. $(x - 7)(x + 7)$ **9.** $(2x - 1)(2x + 1)$ **11.** $(9 - 4y)(9 + 4y)$ **13.** $(x - 0.5)(x + 0.5)$

15. $(c - d)(c + d)$ **17.** $(ab - c)(ab + c)$ **19.** $(1 - 10x)(1 + 10x)$

21. $(4xy^3 - 5)(4xy^3 + 5)$ **23.** $(3 - 8c^2)(3 + 8c^2)$ **25.** $(5b^n - a)(5b^n + a)$

27. $(4a - 7b^{2m})(4a + 7b^{2m})$ **29.** $(2a^{3n} - 9b^n)(2a^{3n} + 9b^n)$

31. $(y^m - 0.1)(y^m + 0.1)$ **33.** $(m^{2x} - n^y)(m^{2x} + n^y)$ **35.** $\left(\frac{2}{3}a - \frac{5}{6}b\right)\left(\frac{2}{3}a + \frac{5}{6}b\right)$
37. $\left(\frac{1}{10}y^n - \frac{2}{3}z^k\right)\left(\frac{1}{10}y^n + \frac{2}{3}z^k\right)$ **39.** $(3x^2y^4 - 4z^3)(3x^2y^4 + 4z^3)$
41. $(a^{x+1} + b^{y+1})(a^{x+1} - b^{y+1})$ **43.** $(x - k - y)(x - k + y)$

45. $[A^{(2x+3)^2} + B^{(y+1)^2}][A^{(2x+3)^2} - B^{(y+1)^2}]$ **47.** $\frac{\sqrt{3}}{4}(b - a)(b + a)$ **Page 96,**
Exercises 1. $(a - 1)(a^2 + a + 1)$ **3.** $(a + 1)(a^2 - a + 1)$ **5.** $(c + 3)(c^2 - 3c + 9)$
7. $(m - 3)(m^2 + 3m + 9)$ **9.** $(m - n)(m^2 + mn + n^2)$ **11.** $(2x - 1)(4x^2 + 2x + 1)$
13. $(2y + 3)(4y^2 - 6y + 9)$ **15.** $(x - 6)(x^2 + 6x + 36)$ **17.** $\left(a + \frac{1}{2}\right)\left(a^2 - \frac{1}{2}a + \frac{1}{4}\right)$
19. $(ab + c)(a^2b^2 - abc + c^2)$ **21.** $(y^2 + 2)(y^4 - 2y^2 + 4)$
23. $(2a + 3b)(4a^2 - 6ab + 9b^2)$ **25.** $(x - 4y^2)(x^2 + 4xy^2 + 16y^4)$
27. $(b + 3a^2)(b^2 - 3ba^2 + 9a^4)$ **29.** $(x^a + 1)(x^{2a} - x^a + 1)$
31. $(y^b - 4)(y^{2b} + 4y^b + 16)$ **33.** $\left(\frac{1}{2}a - \frac{1}{3}b\right)\left(\frac{1}{4}a^2 + \frac{1}{6}ab + \frac{1}{9}b^2\right)$
35. $\left(\frac{1}{7}a^xb^y - \frac{1}{2}c^2\right)\left(\frac{1}{49}a^{2x}b^{2y} + \frac{1}{14}a^xb^yc^2 + \frac{1}{4}c^4\right)$ **37.** $a^2(a - 2)(a^2 + 2a + 4)$
39. $2x(x^2 + 3y^2)$ **41.** $4x(3x^2 + 1)(x^2 + 3)$ **Page 99, Exercises 1.** $4(x + 3)$
3. $ab(a + b)$ **5.** $5(m^2 - 6m - 6)$ **7.** $c(x - 2)(x + 2)$ **9.** $(8m - 3)(m - 1)$
11. $4(k - 2)(k + 2)$ **13.** $y(y - 3)(y + 3)$ **15.** $a(a - 1)(a^2 + a + 1)$
17. $3(x + 2)(x^2 - 2x + 4)$ **19.** $ab(x - 3)(x^2 + 3x + 9)$
21. $(x^2 + y^2)(x^4 - x^2y^2 + y^4)$ **23.** $(c - 3d)(c - 3d + 1)$ **25.** $(5 - c)(7 - c)$
27. $(x + 2)(y - x)(y + x)$ **29.** $(b + c)(x + y)$ **31.** $(m - n)(x + y)$
33. $(x + 1)(x^2 + 1)$ **35.** $3(y - 2)(y - 1)(y + 1)$ **37.** $(a^2 - 3)(5a + 2)$
39. $a(1 - a)^2(1 + a)$ **41.** $(x + y + c)(x + y - c)$ **43.** $(x - y - 1)(x + y + 1)$
45. $(a + b + c)(a - b - c)$ **47.** $(x - 3 - 2y)(x - 3 + 2y)$
49. $(1 - x - y)(1 + x + y)$ **51.** $(x + y - c)(x - y + c)$ **53.** $(a + b + 4)(a + b + 3)$
55. $(m - n + 6)(m - n - 5)$ **57.** $(x - a + b)(x + a - b)$
59. $(b^2 + b + 3)(x^2 + y^2)(x - y)(x + y)$ **61.** $(6a^2 + 2a + 9)^2$
63. $(x - 3)(x + 3)(a^3 + a + 1)$ **65.** $(r - t - 2m + 1)(r - t + 2m - 1)$
67. $a(a + 1)(a^4 + 2a^3 + 4a^2 + 3a + 3)$
69. $(x^2 + 2xy + y^2 + 1 - x - y)(x^2 + 2xy + y^2 + 1 + x + y)$ **Page 102, Exercises**
1. 0 **3.** $(x + 2)(x^2 - x + 2)$ **5.** $(x - 1)(x^2 + x + 5)$ **7.** $(2x + 1)(x - 1)$
9. $(x + y)(x^4 - x^3y + x^2y^2 - xy^3 + y^4)$ **11.** $2(x - 3)(x^2 + 3x + 9)$
13. $(x - 3)(x + 3)$ **15.** $(x + 3)(x - 1)$ **17.** $(x - 1)(x - 5)(x + 4)$
19. $(a - 1)(a^4 + a^3 + a^2 + 1)$ **21.** $(x - 2)(x^2 - x + 1)$
23. $(x - y)(x^6 + x^5y + x^4y^2 + x^3y^3 + x^2y^4 + xy^5 + y^6)$
25. $a(x + 625)\left(x^2 + \frac{1}{25}\right)\left(x + \frac{1}{5}\right)\left(x - \frac{1}{5}\right)$ **27.** $|(x + 1)(x^2 + 1)|$
29. $x^2(x - 2)(x + 2)(x^2 + 5)$ **Page 104, Exercises 1.** 180 **3.** $180a^4b^3$ **5.** $72x^2y^2$
7. $60a^3bc^4$ **9.** $(a + b)(m + n)(c - d)^2$ **11.** $2(x - y)(x + y)^2$ **13.** $x(x + 3)(x - 3)$
15. $(a + b)^2(a - b)^2$ **17.** $(m - 2)^2(m - 3)$ **19.** $(c - 3)(c + 3)(c - 4)(c + 4)$
21. $(x + y)(x^2 - xy + y^2)$ **23.** $(2x + 3)(x - 1)^2(x + 1)$
25. $10(x + y + 1)(x + y - 1)$ **27.** $(b - 1)^2(b^2 + 2b + 2)$
29. $(a + 2b + 9)(a + 2b - 9)^2$ **31.** $30(x + 4)(x + 5)^2$
33. $(x - 1)^2(x + 1)(x + 2)^3(x + 3)$ **Page 105, Checking Your Understanding**
1. $2x^2 + 5x - 3$ **2.** $x^2 + 2xy + y^2$ **3.** $y^2 - 9x^2$ **4.** $5 - 4(x + y)$
5. $3ab^2(2a + 5b + 1)$ **6.** $(x + 7)(x - 3)$ **7.** $(3x - 5)(2x + 3)$ **8.** $(2y - 5)^2$
9. $(2x - 9y)(2x + 9y)$ **10.** $(x - 2)(x^2 + 2x + 4)$ **11.** $(3x + 1)(9x^2 - 3x + 1)$
12. $(x - 3)(x - 1)(x + 1)$ **13.** $y^2(7 + y^2)(7 - y^2)$ **14.** $36x^2(x + 3)(x - 2)$
Pages 107-108, Exercises 1. -6 **3.** $\frac{9}{16}$ **5.** -4 **7.** 13 **9.** -6 **11.** 4
13. $c - d$ **15.** $c - 1$ **17.** $b + 4$ **19.** $\frac{1}{a}$ **21.** $a - b$ **23.** $a^2 - ab + b^2$ **25.** $\frac{T}{g - f}$
27. $\frac{2A}{b + c}$ **29.** $\frac{rl - a}{r - 1}$ **31.** $\sqrt{\frac{A + \pi r^2}{\pi}}$; $\sqrt{\frac{\pi R^2 - A}{\pi}}$; $\frac{A}{\pi(R + r)}$ **33.** $a - 3$
35. Identity; all real numbers **37.** $a^2 + b^2$ **Pages 110-111, Exercises 1.** 5
3. $-3, 0$ **5.** $4, 6$ **7.** $3, -8$ **9.** $1, 2$ **11.** $-3, 2$ **13.** $-\frac{3}{5}, \frac{2}{3}$ **15.** $-8, 10$ **17.** $-\frac{7}{2}$

19. $-7, 2$ **21.** $\frac{1}{2}, 6$ **23.** $\frac{1}{4}$ **25.** $-\frac{1}{4}, -\frac{1}{6}$ **27.** $\frac{2}{7}, \frac{4}{3}$ **29.** $-a, \frac{7}{2}a$ **31.** $a, -\frac{2}{5}a$
33. $x = -9, 3$; y is any real number **35.** $5, 7$ **37.** $-4, -2, 1, 3$

Chapter 4 Fractions and Fractional Equations

Page 119, Exercises 1. $-\frac{x-2}{y-2}$; $-\frac{2-x}{2-y}$; $\frac{2-x}{y-2}$ **3.** $\frac{6-x}{y-x}$; $-\frac{6-x}{x-y}$; $-\frac{x-6}{y-x}$
5. $(3-a)(b-4)$ or $(a-3)(4-b)$ **7.** $(4-z)(2-x)$ or $(z-4)(x-2)$
9. $(b-a)(c-d)$ or $(a-b)(d-c)$ **11.** $(a-1)(b-2)$ or $(1-a)(2-b)$
13. $a-[b-(c-d)]$ **15.** $-(x-1)^2$ **17.** 15 **19.** $(b-a)^n$ **Pages 121-122,**
Exercises 1. $\frac{3}{13}$ **3.** $\frac{y^n}{4x^3}$ **5.** $2x^3y^2$ **7.** $\frac{-2}{y^2}$ **9.** $\frac{b}{x-y}$ **11.** $\frac{m-4}{m+7}$ **13.** $x-3$ **15.** $\frac{4x+1}{3x-1}$
17. $\frac{-3x+5}{x+13}$ **19.** $\frac{y-x}{y(x+y)}$ **21.** $\frac{a+b-2}{2-a+b}$ **23.** $\frac{1}{ax-1}$ **25.** $\frac{x^2+2x+4}{1-3x}$ **27.** $\frac{a+b}{a^2+ab+b^2}$
29. $\frac{x-2}{y^2+3y+9}$ **31.** $\frac{x^2+xy+y^2}{2(x+y)}$ **33.** $\frac{a+2}{a-5}$ **35.** $\frac{(a+2)(a-2)}{a^4-4a^2+16}$ **37.** $\frac{a+b}{a}$ **39.** $\frac{x+4y}{x^2}$
41. $x^n + 9y^n$ **43.** $xy+2$ **45.** $\frac{1}{x+1}$ **47.** $x^{n-1} - x^{n-2} + \cdots x - 1$ **Page 124,**
Exercises 1. $\frac{3b^2}{a}$ **3.** $\frac{3a}{2c}$ **5.** $\frac{3a}{4b}$ **7.** x **9.** $\frac{a-b}{6}$ **11.** $\frac{m-n}{(m^2-1)(m+n)}$ **13.** $\frac{3(x-5)}{4(x-7)}$
15. $\frac{3}{4(y+3)(y+2)}$ **17.** 1 **19.** -1 **21.** $\frac{-x}{y(7+x)}$ **23.** $\frac{aby}{x+y}$ **25.** $\frac{-1}{y}$ **27.** $\frac{a^4-a^2b^2+b^4}{a^2+ab+b^2}$
29. $\frac{-a+b-c}{a+b-c}$ **Page 126, Exercises 1.** $\frac{9bxy^2}{a}$ **3.** $\frac{2}{n^2}$ **5.** $\frac{y}{x-y}$ **7.** $m-n$ **9.** $\frac{b-1}{b(b+1)}$
11. $\frac{x-2}{3}$ **13.** $\frac{2}{t^3(t-3)}$ **15.** $\frac{2(y-x)}{y}$ **17.** $\frac{-12}{m^3+m^2+m+1}$ **19.** $\frac{3x(2x+3)}{(x-1)(1-2x)}$
21. $\frac{a^2+2a+4}{a^3+8}$ **23.** $\frac{a-b}{b+c}$ **25.** $\frac{(x-y+z)(x+y-z)}{x+y+z}$ **27.** $\frac{m-1}{m-3}$ **29.** $\frac{x^n}{x^n-5}$
Pages 128-129, Exercises 1. $\frac{6a+3b+2c}{12}$ **3.** $\frac{6x^2-4x+9}{6x^3}$ **5.** $\frac{yz+xz+xy}{xyz}$ **7.** $\frac{6x-11}{24}$
9. $\frac{-(11x+1)}{4x}$ **11.** $\frac{3}{3-2c}$ **13.** $\frac{-6a^2-3ab+3b^2}{2a^2b^2}$ **15.** $\frac{3x^2-28x-2}{3x}$ **17.** $\frac{-4}{x^3-1}$
19. $\frac{a^3-2a^2-10a+10}{a^2-9}$ **21.** $\frac{-2(3x+2)}{(x^2-16)(x-1)}$ **23.** $\frac{-2}{ab}$ **25.** $\frac{-s^2+2s+2st+t^2}{t^2-s^2}$ **27.** 0
29. $\frac{-t-2}{(t-1)(t-3)}$ **31.** $\frac{-2a^2+3}{(a^3-1)(a+1)}$ **33.** $\frac{x^2}{(x-1)^2}$ **35.** $x^2+y^2 = \frac{4t^2+(1-t^2)^2}{(1+t^2)^2} = 1$
Page 131, Exercises 1. $\frac{x+1}{x-1}$ **3.** $\frac{3}{3a+2}$ **5.** $\frac{y+x}{y-x}$ **7.** $\frac{1}{c}$ **9.** $\frac{m^4-m^2+2m-1}{m^2}$ **11.** $-\frac{1}{z}$
13. $x-y$ **15.** $\frac{4ab}{a^2-b^2}$ **17.** $(x-2)(x-9)$ **19.** $\frac{3(x+12z)}{x+z}$ **21.** 1 **23.** $\frac{2a+1}{2}$
25. $x^2+9x+18$ **Page 133, Exercises 1.** -3 **3.** $\frac{1+xy}{1-xy}$ **5.** $\frac{b}{b-a}$ **7.** $\frac{a}{b}$ **9.** a
11. a **13.** $\frac{2x-3}{3x-1}$ **15.** $\frac{x+3}{x-3}$ **17.** $2x^2-1$ **19.** $\frac{x}{(a-1)(x-3y)}$ **21.** -1 **23.** $\frac{1}{x^2+x+1}$
25. $\frac{99}{70}$ **27.** $\frac{55}{34}$ **Page 134, Checking Your Understanding 1.** -5
2. $(a-3)(b+4)$ **3.** $\frac{2x-3y}{y-2x}$ or $\frac{3y-2x}{2x-y}$ **4.** $\frac{-3a}{b}$ **5.** $\frac{2y(y+2)}{y+3}$ **6.** $\frac{3x-4}{(x+2)(x^2-9)}$
7. $\frac{2x-2}{3-x}$ **8.** $\frac{3x^2-2y^2}{x(x^2-y^2)}$ **9.** $\frac{bc^3}{a}$ **10.** $\frac{a^2}{a-b}$ **11.** $\frac{x^2+x+1}{x^2}$ **12.** $\frac{2(x+2)}{x(x-1)}$ **13.** $x+1$
14. $3(x-1)$ **15.** $\frac{y+x}{y-x}$ **Page 137, Exercises 1.** 9 **3.** 2 **5.** $-\frac{2}{3}$ **7.** 6 **9.** 1
11. 1 **13.** no solution **15.** no solution **17.** $8\frac{1}{2}$ **19.** ab **21.** $\frac{wa}{F}$ **23.** $\frac{Vr_1r_2}{r_2-r_1}$
25. $\frac{r_1r_2r_3}{r_2r_3 + r_1r_3 + r_1r_2}$ **27.** $\frac{S(1-r)}{1-r^n}$ **29.** no solution **31.** -3 **33.** $-4, 1$ **35.** $x < \frac{2}{7}$
37. $\frac{13}{10}$ **Page 140, Exercises 1.** $0, 3$ **3.** $0, -4$ **5.** $2, -5$ **7.** no solution **9.** $-\frac{4}{3}, 2$
11. $\frac{3}{2}, 2$ **13.** no solution **15.** no solution **17.** 1 **19.** no solution **21.** $-\frac{5}{4}$
23. no solution **25.** $\frac{-a-b+2}{3}, \frac{-a-b-2}{3}$ **27.** no solution **29.** -3 **31.** $0, \pm\sqrt{5}$
Pages 143-145, Exercises 1. $\frac{2}{6}$ **3.** $4\frac{4}{9}$ h **5.** $18\frac{2}{3}$ h **7.** $\frac{29}{14}$ **9.** 200 km **11.** 30 min
13. $4, 8$ **15.** $13\frac{1}{3}$ h **17.** $3\frac{9}{19}$ **19.** $27\frac{3}{11}$ min **21.** $10\frac{10}{11}$ min
23. 40 km/h, 30 km/h **25.** $\frac{1}{7}, \frac{2}{3}$ **27.** Anne 3 h, Bernice 4 h **Pages 149-150,**
Exercises 1. $\frac{1}{500}$ **3.** $\frac{x}{x-2}$ **5.** $\frac{1}{20}$ **7.** $\frac{\pi}{1}$ **9.** Lois 21.75, Raymond 29.00

11. 50 m by 60 m **13.** no **15.** no **17.** $\frac{21}{8}$ **19.** -4 **21.** $10.36 **23.** $93.10
25. 875 cm **27.** $2.08 **29.** 16 cm **31.** 9 **33.** 12 **35.** 24, 36, 48 **37.** 99 m²
39. 36 **41.** 27 **43.** 6 **45.** 5:9
47. $\frac{x}{y} = \frac{a}{b}$, $xb = ya$, $xb + xy = ya + xy$, $x(b + y) = y(a + x)$, $\frac{x}{y} = \frac{a+x}{b+y}$
Page 151, Checking Your Understanding 1. no solution **2.** 5, 10 **3.** 2 **4.** 0, -1
5. $\frac{7}{13}$

Chapter 5 Graphs, Linear Equations, Functions and Relations
Pages 161-162, Exercises 1. $A(3, 0), B(-2, -3), C(1, 5), D(-4, 1)$
3. $A(-4, 0), B(0, 3), C(4, -1), D(0, -5)$ **11.** 6
13. Radius is 2 units; m$\angle COB = 60°$; m$\angle BOA = 30°$ **Page 166, Exercises**
27. $2x - 3y - 7 = 0$ **29.** $3x - y + 2 = 0$ **31.** $3x + y = 0$ **33.** $2x - y - 1 = 0, x \neq 0$
Page 171, Exercises 1. 2 **3.** $\frac{1}{4}$ **5.** $-\frac{2}{3}$ **7.** 2 **9.** -4 **11.** 0 **13.** undefined **15.** 2
17. $-\frac{4}{5}$ **19.** $-\frac{3}{7}$ **21.** undefined **23.** 3 **25.** $y \geq -15$ **27.** $\frac{2}{3}$ **Pages 176-177,**
Exercises 1. $x = -2; y = 6$ **3.** $x = 6; y = -6$ **5.** $x = \frac{1}{2}; y = -1$ **7.** none; $y = 3$
9. $m = 2; y = 4$ **11.** $m = -\frac{1}{2}; y = \frac{1}{2}$ **13.** $m = \frac{3}{4}; y = -6$ **15.** $m = 0; y = -\frac{1}{2}$
17. $y = -2x$ **19.** $y = -\frac{1}{2}x + 7$ **21.** $y = -\frac{1}{2}x + 6$ **31.** $w = -3t + 150$
33. $y = 3x + 5; y = -2x + 6; y = 3x - 5$ **37.** $y = -\frac{3}{4}x + 3$
39. diagonal $AC \perp$ diagonal BD
41. $w = -3t + 150, t < 16; w = 1.5t + 102, t \geq 16$ **Pages 179-180, Exercises**
1. $y = \frac{3}{2}x - \frac{5}{2}$ **3.** $y = \frac{1}{4}x - \frac{9}{3}$ **5.** $y = 5$ **7.** $y = \frac{4}{3}x + \frac{1}{3}$ **9.** $y = -\frac{7}{5}x + 7$ **11.** $y = x$
13. $y = 3x - 8; y = -8$ **15.** $y = -\frac{1}{2}x - 2$ **17.** $12x + 5y = 16$ **19.** $4x + 3y = -1$
21. $y = \frac{1}{3}x + \frac{5}{2}$ **Page 181, Checking Your Understanding 8.** $\frac{7}{2}$ **9.** -2
10. $y = \frac{5}{4}x - 3$ **11.** $y = -10x + 7$ **Pages 185-186, Exercises 1.** yes **3.** no
5. yes **7.** no **9.** no **11.** Range: even integers **13.** Range: $\cdots -5, -2, 1, 4, 7 \cdots$
15. $(-1, 5)(0, 0)(1, -3)(2, -4)(3, -3)(4, 0)(5, 5)$ **17.** no **19.** yes **21.** -21
23. $4k - 1$ **25.** -0.88 **27.** 0 **29.** $2a - 1$ **31.** decreases; increases
35. $(\pm 5, 0)(\pm 4, 3)(\pm 3, 4)(\pm 2, \sqrt{21})(\pm 1, 2\sqrt{6})(0, 5)$ **Pages 189-190, Exercises**
1. Range; $y > 3$ **3.** $y \geq 4$ **7.** $y = \frac{5}{2}x - 5$ **9.** $y = -\frac{2}{5}x + \frac{27}{5}$
11. $p(t) = 0.03t + 0.35$ **13.** $a(t) = -400t + 10\ 000$ **15.** $C(n) = 5n + 2750$
17. for $k \leq 500, C(k) = 0.04k + 10; k > 500, C(k) = 0.05k + 5$
Page 193, Exercises 1. relation contains pairs $(1, 2)$ and $(1, 0)$ among others
3. relation contains $(1, 0)$ and $(1, 1)$ among others **Page 196, Exercises**
1. $\{(1, 2)(3, 0)(1, 1)\}$ **3.** $\{(2, 1)(4, 3)(6, 5)(1, 8)\}$ **5.** $y = -\frac{1}{2}x - \frac{3}{2}$ **7.** $y = \frac{1}{3}x - \frac{5}{3}$
9. $y = 2x - 3$ **11.** f **13.** k **15.** no, yes **17.** yes, no **19.** yes, yes **23.** yes, yes
25. 3 **27.** a **Page 197, Checking Your Understanding 1.** no **2.** yes **3.** yes
4. yes **5.** -7, Answers will vary. **9.** 15

Chapter 6 Systems of Linear Equations and Inequalities
Page 205, Exercises 1. $(3, -3)$ **3.** $(5, 0)$ **5.** $(-2, 3)$ **7.** equivalent, dependent
9. $\left(4, -2\frac{1}{2}\right)$ **11.** $(0, 6)$ **13.** $\left(1\frac{1}{2}, -1\right)$ **15.** equivalent, dependent **17.** $\left(-\frac{4}{3}, 8\right)$
19. $(2, 1)$ **21.** $(2, 2), (-6, 6)$ **Pages 208-209, Exercises 1.** $(1, 2)$ **3.** $(-3, -2)$
5. $(-5, 4)$ **7.** dependent equations, all points in common **9.** $(5, 4)$ **11.** $(2c, 0)$
13. $\left(\frac{2a + b}{2}, \frac{2a - b}{2}\right)$ **15.** $(2.5, 3.5)$ **17.** $\left(-\frac{3}{2}, 4\right)$ **19.** $\left(-\frac{9}{16}, \frac{3}{8}\right)$ **21.** no solution
23. $\left(\frac{7}{3}, \frac{2}{3}\right)$ **25.** $(m + n, m - n)$ **27.** $a = 7, b = -5, d = 6, e = -4$ **Page 212,**
Exercises 1. $(4, -1, 3)$ **3.** $(-1, 4, 8)$ **5.** $(2, 5, -1)$ **7.** $(1, 1, 1)$ **9.** $\left(\frac{8}{5}, \frac{4}{5}, -\frac{9}{5}\right)$
11. no solution **13.** $(0.2, 0.4, 0.6)$ **15.** $\left(\frac{3}{4}, \frac{5}{6}, \frac{1}{8}\right)$ **17.** $(6, -7, -13)$

19. $(5b, 5b, -5b)$ **21.** $(2a, 3b, a - b)$ **Page 216, Exercises 1.** $(3, 1)$

3. $(-15, 25)$ **5.** $(9, -16)$ **7.** $(2, 3)$ **9.** $\left(\frac{5}{7}, \frac{5}{6}\right)$ **11.** $m = 2, n = -2$ **13.** $(6, 5)$

15. $\left(\frac{5}{13}, \frac{-5}{12}\right)$ **17.** $\left(-\frac{1}{2}, \frac{1}{3}\right)$ **19.** $m = -\frac{1}{2}, n = \frac{1}{2}$ **21.** no solution **23.** no solution

25. $\left(\frac{2}{m + n - p}, \frac{2}{m - n + p}, \frac{2}{-m + n + p}\right)$ **27.** no solution **Page 217, Checking Your**

Understanding 1. $(1, 5)$ **2.** $(-1, 1)$ **3.** no solution **4.** $(-3, -4)$ **5.** $(1, 3)$

6. $(2a, b)$ **7.** $(-1, 4, -3)$ **8.** $\left(\frac{1}{2}, 2\right)$ **9.** $(7, -3)$ **Page 219, Exercises**

1. 44 dimes, 31 nickels **3.** 50 kg @ \$8.40, 130 kg @ \$7.50 **5.** 50 dozen

7. soap 49¢, toothpaste 87¢ **9.** nickels: $\frac{10t - v}{5}$, dimes: $\frac{v - 5t}{5}$

11. egg 77¢, hamburger 91¢, roast beef \$1.43 **Page 221, Exercises**

1. \$2000 at $6\frac{1}{2}$%, \$3000 at 7% **3.** \$4000 at 7%, \$12 000 at 4%

5. \$3600 at $7\frac{1}{2}$%, \$2800 at $6\frac{1}{2}$% **7.** \$5000 at 5%, \$10 000 at 8% **Page 223,**

Exercises 1. 42 **3.** 74 **5.** 56 **7.** 27 **9.** 42, 32 **11.** 2382

Chapter 7 Exponents, Radicals, and Complex Numbers

Pages 233-234, Exercises 1. a^8 **3.** a^4 **5.** a^{12} **7.** $x^5 y^5$ **9.** m^3 **11.** $\frac{-8}{125}$

13. $2a^5$ **15.** $x^6 y^9$ **17.** $\frac{4c^4}{b^6}$ **19.** $8ab^2$ **21.** $x^3 y^4$ **23.** x^{20} **25.** $(x - y)^4$ **27.** $a^{2n} b^{3n}$

29. $(x + y)^4$ **31.** $2z$ **33.** b^{3n} **35.** $a^{2m} b^{n-2}$ **37.** $(a - 2)^6$ **39.** $4x^7 y^6$

41. $x^2 + 2xy + y^2$ **43.** $\frac{9b^4}{a^2}$ **45.** b^{10} **47.** $a^{x^2 - 4}$ **49.** $y = 24a^{19}$

51. $2^9, 2^{12}, 2^{10}, 2^8$; $16^2, 8^3, 2^{10}, 4^6$ **Pages 237-238, Exercises 1.** $5, -5$ **3.** 3

5. $3, -3$ **7.** 4 **9.** -7 **11.** ± 13 **13.** 9 **15.** -4 **17.** -1 **19.** no root **21.** 10

23. no root **25.** $3y^2$ **27.** xy^2 **31.** $-3x^3$ **33.** $-2a^3 b^5$ **35.** $2x^2 y$ **37.** $-1.2p^2$

39. $0.2a$ **41.** $x^3 y^8$ **43.** $-100x^8 y^2$ **45.** $5x^2 y$ **47.** $x + 2$ **49.** $x - 3$ **51.** $-3(a - b)^4$

53. a^2 **55.** $3x + 3$ **57.** $(x + y)(a + b)^2$ **59.** $4x^3$ **61.** $10x^{10} y^5$ **63.** $(9x + 3y)$

65. $5x$ **67.** $2x^2 y$ **Pages 241-242, Exercises 1.** 5 **3.** -4 **5.** 243 **7.** $\frac{1}{4}$ **9.** $\frac{8}{27}$

11. 1.1 **13.** b^3 **15.** $\frac{3a^2}{b^4}$ **17.** $a^{\frac{4}{5}}$ **19.** $b^{\frac{5}{6}}$ **21.** $c^{\frac{7}{12}}$ **23.** $y^{1.25}$ **25.** $b^{\frac{4}{3}}$ **27.** $n^{\frac{5}{4}}$ **29.** $x^{\frac{1}{6}}$

31. $\frac{x^{\frac{2}{3}}}{y^{\frac{2}{3}}}$ **33.** $\frac{x^{\frac{3}{8}}}{y^{\frac{1}{4}}}$ **35.** $b^{\frac{n}{6}}$ **37.** $x^{\frac{5}{36}} y^{\frac{1}{18}}$ **39.** $(a + b)^3$ **41.** $x^3 yz$ **43.** $6x^4 y^3$ **45.** x^b

47. $\frac{3x^2 y^4}{4}$ **49.** $a - b$ **51.** $\frac{7}{3}$ **Pages 245-246, Exercises 1.** 2 **3.** 4 **5.** $\frac{1}{2}$ **7.** $\frac{1}{2}$

9. $-\frac{1}{64}$ **11.** 2 **13.** 12 **15.** x^3 **17.** $\frac{b^2}{3}$ **19.** b^7 **21.** a **23.** $\frac{1}{x^8}$ **25.** $\frac{1}{n^5}$ **27.** $\frac{1}{m^9}$ **29.** $\frac{x^2}{y}$

31. $\frac{y}{x^2}$ **33.** $\frac{y^9}{x^6}$ **35.** $x^9 y^6$ **37.** $\frac{3cd^{11}}{4}$ **39.** 6 **41.** $\frac{1}{(x + y)^3}$ **43.** $y^4 - 1$ **45.** $x^{\frac{7}{3}} - x^{\frac{5}{6}} - x^{\frac{4}{3}}$

47. $x^2 - 4y^2$ **49.** $x^{-4} - y^{-4}$ **51.** $a^{-1} + b^{-1}$ **53.** $a^{-\frac{1}{2}} - b^{-\frac{1}{2}}$ **Page 246, Checking**

Your Understanding 1. $x^6 y^3$ **2.** $x^5 z^8$ **3.** $9(a - 4)^{2n-2}$ **4.** 27 **5.** $-\frac{243}{32}$ **6.** z

7. $m^{\frac{1}{2}}$ **8.** 9 **9.** $\frac{1}{128}$ **10.** $\frac{a}{2}$ **11.** $x^8 y^5$ **12.** $\frac{c^{\frac{9}{2}}}{a^4 b^3}$ **13.** -3 **14.** -1 **15.** $3ab$ **16.** $4a^2 b$

Page 249, Exercises 1. $2\sqrt{2}$ **3.** $2\sqrt{6}$ **5.** $2\sqrt[3]{3}$ **7.** $5\sqrt{2a}$ **9.** $3x\sqrt[3]{2x}$

11. $4y\sqrt{3x}$ **13.** $7a^2 b\sqrt{2b}$ **15.** $2x\sqrt[3]{5xy}$ **17.** $6x^2\sqrt{3x}$ **19.** $10a^2\sqrt[3]{a}$ **21.** $\sqrt{10}$

23. 6 **25.** $\sqrt[3]{6}$ **27.** $3\sqrt{6}$ **29.** $a\sqrt{bc}$ **31.** 1 **33.** 5 **35.** $y\sqrt{6}$ **37.** 150 **39.** 240

41. $15(x - y)\sqrt{10(x - y)}$ **43.** $2x(x - y)\sqrt[3]{2(x - y)^2}$ **45.** $12\sqrt{3}$ **47.** 12

49. $2xyz^3\sqrt[5]{xy^5}$ **51.** $\sqrt{10} - 5\sqrt{3}$ **53.** $560x^2 y$ **55.** $64xy^4$ **57.** a^{2n} **59.** $x\sqrt[6]{x}$

61. $x^2 + 2x + 1$ **63.** x^{n+1} **65.** $2x^6 y^4\sqrt[3]{x}$ **67.** $13 + \sqrt{6}$ **Page 252, Exercises**

1. 2 **3.** $\sqrt{10}$ **5.** 2 **7.** $\sqrt{5}$ **9.** $\sqrt[3]{4}$ **11.** $2\sqrt[3]{ab}$ **13.** $\frac{2\sqrt{5}}{5}$ **15.** $\frac{x\sqrt{3}}{y}$ **17.** $\frac{2\sqrt{15}}{3}$

19. $\frac{\sqrt{14x}}{7}$ **21.** $\frac{\sqrt[3]{6}}{2}$ **23.** $\frac{\sqrt{15}}{6}$ **25.** $\frac{\sqrt{ab}}{b}$ **27.** $\frac{5\sqrt[3]{9x}}{3x}$ **29.** $\frac{\sqrt[3]{abc}}{b}$ **31.** $\frac{\sqrt{10y}}{2xy}$ **33.** $\frac{x\sqrt{10y}}{5}$

35. $\frac{\sqrt{10xy}}{12x}$ **37.** a **39.** x^2 **41.** $2a^2$ **43.** $9\sqrt{x}$ **45.** $\frac{\sqrt[8]{250x}}{5}$ **47.** $\frac{c\sqrt{3}}{2}$ **49.** $\frac{\sqrt{x-y}}{x-y}$

51. $\frac{1}{x}$ **53.** $\frac{\sqrt[4]{x}}{x^2}$ **Page 254, Exercises 1.** $\frac{\sqrt{15}}{3}$ **3.** $\frac{3\sqrt{2}}{2}$ **5.** $\sqrt{3}$ **7.** $\frac{3\sqrt[3]{4}}{2}$ **9.** $\frac{\sqrt{6}}{9}$

11. $\sqrt[3]{2}$ **13.** $\frac{\sqrt[3]{25}}{3}$ **15.** $\frac{\sqrt[3]{ab^2}}{ab}$ **17.** 0.5773 **19.** 0.8163 **21.** $\frac{\sqrt[3]{36xy^2}}{6y}$ **23.** $\frac{\sqrt{x+y}}{x^2+2xy+y^2}$

25. $\frac{\sqrt[4]{x^3}}{x}$ **27.** $\frac{2\sqrt{2}+1}{7}$ **Page 256, Exercises 1.** $\sqrt{5}$ **3.** $\sqrt{a}$ **5.** $\sqrt{3}$ **7.** $\sqrt{xy}$

9. $3y\sqrt{y}$ **11.** $\sqrt{2}$ **13.** $2\sqrt{xy}$ **15.** $\sqrt[4]{4xy^2}$ **17.** $\sqrt[5]{a^2bc^4}$ **19.** $\frac{\sqrt[3]{3x^2}}{x}$ **21.** $\frac{a^4\sqrt{3}}{y}$

23. $\frac{x^3\sqrt{5y}}{y}$ **25.** $\frac{\sqrt{2ab}}{b^3}$ **27.** $\sqrt[2m]{9x^{2n}y^k}$ **29.** $z\sqrt{2zw}$ **31.** $\sqrt{10a+15b}$ **Page 259,**

Exercises 1. $6\sqrt{3}$ **3.** $5\sqrt{3}$ **5.** $9\sqrt{3}$ **7.** $6\sqrt{x}$ **9.** $\sqrt[3]{2}$ **11.** $\frac{\sqrt{6}-6\sqrt{3}}{6}$

13. $\sqrt{7}-3\sqrt{11}$ **15.** $7+2\sqrt{10}$ **17.** $5+2\sqrt{6}$ **19.** $2+\sqrt{3}$ **21.** $\frac{3(\sqrt{6}+\sqrt{2})}{2}$

23. $13-2\sqrt{42}$ **25.** $\frac{a(\sqrt{a}-\sqrt{b})}{a-b}$ **27.** $\frac{(x+y-1)}{xy}\sqrt{xy}$ **29.** $\sqrt[3]{4}+2\sqrt[3]{6}+\sqrt[3]{9}$ **31.** $2b\sqrt{x}$

33. -4 **35.** $\frac{(2x-1)\sqrt{x^2-1}}{x^2-1}$ **37.** $x^2+2x-(x+1)\sqrt{x^2+x}$ **39.** $t+1-9t^2$

Page 261, Exercises 1. $\sqrt[6]{200}$ **3.** $a\sqrt[6]{a}$ **5.** $x\sqrt[6]{xy^3}$ **7.** $ab\sqrt[6]{a^2b^3}$ **9.** $y\sqrt[6]{32x^5y}$

11. $x\sqrt[12]{x^5}$ **13.** $4x\sqrt[18]{x^{17}}$ **15.** $\frac{\sqrt[6]{108}}{3}$ **17.** $(a-b)\sqrt[4]{a-b}$ **19.** $\sqrt[3]{4}+2\sqrt[6]{108}+3$

21. $\frac{\sqrt[25]{x^{20}y^{13}}}{y}$ **23.** $\frac{a\sqrt[9]{a^6b^2}}{4}$ **25.** $\frac{x\sqrt[60]{x^{45}y^{38}}}{y}$ **Pages 264-265, Exercises 1.** 16

3. no solution **5.** 39 **7.** 29 **9.** 2 **11.** 4 **13.** 9 **15.** $2, 8$ **17.** no solution **19.** $3, 5$

21. 81 **23.** $\frac{17}{4}$ **25.** $S=\frac{1}{2}gt^2$, approx. 44 m **27.** 5 **29.** $x=a$ **31.** 5 **33.** $0, 4$

35. $\frac{1}{9}$ **Page 265, Checking Your Understanding 1.** $5\sqrt{10}$ **2.** $3z^2\sqrt{3z}$

3. $\frac{3}{2a}\sqrt[4]{4a}$ **4.** $\sqrt{3b}$ **5.** $6\sqrt[3]{2}$ **6.** $\frac{3s\sqrt{7s}}{t}$ **7.** $\frac{-\sqrt{3}}{4}$ **8.** $\frac{\sqrt[3]{20}}{5}$

9. $-2\sqrt{2}-2\sqrt{6}$ **10.** $\frac{5\sqrt{15}-16}{7}$ **11.** 7 **12.** 1

Page 268, Exercises 1. i **3.** $i\sqrt{6}$ **5.** $7i$ **7.** $\frac{1}{4}i$ **9.** $i\sqrt{3}$ **11.** $4\sqrt{2}i$ **13.** $\frac{2}{3}i$

15. $2\sqrt{7}i$ **17.** -2 **19.** i **21.** $1.45-0.6i$ **23.** $2-2i$ **25.** $2+i$ **27.** $\frac{6-\sqrt{7}i}{4}$

29. $-2\sqrt{5}$ **31.** $\sqrt{22}i$ **33.** $-1+\sqrt{14}i$ **35.** $1-i$ **37.** $\frac{15-\sqrt{10}i}{5}$ **39.** $(4+\sqrt{2})i$

41. $(7+\sqrt{6})i$ **43.** $x<\frac{7}{2}$ **45.** $\frac{1}{3}+\frac{\sqrt{2}}{3}i$ **Page 271, Exercises 1.** $-6\sqrt{10}$ **3.** -10

5. $\sqrt{3}i$ **7.** $\frac{\sqrt{2}}{2}$ **9.** $-\sqrt{21}i$ **11.** $\frac{-\sqrt{5}i}{5}$ **13.** $10-2i$ **15.** $-5+9i$ **17.** $5+i$

19. $-16+8i$ **21.** 26 **23.** $-40-42i$ **25.** $\frac{3}{34}+\frac{5}{34}i$ **27.** $\frac{9}{41}-\frac{40}{41}i$ **29.** $\frac{5}{34}+\frac{37}{34}i$

31. 169 **33.** 25 **35.** i **37.** $-i$ **39.** $2+3i$ **41.** $-i$ **43.** 5 **45.** i **47.** $-i$

49. $3c+5di$ **51.** $3y^2-8x^2-14xyi$ **53.** $9x^2-4y^2-12xyi$ **55.** $2x^3+6x$

57. $a=6, b=2$ **Page 275, Exercises 11.** $2+3i$ **13.** $4+3i$ **17.** $5+i$

15. $-7+i$ **21.** both members equal $\sqrt{a^2c^2+b^2c^2+a^2d^2+b^2d^2}$ **Page 276,**

Checking Your Understanding 1. $-2\sqrt{3}i$ **2.** $-i$ **3.** $2-\frac{\sqrt{6}}{2}$ **4.** 6 **5.** $21-8i$

6. $-7+7i$ **7.** -10 **8.** $34-2i$ **9.** $-\frac{36}{29}+\frac{3}{29}i$ **10.** $-\frac{1}{58}+\frac{17}{58}i$ **12.** $8+7i$

Chapter 8 Quadratic Functions and Quadratic Equations

Page 284, Exercises 13. $-1, 2$ **15.** $1, 2$ **17.** ± 5 **19.** $\frac{5}{2}$ **21.** no real solution

23. $-1, \frac{5}{2}$ **29.** $\frac{9}{2}$ **31.** $(-1, 0), (3, 0); -1, 3$ **33.** $(-5, 0), (6, 11)$ **Page 287,**

Exercises 1. ± 7 **3.** ± 5 **5.** $\pm 3\sqrt{2}$ **7.** ± 2.5 **9.** ± 4 **11.** $\pm 7\sqrt{2}$ **13.** $\pm i\sqrt{5}$

15. $\pm\sqrt{3}$ **17.** $\pm i\sqrt{5}$ **19.** $\pm\frac{i\sqrt{15}}{5}$ **21.** $\pm2\sqrt{2}$ **23.** ±9 **25.** $\frac{5}{2}, -\frac{1}{2}$ **27.** $1\pm2i$

29. $\frac{-3\pm i\sqrt{2}}{2}$ **31.** $r=\pm\sqrt{\frac{V}{\pi h}}$ **33.** $t=\pm\sqrt{\frac{2s}{g}}$ **35.** $\pm(1+\sqrt{3}), \pm(1-\sqrt{3})$

37. approx. 1 unit thick (0.9745) **Page 291, Exercises 1.** $\frac{9}{4}$ **3.** $\frac{1}{9}$ **5.** 0.0025

7. $3, -1$ **9.** $-5, 7$ **11.** $-6, 9$ **13.** $-8, -6$ **15.** $1, 8$ **17.** $\frac{2}{3}, 1$ **19.** $\frac{-8\pm\sqrt{34}}{5}$

21. $\frac{-1\pm\sqrt{5}}{2}$ **23.** $\frac{-1\pm\sqrt{11}}{5}$ **25.** $1\pm2i$ **27.** $\frac{1\pm i\sqrt{3}}{2}$ **29.** $\frac{4\pm\sqrt{10}}{6}$ **31.** $-a, -2a$

33. $7c, -5c$ **35.** $\frac{9}{4}$ **37.** $\frac{-\sqrt{3}\pm i\sqrt{17}}{2}$ **39.** $\frac{e\pm\sqrt{e^2+4df}}{2d}$ **41.** $\frac{3+\sqrt{5}}{2}$ **Pages 294-295,**

Exercises 1. $-1, -\frac{5}{3}$ **3.** $3, -4$ **5.** $\frac{1}{2}, -\frac{1}{4}$ **7.** $1, -2$ **9.** $\frac{-3\pm\sqrt{17}}{4}$ **11.** $\frac{-1\pm i\sqrt{3}}{2}$

13. $\frac{-1\pm\sqrt{3}}{4}$ **15.** -3 **17.** ±9 **19.** $\frac{6\pm\sqrt{3}}{11}$ **21.** $\frac{0.7\pm\sqrt{0.97}}{2}$ **23.** $\frac{1\pm i\sqrt{59}}{6}$

25. $\frac{-2b\pm\sqrt{4b^2+2c}}{2}$ **27.** $\frac{-1\pm\sqrt{1-4a}}{2a}$ **31.** $1, -\frac{5}{8}$ **33.** $\frac{\sqrt{6}}{2}, \frac{2\sqrt{6}}{9}$ **35.** $\frac{\pm1-\sqrt{4a^2+1}}{2}$

37. 84 **Page 298, Exercises 1.** irrational, $\neq$ **3.** rational, $\neq$ **5.** rational, $=$
7. imaginary, $\neq$ **9.** imaginary, $\neq$ **11.** rational, $=$ **13.** rational, $\neq$ **15.** irrational, $\neq$
17. imaginary, $\neq$ **19.** irrational, $\neq$ **21.** irrational, $\neq$ **23.** ±1 **25.** ±16 **27.** $20, -4$
29. $m>9$ **31.** $k\le\frac{2}{5}$ **35.** sum 5; product 6 **37.** sum $\frac{7}{3}$; product $-\frac{2}{3}$ **Page 301,**

Exercises 1. $\pm i\sqrt{3}, \pm\sqrt{3}$ **3.** $\pm4, \pm4i$ **5.** $\pm i\sqrt{6}, \pm i\sqrt{3}$ **7.** $\pm\sqrt{5}, \pm2\sqrt{2}$

9. $\pm1, \pm2$ **11.** $\pm1, \pm3$ **13.** $\pm\frac{\sqrt{3}}{3}i, \pm\sqrt{2}$ **15.** $\pm1, \pm\sqrt{6}$ **17.** $6, -4$

19. $\frac{1\pm\sqrt{37}}{2}, \frac{1\pm i\sqrt{3}}{2}$ **21.** 64 **23.** $2, -\frac{1}{2}$ **25.** $\pm1, \pm2$ **27.** 13 **29.** $\pm\frac{\sqrt{210}}{9}, \pm\frac{4}{9}\sqrt{15}$

31. $\frac{\sqrt{3}}{9}, \frac{\sqrt{5}}{25}$ **Page 305, Exercises 1.** $3, -1$ **3.** $-1, -\frac{5}{2}$ **5.** $4, 9$ **7.** $\frac{\pm\sqrt{6}}{3}$

9. $\frac{-1\pm\sqrt{129}}{4}$ **11.** $\pm\frac{\sqrt{5}}{3}i$ **13.** no solution **15.** -1 **17.** 2 **19.** 4 **21.** 6 **23.** 7

25. 1, 2, 3, 6 **27.** $\frac{1\pm i\sqrt{95}}{6}$ **29.** 2 **31.** 10, 15 **33.** (0, 1) **Page 307, Exercises**
1. $x^2+x-12=0$ **3.** $x^2+4x+3=0$ **5.** $x^2-3x=0$ **7.** $3x^2+x-2=0$
9. $8x^2+10x-3=0$ **11.** $x^2-11=0$ **13.** $x^2-10x+26=0$ **15.** $x^2-6x+7=0$
17. $x^2-2\sqrt{5}x+5=0$ **19.** $x^3-6x^2+11x-6=0$ **21.** $x^3+4x^2-7x-10=0$
23. $\frac{1-b}{2}, \frac{1+b}{2}$ **Page 308, Checking Your Understanding 1.** $4, -2$ **2.** $\frac{1}{2}, -5$

3. $\pm\frac{9}{2}$ **4.** $\pm\frac{6}{7}$ **5.** $\pm\frac{2}{5}i\sqrt{15}$ **6.** $9, -1$ **7.** $\frac{1}{3}\pm\frac{1}{3}\sqrt{7}$ **8.** $\frac{3}{2}\pm\frac{3}{2}\sqrt{21}$ **9.** $-\frac{1}{2}\pm\frac{\sqrt{5}}{2}$
10. $\frac{1}{10}\pm\frac{1}{10}i\sqrt{39}$ **11.** one, rational **12.** two, complex **13.** two, rational
14. $\pm2, \pm2i$ **15.** $\pm1, \pm i$ **16.** $-\frac{9}{2}\pm\frac{1}{2}\sqrt{13}$ **17.** $\frac{7}{3}$ **18.** $3x^2-14x+15=0$
19. $x^2-6x+25=0$ **Page 312, Exercises 1.** $-3, \left(\frac{1}{3}, -\frac{8}{3}\right), x=\frac{1}{3}$

3. $0, \left(-\frac{1}{2}, -\frac{1}{4}\right), x=-\frac{1}{2}$ **5.** $3, (1, 4), x=1$ **7.** $-4, (2, -12), x=2$
9. $2, \left(\frac{5}{2}, -\frac{17}{4}\right), x=\frac{5}{2}$ **11.** $0, (2, -4), x=2$ **13.** $0, \left(\frac{3}{2}, \frac{9}{2}\right), x=\frac{3}{2}$ **15.** $6, (0, 6), x=0$
17. $5, (-1, 6), x=-1$ **19.** $3, (0, 3), x=0$ **21.** $1, (0, 1), x=0$ **23.** $-\frac{1}{2}, (1, 0), x=1$

25. axis is $x=-\frac{b}{2a}$ and $\left[\frac{-b-\sqrt{b^2-4ac}}{2a}+\frac{-b+\sqrt{b^2-4ac}}{2a}\right]\div2=-\frac{b}{2a}$ **Page 316,**
Exercises 27. $y=32x^2+16x-336$ **Pages 321-322, Exercises 1.** ±9
3. 9 and 15; -9 and -15 **5.** 41, 42 **7.** 12 or $-\frac{25}{2}$ **9.** 36 and 30; 1 and -5
11. 120 m by 160 m **13.** $4+2\sqrt{2}$ (equal sides), $4+4\sqrt{2}$ (hypotenuse)
15. 45 cm; 108 cm **17.** 2 h **19.** 888 km/h **21.** 4, 18, 78 **23.** $e\sqrt{3}$
25. $\left(\frac{13+3\sqrt{17}}{2}\right)\pi$ cm² **27.** $OA=42$ cm; $OB=40$ cm **Page 327, Exercises**

7. -0.6 **9.** 2.1 **11.** $-2.3, 1.9$ **19.** $\pm 3, \pm 1, 5$ **21.** $(1, 0), (-2, 30)$ **Page 331, Exercises 1.** $\pm 2, \pm 2i$ **3.** $x - 2$ **5.** $2, -2 \pm 2\sqrt{2}$ **7.** $\pm 1, \pm 2, \pm \frac{1}{3}, \pm \frac{2}{3}$ **9.** $\pm 1, \pm 2, \pm \frac{1}{3}, \pm \frac{2}{3}$ **11.** $-1, -1, 2$ **13.** $-\frac{2}{3}, \frac{1}{2}, 0$ **15.** $2, 3 \pm \sqrt{13}$ **17.** $5, \frac{2 \pm i}{5}$

19. $-3, \frac{1}{5}, 2$ **21.** $0, -1, 2, 3$ **23.** $\pm 1, \pm \left(\frac{1}{2} + \frac{\sqrt{3}}{2}i \right), \pm \left(-\frac{1}{2} + \frac{\sqrt{3}}{2}i \right)$

25. 10 cm, 7 cm, 5 cm **27.** $(2, -130)(-1, -160)$ **Page 332, Checking Your Understanding 1.** opens up, min at vertex at $x = -\frac{3}{2}$; axis of sym. $x = -\frac{3}{2}$ **2.** opens down, max at vertex at $x = -4$; axis of sym. $x = -4$ **3.** opens up, min at vertex at $x = -\frac{3}{4}$; axis of sym. $x = -\frac{3}{4}$ **4.** 12 **5.** $4, 8, 4\sqrt{5}$

6. expressway 60 km/h, 7.5 h; scenic route 45 km/h, 10 h **9.** $0, \frac{\sqrt{6}}{2}i$

10. $-3, 2, \pm i$ **11.** $2, \frac{-3 \pm \sqrt{5}}{2}$ **12.** $-2, 1 \pm i\sqrt{3}$

Chapter 9 Conics and Systems of Equations Involving Quadratics
Pages 344-345, Exercises 1. 10 **3.** 5 **5.** $\sqrt{130}$ **7.** 10 **9.** $2\sqrt{34}$ **11.** 1.5
13. $\left(\frac{11}{2}, 0 \right)$ **15.** $\left(\frac{7}{2}, -\frac{1}{2} \right)$ **17.** $\left(0, -\frac{9}{2} \right)$ **23.** $M \left(2\sqrt{6}, \frac{23}{3} \right), \overline{AB} = \frac{2}{3}\sqrt{58}$ **27.** 32
Page 348, Exercises 1. $x^2 + y^2 = 16$ **3.** $x^2 + (y - 4)^2 = 9$
5. $(x + 2)^2 + (y + 4)^2 = 36$ **7.** $(x - 4)^2 + (y + 3)^2 = 13$
15. $(x - 8)^2 + (y - 12)^2 = 100$ **17.** $x^2 + (y - 4)^2 = 13$
19. $\left(x - \frac{3}{2} \right)^2 + \left(y + \frac{11}{2} \right)^2 = \frac{5}{2}$ **21.** $(0, -\sqrt{3} + \sqrt{5}), (0, -\sqrt{3} - \sqrt{5})$ among others
23. $(x + 2)^2 + (y - 3)^2 = 4$ **Pages 351-352, Exercises 1.** $(\pm 3, 0), (0, \pm 2)$
3. $(\pm 2, 0), (0, \pm 6)$ **5.** $(\pm 1, 0), (0, \pm 6)$ **7.** $(\pm 12, 0), (0, \pm 11)$
9. $(\pm \sqrt{5}, 0), (0, \pm \sqrt{13})$ **17.** $\left(0, -2 \pm \frac{2\sqrt{15}}{5} \right)$ **19.** $\frac{x^2}{25} + \frac{y^2}{9} = 1$ **21.** $\frac{x^2}{25} + \frac{y^2}{16} = 1$
Page 356, Exercises 17. $y = \frac{1}{12}x^2$ **19.** $y = -\frac{1}{4}(x^2 + 6x - 11)$

21. $\left(0, -\frac{3}{4} \right), y = \frac{3}{4}$; $\left(0, -\frac{1}{4} \right), y = \frac{1}{4}$; $\left(0, -\frac{1}{12} \right), y = \frac{1}{12}$; $(0, 1), y = -1$; $\left(0, \frac{1}{4} \right), y = -\frac{1}{4}$;

$\left(0, \frac{1}{16} \right), y = -\frac{1}{16}$ **Page 360, Exercises 13.** $\frac{y^2}{9} - \frac{x^2}{16} = 1$ **15.** $y = \pm \frac{b}{a}x$

17. $4x - 5y = 22$ and $4x + 5y = 2$ **19.** $\frac{x^2}{4} - \frac{y^2}{5} = 1$ **Page 365, Checking Your**

Understanding 1. a. $\sqrt{117}, \left(-\frac{5}{2}, 6 \right)$ **b.** $\sqrt{53}, \left(3, -\frac{1}{2} \right)$ **c.** $5, \left(\frac{9}{2}, -4 \right)$
2. No, the Pythagorean Theorem does not hold. $a^2 + b^2 \neq c^2$
3. $(x - 2)^2 + (y + 3)^2 = 17$ **4.** $(x - 1)^2 + (y - 2)^2 = 169$ **Page 369, Exercises**
25. $50(\pi - \sqrt{3})$ **Page 372, Exercises 1.** $x < -3$ or $x > 4$ **3.** $-3 < x < 4$
5. $1 < x < 2$ **7.** $-9 < x < 1$ **9.** no solution **11.** real numbers except $-\frac{3}{2}$
13. no solution **15.** no solution **17.** all real numbers

19. real numbers except $\frac{\sqrt{5}}{2}$ **21.** all real numbers **23.** $5 < x < 7$

25. $x < \frac{5}{2}$ or $x \geq 11$ **Page 377, Exercises 1.** 20 **3.** $V = \frac{C}{P}$

5. 3.6 **7.** $\frac{1}{12}$ **9.** $6\frac{1}{4}$ **11.** 5 **13.** 25 **15.** 5 m **17.** 180N **Page 380, Exercises**
1. $(3, 4), (4, 3)$ **3.** $(3, 4), \left(-\frac{7}{5}, -\frac{24}{5} \right)$ **5.** no solution **7.** $(4, 1), \left(-\frac{1}{2}, -8 \right)$
9. $(5, 3), \left(-4\frac{1}{3}, -1\frac{2}{3} \right)$ **11.** $(1, 9), (9, 1), (-1, -9), (-9, -1)$ **13.** $(5, 12)$
15. $(2, 1), (0.2, -1.7)$ **17.** $(\pm 4, 0)$ **19.** $(\pm 5.4, \pm 2.7)$ **21.** $(2, 8)$ **23.** $(\pm 3, 4)$ **Page 383, Exercises 1.** $(3, 6), (-2, 1)$ **3.** no solution **5.** $(\pm 3, \pm 2)$ **7.** $(4, 3), (-3, -4)$
9. $(7, -1), \left(\frac{41}{9}, \frac{35}{9} \right)$ **11.** $(\pm 3, \pm 4)$ **13.** $\left(\pm \frac{5\sqrt{7}}{4}, \pm \frac{9}{4} \right)$
15. $(16, \pm \sqrt{35})$ **17.** $(5, 7), (1, -1)$ **19.** $(3, 2), (-3, -2)$ **21.** $\left(\frac{1}{2}, \frac{1}{2} \right)$
23. $(0, 0), (8, 4)$ **25.** $(-1, -5), (-1, 1)$
27. $(-2, 4, 6), (4, -2, 6), (3 - \sqrt{17}, 3 + \sqrt{17}, 2), (3 + \sqrt{17}, 3 - \sqrt{17}, 2)$

Pages 385-387, Exercises 1. 1, 4 **3.** 40 km/h, 50 km/h **5.** 60 km/h, 72 km/h
7. 51 **9.** 93 **11.** approx. 2.9 **13.** 20 m × 8 m **15.** 10.6 cm **17.** 42, 12
19. 7.33 cm **21.** 5 m, 5 m, 6 m **23.** 12 d, 16 d **Page 387, Checking Your
Understanding 3.** $-3 < x < 5$ **4.** $x \le \frac{1}{2}$ or $x \ge 1$ **5.** no solution **6.** 6 **7.** $\frac{20}{3}$
8. $\left(\frac{8}{3}, \pm\sqrt{5}\right)$ **9.** no real number solution **10.** $(0, \pm 3)$

Chapter 10 Exponential and Logarithmic Functions
Page 395, Exercises 1. $\sqrt[4]{5}$ **3.** $\sqrt[4]{3125}$ **5.** $\sqrt[5]{100^6}$ **7.** $2^{0.75}$ **9.** $2^{0.375}$ **11.** $2^{0.6}$
13. $5^{1.414}$ **15.** $10^{3.464}$ **17.** $9^{2.732}$ **19.** 81 **21.** $2^{3-\sqrt{3}}$ **23.** x^{-4} **25.** $3^{2\sqrt{2}}$ **27.** $2^{3\pi+2}$
29. $(xy)^{\sqrt{3}}$ **31.** $3^{-0.828}$ **33.** $10^{1.707}$

35. $\left(\frac{1}{2}\right)^{\sqrt{2}}$, $\frac{1}{\sqrt{2}}$, $\sqrt[5]{2}$, $2^{0.21}$, $\sqrt[3]{2}$, $\sqrt{2}$, $\sqrt[3]{2^2}$, $2^{\sqrt{2}}$, $\sqrt{2^3}$, $2^{\frac{\pi}{2}}$ **37.** 27 **39.** 1 **Page**

398, Exercises 9. 1.4 **11.** 1.2 **13.** 1.2 **15.** 0.7 **17.** 3.3 **19.** 0.4 **21.** 0.6
23. 1.8 **27.** 1.8 **33.** The graph is translated vertically.
35. D: reals, R: positive reals **37.** D: reals, R: real numbers greater than 2
39. D: reals, R: $0 < y \le 1$ **41.** D: reals, R: $y \ge 3$ **Page 400, Exercises 1.** 2 **3.** 3
5. -2 **7.** -3 **9.** 6 **11.** 9 **13.** 4 **15.** 0.5 **17.** 3 **19.** 2 **21.** -2 **23.** $-\frac{3}{2}$ **25.** 0.25
27. $\frac{1}{3}$ **29.** no solution **31.** all real numbers **33.** $-\frac{1}{3}, 2$ **35.** $a + 1$ **37.** 8 **39.** $4a$
Page 403, Exercises 1. $\log_2 16 = 4$ **3.** $\log_2 8 = 3$ **5.** $\log_2 \frac{1}{2} = -1$ **7.** $\log_5 1 = 0$
9. $\log_5 0.2 = -1$ **11.** $\log_{10} 0.1 = -1$ **13.** $\log_{\frac{1}{2}} 4 = -2$ **15.** $\log_7 7 = 1$
17. $10^3 = 1000$ **19.** $4^3 = 64$ **21.** $2^0 = 1$ **23.** $5^{-2} = 0.04$ **25.** $10^{-2} = 0.01$
27. $\left(\frac{1}{3}\right)^3 = \frac{1}{27}$ **29.** 2 **31.** 3 **33.** 5 **35.** -1 **37.** -1 **39.** 4 **41.** $\log_{\sqrt{35}} \frac{1}{35} = -2$
43. $0.2^{-1} = 5$ **45.** m **47.** 1 **49.** $\frac{1}{4}$ **51.** -2.5 **53.** 0 **55.** 1 **Page 405, Exercises**
1. 1 **3.** 64 **5.** $\frac{1}{6}$ **7.** 5 **9.** 10 **11.** 81 **13.** 125 **15.** 4 **17.** $\frac{1}{3}$ **19.** $\frac{3}{4}$ **21.** 9 **23.** 4
25. $\frac{\sqrt{3}-2}{3}$ **27.** ± 8 **29.** $\frac{1}{15}, -\frac{1}{17}$ **31.** $(4, 5)$ **33.** $10 \pm 3\sqrt{11}$, $10 \pm \sqrt{101}$
Page 408, Exercises 9. 2.6 **11.** 3.3 **13.** 0.6 **21.** D: $x > 1$, R: reals
23. D: $x > -2$, R: reals **25.** D: positive reals, R: reals
35. for increasing a, graph is less steep **37.** for increasing a, graph is more steep
39. for increasing a, graph is translated upward **Page 409,**

Checking Your Understanding 1. 8 **2.** $5^{2\pi-1}$ **3.** $\frac{1}{z^{\sqrt{2}}}$ **5.** 8.8 **6.** $\frac{3}{2}$ **7.** 1

8. $\log_2 16 = 4$ **9.** -3 **11.** 4 **12.** $\frac{1}{5}$ **Page 413, Exercises 1.** 6.62 **3.** 0.360
5. 709 **7.** 8790 **9.** 0.796 **11.** 0.116 **13.** 8.86 **15.** 7.30 **17.** 213 **19.** 0.900
21. 0.9201 **23.** 0.4216 **25.** 1.4914 **27.** 2.6981 **29.** $0.9590 - 1$ **31.** $0.4757 - 2$
33. $0.8531 - 3$ **35.** $0.4771 - 3$ **37.** 0.8965 **39.** 1.1004 **41.** 3.1644 **43.** 8.52
45. 3070 **47.** 0.0304 **49.** -0.5229 **51.** 1.4619 **53.** 694 **55.** 0.4969 **57.** 8
59. 2 **Page 417, Exercises 1.** 0.6075 **3.** 0.8657 **5.** 1.9325 **7.** $0.1987 - 2$
                  c m c m c m m c
9. 2.6395 **11.** $0.7505 - 1$ **13.** $0.8325 - 2$ **15.** $0.8621 - 3$ **17.** 0.9687
19. $0.6742 - 1$ **21.** 704 **23.** 4551 **25.** 0.4481 **27.** 0.005077 **29.** 592
31. 0.07938 **33.** 0.08964 **35.** ± 778 **37.** 9 **39.** 3 **41.** 0.2385 **43.** 309.0
45. approx. 4.217 **Page 421, Exercises 1.** 935.7 **3.** 20.11 **5.** 29.50 **7.** 0.007672
9. 15 650 **11.** 0.2511 **13.** 3.214 **15.** 8245 **17.** 231.6 **19.** $-204\,700$ **21.** -160.9
23. -352.3 **25.** 9.226 **27.** 4.511 **29.** 7.360 **31.** 2.000 **33.** $\log 5x^2$
35. $\log \frac{x^2}{y}$ **37.** $\log x^4$ **39.** $\frac{1}{2}\log x + 2\log y$ **41.** 98.83 **43.** 402.3 **45.** 2 **47.** 3.322

49. 3.114 **Page 425, Exercises 1.** 0.5850 **3.** 2.557 **5.** 0.8982 **7.** 12.93
9. 0.1575 **11.** 0.2736 **13.** approx. 4 093 000 **15.** approx. 177 g (177.4)

17. approx. 11.6 cm (11.60) **19.** 4.25 **21.** approx. \$1114 **23.** 0.6825 **25.** 2.004
27. approx. 7.5 years (7.525) **29.** 2125 g **31.** approx. 12.5 years (12.54)
33. ±0.4897 **35.** approx. 132 (132.2) **Page 426, Checking Your Understanding**
1. 0.6839 **2.** 9.040 **3.** 3.040 **4.** 3.8451 **5.** $0.8325 - 1$ **6.** 5510 **7.** 0.01060
8. 3.9402 **9.** 37.55 **10.** 0.08021 **11.** 5.227 **12.** -8.877 **13.** 2.680 **14.** 2.387
15. 0.4150

Chapter 11 Sequences and Series
Page 434, Exercises 1. 39 **3.** $a + 44$ **5.** 5 **7.** $-\frac{13}{10}$ **9.** $-4, -1, 2, 5, 8$
11. 15 **13.** 17 **15.** $\frac{9}{2}x^2$ **17.** $x + 1 - \frac{35}{x-1}$ **19.** -19

21. The sequence is the sequence of successive even-numbered terms
of A. First term: $a + d$. Common difference: $2d$. **Pages 439-440, Exercises**
1. $S = 200, A = 20$ **3.** $S = -1672, A = -88$ **5.** $S = 1335, A = 26.7$
7. 5050 **9.** 192 **11.** -1800 **13.** \$1.63, \$44.98 **15.** \$3390
17. 40, 56, 72 **19.** 275 **21.** 112 **23.** $1\frac{1}{2}$% **25.** 15 **27.** $\frac{25}{9}$ **Page 444,**
Exercises 1. 3, 1 **3.** 729, 3 **5.** 2; 3, 6, 12 or -2; 3, -6, 12
7. $\frac{1}{2}$; $-320, -160, -80$, or $-\frac{1}{2}$; 320, -160, 80 **9.** 6 **11.** $\frac{1}{9}$ **13.** $-3, 9$
15. $\frac{1}{36}, \frac{1}{12}$ **17.** $\pm ar^4$
19. $x + 2, x^2 + 3x + 2, x^3 + 4x^2 + 5x + 2, x^4 + 5x^3 + 9x^2 + 7x + 2$ **21.** $0, \frac{11}{2}$
Pages 450-451, Exercises 1. $3\left(\frac{1}{2}\right)^0 + 3\left(\frac{1}{2}\right)^1 + 3\left(\frac{1}{2}\right)^2 + 3\left(\frac{1}{2}\right)^3$; $\frac{45}{8}$
3. $1(-2)^0 + 1(-2)^1 + 1(-2)^2 + 1(-2)^3 + 1(-2)^4$; 11 **5.** 86 **7.** 135, 200
9. 1, 5 **11.** 3 840 000 **13.** approx. 12 580/mL **15.** \$24 157.65, \$115 734.15
17. \$167 772 **19.** 468 **21.** 728 **23.** $-\frac{1}{2}$ **Pages 454-455, Exercises**

1. 16 **3.** no **5.** 6 **7.** $\frac{42}{5}$ **9.** $4 + \sqrt{2}$ **11.** $\frac{4}{11}$ **13.** $\frac{41}{333}$ **15.** $\frac{3}{7}$
17. $-\frac{1}{3}$; $\frac{1}{16}, -\frac{1}{48}, \frac{1}{144}$ **19.** $\frac{1}{1-x}$ **21.** $\frac{\sqrt{3}-1}{2}$ **23.** 1152
25. 8, $\frac{3}{4}$; $4(3 + \sqrt{21})$, $\frac{5 - \sqrt{21}}{8}$ **Page 456, Checking Your Understanding**
1. $-\frac{127}{3}$ **2.** $\frac{14}{3}, \frac{16}{3}, 6, \frac{20}{3}, \frac{22}{3}$ **3.** -10 **4.** 5700 **5.** 138 **6.** -7525 **7.** 20 **8.** 21
9. $-\frac{255}{64}$ **10.** 5 **11.** 24 **12.** 9

Chapter 12 Permutations, Combinations, and Probability
Page 466, Exercises 1. 60 **3.** 24 **5.** 24 **7.** 219 024 **9.** 720 **11.** 60 **13.** 36 504
15. 66 **Pages 470-471, Exercises 1.** 360 **3.** 336 **5.** 5040 **7.** 2520 **9.** 90
11. 24 **13.** 60 480 **15.** 72 **17.** 6 **19.** 1728 **21.** 120 **23.** 288 **25.** $(n - 1)!$, 12
Pages 475-476, Exercises 1. 142 506 **3.** 21 **5.** 28 **7.** 120 **9.** 72 **11.** 100
13. 45 **15.** 1, 6 **17.** $_nC_2 - n$ **19.** a 19-gon
21. $_nC_r \overset{?}{=} {}_nC_n - r$, $\frac{n!}{(n-r)!\,r!} \overset{?}{=} \frac{n!}{(n-(n-r))!\,(n-r)!}$, $\frac{n!}{(n-r)!\,r!} \overset{?}{=} \frac{n!}{r!\,(n-r)!}$ **23.** 420
Page 481, Exercises 1. $\frac{2}{7}, \frac{5}{7}$ **3.** $\frac{1}{4}$ **5.** $\frac{1}{2}, \frac{1}{4}$ **7.** $\frac{3}{20}$ **9.** 3 to 2 **11.** $\frac{1}{12}, \frac{1}{2}$
13. 35 to 31 **Pages 486-487, Exercises 1.** $\frac{1}{9}, \frac{1}{12}$ **3.** $\frac{11}{850}$ **5.** $\frac{5}{12}$ **7.** $\frac{2}{13}, \frac{5}{13}, \frac{7}{13}$
9. $\frac{12}{25}$ **11.** $\frac{23}{25}$ **13.** $\frac{13}{25}$ **15.** $\frac{46}{81}$ **17.** $\frac{8}{17}$ **19.** $\frac{1}{13}$ **Page 488, Checking Your**
Understanding 1. 1024 **2.** 210 **3.** 2520 **4.** 10 **5.** 35 **6.** 20 **7.** $\frac{2}{5}$, 3 to 2
8. $\frac{1}{12}$

Chapter 13 Introduction to Matrix Algebra
Page 498, Exercises 1. $\begin{bmatrix} 3 & 1 \\ -7 & 4 \\ 10 & -5 \end{bmatrix}$ **3.** $\begin{bmatrix} 2 & -4 \\ -6 & 8 \\ 10 & -12 \end{bmatrix}$ **5.** $\begin{bmatrix} 4 & -1 \\ -1 & 3 \end{bmatrix}$ **7.** $\begin{bmatrix} -6 & 6 \\ -4 & 10 \end{bmatrix}$

9. $\begin{bmatrix} 2 & 0 & 4 \\ 1 & -1 & 1 \\ -3 & 2 & 1 \end{bmatrix}$ **11.** no product exists **13.** $\begin{bmatrix} 1 & 0 \\ 0 & 1 \end{bmatrix}$ **15.** $\begin{bmatrix} -2 & 0 & 0 \\ 0 & -2 & 0 \\ 0 & 0 & -2 \end{bmatrix}$

17. Show, for example, that $\begin{bmatrix} a & b \\ c & d \end{bmatrix} + \begin{bmatrix} e & f \\ g & h \end{bmatrix} = \begin{bmatrix} e & f \\ g & h \end{bmatrix} + \begin{bmatrix} a & b \\ c & d \end{bmatrix}$.

Pages 500-501, Exercises 1. 38 **3.** 0 **5.** $\begin{bmatrix} \frac{1}{9} & -\frac{2}{9} \\ \frac{2}{9} & \frac{5}{9} \end{bmatrix}$ **7.** $\begin{bmatrix} \frac{1}{3} & 0 \\ \frac{4}{15} & -\frac{1}{5} \end{bmatrix}$

9. A^{-1} does not exist **11.** $\begin{bmatrix} \frac{18}{25} & \frac{24}{25} \\ -\frac{16}{25} & \frac{12}{25} \end{bmatrix}$ **13.** $\begin{bmatrix} 11 & 17 \\ 5 & -5 \end{bmatrix}$ **15.** -140 **17.** -140

19. all matrices such that $bc = 1$ **25.** $\begin{bmatrix} 2 & 0 \\ 0 & \frac{3}{2} \end{bmatrix}$ **Pages 503-504, Exercises**

1. $\begin{bmatrix} 9 & 5 \\ -5 & 5 \end{bmatrix}$ **3.** $\begin{bmatrix} -1 & 3 \\ 0 & 2 \end{bmatrix}$ **5.** $\begin{bmatrix} 0 & 1 \\ -1 & 0 \end{bmatrix}$ **7.** $\begin{bmatrix} \frac{1}{3} & \frac{10}{3} \\ 4 & \frac{22}{3} \end{bmatrix}$ **9.** $\begin{bmatrix} \frac{12}{7} & \frac{12}{7} \\ \frac{8}{7} & -\frac{6}{7} \end{bmatrix}$ **11.** $\begin{bmatrix} 1 & 1 \\ 0 & 2 \end{bmatrix}$

13. any matrix of the form $\begin{bmatrix} a & b \\ -2a & -2b \end{bmatrix}$ **Page 507, Exercises 1.** $(2, 3)$

3. $(3, -2)$ **5.** $(1, 2)$ **7.** $(4, 12)$ **9.** $\left(\frac{ms - nr}{hs - nk}, \frac{nr - ms}{hr - mk} \right)$ **Page 508, Checking Your**

Understanding 1. $\begin{bmatrix} -1 & 2 \\ -\frac{5}{2} & 7 \end{bmatrix}$ **2.** $\begin{bmatrix} 3 & 2 \\ -\frac{7}{2} & 1 \end{bmatrix}$ **3.** $\begin{bmatrix} -1 & 6 \\ 8 & 12 \end{bmatrix}$ **4.** $\begin{bmatrix} -2 & -4 \\ -\frac{17}{2} & 13 \end{bmatrix}$ **5.** 10

6. -6 **7.** 0 **8.** $\begin{bmatrix} -2 & 0 \\ \frac{1}{2} & 3 \end{bmatrix}$, or B **9.** does not exist **10.** $\begin{bmatrix} -\frac{1}{2} & 0 \\ \frac{1}{12} & \frac{1}{3} \end{bmatrix}$, or D

11. $\begin{bmatrix} \frac{9}{10} & \frac{3}{5} \\ \frac{51}{20} & \frac{6}{5} \end{bmatrix}$ **12.** $(-1, 3)$ **13.** $(-1, 3)$

Chapter 14 Circular and Trigonometric Functions

Page 517, Exercises 1. 315° **11.** $\frac{\pi}{6}^R$ **13.** $\frac{5\pi}{6}^R$ **15.** $\frac{\pi}{40}^R$ **17.** π^R **19.** 360°
21. 144° **23.** 240° **25.** 60° **27.** $-45°$ **29.** 90° **31.** 0° **33.** 225° **35.** 315°
37. 0.018^R **39.** 57.30° **41.** $r^2(\pi - 3)$ **43.** 45° **45.** 330° **Page 521, Exercises**

1. 0 **3.** $\frac{-\sqrt{2}}{2}$ **5.** $\frac{\sqrt{3}}{2}$ **7.** $-\frac{1}{2}$ **9.** $\frac{-\sqrt{2}}{2}$ **11.** $-\frac{1}{2}$ **13.** $-\frac{\sqrt{3}}{2}$ **15.** 0 **17.** 30°, 150°
19. 240°, 300° **21.** 210°, 330° **23.** 120°, 240°

25.

$\sin \theta$	0	$\pm\frac{1}{2}$	$\pm\frac{\sqrt{2}}{2}$	$\pm\frac{\sqrt{3}}{2}$	± 1	$\pm\frac{\sqrt{3}}{2}$	$\pm\frac{\sqrt{2}}{2}$	$\pm\frac{1}{2}$	0	0
$\cos \theta$	1	$\frac{\sqrt{3}}{2}$	$\frac{\sqrt{2}}{2}$	$\frac{1}{2}$	0	$-\frac{1}{2}$	$-\frac{\sqrt{2}}{2}$	$-\frac{\sqrt{3}}{2}$	-1	1

27. $\sin \theta > 0$ in quadrants 1 and 2, $\cos \theta > 0$ in quadrants 1 and 4 **29.** $\frac{-\sqrt{3}}{2}$
31. $\frac{\pi}{4}^R, \frac{3\pi}{4}^R, \frac{5\pi}{4}^R, \frac{7\pi}{4}^R$ **Pages 524-525, Exercises 1.** 0.9962 **3.** 0.9283
5. 0.7716 **7.** 0.9922 **9.** 0.5854 **11.** 0.9511 **13.** 0.7443 **15.** 0.9239 **17.** 0.5913
19. 0.9896 **21.** 0.7120 **23.** 0.3875 **25.** 4°50', 0.0844^R **27.** 6°40', 0.1164^R
29. 51°0', 0.8901^R **31.** 0.8415 **33.** 0.6088 **35.** 0.5404 **37.** 216°, 324°

39. $171°14'$, $188°46'$ **41.** B is the complement of A. **Page 528, Exercises**
1. -0.1735 **3.** -0.2588 **5.** -0.9397 **7.** -0.2588 **9.** 0.3420 **11.** 0.6947
13. 0.7071 **15.** -0.7071 **17.** 0.6947 **19.** -0.9026 **21.** -0.7566 **23.** -0.5664
25. -0.5000 **27.** 0.8660 **29.** -0.9923 **31.** -0.9336 **33.** -0.5700
35. no solution **37.** $217°15'$, $322°45'$ **39.** $30°, 150°, 210°, 330°$ **41.** $150°$

Page 534, Exercises 1. $3, 2\pi$ **3.** $2, 2\pi$ **5.** $1, \frac{\pi}{2}$ **7.** $1, \pi$ **9.** $3, \frac{\pi}{2}$ **11.** $1, 2\pi$
13. $2, 4$ **15.** $\frac{2}{3}, \frac{4\pi}{3}$ **17.** $1, \frac{1}{2}$ **Page 538, Exercises 1.** 1 **3.** $\sqrt{2}$ **5.** not defined
7. -0.8391 **9.** -1.192 **11.** 2 **13.** π **15.** π **17.** $\frac{\pi}{4}$ **25.** $\frac{\pi}{2}$ **27.** 4π **29.** 3π
31. 2π **33.** 2π **37.** $\cdots \frac{\pi}{8}, \frac{3\pi}{8}, \frac{5\pi}{8}, \frac{7\pi}{8}, \cdots$, in general $(2k + 1)\frac{\pi}{8}$ **Page**
541, Exercises 1. $27.70, 75.06, 69°45'$ **3.** 0.8868 **5.** approx. 12.0 m (11.97)
7. approx. 798 m (797.9) **9.** $29°14'$ with 18.5 m side, $60°46'$ **11.** $20°34'$
13. apothem 18.47 cm, radius 19.42 cm **Page 542, Checking Your Understanding**
2. $\frac{\pi}{3}$ **3.** 135 **4.** $\frac{5\pi}{4}$ **5.** -60 **6.** $\frac{-\sqrt{2}}{2}$ **7.** $-\frac{1}{2}$ **8.** -1 **9.** $\frac{1}{2}$ **10.** 0.2588 **11.** 0.9986
12. 0.1544 **13.** $29°35'$ **14.** 1.2923 **18.** $\sqrt{3}$ **19.** $\frac{\sqrt{3}}{3}$ **20.** -2 **21.** $\frac{-2\sqrt{3}}{3}$
22. $c \doteq 28.25$, $b \doteq 22.56$, $m \angle A = 37°$
23. $m \angle B \doteq 29°03'$, $m \angle A \doteq 60°57'$, $c \doteq 103.0$

Chapter 15 Trigonometric Identities

Page 549, Exercises 11. $2\cos x - \cos^2 x$ **13.** $\frac{\sin^2 \theta + 1}{\sin \theta}$
15. $\cos^2 x - 2\cos x + 1$, or $(\cos x - 1)^2$ **17.** $\frac{1}{\csc^2 x - 1}$ **19.** $\frac{\sin^2 2\theta + 1}{\sin 2\theta}$
21. $\cos \theta - \sin \theta$ **23.** $\cos x - \cos^2 x$ **25.** $\log(1 + \sin x) - \log(1 - \sin x)$
Pages 552-553, Exercises 27. $\frac{\pi}{4}, \frac{5\pi}{4}$ **29.** $\frac{\pi}{6}, \frac{5\pi}{6}, \frac{7\pi}{6}, \frac{11\pi}{6}$ **31.** $\frac{\pi}{2}, 3.4814, 5.9334$
39. $\frac{\pi}{6}, \frac{5\pi}{6}, \frac{7\pi}{6}, \frac{11\pi}{6}$ **41.** $\frac{\pi}{6}, \frac{5\pi}{6}$ **47.** $\left((2k \pm 1)\frac{\pi}{3}, \frac{1}{2}\right)$
49. $\left((8k + 1)\frac{\pi}{4}, \frac{\sqrt{2}}{2}\right)$, $\left((8k + 5)\frac{\pi}{4}, \frac{-\sqrt{2}}{2}\right)$ **Page 556, Exercises 1.** 7 **3.** 6.56
5. 3.09 **7.** 11.97 **9.** $24°37'$ **11.** $47°9'$ **13.** $120°$ **15.** $123°12'$ **17.** $71°47'$
19. 6.5 km **21.** $c = \sqrt{a^2 + b^2 - 2ab \cos 90°}$, or $c = \sqrt{a^2 + b^2}$ **23.** $60°$
25. $5°25'$, 10.5 km **Page 559, Exercises 1.** 6 **3.** 0.7660 **5.** 1.9284 **7.** 3.4470
9. 6 **11.** 13.47 **13.** $30°57'$ **15.** $15°22'$ **17.** 108.5 m **19.** $28, 30$ **Page 563,**
Exercises 1. 106.05 **3.** $10.63, 10.06$ **5.** 2.80 km **7.** $22°37'$ **9.** approx. 894 m^2
11. $m \angle A = 49°$, $b \doteq 31.15$, $c \doteq 52.80$ **13.** 68.40 m, 53.21 m
15. $91°12'$, approx. 102 **Page 564, Checking Your Understanding**
1. $\cos^2 x$ **2.** $1 + \sin x$ **5.** 18.69 **6.** $38°38'$ **7.** 23.940
8. $35°16'$ **9.** approx. 146 cm **Page 569, Exercises 15.** $\frac{\sqrt{6} + \sqrt{2}}{4}$
17. $\frac{\sqrt{2} - \sqrt{6}}{4}$ **19.** $\frac{\sqrt{6} - \sqrt{2}}{4}$ **21.** $\frac{\pi}{3}, \frac{5\pi}{3}$ **23.** $\frac{\pi}{3}, \frac{2\pi}{3}$ **29.** $(4k - 1)\frac{\pi}{4}$
31. $(4k + 3)\frac{\pi}{2} \pm 0.8411$ **Page 572, Exercises 1.** approx. 0.38
3. approx. 0.26 **5.** approx. 0.38 **7.** approx. 0.414
19. 0 **21.** no solution **23.** $\frac{\pi}{3}, \frac{2\pi}{3}, \frac{4\pi}{3}, \frac{5\pi}{3}$ **25.** $0, \frac{\pi}{6}, \frac{5\pi}{6}, \pi$ **27.** $\frac{2\pi}{3}, \frac{4\pi}{3}$
33. 4096 **Page 577, Exercises 1.** $\frac{\pi}{3}$ **3.** $\frac{5\pi}{6}$ **5.** $\frac{\pi}{3}$ **7.** $-\frac{\pi}{6}$ **9.** $\frac{\sqrt{2}}{2}$
11. $\frac{\sqrt{3}}{3}$ **13.** 0.4 **15.** -2 **17.** $\frac{15}{17}$ **19.** $\frac{8}{17}$ **21.** $\frac{1}{4}$ **23.** $\sqrt{3}$ **25.** $-\frac{119}{169}$ **27.** $\frac{\sqrt{2} - \sqrt{6}}{4}$
31. ± 2

INDEX

BCDEFGH 084321
Printed in the United States of America